Evaluation Guide for MERRILL GENERAL SCIENCE

MERRILL GENERAL SCIENCE is a textbook that discusses basic concepts of science and important applications. The emphasis throughout the text is on making science concepts, especially physical science concepts, relevant to students using the text. To increase student understanding and to challenge students to think about science and technology in their world, many text features are included.

To examine examples of the format and features of MERRILL GENERAL SCIENCE, please turn to the following pages.

pp. 2–3   A **large color photograph, unit opening paragraph, and questions** introduce each of the six units in the text and preview the chapters that follow.

pp. 48–49   Each of the **28 chapters** begins with a **color photo** and **introductory paragraph** designed to interest students. A **goal** statement lists the main objective of the chapter for students.

p. 100   Blue **student margin notes** in question form aid reading comprehension and students' review of text material.

p. 199   **Vocabulary terms** are printed in boldface type where they are defined. Difficult words are **respelled phonetically**.

p. 258   **Example** problems help students understand how to do mathematical calculations needed for some general science concepts.

pp. 296, 323   **Diagrams, illustrations,** and **photographs** throughout the text help students visualize concepts presented.

p. 307   Two full-page **activities** are included in each chapter to reinforce or extend chapter concepts. **Illustrations** clarify procedure steps.

p. 353   **Tables** within the text summarize information.

p. 370   A **Skill Inquiry** in each chapter provides in-depth study of a practical science skill.

p. 386   A **Career Profile** in each chapter emphasizes the importance of studying science in preparation for a variety of careers.

p. 463   **Review and Reflect** questions appear at the ends of selected sections throughout each chapter to help students check their understanding of the text material.

pp. 546–547   The final section in each chapter is an optional **Information** or **Choices** discussion of an additional concept or a current issue.

pp. 572–573   A **Summary** of major concepts, a **Vocabulary** list and exercise, **Main Ideas** and **Applications Questions**, **Investigations** and **Readings** for Further Study appear in each two-page Chapter Review.

p. 616   The **Appendices** provide quick reference information about SI units, safety and first aid, and math calculations.

p. 624   The **Glossary** lists all vocabulary terms and their definitions.

p. 629   The **Index** provides a complete subject list, including page references for illustrations, tables, and activities.

Merrill
General Science

TEACHER'S ANNOTATED EDITION

AUTHORS

Richard H. Moyer
University of Michigan–Dearborn, Michigan
Jeanne E. Bishop
Westlake Public Schools–Westlake, Ohio

Content Consultants

Dr. Philip E. Barnhart, Associate Professor of Physics and Astronomy
Otterbein College, Westerville, Ohio
Dr. Orin G. Gelderloos, Professor of Biology and Environmental Studies
University of Michigan–Dearborn, Michigan
Robert C. Smoot, Science Department Chairman and Chemistry Teacher
McDonogh School, McDonogh, Maryland
Dr. Sidney E. White, Professor of Geology
The Ohio State University, Columbus, Ohio

CHARLES E. MERRILL PUBLISHING COMPANY
A Bell & Howell Company
Columbus, Ohio
Toronto   London   Sydney

Preface

MERRILL *GENERAL SCIENCE* Teacher's Annotated Edition provides answers to all questions in the text, suggestions for effective teaching, background information, performance objectives, and other useful teacher information. Both experienced and inexperienced teachers will find the Teacher's Annotated Edition a valuable teaching aid.

The Teacher's Annotated Edition consists of a pupil's text overprinted with red annotations and a Teacher's Guide bound at the front of the book. The annotations are labeled as INTRODUCING THE CHAPTER, ACTIVITY, DEMONSTRATION, SUGGESTION, or BACKGROUND. Answers to the blue student margin questions are shown with red tint blocks over the appropriate pupil's text. Also, answers to Vocabulary exercises and multiple-choice Main Ideas questions in the Chapter Reviews are indicated by annotations.

The Teacher's Guide includes answers to the balance of the Chapter Review questions and all Review and Reflect questions. It also provides additional teaching strategies for each unit and chapter of the text. The introductory part of the Teacher's Guide explains the philosophy and teaching features of the MERRILL *GENERAL SCIENCE* program. Also included are a complete planning guide, lists of supplemental materials such as audiovisuals and software, safety information concerning activities, and a complete materials list for all the activities in the text. Performance objectives and their use are explained. Then, goals and performance objectives are listed for each chapter of the text. The Teacher's Guide concludes with a questionnaire for your comments concerning the MER-RILL *GENERAL SCIENCE* program.

Project Editor: Michele J. Wigginton; *Editors*: Robert Davisson, Mary Beth Gallant; *Project Designer*: Joan Shaull; *Production Editor*: Janice Wagner

ISBN 0-675-07688-9

Published by
CHARLES E. MERRILL PUBLISHING COMPANY
A BELL & HOWELL COMPANY
Columbus, Ohio 43216

Table of Contents

Merrill General Science helps

MERRILL GENERAL SCIENCE not only teaches students the basic principles of science—it also shows them science at work in their world. Practical applications, technological advances, and current science issues keep the interest level high in this exceptional text.

MERRILL GENERAL SCIENCE teaches students the science that will help them cope with rapid changes in technology . . . it whets their interest in the world around them . . . it gives them opportunities to think as scientists think.

Students will become aware of how science and technology influence their daily lives . . . and how science knowledge is applied in a wide variety of careers.

Gives students a solid science background

MERRILL GENERAL SCIENCE covers all areas of science—earth, space, life, and physical sciences—with a special emphasis on the basic principles of chemistry and physics. Unlike most other texts, it demonstrates how different areas of science are interrelated.

students make sense of the world

The program is suitable for use with all students. It can be presented as a final high school science course or as preparation for more specialized secondary science courses.

MERRILL GENERAL SCIENCE is structured to give all students a solid background in science:

- Activities reinforce concepts and teach scientific methods and proper laboratory techniques.
- Exciting special features present new developments, issues, and career opportunities.

- Built-in reading aids enhance reading and comprehension.
- A complete **Teacher's Annotated Edition** gives the kind of help secondary science teachers want.
- The **Teacher Resource Book** includes a variety of materials that help teachers present all aspects of the program.

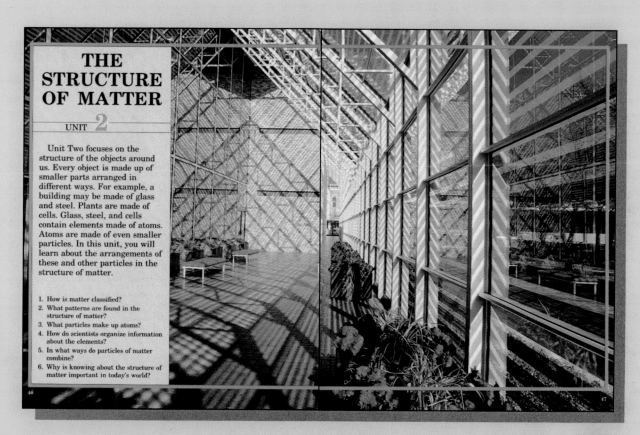

THE STRUCTURE OF MATTER

UNIT 2

Unit Two focuses on the structure of the objects around us. Every object is made up of smaller parts arranged in different ways. For example, a building may be made of glass and steel. Plants are made of cells. Glass, steel, and cells contain elements made of atoms. Atoms are made of even smaller particles. In this unit, you will learn about the arrangements of these and other particles in the structure of matter.

1. How is matter classified?
2. What patterns are found in the structure of matter?
3. What particles make up atoms?
4. How do scientists organize information about the elements?
5. In what ways do particles of matter combine?
6. Why is knowing about the structure of matter important in today's world?

46

47

Content that goes beyond just

Physical science emphasis

Today's students need solid science instruction, especially in the physical sciences.

That's why MERRILL GENERAL SCIENCE emphasizes physical science concepts—not only in the units on physical science—but also throughout units on life, earth, and space sciences. As students build a firm foundation in physical science, they gain a deeper understanding of all the sciences.

Although the text is arranged in a logical sequence, the interrelationships among the sciences are shown throughout the text—especially in practical applications.

SUPPOSE you are going to buy a used car. In order to decide which car to buy, you need information. You might ask a salesperson about the age and general condition of several cars. You might look at the cars carefully and take a test drive in some of them. Scientific information is gained in a way similar to the way any information is gained. What methods do scientists use to get information?

SCIENCE PROCESSES

2:1 Scientific Methods

A primary way of getting information is asking questions. Everyday people ask many questions to get information. People ask directions, what time it is, and how things work. People also get information by making observations and trying things out. For example, you can look out a window if you want to know if it is raining. You know what kinds of soft drinks you like because you have tasted several different ones.

Scientists get information by asking questions, making observations, and trying things out in a systematic way. They use processes called **scientific methods.** In this chapter, a general model of scientific methods is presented. Figure 2–1 illustrates the major parts of this model. While you are reading this chapter, think of ways you might vary from this model if you were to do the tests described.

Scientific methods are not limited to use by scientists only. They can be applied to everyday situations. For example, the makers of most dishwashing detergents claim that their product is best. Obviously they cannot all be best. The question is, which one really is best? You can use scientific methods to find the answer to this question.

GOAL You will learn about the methods scientists use to answer questions and solve problems.

How do scientists get information?

27

4T

science facts

Applications of science

The applications of science concepts outside the classroom are shown throughout the text—in the narrative, in the illustrations, and in a variety of special features.

Scientific concepts are explained through familiar examples. And, students learn how advancements in science lead to technological changes. So students gain a more practical understanding of complex scientific concepts, and a better understanding of the technology that surrounds them.

Scientific methods and tools

The first unit introduces the processes— measurement, scientific methods, and problem solving—that students need to study science. The rest of the program reinforces the idea that science is a process, and gives students plenty of opportunities to master basic science skills.

Becoming familiar with these skills also helps students better appreciate scientific endeavors in the world outside the classroom.

FIGURE 14–11. When you see a rainbow, you are seeing sunlight refracted and spread into its component colors by millions of raindrops (a). The same effect happens when white light is refracted by a prism (b). A spectrum is formed because shorter wavelength light (violet) is refracted more than longer wavelengths (red).

What is white light?

How does a color TV produce different colors?

14:6 Colors

Light that appears white to us, such as sun— tually a mixture of colors. As shown in Fig white light can be separated into a spectrum, of a rainbow. When white light passes at an another substance, such as glass or water, the are refracted. Light with shorter wavelengths more than light with longer wavelengths. So, is bent more than blue light, which is bent green light and so on. Red light is refracted th

Any color can be produced by combining diff of light. A color television screen consists of do of three fluorescent substances. These substance either red, blue, or green when their atoms ar an electron beam. With only these colors, the duce almost any color needed in a picture. F when the substances for green and red are l and brain perceive the result as yellow. When stances are lit, we perceive the mixture as whi cess is known as **color addition.**

Objects that do not produce their own ligh have color because of how they reflect light. C grass is green. Sunlight, a mixture of all co blades of grass. The grass absorbs most of the spectrum except green, so the grass appears g ject that appears black absorbs nearly all colo tle light is reflected.

FIGURE 14–3. Special cameras using computers can analyze the infrared radiation given off by dis- eased tissue, such as a tumor, which is warmer than surround- ing healthy tissue (a). X rays are absorbed more easily by dense materials, such as bone, which makes diagnoses of fractures and dislocations possible (b). Hair styl- ists and hospitals use ultraviolet radiation to sterilize instruments (c).

How is visible light produced?

rays. This property makes X rays useful for medical pur- poses. However, X rays change the cells through which they pass, so the radiation must be carefully controlled.

Gamma rays have shorter wavelengths than X rays. Re- call from chapter 4 that gamma rays are given off as ra- dioactive substances decay. Gamma rays generally have much greater penetrating power than X rays. People who work in nuclear power plants, where radioactive fuels are used, are closely monitored for exposure to gamma rays.

REVIEW AND REFLECT

1. What is the wave-particle duality of light?
2. Which has more energy, low or high frequency electro- magnetic radiation?
3. Why must precautions be taken with X rays and gamma rays?

14:3 Producing Light

Recall that electromagnetic radiation is produced by vi- brating charges. Visible light is produced by electrons moving between energy levels in individual atoms. For this to happen, an outside energy source must excite the electrons, raising them to higher energy levels. When the electrons drop back to lower energy levels, light is given off. The wavelength of the light produced depends on the energy given up by each electron as it drops back. A

Experience with science skills

Critical thinking skills—gathering and organizing information, analyzing data, drawing conclusions—are the focus of the two activities in each chapter. Activities are positioned in each chapter to reinforce or extend the concepts just covered.

A concise lab report format for activities features step-by-step instructions and complete follow-up materials. Diagrams and safety tips help students work independently. All activities use inexpensive materials that are readily available.

Activity: How can forces cause motion?

MATERIALS
laboratory burner
clean, empty metal can with cap
hammer
large nail
water
ringstand and ring
fish line
graduated cylinder or 150 mL container
goggles and apron
scissors
oven mitt or hot pad

PROCEDURE

1. Lay the can on its side. Using the hammer and nail, carefully make a hole in the upper left corner of the can as shown in Figure 9–8. **CAUTION:** *The metal edges of the hole may be sharp.*
2. Turn the can over. Make a hole in the upper left corner on this side of the can. (The two holes should be on opposite sides of the can.)
3. Put 150 mL of water in the can and put the cap on.
4. Set up the ring and ringstand as shown. Cut a piece of fish line to attach the can to the ring.

FIGURE 9–8.

5. Gently heat the can until the water boils. **CAUTION:** *Be sure you have punched the two holes in the can before you begin heating. Steam will escape from the holes in the can and can cause severe burns. NEVER heat a liquid in a completely closed system.*
6. Remove the heat from th[...] serve the motion of the ca[...] observations.

DATA AND OBSERVAT[...]

Heat Source	Observa[...]
Present	
Absent	

QUESTIONS AND CON[...]

1. What happened to the [...] heated the water to boilin[...]
2. What happened to the ca[...] moved the heat source?
3. Explain how this activity [...] Newton's Third Law of M[...]
4. Make a sketch showing [...] forces acting on the can.
5. What would happen if y[...] holes on opposite sides bu[...] of the can?
6. What do you think would [...] using a more massive can[...] ment? Explain.
7. You have made a device [...] monly called a Hero's eng[...] ful work could be perfo[...] engine?
8. What is the energy source [...] How could it be made to [...] efficiently?

Activity: How do antacids compare?

MATERIALS
balance
baking soda
congo red indicator
buret
ring stand
buret clamp
500 mL flask
several different
   packages of antacid tablets

mortar and pestle
graduated cylinder
funnel
dilute HCl
dropper
stirring rod
goggles and apron

PROCEDURE

1. Fill a flask with 100 mL of water.
2. Dissolve 3 g of baking soda in it.
3. Mount the buret with a clamp on the ring stand as shown in Figure 6–7.
4. Using a funnel, carefully fill the buret with dilute HCl. **CAUTION:** *HCl causes burns; avoid skin contact. Rinse spills with plenty of water.* Record the initial volume of HCl in the buret.
5. Add six drops of congo red to the baking soda solution.
6. Place the flask under the buret. Allow the HCl to slowly drip into the solution while you gently swirl the flask. Con-

tinue adding HCl until the solution turns light blue.
7. Record the remaining volume of HCl in the buret. Calculate the amount of acid neutralized by subtracting the remaining volume from the initial volume.
8. Crush one antacid tablet with a mortar and pestle.
9. Dissolve the ground tablet in 100 mL of water. Rinse the mortar and pestle with a little water. Add this rinse water to the flask also. Repeat steps 5–7.
10. Repeat steps 8–9, then 5–7 using a different antacid tablet each time. Fill the buret with additional HCl if needed.

DATA AND OBSERVATIONS

Antacid			Baking Soda
Initial Volume			
Remaining Volume			
Volume of HCl Neutralized			

FIGURE 6–7.

QUESTIONS AND CONCLUSIONS

1. Since your stomach contains dilute HCl, what is the purpose of antacids?
2. What might cause excess stomach acid?
3. Which antacid is most effective in neutralizing a milliliter of acid?
4. What kinds of compounds are antacid tablets composed of?
5. Compare the cost of a unit dosage of each sample. Is there a relationship between cost and effectiveness?

125

Special **"Skill Inquiry"** features help students apply science skills in many different real-life situations. These special features—28 in all—appear once per chapter.

Problem solving is taught with a step-by-step approach. Plentiful example problems show the reasoning and the mathematics that lead to the solution of a problem. Example problems are set off and clearly labeled within the text.

EXAMPLE: Writing Chemical Formulas

Problem: What is the chemical formula for iron(III) oxide?

Solution: Refer to Table 6–1 for the oxidation numbers of iron(III) and oxygen.

$$\text{iron(III)} = 3+ \qquad \text{oxygen} = 2-$$

In order to have a net charge of zero, two iron(III) atoms must combine with three oxygen atoms.

$$2Fe^{3+} + 3O^{2-} = Fe_2O_3$$

The formula for iron(III) oxide is Fe_2O_3. Use subscripts to indicate the relative proportions of each type of atom.

Skill Inquiry

Many household products contain chemicals that can be dangerous if not handled properly. Products that contain these chemicals are labeled with safety information. For example, the label of a laundry bleach is shown.

When you purchase a product, you should read the label to find out if the product has special storage requirements. Any potentially dangerous chemical should be stored out of the reach of children. Mr. Yuk® labels and child-proof caps are also useful in protecting children.

When you use a product, you should read the label to find out what precautions you should take. Some product labels also include information about proper disposal of the container when it is empty.

1. How should bleach be stored?
2. What should you avoid when using bleach? Why?

Occasionally accidents happen and someone is burned, poisoned, or otherwise harmed with a household product. Most products contain emergency information. Follow the directions on the label for minor accidents, such as a spill. For more serious accidents, always contact the Poison Control Center in your area, a paramedic, or a doctor immediately. Post the numbers near your phone. When you call, know the product that caused the harm and the approximate amount involved.

3. If you spilled a little bleach on your hands and clothing accidentally while doing laundry, what should you do?
4. If a child accidentally has swallowed some bleach, what should you do?
5. What is the phone number of your local Poison Control Center?

What are coefficients?

Whole numbers placed in front of the [reac]tants and products in chemical equation[s are] [coeffi]cients. Coefficients indicate the relative [numbers of] reactants and products. Only coefficien[ts change] when balancing a chemical equation. [Never change] subscripts in a compound.

EXAMPLE: Balancing Equations

Problem: Write a balanced equation f[or the reaction be]tween iron and oxygen yield[ing iron oxide] (rust).

Solution: First, write the formulas for [the reactants and] the products.

$$Fe + O_2 \rightarrow Fe[_2O_3]$$

Next, balance the equation. T[here are two oxy]gen atoms on the left side of [the equation and] three on the right side. Placin[g a coefficient of 3] in front of the O_2 and a 2 in [front of the Fe_2O_3] results in six atoms of oxyge[n on both sides of] the equation.

$$Fe + 3O_2 \rightarrow 2F[e_2O_3]$$

There are now four iron ato[ms on the right of] the equation and only one o[n the left. Placing] the coefficient 4 in front of th[e Fe results in four] Fe atoms on both sides of the [equation.]

$$4Fe + 3O_2 \rightarrow 2[Fe_2O_3]$$

6:9 Chemical Reactions

All chemical reactions involve chang[es in energy. The] change in energy may be in the form of heat, light, or electricity. The energy of the products is always different from the energy of the reactants. If the energy of the products is less than the energy of the reactants, energy is released during the reaction.

$$\text{reactants} \rightarrow \text{products} + \text{energy}$$

Reactions that give off, or release, energy are called **exothermic** (ek soh THUR mihk) reactions. Burning is an example of an exothermic reaction that produces energy in the forms of light and heat.

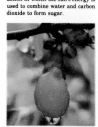

FIGURE 6–10. Photosynthesis is an important series of chemical reactions that are needed for plant growth. It is an endothermic reaction in which the sun's energy is used to combine water and carbon dioxide to form sugar.

The excitement of science

Current topics are highlighted in "Information" or "Choices" special features that conclude each chapter. "Information" pages extend key topics from the chapter. "Choices" pages present various points of view on current issues.

Career information is presented in twenty-eight "Career Profiles." They show daily uses of scientific knowledge and skills in many careers, including nonscience careers.

12:7 Choices: Electricity Use

Demand for electricity increases with each generation of people. It has been predicted that people will use three to six times more electric energy by the year 2000 than we use today. In order to meet the increasing demand for electricity, electric companies have built additional power plants. The c   been increase

The increas ronmental pr energy for pr the air with tains sulfur. with moistur It returns to As more and these environ

Nuclear po clear fuels pr are very dan

What is happening to demand for electric energy?

FIGURE 12–14. Hot water inside a cooling tower is cooled by large fans (a). The water is cooled further as it passes over cascades on the outside of the tower (b).
a

Raindrops are much larger than cloud dr like watermelons compared with peanuts. S rents can keep small droplets suspended as ever, once the droplets grow in size, they beco for the air currents, and fall as precipitation.

Normally, air near the surface of the ear than air at higher altitudes. Therefore, air face tends to rise. As air rises, it cools. Unsta air that keeps rising. As long as the surrou cooler, the air keeps rising. When the risin the same temperature as the surrounding moving upward and becomes stable. Stable earth's surface usually means fair weather, air does not rise and therefore is not coole clouds and precipitation. Air that is unstabl to clouds and rain.

Career Profile

Grace Swanson is a meteorological technician or "met tech." She works at the National Weather Service Forecast Office near Cleveland Hopkins Airport in Ohio. Grace's main job is observing weather conditions. She notes and records data about clouds, visibility, precipitation, relative humidity, and temperatures. Weather forecasters depend on her timely and accurate observations. Grace was trained on duty to be a radar specialist. In a dark room, she studies incoming radar images and analyzes them for precipitation. Radar observations help forecasters determine the amount and intensity of rain or snow. Grace also makes recordings of weather summaries and forecasts. The recordings are broadcast on radio and television. An additional responsibility includes providing airplane pilots with immediate information about both surface and upper air conditions.

Grace was always interested in science. She planned to become an optometrist. However, while in college she took a course about climate. That course got her interested in both climate and weather. Grace rethought her career goals. Eventually she became a met tech.

One does not have to have a college degree to be a met tech. Each met tech is trained on the job. A number of books and manuals must be studied on subjects such as pilot briefing, radar use, and taking weather observations. A test on each of these subjects is required to be certified for this particular work.

10:8 Information: Momentum

Another characteristic of moving objects is momentum. An object's momentum is related to both its mass and velocity. A car and a truck traveling at the same velocity do not have the same amount of momentum. The truck's momentum will be greater since it is more massive. An object's momentum is found by multiplying its mass times its velocity.

$$momentum = mass \times velocity$$
$$p = mv$$

How is momentum calculated?

EXAMPLE: Calculating Momentum

Problem: What is the momentum of a 3000-kg truck moving at 20 m/s?

Solution: The momentum of the truck is equal to its mass times its velocity.

$$p = mv$$
$$p = 3000 \text{ kg} \times 20 \text{ m/s}$$
$$p = 60\ 000 \text{ kg} \cdot \text{m/s}$$

A light object moving rapidly may have more momentum than a slowly-moving massive object. For example, a 2000-kilogram car moving at 25 meters per second has more momentum than a 5000-kilogram truck moving at five meters per second.

FIGURE 10–12. Signs indicating hills are helpful to truck drivers who must decrease the velocity of their trucks in order to prepare for emergency stopping. Decreasing velocity will decrease the truck's momentum (a). The velocity and the mass of a moving vehicle determine its momentum (b).

A brilliant full-color **format** and stimulating photos throughout help clarify concepts and add excitement to the study of science.

Help with reading and studying

The text is organized to help students learn and think about scientific information.

A chapter goal statement, margin questions, and short, numbered sections help students study with purpose. **Vocabulary words** are printed in boldface type, defined in context, and reinforced in the text which follows. Many are phonetically spelled.

Review and Reflect questions at the end of major sections help students review materials and check their understanding.

Two-page **Chapter Reviews** reinforce key chapter ideas:

- **A Summary** highlights at least one main point for each section.
- **Vocabulary and Main Idea** questions use varied formats to keep student interest high.
- **Applications** questions are brief essay questions or problems that require students to use higher level thinking skills.
- **Suggested Readings** and **Investigations** give students of different ability levels opportunities to explore.

CHAPTER 21 REVIEW

SUMMARY

1. Organisms are made of one or more cells. 21:1
2. Scientists use special tools, such as microscopes, to learn about cells.   21:2
3. Some cell parts are common to all types of life. Some types of life have cell parts that are unique.   21:3
4. To remain alive, cells must maintain homeostasis. Homeostasis is maintained by feedback loops.   21:4
5. Materials and wastes move through cell membranes.   21:5
6. Photosynthesis, which takes place in cells that contain chlorophyll, makes use of energy from sunlight to form ATP and glucose.   21:6
7. Cell respiration is an oxidation process that releases the energy stored in glucose.   21:6
8. ATP supplies the energy for the formation and oxidation of glucose.   21:6
9. Enzymes fit in an exact way with other molecules, allowing chemical reactions in cells to take place at low temperatures. 21:7

VOCABULARY

active transport	chloroplasts	mitochondria
ATP	cytoplasm	nucleus
cell membrane	endoplasmic reticulum	photosynthesis
cell respiration	enzyme	ribosomes
cell wall	homeostasis	vacuoles

Choose a word from the list to complete each sentence correctly.

1. _____ is a balance maintained by a system of controls within a cell or an organism.
2. The method of movement of materials through a cell membrane by carrier molecules is called _____.
3. Photosynthesis occurs in the _____ of plant cells.
4. The _____ is the control center of a cell.
5. Energy in cells is stored in a molecule called _____.
6. Respiration in cells occurs in the _____.
7. The _____ is the outermost living part of a cell.
8. Food and water are stored in _____ in cells.
9. The part of a cell that carries proteins is _____.
10. A cell part called the _____ surrounds the cell membranes of some cells, such as plant cells.
11. A(n) _____ is a protein molecule that enables chemical reactions in cells to occur at low temperatures.
12. Proteins are produced in cell _____.
13. _____ is the production of food using energy from sunlight.
14. Another name for biological oxidation in cells is _____.
15. Structures that provide energy for a cell by oxidizing food are _____.

466

QUESTIONS

MAIN IDEAS

Choose the correct answer to complete each sentence.

1. Every type of life *(moves from place to place, shows energy changes, has cell walls)*.
2. All cells *(are about the same size, vary so that the largest is about 10 times larger than the smallest, vary so that the largest is more than 10^4 times bigger than the smallest)*.
3. Cell parts found in all forms of life include *(mitochondria, chloroplasts, lysosomes)*.
4. In every feedback loop, a sensor is connected to something that *(changes an action, performs photosynthesis, performs active transport)*.
5. Movement of carbon monoxide into cells is an example of *(diffusion, active transport, osmosis)*.
6. The products formed in photosynthesis are *(water and carbon dioxide, glucose and oxygen, enzymes and coenzymes)*.
7. Compounds needed for the formation of coenzymes are *(vitamins, carbon monoxide and carbon dioxide, carbon dioxide and water)*.
8. The temperatures at which cell reactions can take place are lowered by *(ATP, enzymes, chlorophyll)*.
9. Cell respiration requires *(sunlight, carbon dioxide, oxygen)*.
10. All cells have *(nuclei, cell walls, cell membranes, chlorophyll)*.

APPLICATIONS

Answer each question in one or more paragraphs.

1. How is a cell nucleus different from an atomic nucleus?
2. Imagine that typical cells are enlarged to be the size of the solar system in comparison to you. What two cell parts (like planets) would you choose to explore first with spaceships? Explain why.
3. Describe the feedback loops that occur when you pick up a pencil and write the answer to a question.
4. Recall what you learned about color in chapter 14. Why does chlorophyll in green plants appear green?
5. Since scientists have not found oxygen (O_2) in the atmospheres of other planets, what can be said about photosynthesis on those planets?

FURTHER STUDY

INVESTIGATIONS

1. Construct a three-dimensional model of a plant or animal cell. Display the model in class with labels.
2. Prepare a report about differing opinions on the value of taking vitamin supplements.
3. Prepare a report on how certain narcotics interfere with diffusion and active transport across the cell membrane.

READINGS

Brown, M. and J. Goldstein, "Receiving Windows for the Cell." *Science Year, 1980*. pp. 42–55.
Pines, Maya. *Inside the Cell*. Enslow Publishers: Hillsdale, NJ, 1980.
Shih, Gene, and Richard Kessel. *Living Images*. Science Books International: Boston, 1982.
Snyderman, Ralph. "Cell Wars." *Science Year, 1981*. 1980. pp. 56–69.

And for teachers . . . .

Help you can rely on

The kind of help secondary science teachers request in a **Teacher's Edition**—in one convenient reference.

A **Teacher's Guide,** in the front of the **Teacher's Annotated Edition,** shows what materials you have at hand . . . helps you adapt the course to your own needs . . . and lists additional resources for class presentations and discussions.

The **Teacher's Guide** also contains complete teaching information for each unit and chapter:
- unit overviews
- ideas for introducing the units
- performance objectives
- specific strategies for teaching concepts, skills, activities
- complete answers to all questions

Safety in the Science Classroom

Careful planning and preparation, as well as being aware of hazards, can help keep accidents to a minimum in the science classroom. Even so, there are no guarantees against accidents. The following guidelines can help you maintain a safe science classroom and/or laboratory. Also, you may want to use the Basic Skills master concerning laboratory safety with your class. The master appears in the *MERRILL GENERAL SCIENCE Teacher Resource Book.*

General Safety

General safety rules are listed in Appendix B of *MERRILL GENERAL SCIENCE.* These general rules should be emphasized to students before any laboratory work is done, and also should be periodically reviewed. Stress to students the importance of adhering to these rules to ensure their own safety as well as the safety of others.

Before Each Laboratory Activity

1. Perform activities yourself before assigning them to students. Previewing enables you to make note of cautions and safety procedures already incorporated into each activity.
2. Arrange the classroom or lab in such a way that equipment and supplies are easily accessible to students. Avoiding confusion where solutions and reagents are being dispensed is important in avoiding spills and broken glassware.
3. Have available only equipment and supplies necessary to complete the assigned activity to help eliminate the problem of students doing unauthorized experiments.
4. Review the procedure to be followed with students. Emphasize cautions found in the activity. Review what students should do if an accident occurs. If chemicals need to be disposed of in a special place, remind students of proper disposal methods.
5. Be sure all students know proper procedures to follow if an accident should occur, and the proper way to use fire extinguishers, fire blankets, showers, and eyewash fountains or bottles. This equipment should be well marked and easily accessible.
6. Discuss proper cleanup procedures with the class. Provide separate refuse containers for combustibles and for noncombustibles, such as glass. When working with chemicals, remind students that reagents should not be poured back into bottles and that waste acids should always be poured into water, never the reverse.

During a Laboratory Activity

1. Make sure that the laboratory is clean and free of clutter. Student books, coats, and other personal items should be stored away from the laboratory tables.
2. Require that students wear safety glasses and aprons when working in the laboratory.
3. Never allow students to work alone in the laboratory.
4. Emphasize that any accident or injury—no matter how insignificant—should be reported to the teacher at once.
5. Remove broken or chipped glassware from use immediately. Also clean up any spills that may occur. Dilute concentrated solutions with water before removing. Use a whisk broom and dust pan to clean up broken glass. Large wads of wet cotton should be used to pick up small pieces of glass.
6. Be sure all glassware that is to be heated is a heat treated type that will not shatter. Remind students that heated glassware looks cool several seconds after heating, but can still cause burns for several minutes.

After the Laboratory Activity

1. Be sure that the laboratory is clean. All work surfaces and equipment should be cleaned thoroughly after use.
2. Be sure students dispose of chemicals and broken glassware properly.
3. Be sure all hot plates and burners are turned off before leaving the laboratory.

Equipment and Supplies

A complete list of the equipment and supplies needed for all the activities in *MERRILL GENERAL SCIENCE* begins on page 32T. The amounts listed are for a class of 30 students working in pairs. Most nonconsumables can be used over and over again for many years. Most consumables and chemicals will need to be replaced each school year. The activities are designed so that simple materials can be used. Many materials may be available locally. A list of scientific suppliers is given on page 39T.

Software

Unit 1
Discovery Lab, MECC (Apple II)
> Introduces to science processes including observation, experimental design, and hypothesis testing.

Measurements: Length, Mass, and Volume, Focus Media (Apple II, Commodore 64)
> Students learn to measure length, mass, and volume in SI units.

Modeling, MECC (Apple II)
> Students develop the concept of a model through experiments with "Black-box" machines.

Unit 2
Chemistry: Series 1, Focus Media (Apple II, TRS-80, Commodore 64 and PET)
> Three different games teach states of matter, atomic structure and bonding, and acids and bases.

Chemistry Volume 1, Prentice-Hall (Apple II, Atari, Commodore 64, IBM PC and PCjr)
> Discusses the atom and atomic models

Chemistry Volume 2, Prentice-Hall (Apple II, Atari, Commodore 64, IBM PC and PCjr)
> Discusses the periodic table.

Introduction to General Chemistry, Compress (Apple II)
> Eight-disk set covers periodic table, nomenclature, balancing equations, and atomic weights.

Molecules and Atoms, SMC (Apple II, IBM PC and PCjr)
> Covers molecules and atoms, the Bohr model, how to draw atoms, ions, and ionic bonding.

Unit 3
ATARILAB Starter Set, Atari (Atari, Apple II, Commodore 64)
> Students analyze objects and events to learn concepts of temperature and energy transfer.

Optics: Mirrors and Beams, HRM (Apple II)
> Teaches students the physics of optical science.

Reflections, HesWare (Apple II, Commodore 64, IBM PC and PCjr)
> Teaches reflection, refraction, and absorption through building of a sound and light show.

Unit 4
Earth Science, MECC (TRS-80)
> Students locate the epicenter of an earthquake, identify 29 minerals, identify five major constellations, and explore the concept of distance.

Earth Science, Atari (Atari 800)
> Teaches definition of solar distances, identification of constellations, and the composition and mineral formations of the earth.

Forecast, CBS (Apple II, Commodore 64, IBM PC and PCjr)
> Students chart weather patterns and learn how atmospheric conditions affect the weather.

Shore Features, CDL (Apple II)
> Tutorial identifying shore and beach features.

Unit 5
Classification, MECC (Apple II, IBM PC)
> Students use a data base inquiry system to enter, search, and sort data and to generate reports. Results are related to the process of scientific classification.

Elementary Biology, MECC (Atari)
> This diskette contains three simulations. In "Circulation," students observe the movement of a blood cell throughout the circulatory system of a fish. In "Odell Lake" and "Odell Woods," students construct food chains.

Genetics, Microcomputer Workshops (Apple II, Commodore 64 and PET)
> Introduction to the basic laws of genetics including dominant, sex-linked recessive, and sex-influenced traits.

The Human Body, CDL (Apple II)
> Tutorial diskette covering the muscular system, digestive system, respiratory system, skeletal system, and nervous system.

Merlan Biology Series, Merlan (Apple II)
> Students learn about mitosis and meiosis.

Unit 6
Energy Search, McGraw-Hill (Apple II, TRS-80)
> Students manage an energy factory and search for new energy sources.

Heatloss, MECC (Apple II with printer)
> Problem-solving program that helps students determine areas and costs of energy-saving improvements to their family home.

Oh, Deer, MECC (Apple II)
> Students manage a herd of white-tailed deer in a residential area over a five-year period.

Power Grid, HRM (Apple II, TRS-80)
> Simulation of an electric utility drawing power from plants fueled by coal, oil, gas, nuclear power, and water power.

And, **fully annotated pupil pages** simplify your classroom instruction. Notes include tips on how to direct material toward the natural interests of students. Whenever appropriate, background information, suggested activities and demonstrations, and specific teaching suggestions are offered.

Natural eutrophication occurs over thousands of years. However, pollutants such as sewage, fertilizers, and organic industrial wastes speed up eutrophication so that it may occur in as little as 20 years. Populations of blue-green algae may increase greatly. When the algae die and decompose, they use dissolved oxygen in the water. As a result of the lower oxygen content, many populations of fish die. This type of eutrophication may be reversed. Lake Erie was considered in advanced stages of eutrophication in the late 1960s. Regulations controlling organic pollutants, such as phosphates, have helped to reverse this trend.

Natural processes cleanse the atmosphere of many pollutants. Air pollutants may be blown away by winds and diluted, combine chemically with other substances and form harmless compounds, or be washed out by precipitation. However, air pollution that is concentrated in certain areas may be complicated by geologic and atmospheric conditions. As shown in Figure 27–3, Los Angeles is located in a geologic area where air circulation is restricted. Temperature inversions prevent smog from rising and becoming diluted.

Although carbon dioxide is listed as an air pollutant in Table 27–1, it is naturally produced as a waste product of respiration and used by plants in photosynthesis. Together these processes form the carbon dioxide–oxygen cycle. The burning of fossil fuels is increasing the concentration of carbon dioxide in the atmosphere. Carbon dioxide and particulate pollution may cause slow temperature changes on the earth. Scientists are not sure if the earth's climate will

FIGURE 27–3. In summer, smog is common in metropolitan Los Angeles. In sunlight, nitrogen oxides and hydrocarbons, abundant pollutants due to traffic in the city, combine to form photochemical smog. Descending warm air from the mountain region forms an inversion layer. The sea breeze moves the smog toward the mountains, where it is trapped. Auto emission regulations have helped reduce the problems.

What natural processes help reduce pollution?

DEMONSTRATION Demonstrate dilution in the air of your classroom: open a bottle of perfume or ammonia in one location. Have students indicate when the odor reaches them. Review diffusion.
ACTIVITY A number of products, such as laundry materials, are now specifically labeled as biodegradable. Have students check their home and store shelves for products with this label. Prepare lists.

Describe some biodegradable and nonbiodegradable materials.

land pollu- cotton, and osers in soil. y short peri- phosphorus, the environ- r many solid odegradable. compose natu- be buried in on.

MIXTURES

INTRODUCING THE CHAPTER   Take a small amount of sugar and add it to a beaker of water. Ask students how to separate the *mixture* of sugar and water. Boil the water away in an evaporating dish or a beaker leaving the sugar behind. In another evaporating dish or test tube, heat some sugar until it becomes carmelized. Note that the sugar has changed *chemically* by combining with oxygen. It cannot easily be changed back to sugar. Use the chapter opening photograph to point out that there are many mixtures.

7:1 Types of Mixtures

Mixtures are important in your life. Your blood is a mixture of solids, liquids, and gases. The air you breathe is a mixture. Many of the foods you eat are mixtures. For example, the milk and cereal you may have had for breakfast or the taco you may have had for lunch are mixtures.

Mixtures can be composed of any combination of solid, liquid, or gaseous substances. A **mixture** is formed when two or more substances are physically combined. Mixtures differ from compounds because the substances in a mixture are not chemically combined. The substances in a mixture retain their chemical properties and can be separated by physical means, such as filtering. Mixtures have a variable composition also. The elements in a compound are always in the same ratio.

Mixtures may be heterogeneous or homogeneous. The properties of a heterogeneous mixture are not the same throughout the mixture. For example, a taco is a heterogeneous mixture. The amounts of vegetables, meats, and cheese are not the same throughout a taco. Homogeneous mixtures are called solutions. **Solutions** have the same properties throughout. Solutions are formed when substances dissolve in other substances.

GOAL   You will learn the characteristics of mixtures, how they are classified, and how they are separated.

How are mixtures different from compounds?

SUGGESTION   Review the classification of matter introduced in chapter 3.

What are some properties of solutions?

139

the forms in- All of these tential. f motion. To g ball. As the e it is able to pins, some of Thus, the ball

and by multi- velocity.

ty²

and a velocity y of the ball? f the mass of city squared.

What is kinetic energy?

BACKGROUND   Kinetic comes from the Greek word *kinetikos*, which means motion.

SUGGESTION   Students may wonder why kg·m²/s² is equated to joules in this example. You may wish to show the following dimension analysis or let students compute it.
$$\text{joule} = F \times d$$
$$= mA \times d$$
$$= \text{kg·m}/s^2 \times m$$
$$= \text{kg·m}^2/s^2$$

$$KE = \frac{1}{2}(7 \text{ kg}) \times (6 \text{ m/s})$$
$$KE = 126 \text{ kg} \times \text{m}^2/s^2 \text{ or } 126 \text{ J}$$

Under ideal conditions, the bowling ball in the example above could do 126 joules of work on the pins. Ideal conditions mean that all of the kinetic energy of the bowling ball can be transferred to the pins. Under real conditions, however, the amount of work done by the ball on the pins will be less than 126 joules. You know that friction between the alley and the ball causes the ball to slow down. The friction produces heat. As the ball rolls down the alley, both the alley and the ball become hotter. Some of the energy of the moving ball is changed to heat. The ball slows down as this energy transfer takes place. When the ball strikes the pins, more energy is changed to heat. The amount of energy gained by the ball and pins is less than the 126 joules of work done on the ball.

BACKGROUND   Some of the energy also is transferred into mechanical energy in the form of sound.

FIGURE 10–5. The explosion of rocket fuel is a chemical reaction. During this chemical reaction, energy in the form of heat, light, and sound is released.

Teacher Resource Book . . .

Extra help for you and your students

Saves you time in preparing classroom presentations . . . helps you emphasize the topics you choose . . . provides for special attention to students working at different ability levels.

Organized by chapter, this 600-page **Teacher Resource Book** includes teaching masters . . . worksheet masters for each activity . . . Basic Skills masters . . . Challenge masters that encourage students to apply their science knowledge . . . Review masters to help students prepare for Chapter Tests.

And, special **"Science and Society"** masters for each unit show students how to relate science to community involvement.

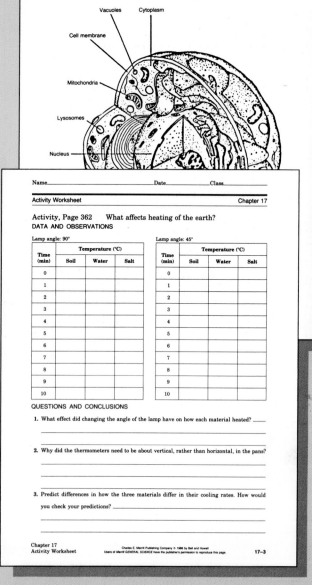

A complete evaluation program is included to help you meet a variety of testing needs. It includes **Chapter Tests, Unit Evaluations,** and a **Final Exam.**

The whole package can be stored in the handy three-ring binder with chapter dividers—so you have ready access to all materials.

Name_____ Date_____ Class_____

Test   Chapter 14

Part A
Write the letter of the best choice on the line to the left.

_____ 1. In the particle model, light is visualized as bundles of energy called ____.
   a. electromagnets   b. photons   c. electrons   d. radons
_____ 2. Which of the following is *not* a part of the electromagnetic spectrum?
   a. beta rays   b. gamma rays   c. X rays   d. visible light
_____ 3. The vibrations of ____ always produce electromagnetic waves.
   a. matter   b. a vacuum   c. sound   d. charged particles
_____ 4. Which of the following has shorter wavelengths than visible light?
   a. infrared   b. ultraviolet   c. radio waves   d. microwaves
_____ 5. Which of the following has the highest frequency?
   a. red light   b. green light   c. blue light   d. radio waves
_____ 6. In AM radio, an audio signal is used to vary the ____ of a carrier wave.
   a. wavelength   b. velocity   c. frequency   d. amplitude
_____ 7. Electrons vibrating between energy levels of atoms produce ____.
   a. X rays   b. visible light   c. radio waves   d. sound
_____ 8. Ultraviolet light, causing a substance to glow and give off visible light, is an example of ____.
   a. fluorescence   b. bioluminescence   c. incandescence   d. polarization
_____ 9. Illuminance depends on both the intensity and ____ of a light source.
   a. color   b. wavelength   c. distance   d. shape
_____ 10. The velocity of light in water is about ____ the velocity of light in air.
   a. 1/10   b. 3/4   c. twice   d. ten times
_____ 11. An object that reflects only red light will appear ____ when placed under white light.
   a. white   b. red   c. blue   d. black
_____ 12. A concave mirror can project a real image because it can ____ light rays.
   a. reflect   b. focus   c. magnify   d. spread out
_____ 13. A ____ mirror can form only a small, wide-angle image.
   a. convex   b. concave   c. flat   d. plane
_____ 14. Most glare from horizontal surfaces is ____.
   a. incandescent   b. refracted   c. diffracted   d. polarized
_____ 15. An element, when heated, gives off light having a characteristic ____.
   a. polarization   b. spectrum   c. focus   d. diffraction
_____ 16. Light from an object placed farther from a convex lens than the focal point will ____.
   a. be totally reflected   c. form a real image
                            d. not be refracted
   wide-angle image.
                            c. flat   d. plane
   c. diffracted   d. polarized
   ht having a characteristic ____.
   c. focus   d. diffraction
   m a convex lens than the focal point will ____.
   c. form a real image
   d. not be refracted

mpany © 1986 by Bell and Howell
e publisher's permission to reproduce this page.   14-11

Name_____ Date_____ Class_____

Challenge   Chapter 3

Using Properties of Matter

In chapter 3, you learn how the chemical and physical properties of a substance determine its use. Certain plastics are used to make desk and counter tops because the plastics can be made smooth and hard. Also, they are more resistant to many cleaning chemicals. Ethylene glycol is a good antifreeze because it has a freezing point that is low and a boiling point that is high compared to the normal temperature ranges in our environment.

Graphite, a form of carbon, is useful as the "lead" in pencils because it is soft. Thus, it will rub easily onto paper. In addition, graphite is nearly black, which makes it visible against the light color of most paper. However, graphite has other properties such as good electrical conductivity, a very high melting point, and chemical inertness which

make it useful in electrical, glassworking, and metalworking technologies.

People in all crafts and professions must understand the properties of the materials with which they work. Then they know how to use these materials safely. They also know how to take advantage of the materials' chemical and physical properties in discovering new uses.

In the left column of the following table, there are several examples of practical uses of materials. Learn more about the underlined material from reference books. Then complete

TABLE OF USES AND PROPERTIES O

Application	Propertie
1. Some cooking pans have copper bottoms.	Thermal conductivi chemical reactivity
2. Gold is used on many electrical contacts.	
3. Aluminum foil is used in the kitchen to wrap foods.	
4. Baking soda is spread on an acid spill.	

Chapter 3
Challenge   Charles E. Merrill Publishing C
                        Users of Merrill GENERAL SCIENCE have

---

Name_____ Date_____ Class_____

Review   Chapter 12

Complete each of the sentences below by writing the correct words on the blanks provided.
1. Electrons travel from one terminal of a battery to the other because of a _____ difference, measured in _____.

2. _____ electricity is electric charge that does not move and is measured in units called _____.

3. An object acquires a positive charge by losing _____, leaving an excess of _____.

4. The quantity of electrons that flows through a conductor per second is called electric _____ and is measured in units called _____.

5. A(n) _____ is used to reduce the voltage of _____ current from a transmission line.

Solve the following problem. Write your answer on the blank provided. Show your work in the space below each problem.

_____ 6. A lamp is connected to a 120-volt outlet. If the resistance of the light bulb is 30 ohms, how much current will flow?

_____ 7. How much power is used by a refrigerator that allows 3.5 amperes of current to flow at 110 volts?

_____ 8. What is the resistance of the refrigerator in the problem above?

_____ 9. What will it cost to operate a 1500-watt air conditioner for 24 hours if the cost of electricity is 11¢ per kilowatt-hour?

Chapter 12
Review   Charles E. Merrill Publishing Company © 1986 by Bell and Howell
                Users of Merrill GENERAL SCIENCE have the publisher's permission to reproduce this page.   12-8

Using *MERRILL GENERAL SCIENCE*

Philosophy and Themes

Advancements in science and the technology it spawns have produced a rapidly changing world. Students of the 80s and beyond must be well prepared in science and, more importantly, in the application of the sciences to everyday life. The major goal of *MERRILL GENERAL SCIENCE* is to help students recognize and appreciate the application of science to everyday living.

The text presents a wide range of life, earth and physical science topics with major emphasis on the physical sciences. Students develop a strong conceptual understanding of the physical sciences, which is reinforced throughout the study of space, earth, life, and environmental science material. Throughout the text, science concepts are explained using familiar examples. In addition, students are exposed to the excitement of science through discovery of its importance beyond the classroom and laboratory.

MERRILL GENERAL SCIENCE is current, interesting, understandable, and relevant, providing a general science background in an easily readable form. Emphasis is placed on scientific processes so that students develop an appreciation for the wonders of the scientific enterprise.

Based on this philosophy, the text contains the following unifying themes.

1. Chemistry and physics concepts provide a basis for understanding earth and life science.
2. Integration of physical, earth, and life sciences provides comprehensive treatment of general science concepts.
3. Observation and experimentation are the bases for scientific discovery and problem solving.
4. All living and nonliving processes involve the transfer of energy.
5. Classification of objects or events simplifies the study of science.
6. Scientific decisions affect people's lives.
7. Science and technology are dynamic.
8. A general understanding of science is important in many aspects of daily life.

Organization and Sequence

MERRILL GENERAL SCIENCE is divided into six units. These units are subdivided into 28 chapters.

Each chapter is divided into numbered sections. The numbered sections will be useful to you in planning lessons and giving assignments. Students will find the numbered sections helpful in locating specific topics. The units, chapters, and sections are listed in the Table of Contents on page v.

Unit One, The Tools of Science, presents basic science concepts of measurement, scientific notation, scientific methods, and problem solving. The use of SI and metric measurements is explained. Scientific methods are presented, not as a rigid procedure, but rather as a dynamic process that varies depending on the topic of study.

Unit Two, The Structure of Matter, introduces concepts of chemistry. The properties of matter and of atomic and subatomic structure are discussed. Interactions of matter are detailed in studies of bonding, reactions, and mixtures. Applications of chemistry are presented, too.

Unit Three, The Nature of Energy, begins with a discussion of a familiar phenomenon, motion. This introduction is the basis for explanation of more abstract concepts, such as force and pressure. Heat and electricity also are presented. The unit concludes with a discussion of waves, specifically in terms of sound and light.

Unit Four, The Systems of Our World, presents a study of the universe and our solar system. An indepth discussion of the earth follows, including studies of the oceans, atmosphere, geology, and earth history.

Unit Five, The Patterns of Life, presents an overview of life science topics. The cell is examined in some detail. Classification of organisms is presented. The human body is discussed in terms of body systems and homeostasis. The importance of health maintenance is stressed. Genetics and ecology conclude the unit.

Unit Six, The Influence of Science, presents some realities of science in our world. Science does not exist in a vacuum. So, many questions of ethics and values are involved in decisions that depend on science knowledge. In the presentation of environmental science, energy resources are analyzed in terms of pollution problems and resource management techniques.

Teacher's Annotated Edition

Teacher's Guide

The Teacher's Guide for *MERRILL GENERAL SCIENCE* is designed to make the features of the text more useful to you as you teach the course, to give you information that aids in adapting your course to your teaching style, and to provide you with additional references and resources you may want to use in your presentations, discussions, or other classroom teaching. The first pages of the Teacher's Guide include this material.

Beginning on page 41T, unit-by-unit and chapter-by-chapter information is provided. This information includes unit overviews, introducing the unit ideas, and ideas for teaching each chapter. Select whatever activities, demonstrations, analogies, background, or other information you feel will be helpful to your students. For each **Activity,** preparation notes are provided to assist you in getting ready for student laboratory work. Sample data, where applicable, and answers to Questions and Conclusions are given, too.

The students' **Goal** for each chapter is followed by a list of specific **Performance Objectives.** Thus, you know what to emphasize to make sure your students achieve the objectives. When you are designing your course of study or tests, the objectives can serve as a framework. The Chapter Review and Chapter Test masters in the *MERRILL GENERAL SCIENCE Teacher Resource Book* are based on these performance objectives.

Answers to Review and Reflect identifies the pupil's pages where questions are asked and provides complete answers, unhampered by space constraints on the pupil's page. **Chapter Review** provides answers to all Applications and Main Ideas questions, except multiple-choice questions. Answers to the Vocabulary activities and multiple-choice Main Ideas questions are indicated by red teacher's annotations overprinting the pupil's pages.

Teacher Annotations

Red teacher annotations are divided into five categories. An INTRODUCING THE CHAPTER annotation appears below the chapter title on the chapter opening pages. These annotations suggest motivational strategies. Throughout each chapter, BACKGROUND, ACTIVITY, DEMONSTRATION, and SUGGESTION annotations provide useful information and ideas to teachers. Red tint blocks identify answers to all student margin notes.

Pupil's Edition

Readability

Readability plays a major role in determining the success of a textbook with students. Readability also promotes teachability and aids in classroom management. In *MERRILL GENERAL SCIENCE,* careful attention has been given to readability in an effort to promote comprehension, student interest, and student involvement in science. The text is designed to help students think critically and sense relationships among ideas, as well as build on previous knowledge.

In science classes, students traditionally are expected to learn scientific facts. *MERRILL GENERAL SCIENCE* facilitates teaching not only science content, but also the processes needed to learn science. Balancing content with process is a practical approach to science instruction.

To help students adjust to the amount of factual information presented in science materials, careful attention has been given to vocabulary, sentence construction, paragraph structure, unit and chapter organization, illustrations, and text format. The vocabulary is consistent with the level of students for whom the text was designed. Vocabulary terms are limited to unfamiliar words that are useful in general understanding of science concepts both within the text and in everyday activities. The terms are printed in boldface type, and many are followed by phonetic spellings. Each term is clearly defined and reinforced throughout the discussion. A variety of other text features enhance readability. Some suggestions to aid you are given in Reading Science Information on page 19T.

Photographs and Illustrations

To aid student understanding and to stimulate interest, more than 500 color graphics—including illustrations, diagrams, and photos—are included in *MERRILL GENERAL SCIENCE.* A two-page photograph accompanied by an explanation and questions introduces each unit. Each chapter begins with a large photo and an introductory paragraph depicting students involved in an activity related to the chapter topic. The introductory paragraph is designed to be thought-provoking and motivating. Throughout each chapter, the graphics reinforce, clarify, and provide additional information about concepts discussed in the sections. In activities, diagrams provide models for setting up apparatus. Use these graphics as much as possible in your presentation of the chapter concepts to enhance student comprehension. Many difficult concepts can be understood readily when represented graphically. Help students to think of the graphics and captions as an integral part of the text, not something to be skipped over.

Margin Notes and Review Questions

Questions, printed in blue, are placed in the margin of the pupil's text to aid reading comprehension. Encourage students to answer the questions as they read each section. Point out that the questions highlight main points and are useful for note-taking or outlining. Answers to all of the margin notes are marked with red tints in the Teacher's Annotated Edition.

Review and Reflect questions are designed for checking the recall and understanding of ideas presented in one or more sections. The questions are useful to students as a self-test, to teachers as a check of student reading comprehension, and for class discussion. If they cannot answer the Review and Reflect questions, students should reread the sections immediately preceding the questions. Answers to Review and Reflect questions appear chapter-by-chapter in the Teacher's Guide.

Activities

Each chapter of *MERRILL GENERAL SCIENCE* contains two full-page activities. Point out the activity format to students: Materials, Procedure, Data and Observations, Questions and Conclusions. Relate this to the form of a lab report. Call attention to the diagrams, which illustrate procedure steps. Note the goggles and apron symbols, which are reminders to students that goggles and aprons should be put on before beginning the Procedure. Also, point out Caution statements. Review appropriate lab safety and equipment use guidelines before each activity. Appendix B in the pupil's edition, Laboratory Safety in this Teacher's Guide on page 31T, and the Basic Skills masters in the Teacher Resource Book may be helpful. Additional information about the activities, including instructions for preparing solutions and alternative materials or procedures, is given chapter-by-chapter in the Teacher's Guide. Sample data, if applicable, and answers to Questions and Conclusions are also provided.

Special Features

Each chapter contains a Career Profile, a Skill Inquiry, and an Information or a Choices section. The Career Profiles may be used to highlight career possibilities for students to consider. Emphasize the importance of scientific knowledge in many careers, even those that may seem to be unrelated to science. An assortment of careers requiring various levels of education is presented.

Skill Inquiries are in-depth studies of topics related to Chapter concepts. Use the Skill Inquiries to illustrate the application of science skills in many different situations. Stress the importance of practical science knowledge.

Information or Choices sections conclude each chapter. These sections may serve as springboards for investigation or discussion of concepts beyond the general information presented in the main part of the chapter. When you use these sections, point out the identifying characteristics, such as the symbol next to the section number, to students. Use the Review and Reflect questions and blue margin notes accompanying these sections to provide a framework for class discussion or student review of the topics presented. Note that since these sections are optional they are not covered in the Chapter Review and no vocabulary terms are boldfaced within them.

Chapter-End Materials

Two pages of Chapter Review materials appear at the end of each chapter. The Summary lists at least one main point from each section. A blue section number keys each statement to the section from which it derives. The Summary provides a concise review of major chapter concepts to aid students' reading and note-taking.

The boldface terms in the chapter are listed as Vocabulary in the Chapter Review. Use the vocabulary activity to check students' knowledge of the meanings of the terms. Note that the format of the vocabulary activities varies with each chapter. Multiple choice, completion, and question-answer formats provide variety so that students do not become bored with routine chapter reviews.

Chapter-end Questions are divided into two categories. Main Ideas questions are objective, short answer questions which can be used to check factual recall. Like the vocabulary activity, the Main Ideas format varies from chapter to chapter. Applications questions require higher level cognitive skills. Students generally need to synthesize chapter information and use it to answer brief essay questions or solve problems.

Further Study presents suggestions for extending the chapter. The wide range of Investigations enables you to assign them to students at many different ability levels. The readings provide an opportunity for interested students at various reading levels to learn more about the chapter topics. Red annotations indicate the approximate reading level of each reading: + for above the reading level, 0 for the same reading level, and − for below the reading level of the MERRILL GENERAL SCIENCE text. Encourage students to read additional science articles in newspapers and magazines or books about scientists and scientific studies, and to watch science programs on television. Also, encourage students to come up with their own ideas for investigations.

Appendixes, Glossary, and Index

Three appendixes are included in the pupil's edition of MERRILL GENERAL SCIENCE. Each is intended for quick reference in areas where periodic review may be needed. Appendix A lists SI base and derived units. Appendix B lists classroom and laboratory safety guidelines, as well as first aid. Appendix C explains basic steps in the manipulation of algebraic equations to solve for an unknown variable.

The Glossary is a listing of all the boldface vocabulary terms that appear in the text, and their definitions. Many terms are accompanied by phonetic spellings. A pronunciation key is provided with the Glossary. The complete Index allows students to quickly locate key terms and topics in the text. References to illustrations, activities, and tables are given in addition to text references.

Teacher Resource Book

To supplement your teaching resources, a Teacher Resource Book is provided with MERRILL GENERAL SCIENCE. This three-ring binder with chapter tab dividers contains more than 350 blackline masters for use with your students. Included are a series of Basic Skills masters such as a reading inventory of the pupil's edition, lab safety and equipment use guidelines, and a basic math skills worksheet. Teaching Masters, Activity Worksheets, Challenges, Chapter Reviews, and Chapter Tests are provided for each chapter. With each chapter, a planning guide indicates when to use the masters with corresponding text material. For each unit, a Science and Society master is designed to get students involved in science at the community level. Unit Evaluations are provided also, for review and/or testing. A final exam master is included to facilitate evaluation of comprehensive learning. Reduced pupil's pages with answers shown in red are included for each master.

Planning the Course

MERRILL GENERAL SCIENCE is organized to provide an understanding of the physical sciences as a basis for understanding the space, earth, life, and environmental sciences. The text is flexible enough for you to adapt it to your classes. You are in the best position to design a general science course that meets your students' needs. To assist you in the development of the best possible general science course for your students, a planning guide is provided.

MERRILL GENERAL SCIENCE may be used in a full-year course or a one-semester course. Depending on the length of your course, the Planning Guide shows the number of class sessions recommended for teaching each chapter. The recommendations for a full-year course are based on 180 classroom periods of approximately 45 minutes each. Similarly, the one-semester course is based on 90 classroom periods. Two additional laboratory periods are needed for each chapter if the activities are to be completed.

Within each chapter, some sections require primary emphasis in order for major concepts to be developed adequately. Sections of secondary emphasis, as designated in the Planning Guide, may be used if you have the time. Use the Planning Guide to help you schedule the topics you plan to present, gauge the amount of time you will spend on each topic, and determine which topics should be given the most emphasis.

The Planning Guide is not intended as a rigid schedule. It is intended to help you develop and follow a schedule that will enable you to complete your goals for the school year or semester. Use it in relation to the interests and abilities of the students you teach, the materials available for activities, and the time available for teaching. You may decide to devote more time and emphasis to some topics by using some of the materials provided in the MERRILL GENERAL SCIENCE Teacher Resource Book.

Planning Guide

Chapter	Class Sessions		Emphasis Level	
	Semester Course	Full-Year Course	Primary	Secondary
1	5	6	1:1–1:10	1:11
2	5	6	2:1–2:7	2:8
3	5	6	3:1–3:7	3:8
4	3	6	4:1–4:3; 4:6	4:4–4:5; 4:7–4:8
5	2	6	5:1–5:3	5:4–5:8
6	4	7	6:1–6:4; 6:7, 6:8	6:5–6:6; 6:9–6:10
7	—	5	7:1–7:7	7:8
8	—	6	8:1–8:8	8:9
9	4	7	9:1–9:6	9:7–9:9
10	4	7	10:1–10:5	10:6–10:8
11	4	7	11:1–11:5	11:6–11:7
12	3	7	12:1–12:3	12:4–12:7
13	3	7	13:1–13:3	13:4–13:10
14	3	7	14:1–14:5	14:6–14:9
15	4	7	15:1, 15:2, 15:4–15:6	15:3, 15:7
16	4	7	16:1, 16:3, 16:4–16:8	16:2, 16:9, 16:10
17	4	7	17:1–17:6; 17:8	17:7, 17:9
18	4	8	18:1–18:3; 18:5, 18:6, 18:8–18:10	18:4, 18:7, 18:11
19	4	7	19:1–19:3; 19:5–19:9	19:4, 19:10
20	4	8	20:1–20:9	20:10
21	3	6	21:1–21:6	21:7, 21:8
22	3	5	22:1–22:7; 22:9	22:8, 22:10
23	4	7	23:1; 23:3–23:10	23:2, 23:11, 23:12
24	4	6	24:1–24:7	24:8
25	3	5	25:1–25:6	25:7, 25:8
26	4	7	26:1–26:4, 26:8, 26:9	26:5–26:7, 26:10
27	—	5	27:1–27:5	27:6–27:8
28	—	5	28:1–28:7	28:8

Reading Science

Although we think of science study as one in which students conduct experiments and discover scientific data, we find that the dissemination and acquisition of data among scientists is through the reading of printed materials. Thus, by reading, scientists are able to know the information their colleagues have discovered.

Science writing can be described as intense, precise, specific, and "jammed" with facts, among which are many interrelationships. This compact writing often presents difficulties to students, who in most cases, have learned to read by using more casual, narrative material. Specifically, students must master technical vocabulary representing scientific concepts. These concepts are in ascending order with new knowledge building on what has been learned. Thus, students must note not only the facts, but the interrelationships among them. They must discern the organization of the information and learn to make a critical interpretation and application of the data.

Essentially, when reading this text, students need the skills:

1. to understand the purpose of the assignment.
2. to use the various parts of the textbook effectively.
3. to understand the vocabulary, which includes technical terms as well as general words used technically, such as "cell."
4. to gain accurate information from the graphic aids: pictures, tables, diagrams, charts, and graphs.
5. to read for exact meaning and to see the organization of the information; to note main ideas and to relate the appropriate details to each.
6. to read directions accurately.
7. to evaluate science materials in noting evidence, drawing conclusions, making judgements, and seeing implications.
8. to apply data from reading to practical problems and to their own experiences.

The ability to note the author's organization of data and to organize this information for oneself is a most important requisite for adequate comprehension of science materials. Specific techniques include:

1. taking notes that will give students practice in recognizing main ideas and related details and in noting the interrelationships of the main ideas and details.
2. investigating what the students know and do not know about the topic(s) to be studied. Help them recall whatever background they may have. Begin immediately to help them apply the information to their personal experiences.
3. previewing the reading assignment. Note topical headings that indicate the organization, and discuss the various graphic aids and the ideas they show. To help students begin to understand the scope and emphasis of the chapter, note the summary ideas, the vocabulary, and the specific questions at the chapter end.
4. establishing questions for the students to keep in mind as they read. These questions will guide their reading and assist their concentration. Keep the questions few in number, usually one or two per section. Often you can evolve these questions as you preview the assignment with students.

Two other major areas in which students need instruction are the understanding of technical terms and the use of graphic aids. Definitions of technical terms can be obtained from the glossary. Meanings also can be gained from the context (a new term often is defined when it is introduced) and from the meanings of word parts (roots, prefixes, and suffixes). Graphic aids seem simple to use, but students need instruction in reading and interpreting the information contained in tables, charts, graphs, diagrams, and pictures.

The text, MERRILL GENERAL SCIENCE, is designed to assist you in helping your students to read competently in the following ways.

1. The topical headings in each chapter are the author's organization of the information. Look at these in a preview before reading, and aid students in noting the development and progression of information.
2. The text has numerous graphic aids. Discuss information from these to give students practice in noting the information. These aids can be very helpful to a slow reader. A Basic Skills master in the Teacher Resource Book may be helpful in giving students practice interpreting graphs and tables.

3. Note the Review and Reflect questions and blue margin notes throughout each chapter. Alert your students to the purpose of these questions so that their understanding of data can build progressively.

4. Use the end-of-chapter features for review, extension, enrichment, and skill application. The Summary lists the main ideas of the chapter. Vocabulary lists the important words from the chapter. The Questions are excellent for review. The Investigations and "Readings" are suggestions for extension and enrichment.

If we think of science as learning through discovery, then as teachers we must make that possible by aiding students' development of a basic conceptual background and competence in the reading-study skills.

Bibliography

For more information on developing reading skills:

Barbe, Walter B., et al. *Reading Skills Check List and Activities, Advanced Level.* The Center for Applied Research in Education, Inc.: West Nyack, NY, 1976.

Bork, Alfred, *Learning With Computers,* Digital Press: Bedford, MA, 1981.

Friedman, Myles I. and Michael D. Rawls, *Teaching Reading and Thinking Skills.* Longman Inc.: New York, 1979.

Heilman, Arthur W., *Principles and Practices of Teaching Reading,* 5th ed. Charles E. Merrill Publishing Co.: Columbus, OH, 1981.

Shepard, David L., *Comprehensive High School Reading Methods,* 3rd ed. Charles E. Merrill Publishing Co.: Columbus, OH, 1982.

Teaching Special Students

Many "special" students compare favorably with "regular" students in their curiosity and desire to learn science. Some even choose science as a career. Special students may, however, be sensitive to failure and lack confidence. Help these students develop a positive self-image. Do not make class or work assignments too long. Use multimedia to develop concepts. Use the same discipline for ALL students. Allow fullest possible participation. Full-time aides facilitate greater participation of some students.

Learning Disabilities

For students who are mentally handicapped, or who have learning disabilities, abstract reasoning and incidental learning are difficult. Because most of these students have experienced failure, give them positive reinforcement often. Provide clear learning goals and concrete references to daily learning skills. Use familiar objects, slower pacing, and greater redundancy in teaching. Stress key ideas. Students with reading problems benefit from repeatedly hearing lessons taped on audio cassettes. Those with limited writing skills may be able to tape-record text question answers.

Behavioral Disabilities

Students with emotional handicaps, autism, and other behavioral disabilities should be taught in a structured environment of fair, consistent, and enforceable rules. Students should be given copies of a stable daily schedule. Any changes in this schedule should be clearly explained in advance. Avoid rearranging furniture unnecessarily. Familiarity in room organization and consistency in teaching style are very important. Use positive reinforcement frequently, and provide students with daily feedback on their progress.

Physical Disabilities

Students requiring wheelchairs or crutches need space for mobility. Students with less conspicuous physical problems, such as diabetes, epilepsy, or allergies, may or may not need special adaptations. Some of these students tire easily. Others are sensitive to particular foods, medications, or laboratory chemicals. Students having cerebral palsy or other fine motor coordination problems may have difficulty holding, pouring, or squeezing equipment and supplies. Be aware of these special students' needs and provide whatever assistance is needed. Having students work in pairs allows them to help each other, although each should contribute something.

Visual Disabilities

Students who have partial sight or are totally blind depend on touch and hearing. These students should sit where they can hear instructions and descriptions easily. Lessons and student answers can be tape-recorded for further study. Provide concrete objects and models. Tactile pictures that have raised and differential textures can be made from self-sticking materials such as weatherstripping, velour, and Velcro®. Peer friends may help in providing more detailed descriptions of visuals and visual presentations. Some laboratory aids for students with visual impairments are available from these suppliers.

The American Printing House for the Blind
1839 Frankfort Avenue
P.O. Box 6085
Louisville, KY 40206

Dr. Ken Ricker
Department of Science Education
University of Georgia
Athens, GA 30601

Hearing Disabilities

Make liberal use of visuals and the printed word when teaching students who have hearing loss. Use the senses of sight and touch. Let these students sit near the front of the room in order to "read" your body language and/or your lips. Avoid standing in front of a bright window, talking with your back to the class, or talking while your lips are hidden from students' view. Men with mustaches may pose an additional problem for these students, as the lips are

partially hidden. Write all instructions, and provide descriptive handouts. The class notes of a hearing peer or your own outline may be copied for the student with a hearing disability. If an interpreter signs class activities, light should continue to shine on the interpreter even when other lights in the room are darkened for visual presentation.

Multicultural and Bilingual Students

It is important that multicultural or bilingual students not feel inferior because they use English as a second language or because they speak a language other than English. The language a student brings to school must not influence your expectations of the student's academic performance, as it is often lack of comprehension, not inherent academic deficiency, that results in low achievement. Thus, to be most effective, you must incorporate the students' native language into your course instruction. If you yourself are not proficient in a student's language, the help of a bilingual aide may be effective. Also, be sensitive to cultural differences in these students when interpreting student behavior. You may need to modify your instructional technique to accommodate these differences. Realize that "obvious" proper behavior for students of the majority culture may not be obvious to a multicultural student. Make your expectations clear and explicit, and understand that a student's unwillingness to respond to questions or participate in a group activity may be due to cultural values.

Evaluating Supplemental Materials

Supplemental materials offer teachers excellent opportunities for presenting new concepts, reinforcing concepts, and stimulating and enriching discussions. The materials include films, filmstrips, film-loops, and computer software. The following suggestions are offered to aid you in choosing supplemental materials that are meaningful to your students and appropriate for your classroom situation.

1. Determine if the instructional objectives of the material are important to you and if the material will serve a purpose in your classroom.
2. Determine if the material is compatible with your behavioral and instructional objectives. The material should reflect the content, termi-

nology, teaching style, and educational philosophy generally encountered by your students.
3. Determine if the focus of the material is narrow enough to allow thorough treatment of a topic.
4. Determine the accuracy of the material.
5. If students are to use the materials individually without teacher assistance, determine that the instructions for use are clear and understandable to students.
6. Determine if the material is appropriate for the ability levels of your students. Important points to consider are the reading level of the material and prerequisite skills or knowledge needed by students to successfully use the materials.

7. Preview the material before use to determine technical quality. Both visual and audio portions of the material should be clear and understandable.

Tips for Evaluating Software

The computer is becoming a widely used tool in the science classroom. Computer software generally falls into six broad categories: tutorials, quiz programs, simulations, interface programs, data analysis programs, and teacher aid packages.

Tutorials often are comprised of drill and practice exercises. Using the computer for this type of activity is valuable, because many students view using the program as a game. Also, because the computer does not tire of repeating the same information, students can review materials as many times as needed. Programs of this type often are useful for remedial work, because the lesson can move fast or slow depending on how the student responds to questions asked.

When considering buying tutorial software, try to find programs in which the text is in both upper and lower case letters. Reading text in all uppercase can be difficult for poor readers. Students should be able to control the pace of the text presentation to avoid frustration. In addition, the use of graphics can stimulate student interest and facilitate learning.

Quiz programs may be combined with tutorial programs, or may come as a separate package. These quizzes may be used as self-checks for students to determine whether or not they are mastering the assigned material. Before buying one of these programs, determine if it correlates with your text or with other student material. A convenient feature to look for is the ability to generate the tests on a printer. This option is important especially if the random generation of quiz questions requires disk reading for each item. Also, determine the type of answers required to complete the tests. Multiple choice type answers may be more appropriate if your students are below average spellers.

Simulations allow students to role-play many real-life situations. As a result of the decisions they make, students affect the outcome of a situation. Simulations are most valuable when they are keyed to real hands-on experiences, either as a pre-lab experience or a post-lab extension. Simulations are useful in developing divergent thinking, because different outcomes teach students that there can be more than one solution to a problem. When considering buying this type of program, determine whether the simulation leads or follows a laboratory experience that you are capable of providing. The graphics in these programs should be clear and easily understood. Ideally, these programs should be able to be run by students with little teacher assistance or intervention.

Interface programs allow students to enter analog data, providing options for more accurate experiments in the classroom laboratory. Computers can be adjusted to directly record temperature changes, light, sound, pH, heat, blood pressure, and heart rate. Before buying a program of this type, determine that your computer has the ability to interface with the program. Some computers must be specially adjusted to use the interface equipment. In order to make the best use of this type of equipment, you should have constant access to the computer in your laboratory, since the equipment takes some time to set up.

Data analysis packages that accept data from many classroom experiments and provide instant graphs are becoming more common. These programs provide easy and accurate curve fitting for science projects and generate descriptive statistics and graphs. One drawback to these packages is the need for a more sophisticated knowledge of statistics than most students have.

Teacher aid packages include test writers, question banks, and gradebooks. These programs may save time, but consider your accessibility to the computer before investing.

In general, see and use a software package before you buy it. Be certain the software will run on your computer, and check memory capacity and other requirements before investing. Examine the instructional objectives of the software to be sure they relate to your course. Determine that the instructions are clear, and that both you and your students can understand and follow them. Finally, determine whether the software will be interesting for students to use, or whether it will be boring. More information about evaluating software for use in science teaching is available from the National Science Teachers Association. The following list of software is provided for your reference. You may want to evaluate some of these materials for use with your general science classes.

Software

Unit 1

Discovery Lab, MECC (Apple II)
Introduces to science processes including observation, experimental design, and hypothesis testing.

Measurements: Length, Mass, and Volume, Focus Media (Apple II, Commodore 64)
Students learn to measure length, mass, and volume in SI units.

Modeling, MECC (Apple II)
Students develop the concept of a model through experiments with "Black-box" machines.

Unit 2

Chemistry: Series I, Focus Media (Apple II, TRS-80, Commodore 64 and PET)
Three different games teach states of matter, atomic structure and bonding, and acids and bases.

Chemistry Volume 1, Prentice-Hall (Apple II, Atari, Commodore 64, IBM PC and PCjr)
Discusses the atom and atomic models

Chemistry Volume 2, Prentice-Hall (Apple II, Atari, Commodore 64, IBM PC and PCjr)
Discusses the periodic table.

Introduction to General Chemistry, Compress (Apple II)
Eight-disk set covers periodic table, nomenclature, balancing equations, and atomic weights.

Molecules and Atoms, SMC (Apple II, IBM PC and PCjr)
Covers molecules and atoms, the Bohr model, how to draw atoms, ions, and ionic bonding.

Unit 3

ATARILAB Starter Set, Atari (Atari, Apple II, Commodore 64)
Students analyze objects and events to learn concepts of temperature and energy transfer.

Optics: Mirrors and Beams, HRM (Apple II)
Teaches students the physics of optical science.

Reflections, HesWare (Apple II, Commodore 64, IBM PC and PCjr)
Teaches reflection, refraction, and absorption through building of a sound and light show.

Unit 4

Earth Science, MECC (TRS-80)
Students locate the epicenter of an earthquake, identify 29 minerals, identify five major constellations, and explore the concept of distance.

Earth Science, Atari (Atari 800)
Teaches definition of solar distances, identification of constellations, and the composition and mineral formations of the earth.

Forecast, CBS (Apple II, Commodore 64, IBM PC and PCjr)
Students chart weather patterns and learn how atmospheric conditions affect the weather.

Shore Features, CDL (Apple II)
Tutorial identifying shore and beach features.

Unit 5

Classification, MECC (Apple II, IBM PC)
Students use a data base inquiry system to enter, search, and sort data and to generate reports. Results are related to the process of scientific classification.

Elementary Biology, MECC (Atari)
This diskette contains three simulations. In "Circulation," students observe the movement of a blood cell throughout the circulatory system of a fish. In "Odell Lake" and "Odell Woods," students construct food chains.

Genetics, Microcomputer Workshops (Apple II, Commodore 64 and PET)
Introduction to the basic laws of genetics including dominant, sex-linked recessive, and sex-influenced traits.

The Human Body, CDL (Apple II)
Tutorial diskette covering the muscular system, digestive system, respiratory system, skeletal system, and nervous system.

Merlan Biology Series, Merlan (Apple II)
Students learn about mitosis and meiosis.

Unit 6

Energy Search, McGraw-Hill (Apple II, TRS-80)
Students manage an energy factory and search for new energy sources.

Heatloss, MECC (Apple II with printer)
Problem-solving program that helps students determine areas and costs of energy-saving improvements to their family home.

Oh, Deer, MECC (Apple II)
Students manage a herd of white-tailed deer in a residential area over a five-year period.

Power Grid, HRM (Apple II, TRS-80)
Simulation of an electric utility drawing power from plants fueled by coal, oil, gas, nuclear power, and water power.

Audiovisual Materials

Unless indicated otherwise, all listings are 16 mm films.

Chapter 1
Make Mine Metric, Pyramid.
Measuring, McGraw-Hill
Metrics for Measurement, BFA
Powers of Ten, revised, Pyramid.
The Search for Solutions (Series of 9 films), Search for Solutions.
Filmstrip: *Introducing the Metric System*, National Geographic.

Chapter 2
Nature of Science: Forming Hypotheses, Coronet.
Nature of Science: Testing Hypotheses, Coronet.
Observing and Describing, McGraw-Hill.
School Lab Safety, Handel.
The Scientific Method, EBEC.
What is Science? (2nd ed.), Coronet.

Chapter 3
Explaining Matter: Molecules in Motion, EBEC.
Learning About Air and Water, National Geographic.
The Nature of Matter, McGraw-Hill
Particles in Motion: States of Matter, National Geographic.
What Are Things Made Of?, Coronet.

Chapter 4
The Atom, A Closer Look, Walt Disney.
Atomic Structure, Prentice-Hall.
An Introduction to the Atom, National Geographic.

Chapter 5
Atom in the Hospital (2nd ed.), Handel.
Atomic Structure and the Periodic Table, EBEC.
Filmstrip: *Chemical Elements*, Science Software.
Filmstrip: *The Periodic Table*, Science Software.

Chapter 6
Balancing Chemical Equations, Prentice-Hall
Chemical Bonding, Prentice-Hall
Introduction to Chemical Nomenclature, Prentice-Hall
Naming Chemical Substances, Prentice-Hall
Oxygen—An Introduction to Chemistry, Barr.
The World of Molecules (2nd ed.), Churchill.

Chapter 7
Crystallization, Churchill.
Filmstrip: *Solution Process and Theory*, Science Software.

Chapter 8
Chemistry in Nature, Centron.
Chemistry: Science Studies Hazardous Waste Materials Problems, Science Screen.
Mars: Chemistry Looks for Life, Ward's
Oil—From Fossil to Flame, Centron.

Chapter 9
Airplanes and How They Fly, Centron.
Space Shuttle: Mission to the Future, National Audio Visual Center.
Splash: Science and Swimming, Centron.
Thonk! Science and Hitting a Ball, Centron.
Zero G, Films, Inc.

Chapter 10
Attraction of Gravity, BFA.
Black Holes of Gravity, Time-Life.
Mac's Mill, Bullfrog.
Pedal Power, Bullfrog.
Principles of Lubrication, International.
Simple Machines—Using Mechanical Advantage, Barr.
Water Power, Bullfrog.

Chapter 11
Energy: The Fuels and Man, National Geographic.
Heat and Temperature, Coronet.
How to Make a Solar Heater, Handel.
Saving Energy at Home, Ramsgate.

Chapter 12
Electricity All About Us (2nd ed.), Coronet.
Electricity—The Energy of Electrons, Barr.
Magnets: The Dragon's Secret, EBEC.

Chapter 13
Learning About Sound, EBEC.
Listen! Hear!, National Geographic.
Quiet, Please!, Fenwick.

Chapter 14
A Visit to Spectrum II, Agency for Instructional Television.
Color from Light, Churchill.
Light and Its Relation to Color, Science Software.
Light is Many Things, Barr.
The Amazin' Laser, Educational Dimensions.
The Light of the 21st Century, Time-Life.

Chapter 15
Charting the Universe with Optical and Radio Telescope, EBEC.
Galaxies and the Universe, Coronet.
Measuring in Astronomy, BFA.

The Night Sky, EBEC.
Space Science: Galaxies and the Universe, EBEC.
Slide Set: *Hale Observatories*, Cal Tech Bookstore, Pasadena, California.
Slide Set: *Hodge Slide Set for Astronomy No. 51, Galaxies and the Universe*, McGraw-Hill.

Chapter 16
The Active Sun, McGraw-Hill.
The Earth in Motion, EBEC.
Mars—Is There Life?, NASA.
Mercury, NASA.
Our Planets—No Place Like Earth, Time-Life.
Solar System, International.
The Wanderers: Paths of the Planets, BFA.

Chapter 17
Above the Horizon, Universal.
Inconsistent Air, McGraw-Hill
Snow, BFA.
Tornado, National Weather Service.
Weather Forecasting, EBEC.
What Makes Clouds?, EBEC.
What Makes the Wind Blow?, EBEC.

Chapter 18
Comparing Rocks, EBEC.
Erosion and Weathering, EBEC.
Glacier on the Move, EBEC.
The Hidden Earth, McGraw-Hill.
The Interior of the Earth, McGraw-Hill.
Rocks and Minerals: How We Identify Them, Coronet.
Rocks That Originate Underground, EBEC.
Strata: Earth's Changing Crust, BFA.
Soils: An Introduction, BFA.
Volcanoes: Exploring the Restless Earth, EBEC.

Chapter 19
The Beach: A River of Sand, EBEC.
Challenge of the Oceans, McGraw-Hill.
Currents, Time-Life.
Earth Beneath the Sea, McGraw-Hill.
Ocean Currents, McGraw-Hill.
Oceanography: A Voyage to Discovery, Universal.

Chapter 20
Continental Drift, Universal.
The Drifting of the Continents, Time-Life.
Evidence for the Ice Age, EBEC.
History: Layer by Layer, McGraw-Hill.
Reflections on Time, EBEC.
Rise and Fall of the Great Lakes, Pyramid.

Chapter 21
Biology: Exploring the Living World, EBEC.
Diffusion and Osmosis (2nd ed.), EBEC.
Food: Energy for Life, Coronet.
Learning About Cells, EBEC.
The Living Cell: An Introduction, EBEC.
Photosynthesis (2nd ed.), EBEC.
Filmstrips: *Investigating Cells*, (series of 5 with cassettes), EBEC.

Chapter 22
Animals with Backbones, Coronet.
Animals without Backbones, Coronet.
Bacteria—Friend and Foe, EBEC.
Darwin and the Theory of Natural Selection, Coronet.
Flowering Plants and Their Parts, EBEC.
Growth of Seeds, EBEC.
Microorganisms That Cause Disease, Coronet.
The Protist Kingdom, BFA.
The Rotten World Around Us, Films, Inc.
This Was the Beginning: Part 1—The Invertebrates; Part 2—The Vertebrates, International.
Viruses (2nd ed.), Coronet

Chapter 23
Body Defenses Against Disease, EBEC.
The Digestive System, EBEC.
Drugs and the Nervous System (2nd ed.), Churchill.
The Endocrine System (2nd ed.), EBEC.
The Heart and the Circulatory System, EBEC.
The Human Brain, EBEC.
The Lungs and the Respiratory System, EBEC.
Work of the Blood, EBEC.

Chapter 24
Genetics and Plant Breeding, BFA.
Genetics: Chromosomes and Genes (Meiosis), Coronet.
Genetics: Human Heredity, Coronet.
Inheriting Your Physical Traits, Coronet.

Chapter 25
Adaptations of Plants and Animals, Coronet.
The Ecosystem, Network of Life, BFA.
Environment, BFA.
Food Chains—A Bond of Life, Barr.
Food Cycle and Food Chains, Coronet.
Introducing Ecology, Coronet.
Filmstrips: *Land Biomes of the World* (8 filmstrips, 4 cassettes), Eye Gate.

Chapter 26
Dawn of the Solar Age: Solar Energy, Time-Life.
Dawn of the Solar Age: Wind and Water, Time-Life.
Energy, BFA.
Energy: The Fuels and Man, National Geographic.
Energy: The Problems and the Future, National Geographic.
Nuclear Energy, National Geographic.
The Sun: Its Power and Promise, EBEC.

Chapter 27
Garbage, BFA.

The Garbage Explosion, EBEC.
Hydrogen Car, Los Alamos National Laboratory.
Man's Effect on the Environment, BFA.
Pollution Solution, NASA.

Chapter 28
Erosion, BFA.
The House of Man, Parts I and II, EBEC.
The Problem with Water is People, McGraw-Hill.
Problems of Conservation: Forest and Range, EBEC.
Problems of Conservation: Wildlife, EBEC.
The Water Crisis, Time-Life.

Software Distributors

Atari, Inc.
1265 Borregas Ave.
P.O. Box 427
Sunnyvale, CA 94086

Cambridge Development
Laboratory (CDL)
100 Fifth Avenue
Waltham, MA 02154

CBS Software
One Fawcett Place
Greenwich, CT 06836

Compress
Division of Wadsworth Inc.
P.O. Box 102
Wentworth, NH 03282

Focus Media, Inc.
839 Stewart Avenue
Garden City, NY 11530

HesWare
150 North Hills Drive
Suite 35
Brisbane, CA 94005

HRM Software
175 Tompkins Avenue
Pleasantville, NY 10570

Merlan Scientific Ltd.
247 Armstrong Avenue
Georgetown
Ontario, Canada L7G 4X6

McGraw-Hill
1221 Avenue of the Americas
New York, NY 10020

Microcomputer Workshops
Courseware
225 Westchester Avenue
Port Chester, NY 10573

Minnesota Educational
Computing Consortium
(MECC)
3490 Lexington Avenue North
St. Paul, MN 55112

Prentice-Hall
General Publishing Division
P.O. Box 819
Englewood Cliffs, NJ 07632

Science Management Corp. (SCM)
1011 Route 22
P.O. Box 6800
Bridgewater, NJ 08807

Film Distributors

Agency for Instructional Television
P.O. Box A
1111 West 17th Street
Bloomington, IN 47401

Barr Films
P.O. Box 5667
3490 East Foothill Blvd.
Pasadena, CA 91107

BFA Educational Media
P.O. Box 1795
2211 Michigan Avenue
Santa Monica, CA 90404

Bullfrog Films
Oley, PA 19547

Centron Educational Films
1621 West 9th Street
Lawrence, KS 66044

Churchill Films
662 West Robertson Blvd.
Los Angeles, CA 90069

Coronet Instructional Media
65 E. South Water St.
Chicago, IL 60601

Educational Dimensions Corp.
Box 126
Stamford, CT 06904

Encyclopaedia Britannica
Education Corp. (EBEC)
425 North Michigan Avenue
Chicago, IL 60611

Eye Gate Media
P.O. Box 303
Jamaica, NY 11435

Fenwick Productions
Box 277
West Hartford, CT 06107

Films, Inc.
1144 Wilmette Avenue
Wilmette, IL 60091

Handel Films
8730 Sunset Blvd.
West Hollywood, CA 90069

International Film Bureau
332 South Michigan Avenue
Chicago, IL 60604

Los Alamos National Laboratory
P.O. Box 1663, Mail Stop 45
Los Alamos, NM 87545

McGraw-Hill Text Films
110 Fifteenth Street
Del Mar, CA 92014

NASA
Code FAM
Washington, DC 20546

National Audio Visual Center
National Archives and
Records Service
General Services Administration
Washington, DC 20409

National Geographic Society
17th and M Streets NW
Washington, DC 20036

National Weather Service (NOAA)
8060 13th Street
Silver Springs, MD 20910

Prentice-Hall Media
Servcode HC2
150 White Plains Rd.
Tarrytown, NY 10591

Pyramid Films
P.O. Box 1048
Santa Monica, CA 90401

Ramsgate Films
704 Santa Monica Blvd.
Santa Monica, CA 90401

Science Screen Report
11890 West Pico Blvd.
Los Angeles, CA 90401

Science Software Systems
11890 West Pico Blvd.
Los Angeles, CA 90064

The Search for Solutions Booking
Center
708 Third Avenue
New York, NY 10017

Time-Life Films
100 Eisenhower Drive
Paramus, NJ 07652

Universal Education and Visual Arts
100 Universal City Plaza
Universal City, CA 91608

Walt Disney Educational Media Co.
500 S. Buena Vista St.
Burbank, CA 91521

Wards Natural Science Establishment
Modern Learning Aids Division
P.O. Box 1712
Rochester, NY 14603

Reference Books for Teachers

Unit 1

Bitter, Gary, et al. *Activity Handbook for Teaching the Metric System.* Allyn & Bacon: Boston, 1976.

Peterson, Rita, et al. *Science and Society.* Charles E. Merrill Publishing: Columbus, OH 1984.

Barman, Charles, et al. *Science and Societal Issues.* University of Iowa Press: Iowa City, IA, 1980.

Pollard, Michael. *How Things Work.* Larousse: New York, 1981.

Peet, Louise J. *Science Fundamentals: A Background for Household Equipment.* Iowa State University Press: Ames, IA, 1972.

Unit 2

Brady, James, and Gerard Humiston, *General Chemistry: Principles and Structure.* John Wiley & Sons: New York, 1982.

Sherman, Alan, and Sharon Sherman. *Chemistry and Our Changing World.* Prentice-Hall: Englewood Cliffs, NJ, 1983.

Lehninger, Albert. *Short Course in Biochemistry.* Worth Publishers: New York, 1973.

Hittle, David, et al. *Sourcebook for Chemistry and Physics.* Macmillan Publishing: New York, 1973.

Ehrlich, Paul, et al. *Ecoscience.* W. Freeman & Co: San Francisco, 1977.

Unit 3

Lunetta, Vincent, and Shimshon Novick. *Inquiry and Problem-Solving in the Physical Sciences.* Kendall/Hunt Publishing: Dubuque, IA, 1982.

Joseph, Alexander, et al. *A Sourcebook for the Physical Sciences.* Harcourt Brace & World: New York, 1961.

Giancoli, Douglas. *The Ideas of Physics.* Harcourt Brace Jovanovich: New York, 1978.

Brooks, Stewart. *Integrated Basic Science.* The C.V. Mosby Company: St. Louis, 1979.

Halliday, David, and Robert Resnick. *Fundamentals of Physics,* 2nd ed. John Wiley & Sons: New York, 1981.

Unit 4

Battan, Louis J. *Weather in Your Life.* W. H. Freeman & Co.,: San Francisco, 1983.

Beatty, J. Kelly, et al. *The New Solar System.* Sky Publishing: Cambridge, MA, 1981.

Burnham, Jr., Robert. *Burnham's Celestial Handbook: An Observer's Guide to the Universe Beyond the Solar System.* In three volumes. Dover Publications: New York, 1978.

Editors of Time-Life Books. *Planet Earth.* Time-Life Books: Chicago, 1983.

Press, Frank and Raymond Siever, *Earth.* 3rd ed. W. H. Freeman & Co.: San Francisco, 1982.

Unit 5

Cronquist, Arthur. *Basic Botany.* Harper and Row: New York, 1982. de Duve, Christian. *A Guided Tour of the Living Cell,* Vols. 1 and 2. Scientific

American Books, W. H. Freeman and Co.: New York, 1984.

Morhalt, Evelyn, et al. *A Sourcebook for the Biological Sciences.* Harcourt Brace & World: New York, 1966.

Norstog, Knut and Andrew J. Meyerriecks. *Biology.* 2d ed. Charles E. Merrill Publishing: Columbus, OH, 1985.

Smith, Robert Leo. *Ecology and Field Biology.* Harper and Row: New York, 1980.

The Human Body, series. U.S. News Books: Washington, DC, 1981–82.

Unit 6

Dorf, Richard C. *The Energy Factbook.* McGraw-Hill: New York, 1981.

Ehrlich, Paul and Anne Erlich. *Extinction: The Causes and Consequences of the Disappearance of Species.* Random House: New York, 1981.

Myers, Norman. *The Primary Source: Tropical Forests and Our Future.* W. W. Norton: New York, 1984.

Troch, Frederick, et al. *Soil and Water Conservation for Productivity and Environmental Protection.* Prentice-Hall: Englewood Cliffs, NJ, 1980.

About Activities

Process Skills

MERRILL GENERAL SCIENCE provides experiences that help students both develop and apply critical thinking process skills. These experiences are provided by the use of higher level divergent questions, laboratory investigations, controlled experiments, and creative activities. Students are given the opportunity to use and apply the basic and complex process skills, thus facilitating their advancement toward higher levels of cognitive thinking. Through integration of these skills, students should develop the ability to reflect and evaluate their approaches to a problem. Students able to think in terms of several solutions to a single problem are not limited to concrete activities. Instead, these students can formulate hypotheses as testable ideas in their minds and can demonstrate deductive patterns of thought. Through integration of the important critical thinking process skills listed below, students develop the ability to think logically and abstractly. The table that follows the list indicates the activities in MERRILL GENERAL SCIENCE that emphasize various process skills.

Basic Process Skills

Observing: Students use one or more senses to increase their perceptions in order to learn more about objects and events.

Classifying: Students group objects or events based on common properties and/or categorize based on existing relationships among objects or events.

Inferring: Students propose interpretations, explanations, and causes from observed events and collected data.

Communicating: Students convey information verbally, both in oral and written forms, and visually through graphs, charts, pictures, and diagrams.

Recognizing and Using **Spatial** Relationships: Students estimate the relative positions of moving and nonmoving objects to one another.

Measuring: Students identify and order length, area, volume, mass, and temperature to describe and quantify objects or events.

Predicting: Students propose possible results or outcomes of future events based on observations and inferences drawn from previous events.

Using **Numbers:** Students transfer or apply ordering, counting, adding, subtracting, multiplying, and dividing to quantify data where appropriate in investigations or experiments.

Complex Process Skills

Interpreting Data: Students explain the meaning of information gathered in scientific situations.

Forming **Hypotheses:** Students make an assumption in order to draw out and test its logical consequences.

Separating and Controlling **Variables:** Students recognize the many factors that affect the outcome of events, and understand the relationship of the factors to one another so that one factor (variable) can be manipulated while the others are controlled.

Experimenting: Students test hypotheses or predictions under conditions where variables are both controlled and manipulated.

Formulating **Models:** Students construct mental, verbal, or physical representations of ideas, objects, or events. The models are then used to clarify explanations or to demonstrate relationships.

Defining Operationally: Students form a working definition that is based upon actual experience in which the student has participated.

Chapter	Activity Page	Basic Process Skills								Complex Process Skills					
		Observing	Classifying	Inferring	Communicating	Spatial	Measuring	Predicting	Numbers	Interpreting	Hypotheses	Variables	Experimenting	Models	Defining
1	12	✓					✓		✓	✓		✓			
	17	✓		✓		✓	✓	✓	✓	✓					
2	36	✓		✓	✓		✓		✓	✓	✓	✓		✓	
	41	✓		✓	✓		✓	✓	✓	✓	✓		✓	✓	
3	62	✓	✓				✓		✓	✓					
	65	✓	✓	✓						✓			✓	✓	
4	78	✓		✓				✓	✓	✓	✓		✓		✓
	85	✓		✓		✓	✓	✓		✓	✓		✓	✓	
5	102	✓	✓	✓						✓		✓	✓		
	109	✓	✓	✓						✓			✓		
6	121	✓	✓	✓			✓		✓	✓				✓	✓
	125	✓					✓	✓	✓	✓			✓		
7	147	✓	✓	✓			✓			✓	✓	✓	✓		
	153	✓								✓					✓
8	168	✓	✓					✓		✓		✓	✓		
	175	✓		✓			✓	✓		✓	✓	✓	✓		
9	193	✓			✓	✓	✓		✓	✓		✓			✓
	195	✓		✓			✓			✓				✓	
10	208	✓			✓	✓	✓		✓	✓			✓		✓
	221	✓		✓			✓	✓		✓		✓	✓		✓
11	231	✓			✓		✓	✓		✓			✓	✓	
	238	✓		✓			✓	✓		✓	✓		✓	✓	
12	256	✓	✓	✓		✓	✓		✓	✓		✓	✓	✓	✓
	262	✓		✓	✓		✓	✓		✓	✓	✓	✓	✓	
13	273	✓	✓	✓		✓				✓			✓	✓	✓
	285	✓		✓		✓	✓		✓	✓		✓			

Chapter	Activity Page	Basic Process Skills								Complex Process Skills					
		Observing	Classifying	Inferring	Communicating	Spatial	Measuring	Predicting	Numbers	Interpreting	Hypotheses	Variables	Experimenting	Models	Defining
14	299	✓			✓	✓	✓			✓		✓		✓	
	307	✓	✓	✓		✓				✓				✓	
15	327	✓				✓	✓	✓	✓	✓	✓		✓		✓
	331	✓	✓			✓	✓			✓		✓		✓	
16	343	✓	✓	✓		✓				✓			✓	✓	
	348	✓	✓		✓	✓	✓		✓	✓				✓	
17	362	✓		✓	✓		✓	✓		✓		✓		✓	
	371	✓	✓	✓				✓		✓	✓		✓		
18	390	✓	✓	✓				✓		✓				✓	✓
	397	✓	✓			✓	✓		✓	✓		✓		✓	
19	406	✓		✓		✓	✓		✓	✓		✓	✓	✓	
	409	✓			✓	✓	✓			✓				✓	
20	430	✓	✓	✓		✓		✓		✓		✓		✓	
	437	✓			✓	✓				✓				✓	
21	456	✓		✓		✓				✓		✓			✓
	459	✓	✓	✓						✓				✓	
22	475	✓	✓					✓		✓	✓		✓		
	477	✓	✓							✓					✓
23	496	✓		✓	✓		✓			✓		✓			
	499	✓		✓	✓		✓	✓		✓		✓			
24	517		✓			✓								✓	
	526	✓	✓	✓	✓				✓	✓					
25	535	✓	✓				✓		✓	✓					✓
	541			✓	✓			✓						✓	
26	562	✓		✓		✓	✓	✓		✓		✓	✓	✓	
	569	✓		✓		✓	✓		✓	✓			✓	✓	
27	580	✓		✓				✓		✓		✓			✓
	586	✓	✓	✓				✓		✓		✓			
28	596		✓		✓				✓	✓	✓				
	608		✓	✓					✓	✓	✓	✓	✓	✓	

Safety in the Science Classroom

Careful planning and preparation, as well as being aware of hazards, can help keep accidents to a minimum in the science classroom. Even so, there are no guarantees against accidents. The following guidelines can help you maintain a safe science classroom and/or laboratory. Also, you may want to use the Basic Skills master concerning laboratory safety with your class. The master appears in the *MERRILL GENERAL SCIENCE Teacher Resource Book.*

General Safety

General safety rules are listed in Appendix B of *MERRILL GENERAL SCIENCE.* These general rules should be emphasized to students before any laboratory work is done, and also should be periodically reviewed. Stress to students the importance of adhering to these rules to ensure their own safety as well as the safety of others.

Before Each Laboratory Activity

1. Perform activities yourself before assigning them to students. Previewing enables you to make note of cautions and safety procedures already incorporated into each activity.
2. Arrange the classroom or lab in such a way that equipment and supplies are easily accessible to students. Avoiding confusion where solutions and reagents are being dispensed is important in avoiding spills and broken glassware.
3. Have available only equipment and supplies necessary to complete the assigned activity to help eliminate the problem of students doing unauthorized experiments.
4. Review the procedure to be followed with students. Emphasize cautions found in the activity. Review what students should do if an accident occurs. If chemicals need to be disposed of in a special place, remind students of proper disposal methods.
5. Be sure all students know proper procedures to follow if an accident should occur, and the proper way to use fire extinguishers, fire blankets, showers, and eyewash fountains or bottles. This equipment should be well marked and easily accessible.
6. Discuss proper cleanup procedures with the class. Provide separate refuse containers for combustibles and for noncombustibles, such as glass. When working with chemicals, remind students that reagents should not be poured back into bottles and that waste acids should always be poured into water, never the reverse.

During a Laboratory Activity

1. Make sure that the laboratory is clean and free of clutter. Student books, coats, and other personal items should be stored away from the laboratory tables.
2. Require that students wear safety glasses and aprons when working in the laboratory.
3. Never allow students to work alone in the laboratory.
4. Emphasize that any accident or injury—no matter how insignificant—should be reported to the teacher at once.
5. Remove broken or chipped glassware from use immediately. Also clean up any spills that may occur. Dilute concentrated solutions with water before removing. Use a whisk broom and dust pan to clean up broken glass. Large wads of wet cotton should be used to pick up small pieces of glass.
6. Be sure all glassware that is to be heated is a heat treated type that will not shatter. Remind students that heated glassware looks cool several seconds after heating, but can still cause burns for several minutes.

After the Laboratory Activity

1. Be sure that the laboratory is clean. All work surfaces and equipment should be cleaned thoroughly after use.
2. Be sure students dispose of chemicals and broken glassware properly.
3. Be sure all hot plates and burners are turned off before leaving the laboratory.

Equipment and Supplies

A complete list of the equipment and supplies needed for all the activities in *MERRILL GENERAL SCIENCE* begins on page 32T. The amounts listed are for a class of 30 students working in pairs. Most nonconsumables can be used over and over again for many years. Most consumables and chemicals will need to be replaced each school year. The activities are designed so that simple materials can be used. Many materials may be available locally. A list of scientific suppliers is given on page 39T.

Nonconsumables

Item	Amount	Used in Activity on page
clothespins, wooden	60	62, 586
cobalt glass	15 pieces	102
coins	150	78
cup, plastic foam	30	78, 175
cup hooks	30	221
dice	30	78
drafting compass	15	348, 397
dropper with bulb	45	65, 125, 153, 459, 477
flashlight	10	343
flashlight bulb and holder	30	62, 256
flask, Erlenmeyer (500 mL)	15	125
forceps	15	121
funnel, glass or plastic	15	125
gloves	15 pairs	569
goggles	30	62, 65, 102, 109, 121, 125, 147, 168, 195, 273, 390, 580
graduated cylinder	15	17, 41, 62, 125, 147, 153, 175, 195, 231, 238, 406, 459, 477,
hammer	15	121, 195
hammer, rubber	15	285
hand lens	15	121, 475
hot plate	15	109, 147, 231, 459
insulation materials, 5 different	15 sets	569
jar, glass (baby food)	60	390
jars, large with lids	60	586
knife, cake	5	437
ladle, not aluminum	15	109

Item	Amount	Used in Activity on page
lamp, high intensity	15	562, 569
lamp, large clamp-on with reflector	15	362
lenses, 3 convex, short focal lengths	15 sets	331
lenses, 2 convex, long focal lengths different diameters	15 sets	331
lens holder (for meter stick)	30	331
light bulbs, 15 and 75 watts	15 sets	327
magnet	15	121
map, world	1 large or 15 small	541
meter stick	15	12, 273, 327, 331, 535
microscope	15	477
microscope, stereo	15	168
mirror, adjustable on stand	15	456
mirror, plane	15	299
mortar and pestle	15	125
nail, large	45	195, 262
objects to measure	large assortment	17
oven mitt	15	195
pan, large, not aluminum	15	109
pan, rectangular cake	45	362, 409
paper clip, large	15	36
paper clips, small	large quantity	262
pen, ball-point	15	168
pen, felt tip	15	36, 193, 517
pencil or crayon, glass marking	15	406, 499
photometer	15	327
ping-pong ball	10	343
pins, straight	30	299, 307

Item	Amount	Used in Activity on page
pipette, graduated with bulb	15	580
protractor	15	36, 299
ring stand and ring	15	125, 147, 195, 331, 362
rubber stopper, for test tube	45	109
rubber stopper, 1 hole for thermometer	45	147, 362
rubber tubing	6 m	499
ruler, metric	30	12, 17, 62, 78, 153, 208, 285, 299, 307, 331, 362, 406, 409, 517, 562, 569
ruler, metric 3-holed	15	36
samples of matter	large assortment	62
scale, bathroom (metric)	3	193
scale, spring	15	221
scalpel	15	475
scissors	15	153, 307, 348, 406, 459, 517, 562
screen, optical (for meter stick)	15	331
slides, microscope	30	477
socket, light bulb with wire and plug	15	327
sphygmomanometer kit	15	496
spoon, large	15	586
spoon, small	15	147, 477
spoon, wooden	15	109
spring, coil (Slinky®)	15	273
stapler	3	221
stethoscope	15	496
stirring rod	15	41, 121, 125, 147, 153, 362, 390, 406
stopwatch	15	193
tape, measuring	3	193

Item	Amount	Used in Activity on page
test tube holder	15	121, 459
test tubes, standard size	180	65, 109, 121, 153, 459
test tube rack	15	65
thermometer	45	109, 147, 231, 238, 285, 362, 562, 569
tongs	15	41
trough (or sink)	15	499
tube, plastic (40 cm × 2.5 cm)	15	285
tuning forks	assortment	285
washers, large steel	90	36, 406
washers, small steel	15	409
wire, enameled, 20–226 gauge	100 m	262
wire, hookup	30 m	62, 256, 262
wire loop, platinum or nichrome	15	102

Consumables

Item	Amount	Used in Activity on page
algae, green	vigorous culture	477
aluminum foil	2 rolls	153, 307
antacid tablets, various kinds	several packages	125
bags, large plastic zip-locking	15	390
baking powder	1 can	65
baking soda	1 box	65, 125
balsa wood sheeting, 30 × 11 cm	90 pieces	175
can, rectangular metal	15	195
can, soup	30	238
cellophane, colored	15 sheets	562

Item	Amount	Used in Activity on page
clay, modeling	large quantity	409
clay, modeling (3 colors)	15 sets	437
corn syrup	1 L	459
cornstarch	1 box	65
coverslips	30	477
detergent, laundry	1 box	168
detergent, low-phosphate	1 box	586
detergent, phosphate	1 box	586
dialysis tubing	150 cm	459
dye, fabric	2 packages	168
egg carton, cardboard	15	109
eggs, hard-boiled	60	41
fabric samples, white, 15 cm × 15 cm (1 each nylon, rayon, polyester, wool, cotton, silk, linen, polyester-cotton blend)	15 assortments	168
filter paper strips, 20 cm	75	153
fishing line	5 m	195
food coloring	4 colors	153
glue, carpenters	15 bottles	175
index cards	60	517
ink, washable black or blue-black	1 bottle	153
jar, glass with lid (baby food)	15	390
labels, self stick	300	17, 390, 475, 477, 580, 586
limestone fragments	1 kg	390
map of North and South America	15	397
newspaper	several	109
oil, vegetable or motor	1 L	586

Item	Amount	Used in Activity on page
paper, adding machine roll	15 rolls	348
paper, black construction	45 sheets	307, 562
paper, colored construction	15 sheets	517
paper, graph	200 sheets	208, 231, 238, 362, 409, 608
paper, white construction	30 sheets	562
pH paper	15 dispensers	390
plant, potted	15	562
plastic wrap	1 roll	562
potting soil	2 kg	475
powders, unknown	several kinds	41
rock fragments, several kinds	large assortment	390
salt, rock	15 kg	362
salt, table	3 kg	41, 406
sandpaper, fine	15 sheets	262
sandpaper, medium to coarse	30 sheets	221
seeds: bean, corn, peanut, pea, oat, squash, and barley	60 each	475
shortening, vegetable	5 kg	109
soap flakes	1 box	586
straw, soda	45	221, 499
string	large quantity	36, 348, 406, 409, 535
sugar, powdered	500 g	147
sugar, granulated	1 kg	147, 477
sugar, cube	15 cubes	147
talc	250 g	65
tallow, beef	2.5 kg	109
tape, cellophane	15 rolls	517

Item	Amount	Used in Activity on page
tape, masking	7 rolls	193, 307, 348, 409, 456, 562, 569
thread	1 spool	459
toothpicks	1 box	153
towels, paper	5 rolls	121, 168, 475, 562, 569
tracing paper	150 sheets	456
tube, cardboard (from kitchen wrap)	15	307
tube, cardboard (from toilet paper)	15	307
vinegar	1 L	65
washing soda	1 box	586
wax paper	2 rolls	307, 475
yeast, dry	30 packets	477

Chemicals

Item	Amount	Used in Activity on page
ammonium chloride (NH_4Cl)	1 kg	147
Benedict's solution	200 mL	459
congo red indicator	15 dropper bottles	125
hydrochloric acid, concentrated (36%)	5 L	102, 125, 390
iodine solution (Lugol's)	15 dropper bottles	65, 459
iron filings	100 g	121
methylene blue solution	15 dropper bottles	580
sodium hydroxide	1 kg	109
solutions, metallic ion for flame tests	several	102
starch solution	500 ml	459
sulfur, powdered	50 g	121

Suppliers

Carolina Biological Supply Co.
2700 York Rd.
Burlington, NC 27215

Central Scientific Co.
11222 Melrose Ave.
Franklin Park, IL 60131

Fisher Scientific Co.
4901 W. LeMoyne
Chicago, IL 60615

LaPine Scientific Co.
6001 S. Knox Ave.
Chicago, IL 60629

Nasco
901 Janesville Ave.
Fort Atkinson, WI 53538

Sargent-Welch Scientific Co.
7300 N. Linder
Skokie, IL 60077

Science Kit and Boreal Labs
777 E. Park Dr.
Tonawanda, NY 14150

Sargent-Welch Scientific of Canada, Ltd.
285 Garyray Dr.
Weston
Ontario, Canada M9L 1P3

VWR Scientific
P.O. Box 855
Columbus, OH 43216

Ward's Natural Science Establishment
P.O. Box 1712
Rochester, NY 14603

Performance Objectives

Books on science education list many valid reasons for teaching the subject. These reasons may range from general goals to more specific goals. A general goal might be to help students acquire habits of critical thinking while a specific goal might be to teach these students the definition of an element and compound. Statements of what science education intends to accomplish are no doubt valid and justifiable. But, how do you know if you are accomplishing these goals in your teaching? Herein lies the value of performance objectives—the behaviors that you, the teacher, can observe and that indicate students are achieving the goals of science education.

In many cases, several types of behaviors will indicate that the students are achieving the objectives. For example, how do you, the teacher, determine that the students are acquiring habits of critical thinking? Some behaviors that you might observe include students:

1. asking questions related to the topic being discussed.
2. gathering data or sharing evidence that supports their answers.
3. questioning or expressing doubt about the hypotheses posed by others.

An unlimited number of behaviors could be cited which would indicate whether students are thinking critically.

Other behaviors will indicate if students are learning other things. These behaviors can be written as performance objectives to aid you in assessing student accomplishment. A good performance objective can usually be written in three parts:

1. the condition,
2. the performance or criterion, and
3. the criterion measure.

The condition tells what causes, stimulates, or motivates the student to perform the behaviors, or under what circumstances those behaviors will be performed. The performance or criterion tells exactly what behavior you are looking for. The criterion measure tells how many of the students have achieved the objective, or to what degree of accuracy or level of performance the behavior should be performed for you to know the students have actually achieved the objective.

Performance objectives are listed for each chapter of MERRILL *GENERAL SCIENCE* in the Teacher's Annotated Edition. They are related to the four broad goals of science education.

A Attitudes: To develop students' attitudes of curiosity and involvement with occurrences in their environment; to develop an appreciation for the contributions of science; and to recognize the value of solving problems in a scientific manner.

P Processes: To develop those intellectual processes of inquiry by which scientific problems and occurrences are explained, predicted, and/or controlled.

K Knowledge: To develop knowledge of facts, terminology, concepts, generalizations, and principles that help students confront and interpret occurrences in their environment.

S Skills: To develop students' abilities to handle, construct, and manipulate materials and equipment in a productive and safe manner; and to develop the ability to measure, organize, and communicate scientific information.

The following are some examples of each type of performance objective.

Attitudes: Students will request permission to perform an investigation listed at the end of a chapter.

Processes: Given data about weather fronts, temperature, and barometer readings, students will predict the weather conditions in their area.

Knowledge: Students will differentiate between covalent and ionic bonding.

Skills: Using a stopwatch, students will count the number of swings a pendulum makes in one minute.

How to Use the Objectives

In the chapter-by-chapter portion of the Teacher's Guide, a specific goal is stated for each chapter. Following the goal statement in the Teacher's Guide, specific performance objectives for each section of the chapter are listed. There may be several objectives in each section. Each objective is numbered to correspond to that section of the chapter. For example, 2:5 is chapter 2, section 5. The following performance objectives, which are not listed for each chapter, apply to all chapters in MERRILL GENERAL SCIENCE.

S   use laboratory materials and equipment in the prescribed manner.

A   conduct one of the investigations at the end of the chapter.

A   read unassigned books or articles related to the chapter.

A   express interest in learning about careers related to the chapter.

From these objectives you should be able to determine and plan for the achievement of the objectives for each section of a chapter.

As you examine the performance objectives, you will find that the criterion or level of performance for each objective is not included. The intent was to create guidelines and not to state levels of expectancies for you. Only you can decide if 100 percent or only 50 percent of your students should be able to accomplish each task. You will need to develop and insert these criterion levels for your own students based on your knowledge of their abilities, your materials, and your own situation.

Remember, a performance objective cannot and should not tell you how to teach. A performance objective can be used in several different ways. It can aid you in planning instruction. It can help you provide evidence that your students are learning if you keep records of students' progress. A performance objective can help you diagnose a student's abilities and better individualize student instruction. Also, a performance objective can help students "tune in" to what you are trying to achieve. Many teachers have found that when they share with students the objectives that are sought, much of the teaching job is accomplished.

Bibliography

The following books are suggested for additional information on educational objectives.

Bloom, Benjamin S. and Madaus, George F., *Evaluation to Improve Learning*. McGraw-Hill Book Co.: New York, 1981.

Bloom, Benjamin S., et al., *Handbook on Formative and Summative Evaluation of Student Learning*. McGraw-Hill Book Co.: New York, 1971.

Bloom, Benjamin S., et al., *Taxonomy of Educational Objectives: Handbook 1: Cognitive Domain*. Longman Inc.: New York, 1977.

Bloom, Benjamin S., et al., eds., *Taxonomy of Educational Objectives: Cognitive & Affective Domains*. Longman Inc., New York, 1969.

Doran, Rodney L., *Basic Measurement and Evaluation of Science Instruction*. National Science Teachers Association: Washington, D.C., 1980.

Farmer, Walter A. and Margaret A. Farrell, *Systematic Instruction in Science for the Middle and High School Years*. Addison-Wesley: Reading, MA, 1980.

Gronlund, Norman E., *Constructing Achievement Tests,* 3rd ed. Prentice-Hall: Englewood Cliffs, NJ, 1982.

Krathwohl, David R., et al., *Taxonomy of Educational Objectives: Handbook 2: Affective Domain*. Longman Inc.: New York, 1969.

Lindvall, C. M., ed., *Defining Educational Objectives*. University of Pittsburgh Press: Pittsburgh, 1964.

Mager, Robert F., *Preparing Instructional Objectives,* 2nd. ed., Pittman Learning, Inc.: Belmont, CA, 1975.

Measuring and Attaining the Goals of Education. Association for Supervision and Curriculum Development: Alexandria, VA, 1980.

Popham, W. James, *Uses of Instructional Objectives: A Personal Perspective*. Pittman Learning, Inc.: Belmont, CA, 1973.

UNIT 1   THE TOOLS OF SCIENCE

Overview

In chapter 1, students are introduced to the concepts of measurement in science. The chapter begins with a discussion of the importance of science. The development of measurement standards is considered. Standard SI and metric measures are presented. In addition, use of scientific notation is explained. The factor-label method of problem solving and use of significant digits are presented in an optional information section at the end of the chapter.

In chapter 2, scientific methods are introduced and developed. Using practical examples, the methods of science are presented, including questioning, testing, analyzing, and concluding. The use of models and the development of laws and theories are also discussed. The chapter concludes with a discussion of the use (and occasional misuse) of statistics.

Introducing the Unit

Many activities make use of tools. Discuss with your students some common examples of tools, such as the tools needed for carpentry, cooking, baseball (and other games), sewing, painting, and so on. Point out that science is involved with acquiring knowledge about the universe and everything it contains. One important tool used by those studying science is measurement.

It is important for students to realize that science is not something that is done only by scientists in laboratories. Science has many practical applications to the "real world" for nonscientists as well. Direct the students' attention to the unit opening photograph. Point out that in many common tasks, such as buying vegetables and fruit, decisions based on observations and measurements are important.

The unit opening questions should be discussed briefly at this time. These questions are designed to be motivational. They provide a framework for students, outlining what will be studied in the unit. It is not expected that students can answer the questions at this time. However, you may want to use the questions to assess students' prior knowledge of the unit concepts.

CHAPTER 1
MEASUREMENT IN SCIENCE

Performance Objectives

GOAL: Students will learn how scientists quantify the properties of objects and use standardized methods of measurement.

OBJECTIVES: When asked to respond after completion of the reading and activities, students will

1:1	K	define and contrast science and technology.
	A/P	appreciate the vast impact of science and technology on society.
1:2	K	state the importance of measurement.
1:3	K/P	recognize that measures must be standardized in order to be meaningful.
	K	identify the International System of Units (SI) as the world-recognized standard for measurement.
	P	infer problems associated with using nonstandard measurements.
1:4	K	identify the meter as the SI standard unit for length.
	P	change linear metric units using the different prefixes.
1:5	K	identify SI units used to measure area.
	P/S	calculate areas using SI units.
1:6	K	identify SI units used to measure volume.
	P/S	calculate volumes using SI units.
1:7	K	identify SI units used to measure mass.
	P/S	calculate masses using SI units.
1:8	K	identify the SI units used to measure time and temperature.
	P	differentiate between Kelvin and Celsius temperature scales.

1:9	K	identify the SI unit used for measuring force.
	K/P	explain the differences between mass and weight.
1:10	S	write and interpret numbers represented in scientific notation.
1:11	A	appreciate the importance of understanding what is being asked in a problem before attempting to solve it.
	S/P	use the factor-label method.
	K	state the rules for determining the number of significant digits.

Teaching the Chapter

Section 1:1 discusses the study of science and the differences between science and technology. You may wish to have students begin their study of this chapter by using the library to investigate and then report on some area of technological advancement.

Each chapter includes a Career Profile. These profiles have been chosen carefully to present students with a wide variety of careers that are related to science and technology. Care has been taken in the selection of these careers to help dispel some sexual and racial stereotypes often associated with science-related careers.

An interesting discussion regarding science stereotypes can be sparked by having students draw a picture of a scientist. Encourage them to draw their first impression. One of the authors of this text has analyzed such pictures drawn by teachers and found that a *majority* portray scientists as Caucasian males wearing lab coats and glasses, working with some type of glassware.

In measuring area and volume (**sections 1:5 and 1:6**), some students may have difficulty with the units. Stress that when calculating an area, as in the first example in **section 1:5**, 4 times 3 equals 12 and meters times meters equals meters squared or m^2.

Section 1:8 deals with time and temperature. The original definition of a second was 1/86 400 of the mean solar day. The second is now defined as the duration of 9 192 631 770 periods of the radiation corresponding to the transition between two levels of the cesium-133 atom. The SI unit for temperature, the kelvin (K), is defined as the fraction 1/273.16 of the thermodynamic temperature of the triple point of water.

Depending on the background of your students, **section 1:10**, Scientific Notation, may present new information or serve as a review. Gauge teaching time accordingly. You may wish to have students work through additional problems. Scientific notation is particularly helpful in problems such as, how many cm^3 are in a m^3? (10^6 cm^3)

Activity, Page 12   Why are units made uniform?

Try to obtain metric rulers and meter sticks that are not also marked in English units. The most effective way for students to learn the metric system is not to convert from English units, but rather to think metrically.

An interesting extension of this activity is to ask students to determine whether they are wider than they are tall. Have them measure their heights and widths (from fingertip to fingertip of outstretched arms). Most people are very nearly as wide as they are tall.

Answers to QUESTIONS AND CONCLUSIONS
1. Measurements probably will differ.
2. Answers will vary. The main reason for variation is that the widths of students' hands differ, therefore their measurements will differ.
3. Answers will vary.
4. Answers will vary.
5. Answers will vary. Students should realize the need for standardization of units because their measurements varied depending on who was doing the measuring.
6. Divide height in centimeters by 10 to determine units of hands.

Activity, Page 17   How well can you estimate?

The purpose of this activity is to give students the opportunity to practice using metric measures in order to gain familiarity. Linear, volumetric, and mass measurements are involved. It is, of course, not important how accurate the students' predictions are as long as they use the correct units and are able to roughly predict in the metric system. Index cards, coins, keys, and various sizes of soda bottles make good objects for students to measure. If glass bottles are used, review Appendix B for safety instructions in the laboratory. It is a good idea to refer to these instructions whenever students are working in the lab. You may also wish to review the use of a balance. The Teacher Resource Book contains a Basic Skills master that may be helpful.

Answers to QUESTIONS AND CONCLUSIONS

1. Answers will vary.
2. Area = $L_1 \times L_2$
   Area = 20 cm × 24 cm
   Area = 480 cm^2 (approximately)
3. Measurements should be similar.
4. To convert milliliters to liters, divide by 1000.
5. Fill the graduated cylinder with some water. Note the water level. Add the object. Note the new water level. Subtract the original water level from this value. The remainder is the volume displaced by the object, which is the object's volume. (Note: cm^3 = mL)
6. a. square meters
   b. cubic centimeters (milliliters)
   c. centimeters

Skill Inquiry, Page 18

The Skill Inquiry for this chapter deals with graphs. Each chapter of the text includes a Skill Inquiry related to the content in that particular chapter. The Skill Inquiries are designed to reinforce and develop skills that assist in the study of science. Discuss graphs with the class. Review interpolation techniques. You may wish to have students bring examples of graphs from newspapers and magazines to class for discussion and analysis.

1. Phoenix, AZ: January: 10.9°C, March: 24.4°C, September: 28.7°C
   Rochester, NY: January: −3.9°C, March: 0.4°C, September: 17.1°C
2. January is coldest. July is warmest.

INTERPOLATED VALUES (°C)

	Phoenix, AZ:	Rochester, NY:
February	13.4	−1.8
April	20.1	7.1
June	28.6	17.8
August	35.7	19.5
October	22.1	10.7
December	13.2	0.2

3. The difference is greatest in August, least in January.
4. Phoenix, AZ: 32.3°C
   Rochester, NY: 19.7°C

Answers to Review and Reflect

Page 8
1. Technology is the practical application of science and scientific knowledge to problems involved with daily living.
2. Answers will vary. Examples could include more efficient fuels and engines; larger aircraft that travel at high speeds; trains for transporting products or for commuter travel; space travel; shipping industry for cargo transport or pleasure cruises.
3. People use measurement to classify items, such as shoes and clothing by size; to assign value to items by pricing; to organize, such as by scheduling. Students may suggest additional examples not mentioned in the text.

Page 11
1. 650
2. 3.8
3. Because actual measurement of this distance could not be made, calculations varied.
4. Measurement has no meaning without the use of standard units. It would be confusing for people to communicate to others without standardized units.
5. Answers will vary. The carpet is not likely to fit, especially if your arm is significantly longer or shorter than the arm of the salesperson.

Page 16
1. area – square meter, m^2
   volume – cubic meter, m^3
   mass – kilogram, kg
2. 15 m^2
3. 1 m
4. 15 000 kg
5. 10 000 cm^2; 1 000 000 cm^3

Page 19
1. kelvin
2. water skiing
3. newton
4. 65 kg

Page 21
1. 0.000 000 004 5
2. 4.2×10^{13}
3. 4.8×10^5 cm^3

Page 23
1. Read the problem carefully and determine given and unknown values.

2. a. $\dfrac{47.5 \text{ km}}{} \left| \dfrac{1000 \text{ m}}{1 \text{ km}} \right| \dfrac{1000 \text{ cm}}{1 \text{ m}} = 4.75 \times 10^7$ cm

b. $\dfrac{1\,209\,600 \text{ s}}{} \left| \dfrac{1 \text{ min}}{60 \text{ s}} \right| \dfrac{1 \text{ h}}{60 \text{ min}} \left| \dfrac{1 \text{ day}}{24 \text{ h}} \right| = 14$ days

3. a. three   **c.** three
   b. one   **d.** six
4. a. 54   **c.** 153 000
   b. 0.65   **d.** 0.24

Chapter 1 Review, Pages 24–25

Answers to APPLICATIONS

1. Answers will vary. Some examples might be mass transportation, air conditioning, freeze-dried foods, and computers. Students need to study science to know how their world functions, to make plans for the future, and to deal more efficiently with daily living.
2. They would be discussing criteria that are used for evaluating various measurements.

3. Not all metric units are SI.
4. See Appendix A.
5. $A = L_1 \times L_2$
   $A = 5.5 \text{ m} \times 6.5 \text{ m}$
   $A = 35.75 \text{ m}^2$
   Buy one can of paint.
6. Astronauts are not massless because the amount of matter they have is not determined by their location.
7. Scientific notation was developed as a means of writing very large and small numbers in a shorter form.
8. **a.** newtons   **d.** meters
   b. kilograms   **e.** square meters
   c. cubic centimeters   **f.** cubic meters
9. $1\,200\,000$ m or 1.2×10^6 m
10. $V = 10 \text{ m} \times 5 \text{ m} \times 3 \text{ m}$
    $V = 150 \text{ m}^3$ or $1.5 \times 10^2 \text{ m}^3$

CHAPTER **2**

SCIENCE PROCESSES

Performance Objectives

GOAL: Students will learn about the methods scientists use to answer questions and solve problems.

OBJECTIVES: When asked to respond after completion of the reading and activities, students will

2:1	K/P	recognize that scientific methods are systematic processes of gaining information.
	A	appreciate that scientific methods are not limited to use by scientists.
	P	explain that scientific methods involve questioning, testing, analyzing, and concluding.
2:2	P/S	identify and define variables in an experiment.
	P	state an experimental hypothesis.
2:3	K/P	explain why it is important to control variables.
	K/P	distinguish between experimental and control groups.
	K/P	classify variables as independent or dependent.
	K/P	contrast quantitative and qualitative observations.
	K	explain how graphs and tables are useful means to record and interpret data.
2:4	S	calculate the average value for a set of data.
2:5	A	recognize that conclusions are limited by the design of the experiment.
2:6	K	define and explain the differences between scientific laws and theories.
2:7	K/P	recognize that scientific models are developed to help visualize that which cannot directly be observed.
2:8	K/P	explain how graphs can be useful or can misrepresent information.

Teaching the Chapter

The emphasis of **section 2:1** is on scientific methods as a means to gain information in order to make decisions. Rather than artificially forcing a rigid list of processes to be followed, the text stresses that there are different ways to conduct experiments.

Sections **2:2** through **2:5** summarize the general steps in the process of scientific methods. As an example, the text discusses a relatively simple experiment regarding flashlight batteries. It would be helpful to perform some of this type of product testing in the classroom. You may wish to have students or groups of students select a product to test and then report their findings in writing or orally.

The terms independent and dependent variables are introduced in **section 2:3.** Your students may be more familiar with the terms manipulated and responding variables, which are sometimes used for independent and dependent variables in lower grades.

A simple algebraic formula for the arithmetic average is presented in **section 2:4.** (Appendix C describes how to manipulate algebraic equations.) Point out to students that the arithmetic average, or mean, is only one type of measure of central tendency. You may wish to explain that one disadvantage of the mean is its sensitivity to extreme values. An example is the average salaries of 12 people working for a small business. The owner earns $80 000, the manager $50 000, and 10 employees each earn $20 000. The average salary for the business is $27 500. Most of the employees would surely disagree that $27 500 represented the average wage!

In **section 2:6,** be sure students understand the difference between laws and theories. Many students hold the misconception that laws are "grown-up" theories.

Have students look through magazines, advertisements, and newspapers for examples of graphs that may be questionable when you present **section 2:8.**

Activity, Page 36   How do selected variables affect a pendulum?

Be sure students measure to the end of the washer when determining the length of the pendulum. The period of a pendulum is given by:

$$T = 2\pi \sqrt{\frac{l}{g}}$$

where l is in cm and g (acceleration due to gravity) is in cm/s^2. An interesting graph can be constructed by taping the strings of different lengths to the chalkboard.

Answers to QUESTIONS AND CONCLUSIONS

1. In Part A, the independent variable was the mass (number of washers), and the dependent variable was the period of the pendulum. In Part B, the independent variable was the angle of release, and the dependent variable was the period of the pendulum. In Part C, the independent variable was the length of the string, and the dependent variable was the period of the pendulum.
2. Part A: angle of release and length of string
   Part B: number of washers and length of string
   Part C: number of washers and angle of release
3. It is necessary to do the experiment in three parts in order to control the variables.
4. The number of washers does not affect the period of the pendulum. The angle of release does not affect the period of the pendulum. As the length of the string increases, the period of the pendulum increases.

Activity, Page 41   How can you use scientific methods?

One method for floating the egg in the middle of the beaker is done by filling the beaker half full with a salt solution and floating the egg in it. Then, carefully pour pure water down the side of the beaker. This limits the amount of mixing, leaving mostly pure water on top of the salt solution. The egg floats at the boundary between the two layers.

You may wish to conduct a sink-float challenge with your students. Have students attempt to design a device that sinks when first placed in a container of water but after 30 seconds rises to the surface and remains afloat. After the object is placed in the water, the students may not touch it or any part of the container, nor may they add anything to the water.

Answers to QUESTIONS AND CONCLUSIONS

1. Salt water was more dense than the egg.
2. Increase the concentration of salt in water.
3. Answers will vary. One method that works is to float an egg in a half beaker of salt water. Carefully pour water down the side of the beaker so not to disturb the floating egg.
4. Techniques will vary. Some answers are varying the amount of salt in water and stirring.
5. Law: An egg will float in the middle of a beaker of water if the bottom half of the beaker contains a salt solution dense enough to float the

egg. Theory: The bottom portion of water contains dissolved salt that increases the density of the solution causing the egg to float. The upper portion of water is not dense enough to affect the floating egg.

6. Ocean water is denser because it contains large amounts of dissolved salts.

Skill Inquiry, Page 38

The concept of the slope of a graph is discussed in the Skill Inquiry for chapter 2. Your students should be able to quickly recognize the relationship between the variables graphed. Stress the point that the relationship between the variables is the main idea presented in the graph.

1. **a.** Independent: month
Dependent: average quiz grade
   b. Independent: time
Dependent: speed
   c. Independent: world population
Dependent: consumption
2. **a.** Positive direct proportion
   b. (a) Positive direct proportion, (b) Negative direct proportion
   c. Positive direct proportion
3. No

Answers to REVIEW AND REFLECT

Page 34

1. Scientific methods are systematic ways of solving problems or finding the answers to questions.
2. The independent variable was the type of battery. The dependent variable was the length of time a battery will illuminate a one-square meter area from a distance of one meter. Lists of other variables may include testing all of the batteries in the same flashlight, in the same place, at the same temperature, and so on.
3. Survey respondents were high school students. Radio stations have a listening audience that includes people from many age groups. People from other age groups may not like rock music.
4. Answers may vary. For example, data can be recorded in the form of photographs, tape recordings, and chart recordings.
5. They are quantitative.

Page 38

1. It must first be organized and then analyzed.
2. A circle graph or a histogram would be suitable.

3. The limitations restrict the conclusions. One cannot make a conclusion about something that was outside the scope of the variables considered.
4. 30.5 days

Page 40

1. A scientific law is something in nature that has been observed repeatedly. A theory is a reasonable explanation for these observations.
2. Yes, theories are considered true as long as they explain observed facts. When they fail to support a new observation, they are changed to make them true again.
3. Models are used to visualize objects that cannot be observed directly. Students may suggest making scale drawings of different arrangements of classroom furniture.
4. Answers will vary. It is difficult and very expensive to send people into space to test the effects of space travel. Models allow studies to be done more economically and safely.

Page 43

1. Graphs are a useful way of summarizing information so that relationships among variables can be understood more easily.
2. Data can be misrepresented if the scales of the graph are exaggerated or diminished.
3. Answers will vary but students should prepare graphs that indicate both cereals contain a low percentage of the RDA for protein.

Chapter 2 Review, Pages 44–45

Answers to MAIN IDEAS

1. information	7. theories
2. theories	8. dependent
3. graph	9. research
4. controlled	10. control
5. independent	11. organize
6. model	12. proved

Answers to APPLICATIONS

1. The inner structure of the earth cannot be observed directly. Developing a model helps scientists test theories about the earth.
2. Answers will vary. They may include the size of tires, weight of bike, weight of rider, and so on.
3. To ensure results are not due to chance, the experiment should be repeated.
4. Student answers will vary but should reflect the idea that a considerable amount of preliminary

information gathering and planning usually precedes any experiment.

5. A theory is based on and explains observed facts. Scientific theories are never considered "proved" but rather are supported by repeated testing and changed when necessary. So to a scientist, a theory is a well-supported idea that explains nature and not just a belief or notion.

6. Many responses are possible. Answers should reflect logical thought about the scientific process, especially advanced preparation and planning as well as proper experimental methodology. For example: Why does the scientist think the chemical may have an effect? How will the scientist test for the presence or the absence of the disease?

UNIT 2   THE STRUCTURE OF MATTER

Overview

Chapter 3 introduces students to matter and how it is classified. Properties and states of matter are presented. The differences between physical and chemical properties and changes are also explored. The optional section on photography describes the chemical changes that occur as film is exposed and developed.

Chapter 4 begins with a brief history of atomic theories before discussing current atomic theory in some detail. Subatomic particles are presented. The chapter concludes with discussions of atomic mass and radioactivity.

In chapter 5, the periodic table is presented as a means to classify the elements. The characteristics of each group are explained with attention given to how their properties influence how they are used. Periodic trends are outlined in the final section of the chapter.

Chapter 6, Bonding and Reactions, begins by contrasting ionic and covalent bonding. Acids and bases are explained, followed by a discussion of organic chemistry. Equations and reactions also are considered. The chapter concludes with a presentation of some of the causes and effects of acid rain.

The concept of mixtures is developed in chapter 7. Solutions and solution concentration are discussed, followed by an explanation of solubility. The chapter concludes by exploring other types of mixtures—suspensions and colloids. Methods of separating mixtures are explored also. The material is integrated in an optional information section on water softeners.

Chapter 8, Chemistry Today, develops the concept of how chemical technology affects society. This chapter begins by considering petroleum, its refining and uses. The history and applications of plastics are then presented, followed by changes in textile technology. The chapter also includes sections on ceramics and alloys. The chapter concludes with a treatment of the impact of technology on society.

Introducing the Unit

Discuss the unit opening photograph with your students. Direct their attention to the unit questions. It is important for students to recognize that substances are used for different purposes because of their chemical and physical properties. Provide simple examples, such as shampoos used for dry, normal, or oily hair, or fertilizers and herbicides used for particular plants.

Students should know the names and symbols of the common elements by the end of chapter 5. You may want to have students begin learning them at this time.

Many different examples are used throughout the text discussion in the following chapters. It is not recommended that you or your students attempt to conduct any experiments based on these examples.

CHAPTER 3
MATTER

Performance Objectives

GOAL: Students will learn about the properties of matter and how it is classified.

OBJECTIVES: When asked to respond after completion of the reading and activities, students will

3:1   K   define matter and inertia.

3:2	K/P	explain why matter is classified.
	K/P	distinguish between homogeneous and heterogeneous matter.
	K/P	distinguish between elements and compounds.
3:3	P	describe the physical and chemical properties of some matter.
	K	explain the difference between physical and chemical properties.
	A	appreciate that the properties of matter determine how that matter will be used.
	K	define boiling point and freezing point.
3:4	K	recognize that matter can exist in four physical states.
3:5	K/P	compare malleability and ductility.
	K	define solubility.
3:6	K	define density.
	S	calculate the density of an object.
3:7	K	identify and explain some chemical properties.
3:8	K	recognize that chemical changes occur in photographic processes.
	A	appreciate how technology has changed photographic processes.

Teaching the Chapter

Review the concept of matter with students (**section 3:1**). Most students will be familiar with the notion that matter is anything that has mass and takes up space. Inertia is defined as a resistance to change in an object's motion. In this sense, the inertia and mass of an object are directly proportional. A greater force is required to change the motion of more massive objects.

Discuss the examples of heterogeneous and homogeneous mixtures in **section 3:2**. To be sure students understand the distinction, ask them to list common examples of each type.

Review Table 3–2 (**section 3:3**) to reinforce the differences between chemical and physical properties. Have your students describe some of the chemical and physical properties of objects in the room.

The Career Profile (page 59) is an illustration of the importance of understanding science concepts in many careers. You may wish to have your students interview someone in a nonscience career and write their own science-related career profile.

Density (**section 3:6**) is a difficult concept for students. Some students may be challenged by the following "discrepant event" demonstration. Float several plastic margarine tub "boats" in a small aquarium. Put as many rocks as possible in the boats. Mark the water level on the side of the aquarium. Now ask students to predict what will happen to the water level if the rocks are dumped overboard. Most will likely predict the water level will rise or else stay the same. Discuss students' reasons. When the rocks are placed on the bottom of the aquarium, the students will observe that the water level clearly drops from its previous level. This is due, of course, to the rocks being more dense than the water. When the rocks are in the boat, they displace an amount of water that has a weight equal to the weight of the rocks (Archimedes principle). When they are on the bottom of the aquarium, they displace only an amount of water equal to their volume. Since rocks are more dense than water, a greater amount of water is displaced by the weight of the rocks than by their volume.

Activity, Page 62   What are some properties of matter?

Review Appendix B for safety and first aid instructions. Suggested items for students to investigate: chalk, aluminum, steel, copper (penny), rubber, and wood. Be sure to include electrical conductors as well as insulators. You may wish to purchase density kits from a science supply house. They usually contain a good assortment of samples of both regular and irregular shapes.

Answers to QUESTIONS AND CONCLUSIONS

1. Answers will vary. They may include descriptions of color, texture, size, shape, and so on.
2. Answers will depend on the samples you supply. Test the conductivity in advance.
3. Again, answers will depend on the samples. Calculate the densities in advance so that you can check student answers.
4. Distilled water is an insulator. Tap water contains dissolved salts that conduct electricity.

Activity, Page 65   What are chemical changes?

Review Appendix B for safety and first aid instructions. Students should wear safety goggles and protective aprons for this activity. Iodine stains can be removed from some fabrics with sodium thiosulfate (photographer's hypo).

Prepare the iodine solution by adding about a milliliter of tincture of iodine to about 500 ml of water. The exact proportions are not important. The solution should only be kept for a day or so. Four of the six unknowns should be the same as the known substances in Part A. At least two should be mixtures, however. Mixtures of any two known substances will work. It is difficult to identify baking powder when mixed with cornstarch since baking powder already has cornstarch as one of its ingredients.

As an extension, you may wish to provide students with three of the unknown substances in liquid form. Their physical properties can be masked by adding food coloring and a few drops of inexpensive perfume.

Answers to QUESTIONS AND CONCLUSIONS

1. When water is added to cornstarch, baking soda, and talc, no chemical reaction is observed. When added to baking powder, fizzing occurs.
2. Answers will depend on the unknown powders you supply.
3. When iodine solution is added to cornstarch, a color change is observed. Fizzing may be observed when iodine solution is added to baking powder. No change is observed when it is added to baking soda and talc.
4. Answers will depend on the unknown powders you supply.
5. When vinegar is added to baking soda, a chemical reaction is observed. No change is observed when vinegar is added to cornstarch or talc. Fizzing may be observed when it is added to baking powder.
6. Answers will depend on the unknown powders you supply.
7. The chemical changes observed were in color and fizzing. See 1, 3, and 5 above.
8. Answers will depend on the unknown powders you supply.
9. Students may mention texture and odor.

Skill Inquiry, Page 52

Review the concepts presented in chapter 2 on scientific methods. Explain to students that most products they buy, such as food, health and beauty aids, and cleaners, are mixtures. Stress the point that good consumers research the quality and cost of the products they use.

1. Beef stock is the most common. Natural flavoring is least common in a; citric acid in b.
2. Soup a probably contains more carrots since they are the second ingredient listed. However, the listing of ingredients only indicates relative amounts within a specific product, so comparisons of different products are uncertain.
3. Students may say that soup a is a better value since it contains more protein, carbohydrate, vitamins, and minerals overall than soup b.
4. Soup b contains less sodium.
5. Soup b contains fewer Calories.

Answers to Review and Reflect

Page 54
1. Elements, compounds, and solutions are all homogeneous matter. Compounds and solutions contain more than one element. Elements and compounds are substances; solutions are mixtures.
2. All matter exhibits inertia, has mass, and occupies space.
3. Answers might include type of sport, level—varsity or junior varsity, first or second string.
4. Physical properties can be observed without chemically changing matter. Chemical properties describe how matter interacts.
5. Answers might include delicate petals, thorny stems, wide range of colors, fragrance.

Page 61
1. Plasma only exists at very high temperatures.
2. These metals are good conductors of heat, which helps cook food evenly.
3. The pine desk would be easier to move because it is less dense than oak. Lower density means less mass in the same volume.
4. White pine. It will float because it is less dense than water.
5. iron

Page 64
1. Answers might include flammability, combustibility, reactivity, acidity, tendency to ionize.
2. Answers might include the difference in cost (steel is generally cheaper) or strength (steel is generally stronger).

Page 67
1. Developed film is a negative.
2. If they were not fixed, they would gradually turn dark if exposed to light.
3. The negative will be dark.

Chapter 3 Review, Pages 68–69

Answers to Applications

1. ice, white pine, oak, leather, butter, cardboard, charcoal
2. The temperature on stars is several thousand degrees Celsius, which causes matter to ionize.
3. Answers might include strength, light weight, and ability to be formed or shaped. Interior construction materials should be nonflammable.

4.
$$D_{ice} = \frac{m}{V}$$
$$.92 \text{ g/cm}^3 = \frac{m}{20 \text{ cm} \times 10 \text{ cm} \times 5 \text{ cm}}$$
$$m = 1000 \text{ cm}^3 \times .92 \text{ g/cm}^3$$
$$m = 920 \text{ g}$$

5. No. The ice cube is more dense than methanol.

6. $D = \dfrac{m}{V} = \dfrac{150 \text{ g}}{125 \text{ cm}^3} = 1.2 \text{ g/cm}^3$

CHAPTER 4

ATOMIC STRUCTURE

Performance Objectives

GOAL: Students will learn how theories of atomic structure have developed and changed.

OBJECTIVES: When asked to respond after completion of the reading and activities, students will

4:1	A	appreciate that scientific knowledge is evolving constantly.
	K	state early atomic theories.
4:2	K	explain current ideas about atomic structure.
	K	define electron, proton, and neutron.
4:3	K/S	recognize that the probable location of electrons in the electron cloud of an atom can be predicted.
	K	explain the octet rule.
4:4	K	explain that the nucleus of an atom contains many subatomic particles and antiparticles.
	K	define antimatter.
4:5	K	define atomic number.
	K/P	recognize that the number of protons in the atoms of an element is always the same, but the number of neutrons may vary.
4:5	K	recognize that each element has a unique atomic number.
	K	define isotope.
4:6	K/S	explain that the mass of an atom is measured in atomic mass units.
	S	determine the atomic number of an atom.
4:7	K	define radioactive elements.
	K	define the three types of radiation.
	S/P	explain transmutation.
4:8	S/K	apply concepts of radioactivity.

Teaching the Chapter

You may wish to initiate a discussion of atomic theory (**section 4:1**) by cutting an apple or a sheet of paper into smaller and smaller pieces following the reasoning of Democritus. It may be helpful to ask students to state what they already know about atomic structure. Emphasize in **sections 4:1 and 4:2** that current beliefs about atomic structure are theories and that scientific theories change as more information is obtained. In this sense, what we know about atomic structure, and indeed much about our universe is constantly evolving.

In **section 4:2**, point out that most of an atom consists of empty space. As another analogy, if your classroom measures about 100 square meters, the nucleus would be about a quarter of a millimeter in diameter (1/10 000 the size of the classroom).

It is not important for students at this level to memorize a list of various subatomic particles. It is important that they realize that subatomic particles exist and are the subject of much research. Alert students to be aware of reports of this research in popular science journals (*Science 8–, Discover, Scientific American*), as well as in newspapers and magazines.

In **section 4:3**, emphasize that only probable locations for electrons can be determined. The electron cloud model helps us realize that the constantly moving electrons produce a cloudlike effect. Many students lose sight of the fact that our conceptions of atomic structure are models. Emphasize this point. Students often interchange a model with reality.

Point out the distinction between physical and mental models.

The word isotope (**section 4:5**) is derived from two Greek words and translates literally as "in the same place," as in the same place on the periodic table.

Activity, Page 78　　How can you make predictions?

Discuss with your students the fact that some events are more likely to occur than others. Probability is a mathematical measure of the likeliness of an event. Probabilities are expressed as a decimal fraction between 0.00 and 1.00. For example, if a coin is tossed, we could expect it to land heads up one half of the time. The probability is one-half, or 0.5. If a coin is tossed 50 times, we could expect 25 heads $(0.5 \times 50 = 25)$. In reality, the outcome will most likely not be exactly 25 heads. When a die is thrown, there are six possible outcomes. The probability of any one number coming up is then 1/6, or 0.167.

Answers to QUESTIONS AND CONCLUSIONS

1. Chances are equal. The probability of a head on each flip is 1 in 2. The results of each flip do not affect the subsequent flips.
2. Yes, but it is not probable.
3. Chances are equal. Student data should support this prediction.
4. Different numbers are more likely to occur because each die has six possible numbers on it.
5. Chances are better for two heads because there are only two different sides to a coin but six different sides to a die.
6. Based on probability data, scientists predict arrangements of electrons in atoms.

Activity, Page 85　　How are theories developed?

To make the black box, place several objects inside a tennis-ball can. (A shoe box may be substituted.) Prepare enough black boxes to allow students to work in groups of two or three. Construct two or three different types of black boxes and distribute them randomly to the class. It is suggested that each of the different black boxes contain some similar elements. It should be stressed to the students that it is not important for them to determine the exact contents of the cans. Rather, they are to devise and test their theories regarding its overall structure. You may wish to supply magnets so students can determine if the contents are magnetic.

Answers to QUESTIONS AND CONCLUSIONS

1. Answers will vary. Encourage students to be specific in their descriptions. Accept drawings.
2. Answers will vary, but students should indicate a logical method of arriving at their hypothesis. Stress the use of scientific methods.
3. Students may describe size, mass, sounds, etc.
4. Students should discover that there are several different types of black boxes.
5. Answers will vary depending on contents.
6. No
7. Theories cannot be proven generally. In this case, students could open the boxes to determine the contents. Stress that scientists are unable to check their theories this way.
8. Scientists cannot see into atoms. They must describe atomic structure based on indirect observations.
9. Students may say that together they came up with more ideas than they could have alone.
10. Answers will vary. Students may say people catch colds from going out in cold weather with wet hair, not dressing warmly, not eating right, or not taking vitamins. People also develop theories about how to get rid of colds, how to break bad habits, how to pass tests, or why people act as they do.

Skill Inquiry, Page 74

The legality of separate actuary tables and rate structures for males and females is controversial. Males traditionally pay higher insurance premiums because their life expectancy is shorter. Historically, females have been paid their pensions in smaller monthly amounts based on the reasoning that they have longer life expectancies. Many people feel that these practices are unfair and amount to sexual discrimination. An interesting class discussion could revolve around these issues.

1. Statistics may show that women drivers are involved in fewer accidents than men drivers.
2. People who have not had many auto accidents or traffic violations may be better drivers than people who have had many auto accidents and traffic violations. So, car insurance rates may be lower for better drivers because they are less likely to have accidents.
3. The man is not expected to live as long as the woman, so the insurance company may collect

fewer premiums from him. Thus, the insurance company may charge men a higher rate.

4. Life expectancy for older people is shorter, so the insurance company will collect fewer premiums from an older person.

5. Answers will vary. Students may mention questions about general health, lifestyle (such as smoking or drinking), family medical history, or driving record.

Answers to Review and Reflect

Page 75

1. **a.** Dalton theorized that all matter is composed of atoms, which are solid spheres. Each element has unique atoms.

   b. Thomson proposed that atoms contain negatively-charged electrons floating in a ball of positively-charged matter.

   c. According to Bohr, an atomic nucleus is a small, dense, positively-charged mass surrounded by electrons traveling in orbits.

2. Electrons are continually moving at high speeds.

3. It has eight outer energy level electrons.

Page 82

1. Leptons and hadrons

2. They have opposite charges.

3. 79

4. All carbon atoms contain six protons. The number of neutrons is different in different isotopes.

5. $^{35}_{17}$Cl; 17 electrons, 17 protons, 18 neutrons

Page 84

1. alpha, α; beta, β; gamma, γ

2. Gamma rays

3. Lead;
   $^{212}_{84}$Po → $^{208}_{82}$Pb + $^{4}_{2}$He

Page 87

1. Half-life is the time it takes for one-half of a radioactive substance to decay.

2. 250 kg; 31.25 kg

3. The amount of error involved in the measurements would make the dating unreliable.

4. using radioactive isotopes to make molecules

Chapter 4 Review, Pages 88–89

Answers to Applications

1. $^{222}_{86}$Rn

2. He did not test his theory.

3. Atoms contain a densely-packed nucleus that contains positively-charged protons and usually neutral neutrons. Negatively-charged electrons are located in a cloud surrounding the nucleus.

4. They must revise the model to fit observations.

5. Accelerated particles collide and break apart into smaller subatomic particles.

6. They cancel each other.

7. The atomic masses listed are averages of all existing isotopes for each element.

CHAPTER 5
THE PERIODIC TABLE

Performance Objectives

GOAL: Students will learn how the elements are organized into the periodic table and how people use the properties of elements to develop useful products.

OBJECTIVES: When asked to respond after completion of the reading and activities, students will

5:1	K/S	represent elements with symbols.
	A/P	explain the history of the periodic table.
	K	describe the modern periodic table in terms of electron arrangement.
	K/P	recognize that properties of elements repeat in each period of the periodic table.
	K/P	distinguish among metallic, nonmetallic, and metalloid elements.
5:2	K	explain the significance of the octet rule.
5:3	K/A	describe ways that elements are named.
	A	explain their position on the controversy regarding the nomenclature of new elements.
5:4	K/P	explain how the properties of A Group metals determine how they will be used.
5:5	K/P	explain how the properties of B Group metals determine how they will be used.

5:6	K	describe properties of metalloids.
	K/P	explain how the properties of metalloids determine how they will be used.
5:7	K	describe the properties of nonmetals.
	K/P	explain how the properties of nonmetals determine how they will be used.
5:8	K	explain several periodic trends.

Teaching the Chapter

You may wish to discuss additional "properties" of weekdays and weekend days (**section 5:2**) such as dances or basketball games, usually held on weekends. You may wish to reinforce the idea of chemical families by discussing some of the "properties" that are sometimes shared within human families.

While it is not necessary for students to memorize the symbols for all the chemical elements, they should attempt to become familiar with some of the more common ones (**section 5:3**). Encourage the use of the symbols whenever possible.

You may wish to have students look up and report on the origin of names and the history of the discovery of some of the elements. Have students use the IUPAC nomenclature system to name several common elements.

As can be seen from the periodic table, metals generally have three or fewer electrons in their outer energy level. Consequently, it is relatively easy for metals to give up one of the outer level electrons. This tendency to lose electrons can be used to explain why metals are good conductors of electricity. Since they tend to lose electrons, electricity can flow through most metals quite readily. Be sure students see that the properties of elements and the compounds they form determine their uses. Use Table 5–4 to discuss this point with your class.

Some students may question why (**section 5:7**) helium is included as a noble gas since it has two, rather than eight, electrons in its outer level. Point out that the first energy level holds only two electrons. Therefore, helium does have an outer level that is completely filled.

When reviewing Table 5–6, you may wish to discuss the effects of phosphates in detergents and run-off from fertilizers on the water quality of lakes and streams.

Activity, Page 102   How can we identify some metals?

Review safety and first aid instructions with students before beginning this activity. See Appendix B. Students should wear safety goggles and an apron for this activity. **CAUTION:** *barium, lithium, and copper compounds are poisonous (barium compounds are very toxic); avoid skin contact.*

Provide students with four to eight different known and unknown solutions. Standard laboratory solutions (0.1 M) can be prepared as follows.
lithium chloride—4.24 g LiCl per liter
sodium chloride—5.85 g NaCl per liter
potassium chloride—7.46 g KCl per liter
calcium chloride—11.1 g $CaCl_2$ per liter
strontium chloride—15.85 g $SrCl_2$ per liter
barium chloride—24.4 g $BaCl_2 \cdot 2H_2O$ per liter
copper(II) chloride—17.05 g $CuCl_2 \cdot 2 H_2O$ per liter
Note: It is quite common for sodium ions to be present as a contaminant. If the yellow sodium color is present, have students view the flames through the cobalt glass (to filter out the yellow) in a slightly darkened room. Dilute hydrochloric acid can be prepared by diluting concentrated hydrochloric acid with an equal amount of distilled water.

DATA AND OBSERVATIONS

Metal Ion	Flame Color	Flame Color/ Cobalt Glass
Li^+	red	violet
Na^+	yellow	invisible
K^+	violet	purple red
Ca^{2+}	yellowish red	green
Sr^{2+}	bright red	violet
Ba^{2+}	yellow green	red violet
Cu^{2+}	blue green	blue violet

Answers to QUESTIONS AND CONCLUSIONS
1. See data table.
2. See data table.
3. It filters out yellow light.
4. Answers will vary. Refer to data table.
5. Answers may include that the burner, wire loops, or solutions were contaminated.

Activity, Page 109   How can you make soap?

Review safety and first aid rules in Appendix B with students before this activity. Students should wear safety goggles and aprons throughout the activity. It is important that students follow the directions very carefully. It might be helpful to review the entire process before students begin. It is important to add the NaOH solution slowly while stirring. Do not use aluminum pans or utensils as they will react with the lye solution. You may want to add a few drops of perfume to the soap mixture.

Prepare 9 M stock solution by dissolving 360 g of NaOH in 1 L of water. To render beef fat, cut the fat into small pieces and place in a large pan with a few centimeters of water and several large spoonfuls of salt. Bring to a boil. Lower heat, cover loosely, and continue heating for several hours, stirring occasionally. Pour liquid portion into a large bowl. Allow to cool, then cover with plastic wrap and place in refrigerator overnight. Tallow will separate from water and harden on top.

Soap can be made using only shortening, however, a much softer, mushier product will be formed. If you use only shortening, increase quantity to 450 g.

Temperatures are rather critical in soap making. Failure to remain within the specified temperature range may result in separation of the soap mixture. The soap must be aged for at least two weeks, longer if possible. After the soap has hardened slightly, you can form it into balls with your hands if you wear the plastic gloves.

Answers to QUESTIONS AND CONCLUSIONS

1. Distilled water and soft water will have similar results.
2. Hard water has many dissolved salts that inhibit suds from forming.
3. Soft water
4. To allow soap molecules to dissolve in water

Skill Inquiry, Page 108

Often it is not practical (or possible) to calculate the variance or exact statistical relationships among variables presented in a graph. Regular patterns or trends, if they exist, can generally be observed quite readily. Trend information is very valuable in understanding the relationships between variables. You may want to refer your students to the Skill Inquiry on page 38. Ask them to describe the trends in the graphs discussed.

1. a. magnesium
    b. chlorine
    c. potassium

2. francium
3. Much smaller than francium; slightly larger than element 109
4. In general, the incidence of all the diseases has decreased in the 10 years shown on the graph. (Some cases of measles, mumps, and rubella may be from the adult population that was not vaccinated.)
5. In the late 1970s, many states passed laws requiring children to be vaccinated for many childhood diseases. The laws led to a decrease in the incidence of these diseases.

Answers to Review and Reflect

Page 92
1. a. 26.98154
    b. gold
    c. 26
2. The properties of elements in the same period are similar; metals, metalloids, and nonmetals are grouped together; easier to answer questions about atomic number, atomic mass, and the number of electrons for different elements.

Page 95
1. fourth
2. Chlorine is more reactive than argon.
3. Fermium, Fm; Lawrencium, Lr; Nobelium, No
4. unnilseptium
5. unnilunium; unnilbium
6. Answers will vary. Attempt to have students recognize the worldwide implications of this problem.

Page 100
1. Groups IA and IIA
2. Group IA—alkali metals; Group IIA—alkaline earth elements
3. Good conductors of heat and electricity; solids are malleable and ductile; high density; metallic luster; one to four electrons in the outer energy level; form compounds by losing or sharing electrons
4. B Group metals are less reactive.

Page 108
1. They have some properties of metals and nonmetals and 3 to 7 outer energy level electrons.
2. Nonmetals are nonconductors, nonlustrous, and brittle. They generally have more outer energy level electrons.
3. four
4. They have a filled outer energy level.

Page 111
1. a. increases
   b. decreases
   c. increases
2. a. increases
   b. increases
   c. decreases
3. Cesium is more reactive. It only needs to lose one electron to obtain a filled outer energy level.

Chapter 5 Review, Pages 112–113

Answers to Main Ideas

1. potassium
2. right
3. Mendeleev
4. eight
5. H
6. It comes from the Latin word *ferrum*, which means iron.
7. Cl
8. 8
9. carbon
10. metal
11. Metals
12. Moseley
13. IA and VIIA
14. transition
15. fifth

Answers to Applications

1. It provides organized, factual information on the elements.
2. Groups are often referred to as families because the elements in a group have similar properties.
3. The Group VIIIA elements, because they have filled outer energy levels.
4. The elements in Group IA are chemically active because by losing one electron, they gain a filled outer energy level. The Group VIIA elements are chemically active because by gaining one electron, they fill their outer energy levels.
5. Aluminum is malleable, ductile, strong, light-weight, and relatively unreactive.
6. a. Named for state and University of California
   b. Named for color of element (Greek "chloros," greenish-yellow)
   c. Named for Mendeleev
   d. Named after planet Neptune
   e. Named for red color of spectra
   f. Named using new IUPAC system
7. Groups are vertical columns and periods are horizontal rows on the periodic table. Similar properties are found within groups. Periods indicate electrons in outer energy levels.

CHAPTER 6
BONDING AND REACTIONS

Performance Objectives

GOAL: Students will learn how elements combine chemically and form compounds.

OBJECTIVES: When asked to respond after completion of the reading and activities, students will

6:1	A	appreciate the magnitude of chemical reactions in the world.
	K	explain that atoms combine by gaining, losing, or sharing electrons.
6:2	K	describe ionic bonding.
6:3	K	describe covalent bonding.
	P	distinguish between ionic and covalent bonding characteristics.
6:4	K	explain the purpose of chemical formulas.
	S/P	distinguish between chemical formulas and chemical reactions.
6:5	K	explain that ions may carry a positive or a negative charge.
	S	distinguish between polyatomic ions and use them to write chemical formulas.
6:6	K/S	define acids and bases and distinguish between the two.
	K	give common examples of household acids and bases.
	S/P	describe how the strength of an acid or a base is measured.
	K	describe the pH scale.
6:7	K	explain why there are so many organic compounds.
	K	define hydrocarbon and describe some common uses.
6:8	K/P	explain the Law of Conservation of Matter.
	S	balance chemical equations.

6:9	K	recognize that all chemical reactions involve changes in energy.
	P	distinguish between endothermic and exothermic.
	K	describe the basic types of chemical reactions.
	K	explain the concept of a polymer.
6:10	A	appreciate the difficulty encountered in trying to solve environmental problems.
	K	define acid rain.
	K/P	describe some means to curtail acid rain.

Teaching the Chapter

Introductory **section 6:1** is meant to help students realize that chemical reactions are occurring in their environment (and inside their bodies). You may wish to perform a commonplace event that represents a chemical reaction such as dropping an antacid tablet in a glass of water. Baking a cake or bread involves chemical reactions. Baking soda ($NaHCO_3$) is a compound made up of sodium, carbon, hydrogen, and oxygen. When baking soda reacts with an acid, a new compound, carbon dioxide (CO_2) is formed. Common baking powder contains an acid and baking soda. During the baking of a cake, the acid and the baking soda react giving off bubbles of carbon dioxide gas. These bubbles are what cause the cake to rise and give it texture.

Ionic compounds (**sections 6:2 and 6:3**) are mostly hard, brittle, solids with high melting points. The solids do not conduct electricity. When melted or dissolved, they do conduct. These differences in properties between covalent and ionic compounds are explained by their different structures. Be sure students realize that ionic compounds are composed of ions, while covalent compounds are made up of molecules. The ions in an ionic crystal are held rigidly in place by the mutual attractions of the oppositely charged particles.

Earlier systems of nomenclature (**section 6:4**) used the Latin name of the element and the suffixes *-ic* and *-ous*. Some chemical supply houses still use this system. Students may be familiar with compounds such as stannous fluoride, which is tin(II) fluoride.

H^+ ions (**section 6:6**) are also called hydride ions. H_2O forms H_3O^+ and OH^- ions. The concentrations of these ions: $[OH^-] = [H_3O^+] = 1.00 \times 10^{-7}$ M.

Acids react with metals. Many metals are dipped in H_2SO_4 to remove oxidation from their surfaces. This process is known as pickling.

When some compounds are mixed with water, an acidic or a basic solution is formed. For example, the oxides of most metals react with water to form bases. These metal oxides are usually called basic anhydrides. Anhydride means without water. In other words, compounds that form bases when added to water are known as basic anhydrides.

Likewise, many nonmetal oxides form acids when added to water. These compounds are called acid anhydrides. When carbon dioxide is added to water, carbonic acid is formed.

$$CO_2 + H_2O \rightarrow H_2CO_3$$

Organic compounds may be saturated or unsaturated. Alkanes are said to be saturated because they contain the maximum number of hydrogen atoms. Unsaturated hydrocarbons containing double and/or triple carbon bonds have fewer than this maximum number of hydrogen atoms.

Plant and animal tissue is made up primarily of proteins. Point out that proteins are composed of polymers (long repeating chains) of amino acids.

In **section 6:8,** be sure students are aware of the relationship between balancing chemical equations and the Law of Conservation of Matter. Students often overlook this important point and become bogged down with the arithmetic of equation balancing.

Activity, Page 121 What are properties of mixtures and compounds?

Review safety and first aid instructions in Appendix B with students before beginning this activity. Students should wear safety goggles and aprons for this activity.

To keep the iron filings off the magnet, have students keep the magnet under the paper. You may have them place the magnet inside a plastic bag.

Although ideally, the iron and sulfur should not be magnetic after heating together, some bits of iron may not chemically combine with the sulfur. In this case, students should still be able to observe that some of the iron sulfide pieces are only weakly magnetic or not at all magnetic, indicating a change in properties.

Answers to QUESTIONS AND CONCLUSIONS

1. No. Both elements kept their individual properties.

2. Yes. A substance with different properties was formed.

3. Iron(II) sulfide, FeS.

4. The properties of compounds differ from the properties of the elements from which they are formed.

5. The mass of the reactants is the same as the mass of the products. Note: Some slight difference might occur due to experimental error.

Activity, Page 125   How do antacids compare?

Review safety and first aid procedures in Appendix B with students before beginning this activity. Students should wear aprons and safety goggles during this exercise.

If an acid is added to pure water, the water will become acidic; the pH of the water solution will become something less than 7. It is sometimes important to keep the pH of a substance constant. For example, the pH of many human systems must remain within a narrow range. To keep the pH of a solution relatively constant, a buffer system is used. A buffer can absorb small amounts of acids or bases without a significant change in pH. A buffer is usually made from a weak acid or a weak base and its salt.

Demonstrate to students the proper way to fill a buret using a funnel. The funnel should never be dropped into the buret or allowed to rest on the top rim of the buret. The funnel should always be supported by holding the stem with the fingers of one hand while the other hand is used to pour.

For stability, use two buret clamps to mount each buret, if available. If burets are not available, you may substitute either syringes or eyedroppers. Standard medicine droppers can be easily calibrated. A milliliter is approximately equivalent to 20 drops.

Purchase congo red. If it is not available, phenolphthalein can be substituted. This indicator will range from colorless (before titration) to pink (after titration). However, phenolphthalein does not have the needed pH range for use with all common antacids. When selecting antacids to use, be sure they are the regular (peppermint) flavor. The fruit flavors contain added coloring that may interfere with the results of the experiment. The HCl solution for this activity can be prepared by adding one part concentrated HCl to 12 parts water.

Answers to QUESTIONS AND CONCLUSIONS

1. Antacids help neutralize excess stomach acid.

2. Spicy or hard to digest foods

3. Answers will vary depending on the tablets used. Do the activity yourself in advance to determine the answers.

4. Mildly alkaline compounds

5. Cost/unit dosage $= \dfrac{\text{cost of sample}}{\text{number of dosages}}$

Skill Inquiry, Page 120

Generally, induced vomiting is not suggested when strong caustics are accidentally ingested. They may cause more severe burns to the esophagus as the substance is regurgitated. Have your students do a home inventory to see if dangerous products are stored safely. You may want to tell your students that you will have a bonus question on the next test asking the phone number of your local poison control center.

1. Out of the reach of children, away from food, tightly capped, upright, in a cool place

2. Combining with ammonia or other household chemicals, transferring to food or beverage containers, contact with skin or eyes, ingesting. Bleach may cause harmful vapors, chemical burns, and it is poisonous.

3. Flood with water 10 to 15 minutes. If irritation persists, call a doctor.

4. Call a poison control center, a paramedic, or a doctor immediately. Labels often give incorrect emergency instructions.

5. Answers will vary.

Answers to Review and Reflect

Page 118

1. Compounds form when atoms or ions bond.

2. Ionic bonds are formed when electrons are transferred. Covalent bonds are formed when atoms share electrons.

3. $K^+ I^-$

Page 123

1. a. potassium bromide   c. ammonium nitrate
   b. silver phosphate   d. silicon carbide

2. a. $Fe_2 (SO_4)_3$ c. $(NH_4)_3 PO_4$
   b. $Cu_2 O$ d. $NaC_2H_3O_2$

3. Parentheses indicate that more than one of the entire ion is needed, not just the last element listed in the ion. In $Al(OH)_3$, there are three hy-

droxide ions. In $AlOH_3$, there is one oxygen atom and three hydrogen atoms.

Page 126
1. Acids are proton donors and bases are proton acceptors.
2. A strong acid forms more ions in solution, which makes it a better conductor.
3. Because all living things contain organic compounds.
4. Alcohol

Chapter 6 Review, Pages 136–137

Answers to Applications
1. There are millions of ways in which elements can combine. Carbon, in particular, forms an immense variety of compounds, including long chains and complex ring structures.
2. Carbon can form long chains and ring structures to a greater extent than any other element.
3. Zinc is much less reactive than iron so it forms a protective layer. The process is called galvanizing.
4. Exothermic reactions produce energy.
5. **a.** $ZnO + C \rightarrow Zn + CO$
   b. $6CO_2 + 6H_2O \rightarrow C_6H_{12}O_6 + 6O_2$
   c. $CO_2 + H_2O \rightarrow H_2CO_3$
   d. $P_4O_{10} + 6H_2O \rightarrow 4H_3PO_4$
6. Polymerization reactions have provided us with numerous forms of plastics, synthetic foods, medicines, textiles, paints, fuels, and chemicals.

CHAPTER **7**

MIXTURES

Performance Objectives

GOAL: Students will learn the characteristics of mixtures, how they are classified, and how they are separated.

OBJECTIVES: When asked to respond after completion of the reading and activities, students will

7:1	K	define mixtures.
	K/P	distinguish between and describe different types of mixtures.
	S	give examples of mixtures.
7:2	K	define solvent and solute.
	K/P	describe effects of a solute on the physical properties of the solvent.
	K	recognize that solutes and solvents can be solids, liquids, or gases.
	S	give examples of solutes and solvents.
7:3	K	distinguish between saturated, concentrated, and dilute solutions.
7:4	K/P	describe basic characteristics of solubility.
	K	distinguish between polar and nonpolar molecules.
	P	explain the solvation process.
7:5	K	recognize that the solubility of solids generally increases with temperature.
	K	recognize that the solubility of gases generally decreases as temperature increases.
	K/P	state and explain factors affecting solubility.
7:6	K/P	compare solutions, colloids, and suspensions.
	K	explain the Tyndall effect.
	K	describe the purpose and give examples of emulsifying agents.
7:7	K/S	state several physical means for separating mixtures.
7:8	K	differentiate between hard and soft water.
	S	describe how an ion exchange water softener operates.

Teaching the Chapter

You may wish to introduce this chapter (**section 7:1**) by mixing together sand, salt, and water. The sand can be filtered and then the salt recovered by boiling. If a condenser is used, the water can also be saved.

Point out that there are many everyday examples of mixtures, including mixed vegetables, milk and cereal, soil, gravel, fruit punch, clouds, and seawater. Let students suggest additional examples of mixtures. You may wish to have students classify them as heterogeneous or homogeneous.

Discuss Table 7–1 (**section 7:2**) with the class. It is important for students to recognize that solutions do not all consist of a solid solute dissolved in a liquid solvent. You may also wish to demonstrate that a salt solution will conduct electricity while a sugar solution will not.

Have students grow crystals (**section 7:3**) as a class project. Some possible questions for students to investigate include: Do all crystals have the same shape? What variables may affect the size or shape of a crystal?

Many common polar solvents (**section 7:4**) are dangerous. These include (but are not limited to) carbon tetrachloride, benzene, acetone, and chloroform. It is recommended that these substances not be used in the classroom. As an assignment, you may wish to have students research the solvents used by dry cleaners. (See Skill Inquiry, chapter 8, and the Career Profile for this chapter.)

Colloids (**section 7:6**) have particles between 10 Å and 1000 Å (10^{-5} cm and 10^{-7} cm). The Tyndall effect can be easily demonstrated with a flashlight in a darkened room by clapping two chalk erasers together, dispersing chalk dust in the air.

Additional information on water softening (**section 7:8**) is usually available from local commercial water softener companies. Many have materials available for schools.

Activity, Page 147   What affects solubility?

Review safety and first aid procedures in Appendix B with students before they begin this activity. Students should wear safety goggles and aprons for the activity. Care should be used placing the thermometer in the rubber stopper.

In Part B, have students graph their results to produce a solubility curve. Have them compare their graph with the one on page 145.

Answers to QUESTIONS AND CONCLUSIONS

1. It is an experimental control to see if equal masses dissolve at equal rates.
2. Mass is not a relevant variable in Part B. To estimate mass:
   determine the mass of the beaker and water.
   determine the mass of the cooled solution. subtract the mass of the beaker and water from the mass of the solution.
3. Solubility increases as particle size decreases.

Stirring increases the rate of solubility. As the temperature increases, more solute dissolves.
4. Similar to Figure 7–5 on page 145. The trends indicated in question 3 should be shown.

Activity, Page 153   How can mixtures be separated using paper chromatography?

Review safety and first aid procedures in Appendix B with students. Be sure to use washable blue-black or black ink to ensure its solubility in water. It will take approximately 15 minutes for the water to soak the strip of filter paper. You may also wish to have students separate the same color(s) of food coloring produced by various manufacturers. An application of this technique would be to have students analyze the chromatograms of several different brands of ink. A hypothetical "crime" could thus be solved.

Answers to QUESTIONS AND CONCLUSIONS

1. and 2. Answers will vary with ink and food color used. You should test your samples before distributing them to your students. You may want to display your results in the lab so students can compare their results.
3. The bands of dye dissolved. The solution colors will be faint because of the low concentration.
4. A light gray solution was formed.
5. Scientists can use chromatography to separate and identify the parts of a solution.

Skill Inquiry, Page 144

It may be helpful to your students if you build models of some of the molecules described in the table. If you have several molecular model kits available, allow students to check their answers.

NH_3—polar CO_2—nonpolar
CH_4—nonpolar CH_3Cl—polar

Answers to Review and Reflect

Page 142

1. A mixture can be any combination of solid, liquid, or gaseous substances. Mixtures may be homogeneous, such as coffee or tea, or heterogeneous, such as concrete or soil.
2. Solution—salt water; solute—salt; solvent—water
3. Ionic and molecular solutes that ionize in solution
4. There is less water, the solvent, in concentrate.

5. Pool, lake, and ocean water contain electrolytes. If lightning strikes the water, the electric current would be conducted to the swimmers.

Page 146
1. Stirring, temperature, particle size, pressure
2. The warmer soft drink would fizz more because the solubility of a gas decreases as temperature increases.
3. Water is polar; grease is nonpolar.

Page 152
1. **a.** solution
   b. solution
   c. suspension
2. **a.** filtering
   b. using a magnet
   c. centrifuge
3. The substances in a mixture are not chemically combined.

Page 155
1. Hard water contains more than 8 ppm dissolved salts. Soft water contains less.
2. Difficulty cleaning, soap scum, boiler and water pipe damage.
3. The hard Mg, Fe, and Ca ions are exchanged for Na ions.
4. Consult your local water supply department.

Chapter 7 Review, Pages 156–157
Answers to Applications
1. The salt lowers the freezing point of the ice, making the water in contact with the ice cream maker colder. The colder water helps the ice cream freeze faster.
2. The substance may be polar, and water is a polar solvent. Benzene is nonpolar. Polar solutes generally dissolve in polar solvents.
3. Excess solute is added to a saturated solution. The solution is heated until the excess dissolves. Then the solution is allowed to cool undisturbed.
4. The wastewater may be warmer than the temperature of the waterway, causing thermal pollution. The warm water promotes the growth of algae, which take dissolved oxygen from the water as they decay. Fish die due to the lower oxygen content of the water.
5. Emulsifying agents contain large molecules that have one polar and one nonpolar end. They cause the two liquids to form a colloid. Homogenization is a process of reducing particle size. The smaller particles have less tendency to separate.
6. Filter the mixture to remove the sand and iron. Use a magnet to separate the iron from the sand. Distill the salt water to separate salt and water.

CHAPTER **8**
CHEMISTRY TODAY

Performance Objectives

GOAL: Students will learn about important advances in technology and the impact of these advances.

OBJECTIVES: When asked to respond after completion of the reading and activities, students will

8:1	A	appreciate the impact of science and technology on the consumer.
8:2	K/A	recognize petroleum as a primary resource for fuels and many other products.
	K	define fossil fuels.
8:3	K	explain how petroleum is separated into fractions.
8:4	K/P	explain how the properties of plastics give rise to its many commercial uses.
	K/A	relate the history of the development of plastics.
8:5	K/P	compare the advantages and disadvantages of natural and synthetic fibers.
	K	describe some uses and characteristics of fiber-reinforced plastics.
8:6	K	describe some characteristics of ceramics.
	K	explain how ceramics are used.
8:7	K	define alloy
	K	name some important alloys and their uses.
8:8	A	recognize that technological advancements have both costs and benefits.
8:9	K	explain why chemicals are added to some foods.

A   recognize the impact of chemicals in society.

Teaching the Chapter

The impact of technology on society is very great. Students, however, may not realize how technology plays a role in many facets of life that may not appear to be "high tech." For this reason, it may be informative to discuss **section 8:1** with the class. Ask students to trace the involvement of science, technology, and people on other consumer goods.

Teaching materials can be obtained from most of the major oil companies at little or no cost (**section 8:2**). Point out to students that fossil fuels are still being formed by earth processes. However, these processes take millions of years. People are using fossil fuels about 50 times faster than they are being replenished.

To increase the yield of gasoline and other products, a process known as cracking is used (**section 8:3**). In cracking, the long hydrocarbon chains of the less valuable heavy fractions are broken apart, or cracked to form the smaller, lighter molecules found in gasoline. Further refining of petroleum includes the removal of impurities (mainly sulfur), treatment with specific additives, and the blending of fractions.

Ceramics (**section 8:6**) generally consist of one or more metals, combined by heating, with nonmetallic elements. Another advantage of ceramics is that there is an abundant supply of the raw materials from which they are made. Most ceramics are made from silicon and aluminum, two of the most abundant substances in the earth's crust.

A series of educational materials on steelmaking (**section 8:7**) is available to teachers from the American Iron and Steel Institute, 1000 16th Street, N.W., Washington, D.C. 20036, or your local chapter of the American Society for Metals.

Discuss the use of alloys in the everyday life of the consumer. For example, many different types of cookware are available. More expensive cookware is made from costly alloys that are more durable. The bottoms of cookware often are made from a cast aluminum alloy or copper for greater heat conductivity. This allows food to cook more evenly.

Be sure students realize that there are costs and benefits in most areas of life (**section 8:9**). While the automobile is a most useful product, there are costs in terms of environmental pollution and highway fatalities associated with their use. Society strives to reduce the costs by requiring exhaust standards, safety standards, and so on.

Some athletes believe that ingesting large doses of the male hormone testosterone, a steroid, will increase muscle bulk and consequently strength. Most scientists believe that steroids will not increase the strength of athletes, and studies indicate that there are many negative side effects. These side effects include decreased fertility, possible increased aggression, liver damage, the development of male secondary sex characteristics in women, and the possible accumulation of fat deposits in arteries.

Draw students' attention to Figure 8–13 to show the scale of chemical production (**section 8:9**). Most students believe that chemicals are produced in laboratory settings similar to their classroom.

Activity, Page 168   How do fabrics compare?

Review safety and first aid procedures in Appendix B with students before this activity. Students should take care handling dye and wear safety goggles and aprons.

It is not necessary to use all of the samples of fabric. In addition, you may substitute other fabrics. Wool is relatively expensive compared to some other fabrics. One method of labeling is to cut corners with scissors.

Answers to QUESTIONS AND CONCLUSIONS

1. Wool, silk, linen, cotton, possibly rayon and poly/cotton blend; these fibers are natural or are made from cellulose.
2. Silk and cotton; natural
3. The fabric will take on the characteristics of the more prominent fabric. For example, a 70/30 percent polyester/cotton blend will act more like a polyester.
4. Extra care must be taken when cleaning natural fibers.

Activity, Page 175   What affects the strength of plywood?

The balsa wood strips should be 2 mm thick. Standard 2 × 4s work well for the two required boards. If the strips are saved from year to year, step 1 can be eliminated.

Answers to QUESTIONS AND CONCLUSIONS

1. Yes. More mass was supported by two strips than one, and more by three strips than two.

The three strips glued together supported the most mass.

2. Answers may vary. However, the amount of mass supported by the two glued strips should (within a rather crude experimental error) be on an order of magnitude of 8 (2^3) times more than that supported by a single strip. The load supported by such a beam varies with the cube of the thickness, when the pieces are glued together. Three strips glued together should support a mass 27 times greater (3^3) than one beam. You may be able to demonstrate this with a spring scale.

3. More than three strips glued together should support a greater mass. However, more than three strips generally will not show any change in mass supported using the cup of water since three strips will support the cup very well.

Skill Inquiry, Page 171

Refer students to section 7:4 and discuss the importance of molecular polarity and stain removal. One commonly used dry-cleaning fluid is perchloroethylene, $Cl_2C = CCl_2$, a nonpolar solvent.

1. Presoak in warm water. Wash.
2. Presoak in warm water. Wash in warm water, rather than hot at first, since blue jeans fade.
3. Take to a dry cleaner or use a commercial dry cleaning product available for consumer use.
4. Treat with paint remover. Wash.
5. Presoak in warm water. Wash in warm water. Bleach could be used since the tablecloth is white.
6. Soak in cool water. Wash.
7. Rub with petroleum jelly. Wash in warm water.
8. Harden gum with ice cube. Remove excess. Hand wash in COLD water since the sweater is wool. Or, take to a dry cleaner.
9. Presoak in cold water.
10. Presoak in warm water. Wash in cold water.

Answers to Review and Reflect

Page 163

1. Will a product meet needs? Is a product or solution safe? How much will a product or solution cost? How long will a product or solution last?
2. Petroleum products include gasoline, diesel fuel, jet fuel, heating oil, lubricating oils and greases, plastics, waxes, and asphalt.

3. Petroleum is a fossil fuel—a product of once-living organisms whose remains were trapped deep in the earth. It would take millions of years for the petroleum supply to be replenished.

Page 171

1. Plastics are used to make disposable products but are not easily recyclable. Because of their non-reactivity, they are very slow to decompose in the environment.
2. Synthetic fibers are prepared mainly from wood pulp, cotton linters, and petroleum.
3. Ceramics are nonmetallic primarily. They withstand very high temperatures. They are brittle.
4. Cement is a ceramic material composed mainly of calcium silicate prepared from chalk or limestone and clay or shale. Concrete is a mixture of cement, sand, gravel, and water.
5. FRPs are lightweight, yet strong and durable. They do not rust or corrode.

Page 174

1. Steel is a strong material. Iron is weaker and more brittle.
2. The materials in one alloy may be scarcer making them more expensive. Also, the cost of processing the materials of one alloy may be greater.
3. Products must be beneficial or desirable to consumers in some way; otherwise, people would not buy them. However, even the most beneficial product can be used (or misused) in ways that are harmful. The manufacture of many beneficial products may also cause a risk of pollution or other environmental damage. People ultimately must decide whether the benefits of a product outweigh its risks.

Page 177

1. The synthetic chemicals may be less expensive. Extracting the naturally occurring chemicals may be destructive of living things and the environment as well as expensive.
2. Salt, sugar, corn syrup
3. Sulfuric acid, H_2SO_4. It is used to make other chemicals, such as fertilizers, dyes, rayon, and in petroleum refining.
4. Additives make food look and taste better, increase shelf life, and add nutritional value.

Chapter 8 Review, Pages 178–179

Answers to Applications

1. Student answers will vary but should include

some of the following ideas. Methods would have to be devised to test the product for quality and safety. Proper packaging and labeling would have to be designed.

2. Once all petroleum is pumped out of the earth, for all practical purposes, it is gone. More might be produced by geological activity but would take millions of years. You may want to compare petroleum with renewable resources such as timber.

3. Student answers will vary. One possible answer is: plastic has been substituted for the front sheet metal of many automobiles. It weighs less, does not easily nick or dent from flying gravel, and is not easily damaged in mild front-end collisions. However, it may warp somewhat with heat or crack in intense cold.

4. The dyes may be better absorbed or more tightly held by the polyester fibers than they are by the cotton. The solvent action of detergent often removes dyes from natural fibers easier than from synthetics.

5. In selecting a site for a brick factory, here are some factors to consider: whether there is a cheap and plentiful fuel, whether there is a nearby supply of raw materials, whether there is likely to be a good market for bricks nearby since bricks are expensive to ship long distances, whether there would be qualified employees available in the area.

6. The alloy would have to melt at a relatively low temperature in order to release the sprinkler before the fire has progressed too far. (Wood's metal melts below the temperature of boiling water.) In addition, it would need to last a long time without corroding, rusting, or weakening significantly.

UNIT 3 THE NATURE OF ENERGY

Overview

In chapter 9, Motion, Newton's basic laws of motion are described. The concepts of inertia, speed, velocity, acceleration, and centripetal force are explained. The chapter concludes with an optional discussion of projectile motion.

Chapter 10, Force and Work, presents the three fundamental forces in nature. Pressure and work are explained in relation to force. On this base, the concept of energy is built. Mechanical advantage, efficiency, and power are defined mathematically. An optional discussion of momentum concludes the chapter.

In chapter 11, Heat, the concept of energy is developed further. The difference in definitions of heat, thermal energy, and temperature is explained. Examples of the processes of thermal energy transfer: convection, conduction, and radiation, are given. Practical uses of information about thermal energy transfer are discussed, also. The chapter ends with a Choices section concerning energy sources.

In chapter 12, static and current electricity are contrasted. Ohm's Law is explained. Practical information about costs of electricity, electromagnets, direct and alternating current are presented, also. The final section presents choices about electricity use.

Chapter 13, Waves and Sound, begins with a general discussion of wave properties. Then, sound waves are discussed specifically. How sounds are produced, the Doppler effect, pitch, tone quality, and volume are each presented. Separate sections are devoted to noise and the speed of sound. An information section about how we hear and hearing loss concludes the chapter.

Chapter 14, the final chapter of this unit, is Light. The wave-particle duality is explained briefly. Then the chapter continues with a more in-depth discussion of light as a wave. The electromagnetic spectrum is highlighted. Mirrors and lenses are discussed, also. The optional last section is about lasers.

Introducing the Unit

Many important and famous scientists are mentioned in this unit. You may want to assign students reports about these scientists now so they will be ready to present the reports when the accomplishments of the scientists are studied. For example, Newton, Galileo, Coulomb, Hertz, Pascal, Ohm, Oersted, and Doppler are among the scientists mentioned in the text. Many other scientists who contributed but are not mentioned also may be of interest to students.

Students often think they will not enjoy studying physical science because it is more abstract than life or earth science. Use the unit opening photograph to point out the practical application of physical science in our world. The motion of buses and cars, the construction of freeways and skyscrapers, the light from lamps and a sunset all can be explained with physical science laws and concepts. Use the unit opening paragraph and questions to motivate student interest. Find out how much students do not know about how their world "works." Emphasize that after studying Unit 3, they will understand better.

CHAPTER 9
MOTION

Performance Objectives

GOAL: Students will learn how motion can be described and about the forces that cause motion.

OBJECTIVES: When asked to respond after completion of the reading and activities, students will

9:1	K	recognize that laws of motion apply to all moving objects.
	A	appreciate that people have studied moving objects for centuries.
9:2	K	define motion as the change in an object's position.
	P/K	compare the motions of objects from different frames of reference.
	K	define speed.
	S	calculate average speed.
9:3	K	explain Newton's First Law of Motion.
	K/P	describe the forces acting on an object.
9:4	K	define velocity and acceleration.
	S/P	calculate the acceleration of an object.
9:5	K	explain Newton's Second Law of Motion.
	S/P	calculate acceleration using Newton's second law.
9:6	K	explain Newton's Third Law of Motion.
	P	apply Newton's laws to moving objects.
9:7	K/P	describe the motion of falling objects.
	S	calculate the velocity of a falling object.

	K	define terminal velocity.
9:8	K	describe circular motion.
	K	explain centripetal force.
	P/K	give common examples of circular motion.
9:9	K	define projectile motion.
	P/K	give examples of projectiles.
	K	describe how projectile motion is applied to orbiting satellites.

Teaching the Chapter

Two of the most famous of the early astronomers referred to in **section 9:1** were Thales and Pythagoras. You may wish to have students observe the sky on a clear night. If they use some reference points, such as trees, buildings, or utility poles, and then observe the sky again after several hours, changes in the apparent position of some stars can be noted.

With **section 9:2,** you may wish to discuss frames of reference in a somewhat broader context. The motion of an object on earth from a reference of the sun would be observed to be moving quite rapidly—about 30 kilometers per second, the speed of the earth around the sun. From a more distant reference point, one would also observe the motion of the solar system around the center of the Milky Way Galaxy. Stress that there is no absolute frame of reference. All motion is relative.

With **section 9:3,** note that Galileo also hypothesized that moving objects will tend to remain in motion and first introduced the idea of inertia. You may wish to discuss the issue of air bags and the mandatory use of seat belts in class.

With **section 9:5,** you could have students perform other calculations that require them to manipulate the equation, solving for force or mass.

When discussing terminal velocity in **section 9:7**, have students discuss how parachutes work. Some students may wish to reconstruct some of Galileo's experiments on vertical motion.

The idea of centripetal force is often difficult for students to grasp. Many think that circular motion causes a force—the so-called "centrifugal" force. Emphasize that the centripetal force must be exerted in order to produce circular motion. The "centrifugal" force is simply the force equal and opposite in response to centripetal force.

Activity, Page 193   How can velocity and acceleration be calculated?

If a metric bathroom scale is not available, let students calculate their mass by dividing their weight in pounds by 2.2. Be sure that students do not try to stop at the 50-meter line but maintain a constant speed, decelerating only after crossing the line.

Answers to QUESTIONS AND CONCLUSIONS

1. The average acceleration for the first 25 meters is a result of the fact that students start from rest position and accelerate quickly to top speed. Very little or no acceleration should occur in the last 25 meters as students run at constant speed.
2. The average acceleration over the entire 50 meters would have been less than the acceleration for the first 25 meters but greater than the acceleration for the final 25 meters. Students should be aware that most of their acceleration should have occurred within the first few meters of the run. After that point, they would have run at a constant speed with little or no acceleration.
3. Answers will vary depending on the final speed at the end of the run, the time it took to stop, and the student's mass. Force is calculated by using the equation $F = m \times a$. The force will be negative, which indicates that the force is acting to decelerate the mass.
4. Answers will vary. See answer to question 3.
5. Answers will vary.

Activity, Page 195   How can forces cause motion?

Review safety and first aid instructions in Appendix B before beginning this activity. Make certain students wear safety goggles and a protective apron for this activity. Before allowing students to apply heat, be sure to inspect each student's apparatus. Make certain the holes are correctly placed and there is water in the can.

Answers to QUESTIONS AND CONCLUSIONS

1. Steam escaped from the holes and the can began to rotate.
2. The can stopped rotating as the water cooled.
3. The pressure within the can exerts the force that expels the steam. An equal force in the opposite direction causes the can to rotate.
4.

5. The forces would balance each other, so there would be no rotation.
6. More force will be required to rotate the can.
7. Answers will vary. A Hero's engine can be used for devices that require rotational motion, such as a pump.
8. The energy source is the laboratory burner. Answers about improvements will vary. Students may mention reducing friction or air resistance.

Skill Inquiry, Page 187

Using the Pythagorean Theorem, students could calculate the net velocity (5 km/s) of the boat as it moves across the river. You could extend the skill with other examples to show the practicality of vector analysis of motion. Situations could include flying with a tail wind, a crosswind, or a head wind, piloting a boat against, with, and across a current. With practice, students can gain a good understanding of interacting vectors using only the skills of drawing to scale and simple mathematics.

1. East at 11 km/h, northwest at 4 km/h
2.

Note: If students use the same scale for both vectors, vector b will be much longer than vector a.

3.

Net velocity vector

4 km/h SE

3 km/h NE

Note: If the diagram is properly constructed, the net velocity vector should be 5 units long in the direction shown. Also, note the addition of vectors head to tail as shown. Only this arrangement will give the correct geometric relationship to allow the resultant vector to have both the correct length and direction.

Answers to Review and Reflect

Page 187

1. Early astronomers described the apparent motions of planets based on observations made from the earth's surface. Apparent movements were a result of earth's rotation and revolution.

2. distance = 640 laps × 6 km/lap = 3840 km

$$S = \frac{d}{t} = \frac{3840 \text{ km}}{24 \text{ h}} = 160 \text{ km/h}$$

3. The ball originally at rest will experience an external force from the club, which will cause the ball to accelerate from its rest position. Once in motion, forces caused by air resistance tend to decelerate the ball. Whether the ball is at rest or in motion, there is a constant force due to gravity acting on it. This force tends to accelerate the ball downward. As a result, the ball falls and strikes the ground. Finally, friction produced by rolling on the grass causes the ball to stop completely. In all cases, forces were responsible for changes in the ball's motion.

Page 192

1. $a = \dfrac{v_f - v_i}{t} = \dfrac{70 \text{ m/s} - 10 \text{ m/s}}{15 \text{ s}} = \dfrac{60 \text{ m/s}}{15 \text{ s}} =$

4 m/s^2

2. $a = \dfrac{v_f - v_i}{t} = \dfrac{0 \text{ m/s} - 5 \text{ m/s}}{5 \text{ s}} = \dfrac{-5 \text{ m/s}}{5 \text{ s}} =$

-1 m/s^2

3. $a = \dfrac{F}{m}$

$a = \dfrac{4 \text{ N}}{2 \text{ kg}} = \dfrac{4 \text{ kg m/s}^2}{2 \text{ kg}}$

$a = 2 \text{ m/s}^2$

4. Force; mass

5. Speed is a measure of the rate of motion. Velocity is a measure of speed and direction of motion.

6. Deceleration is negative acceleration.

Page 194

1. For every force, there is an equal force in the opposite direction.

2. The girl holding the rope exerts a force, equal to her weight, on the rope. In order for the girl to maintain her position, an upward force must be exerted on the girl equal to her weight. The rope provides the upward force. When the bat and ball interact, the force exerted by the ball causes the bat to decelerate. The resultant force exerted by the bat changes both the speed and direction of the ball.

3. When rocket fuel is burned in the engine, a force expels the particles produced by the explosion through the exhaust nozzle. An equal force in the opposite direction propels the rocket.

Page 199

1. $a = \dfrac{\Delta v}{t}$ so $t = \dfrac{\Delta v}{a}$ $t = \dfrac{54 \text{ m/s}}{9.8 \text{ m/s}^2} = 5.53 \text{ s}$

Note: This would be true only if the sky diver accelerated constantly to terminal velocity. In reality, as the sky diver's velocity increases, the force due to air friction increases. This results in an increasing upward acceleration opposing the acceleration of gravity. When the two accelerations are equal, the sky diver has attained terminal velocity. You may want to see if students can reason out this explanation before presenting it to them.

2. An object in circular motion is accelerating because its direction is constantly changing, therefore, its velocity is constantly changing.

3. Friction, which supplies the centripetal force on the car while it is turning, is reduced by water on the pavement.

Page 201

1. Answers may include any thrown object, bullets, satellites, and so on.

2. Gravitational force

3. The curved path is a result of the combined effect of gravity coupled with a horizontal motion.

Answers to Applications

1. 80 km/h + 75 km/h = 155 km/h

2. $t = \dfrac{855 \text{ km}}{570 \text{ km/h}} = 1.5 \text{ h}$

3. d = 3.5 km/h × 0.5 h = 1.75 km

4. A bicycle with less mass is easier to accelerate.

5. F = 180 kg × 0.7 m/s^2 = 126 kg m/s^2 = 126 N

6. The object's weight decreases as its distance from earth increases.

7. v = 9.8 m/s^2 × 4.5 s = 44.1 m/s

8. The bank allows centripetal force to be exerted more nearly "upward" through the suspension of the car, rather than relying totally on the friction of the tires to provide it. This makes greater centripetal force (before skidding occurs) possible and thus greater speeds through the curves.

Chapter 9 Review, Pages 202–203

Answers to Main Ideas

1. Newton's
2. Aristotle, Galileo
3. position
4. 37 m/s
5. m/s or km/h
6. Newton's First Law
7. change
8. m/s^2
9. $F = m \times a$ or $a = \dfrac{F}{m}$
10. It also doubles.
11. third
12. the height at which it was released and the time the object is falling
13. air resistance
14. 0.4 m/s^2
15. 2 m/s^2
16. 4.9 m/s
17. final velocity; initial velocity
18. the gravitational force between an object and the earth

UNIT 3

CHAPTER 10
FORCE AND WORK

Performance Objectives

GOAL: Students will learn about the relationships among forces, work, and energy.

OBJECTIVES: When asked to respond after completion of the reading and activities, students will

10:1	K	state that a change in motion occurs only when the forces on an object are unbalanced.
	K/P	predict what happens when the forces on an object are balanced.
	K	describe the three fundamental forces.
	A	appreciate that although much has been learned about the nature of forces, much remains to be learned.
10:2	S	calculate pressure.
	K	distinguish between pressure and force.
10:3	K	state the definitions of work and energy.
	K	explain that the energy of a closed system is constant.
	S	calculate work.
10:4	K/P	distinguish between kinetic and potential energy.
	S	calculate kinetic and potential energy.
10:5	K/P	explain how forces can be changed by machines.
	K	explain mechanical advantage.
	S	calculate the mechanical advantage of a machine.
10:6	K	define efficiency.
	S	calculate the efficiency of a machine.
10:7	K	explain power.
	S	calculate power.
10:8	K	define momentum.
	S	calculate momentum.
	K	explain that the momentum in any closed system is constant.

Teaching the Chapter

When you discuss **section 10:1**, ask students to list other examples of balanced and unbalanced forces, especially those things students may encounter at school or home.

An interesting enrichment is to ask students to determine the weight of an automobile using only an air pressure gauge and a ruler. The weight can be determined by multiplying the area covered by each tire times the air pressure in the tire, to give the weight supported by that tire. Summing this value for the four tires gives a reasonable approximation of the weight of the car. Since most tire pressure gauges are calibrated in pounds per square inch, the area covered by the tire must be measured in inches. The weight of the car will be in pounds.

Reinforce the concept of work by having students determine the amount of work done in moving an assortment of typical classroom objects (**section 10:3**).

When the bowling ball strikes the pins in the example described in **section 10:4**, some of the energy is changed to heat and mechanical (sound) energy. The gain in heat can be demonstrated by repeatedly striking a block with a hammer. An increase in the temperature can be noted in the hammer and wood.

The ideas of potential and kinetic energy and machines (**section 10:5**) can be reinforced by having interested students construct a mousetrap powered car. The object is to design a car (machine) that utilizes the potential energy stored in the spring of a mousetrap. Challenge students to build a car that will travel the greatest distance. Ideas for construction are discussed in *How to Build a Mousetrap Car* by Al Renner (Dodd-Mead).

Students are often fascinated with the idea of a perpetual motion machine (**section 10:6**). Have interested students prepare a report on inventors' efforts to make a perpetual motion machine. Include an explanation of why they have not been successful.

Remind students that work and energy are both measured in joules. You may wish to have students calculate the horsepower used by the girl in the example in **section 10:7**. Use the equation 750 W = 1 hp so 270 W = 0.36 hp. This activity can be performed easily with the students in your class. It is rare for a student to generate more than 1 hp in this exercise.

Activity, Page 208   What is your reaction time?

In steps 3 and 4, caution students who drop the rulers not to establish a pattern that will aid the students who catch the rulers. Additional values can be calculated easily for Table 10–2 as follows.

$$d = \frac{1}{2} gt^2 \text{ therefore, } g = 2 \, d/t^2$$

where g = 9.8 m/s^2 and d is measured in meters.
1. Generally, reaction time improves with practice.
2. No, generally visual reaction time is best; tactile reaction time is worst.
3. Objects fall at the same rate, 9.8 m/s^2.

Activity, Page 221   What factors affect friction?

Short lengths of 2 × 4s work well for the wood blocks. The scale should be calibrated in newtons. Many commercial scales are incorrectly calibrated in kilograms. If only kilogram scales are available, a newton scale can be placed over the kilogram scale with masking tape. At sea level, 1 kg = 9.8 N.
1. friction
2. No effect
3. The effect of friction increased when more weight was added.
4. increased
5. When the block was rolled across the straws
6. Weight and type of surface

Skill Inquiry, Page 219

Although the mathematical calculations of mechanical advantage and input and output forces are important for students to comprehend, you should also stress the logical and practical implications of using this concept. Discuss several practical applications of MA, including distribution of pulleys and fulcrum placement. Encourage students to think of input force as their own exertion.

1. 4 N
2. 2 m

3. $MA = \dfrac{0.75 \text{ m}}{0.025 \text{ m}} = 30$

input force $= \dfrac{300 \text{ N}}{30} = 10 \text{ N}$

Answers to Review and Reflect

Page 210
1. Electromagnetic, gravitational, and strong nuclear forces
2. Pressure is the force exerted by moving particles per unit area.
3. 250 Pa, 0.250 kPa
4. If you lie down, your body weight will be distributed over a greater area making the pressure on the ice, or force per unit area less.

Page 212
1. Work is a force applied through a distance.
2. 1000 J
3. 150 N

Page 215
1. Kinetic energy is energy of motion; potential energy is energy of position.
2. 24.5 J
3. 180 000 J or 180 kJ

Page 220
1. No machine is 100 percent efficient. Some work is lost in friction, etc.
2. 3
3. 125 N

Page 223
1. Momentum equals mass times velocity.

2. $p_{sports\ car}$ = 1000 kg · 85 km/h
   = 85 000 kg · km/h

   p_{sedan} = 1800 kg · 45 km/h = 81 000 kg · km/h
   The sports car has more momentum.
3. The 7-kg ball will probably knock down more pins because it has more momentum.

Chapter 10 Review, Pages 224–225

Answers to Applications
1. Motion of an object only occurs if the forces on the object are unbalanced. When the forces are balanced, there is no net force on the object. If the net force on a stationary object equals zero, there will be no motion.
2. **a.** 600 N
   b. 30 kPa
3. 5000 Pa or 5 kPa
4. **a.** 6 J
   b. 12 J
5. 150 J
6. 2.8
7. Work in = 35(3) = 105 joules
   Work out = 98(0.75) = 73.5 joules
   Efficiency = 70%
8. Work = 1350 J, power = 540 W

CHAPTER 11
HEAT

Performance Objectives

GOAL: Students will learn about heat, and how it is transferred, used, and conserved.

OBJECTIVES: When asked to respond after completion of the reading and activities, students will

11:1	K/P	distinguish between heat, temperature, and thermal energy.
11:2	K	explain how thermal energy is transferred during change of state.
	K	define heats of fusion and vaporization.
11:3	K	explain that most objects expand when heated and contract when cooled.
	P	distinguish that not all materials expand and contract at the same rate.
	K	explain how the Coefficient of Linear Expansion is used.
11:4	K	define heat capacity.
	K/P	describe why water is often used as a coolant.
	S	calculate heat needed to raise or lower an object's temperature.
	K	define calorie and kilocalorie.
11:5	K/P	compare heat transfer by conduction, convection, and radiation.

11:6	K	define thermal conductance.
	K	explain that materials conduct thermal energy at different rates.
	K	define R-value.
	S	calculate R values.
11:7	A	appreciate problems society faces regarding energy.
	K/P	compare advantages and disadvantages of some alternative energy sources.

Teaching the Chapter

Emphasize the difference between heat and temperature (**section 11:1**). Point out that heat is an amount of thermal energy and is, therefore, measured in joules. Perhaps the two concepts can be best understood by considering the following example. A bathtub is nearly full of water. Imagine the temperature of the water is 50°C. If a glassful of water is removed from the tub, it also has a temperature of 50°C. The fact that the two containers of water have the same temperature means that the molecules of water in each container have the same *average* kinetic energy. However, the heat contained in each is not the same. The water in the tub, being more massive, contains more heat. This can be readily observed by noting that the water in the glass, containing less heat, will reach room temperature relatively quickly. The water in the tub will take several hours to reach room temperature since it contains more heat energy. Large, more massive objects contain more heat than do smaller, less massive objects at the same temperature.

You may wish to extend the previous bathtub discussion in **section 11:5** regarding energy transfer. The bathwater will eventually cool and reach the same temperature as the air in the room. In the process of cooling, the bathwater will transfer heat to the air in the room, and the air will become somewhat warmer. Heat flows from the warmer bathwater to the cooler air. It is not possible for the reverse to occur. Heat will never flow from the air leaving it cooler, and thus, warming the bath water. Heat always flows from warmer objects to cooler ones. Discuss other examples of the second law of thermodynamics. Remind students that the first law of thermodynamics is a restatement of the law of conservation of energy.

You may wish to review atomic structure when you introduce **section 11:6**. The free outer level electrons in metals are able to quickly transfer kinetic energy, explaining the high thermal conductance of metals.

A significant problem in using wastes for fuel (**section 11:7**) is that they are not usually generated near the site where they can be used for fuel.

Activity, Page 231 How is energy absorbed when matter changes state?

Review safety and laboratory procedures in Appendix B with students prior to this activity. Students should wear safety goggles and a protective apron. Be sure students do not use a high heat setting. Temperature setting of hot plate must only be great enough to eventually boil water within laboratory time frame. You will need to determine the correct settings on hot plates before class.

Answers to QUESTIONS AND CONCLUSIONS

1. The graph should begin with a nearly horizontal line at about 0°C (perhaps a little warmer). After the ice melts, the temperature should increase until the water begins to boil. At that point, approximately 100°C, the temperature should again remain constant.
2. The heat of fusion and the heat of vaporization, respectively
3. The original horizontal line would be longer. That is, since it would take more heat to melt more ice cubes (greater mass), the temperature would remain at about 0°C for a longer time.
4. If the ice does not melt, the temperature of the tea should be the same.
5. Answers will vary between 95 to 100°C.
6. As the water began to boil, the added heat was used to change from the liquid to gaseous state.
7. The water would begin to boil faster. However, the basic shape of the graph would remain the same. The temperature at which the water boiled would also be the same.
8. Answers will vary. The graph will show a gradual decrease in temperature with a leveling of the graph at room temperature.

Activity, Page 238 What makes the best radiator?

Review laboratory and safety procedures (Appendix B) with students prior to this activity. Discuss with students how this experiment relates to everyday life. You may have noticed that solar collectors are black. Black absorbs more heat than other colors. For this reason, it is more comfortable to wear light-colored clothing in the sun on a warm day. Dark-colored automobile seats can also become uncomfortably hot in the summer. Dark colors are the best absorbers of radiant energy and also the best radiators. Hot coffee will cool more rapidly in a dark-colored cup than in a light one. Car radiators are usually black because they are designed to cool the engine by transferring heat from the engine to the air.

Answers to QUESTIONS AND CONCLUSIONS

1. the black can
2. the black can
3. Answers will vary.
4. The temperature in the black can rose more rapidly.
5. Silver is the poorest radiator of thermal energy. Therefore, it helps keep hot drinks hot in the thermos and cold drinks cold by not allowing as much thermal energy from the air to transfer to the drink by radiation.
6. Black is a good radiator of thermal energy. It helps keep the engine cool.

Skill Inquiry, Page 230

Obtain some books on landscaping from the library or your local nursery. Have students design the landscape for a model home in their area. Discuss with your students some other considerations when selecting plants such as soil acidity, need for fertilizers or pesticides, light requirements, and so on.

1. Refer to zone chart.
2. California, Alabama, Mississippi, Louisiana, Texas, Arizona, Florida, Oregon, and Washington
3. 3
4. Zone 2, which includes most of Canada
5. Miami
6. Refer to zone chart and table.

Answers to Review and Reflect

Page 233

1. The total amount of energy in a system is constant.
2. Heat is the amount of thermal energy that an ob-

ject is able to transfer to another object. Temperature is a measure of the average kinetic energy of an object.
3. 25 000 J
4. Lay the patio in sections with some kind of divider between the sections that will allow for expansion and contraction.

Page 241

1. Conduction, convection, and radiation
2. 430 kJ
3. 20.67
4. Hot air tends to rise since it is less dense than cooler air. For this reason, the heated air is carried to the roof of the house. If the ceiling is poorly insulated, the snow on the roof will melt faster.

Page 243

1. Oak is more expensive than pine.
2. Advantages—readily available, renewable resource, needs to be disposed of anyway
   Disadvantages—must be collected and transported, must be separated into safe and unsafe materials
3. Uranium ore
4. Students should mention costs of acquisition, mining, transportation; impact on environment; heat of combustion; safety skill

Chapter 11 Review, Pages 244–245

Answers to Main Ideas

1. joules
2. convection, conduction, radiation
3. radiation
4. higher, lower
5. sum
6. joules per gram
7. metals
8. 1000
9. joules per gram Celsius degree
10. higher (4.18 J/g · C°)

Answers to Applications

1. Heat is the amount of thermal energy that an object is able to transfer to another object. Temperature is a measure of the average kinetic energy of the particles in an object.
2. Warm air is less dense than cool air. Warm air rises pushing down the cool air, which can then be warmed. Heat registers located near the floor can help produce convection currents in a room.
3. Warm air rises since it is less dense than cool air.
4. The cookies on the aluminum pan burned. Aluminum has a higher specific heat capacity than

steel. As aluminum cools, it releases more thermal energy per Celsius degree than steel.

5. $H = Cp \times m \times \Delta t$
   $= 4.18 \text{ J/g} \cdot \text{C}° \times 150\ 000 \text{ g} \times 15 \text{ C}°$
   $= 9.4 \times 10^6 \text{ J}$

6. The specific heat capacity of water is much higher than that of air. Therefore, more energy is required to raise the temperature of the water.

7. $R_{total} = 2 \text{ cm } (0.49/\text{cm}) + 2 \text{ sheets}$
   $(0.15/\text{sheet}) + 1 \text{ layer } (0.44/\text{layer}) = 1.72$

8. $H = H_{vap} \times \text{mass}$
   $= \dfrac{2260 \text{ J}}{\text{g}} \times 1000 \text{ g}$
   $= 2260 \text{ kJ}$

9. A two-story house is more efficient to heat for two reasons. First, the warm air moves from the first to the second floor before reaching the roof. Second, a two-story house has less surface area for heat loss.

10. The coals radiate energy to the food and grill. The hot grill conducts heat to the food.

CHAPTER 12
ELECTRICITY

Performance Objectives

GOAL: Students will learn what electricity is, and how it is measured and used.

OBJECTIVES: When asked to respond after completion of the reading and activities, students will

12:1	K	explain how both positive and negative static charges occur.
	K/A	recognize that static electricity can be both a benefit and a nuisance.
	K	state the meaning of coulomb.
12:2	K/P	distinguish between current and static electricity.
	K	define potential difference.
	K/S	identify circuits as being either series or parallel.
12:3	K	explain current and how it is measured.
	K	define resistance.
	K/P	describe the relationship among current, resistance, and voltage.
	S	perform calculations using Ohm's Law
12:4	A/K	explain the function and necessity of circuit breakers and fuses.
	K	define electric power.
	S	calculate power.
	S	calculate the amount of electric energy used.
12:5	K/P	describe the relationship between magnetism and electric current.
	K	explain how an electric motor works.
12:6	K/P	describe how electricity is generated.
	K/P	compare alternating and direct current.
	K	state the function of transformers.
12:7	A	recognize the problems associated with energy production and consumption.

Teaching the Chapter

Depending on the needs of your students, you may want to review atomic structure as discussed in chapter 4.

It is assumed that students have some familiarity with the principles of static electricity from previous science courses. However, you may wish to demonstrate the phenomena illustrated in Figure 12–1. Keep in mind that it is difficult to produce lasting static charges in humid air.

When dealing with circuits, emphasize that each device added to a parallel circuit provides a new pathway for electron flow. This may make the concepts of Ohm's Law and circuit overload easier for students to grasp later in the chapter.

With **section 12:4**, caution students that they should make sure the cause of an overload is removed before a fuse is replaced or a breaker is reset. It may not be obvious to students why amperes times voltage equals watts. This can be shown as follows.

$$P = IV$$
$$\text{watts} = \text{amperes} \times \text{volts} =$$
$$\frac{\text{coulombs}}{\text{second}} \times \frac{\text{joules}}{\text{coulomb}} = \frac{\text{joules}}{\text{second}}$$

You may want to open **section 12:5** by demonstrating Oersted's discovery. Transparent compasses that can be placed on overhead projectors are available. Use a heavy uninsulated wire with a fresh dry cell. Do not allow the wire to remain connected for more than a few seconds as the cell will be quickly depleted. In addition, the wire may become quite hot. If available, demonstrate a simple model motor and other devices that use electromagnets. Instructions for building motors from common materials can be found in many sources.

You may want to begin **section 12:6** by demonstrating that moving a wire in a magnetic field produces a current. Connect a loop of wire to the terminals of a galvanometer and move the wire near the poles of a magnet. If a galvanometer is not available, try using a milliammeter and a coil of wire with several turns. Move a bar magnet back and forth through the coil while observing the meter.

The rate consumers pay for electric power is sometimes based on "peak load." Interested students may want to find out how peak load is determined and why power companies want to reduce peak load. They should also consider what actions consumers can take to reduce peak load.

While studying **section 12:7,** you may wish to arrange a field trip to a fossil fuel or nuclear power plant in your area. In addition, these companies may be able to supply free or low cost films or other teaching materials.

Activity, Page 256   How are circuits different?

The bulbs should be of the same type and have a voltage rating near that of the battery. Caution students not to short circuit the battery terminals. The battery will be depleted rapidly and burns can result from the hot wire as well as melting insulation. In addition, caution students not to insert wires into AC outlets. Be sure students hook up the meter using the correct polarity. Meters should be marked + and − .

Students may discover that, even with the same type bulb, two bulbs in series do not have twice the resistance of one bulb, and two bulbs in parallel do

not have half the resistance of one bulb. This is because the resistance of the bulb increases as the filament becomes hotter.

Answers to QUESTIONS AND CONCLUSIONS
1. All electrons must flow through both bulbs.
2. Unscrewing one bulb breaks the circuit. As a result, electrons cannot flow through the second bulb.
3. The circuit is a series circuit.
4. The electrons are free to flow through one bulb or the other.
5. The circuit is a parallel circuit.
6. The bulbs are brightest in the parallel circuit and dimmest in the series circuit.
7. With one bulb disconnected from the parallel circuit, electrons are still free to flow through the other bulb.
8. The current reading should decrease from step 1a to step 1b. Adding a bulb in series forces all electrons to flow through both bulbs, increasing the resistance and reducing the current. There is no current in 1c because the circuit is broken. In 1d, the current should be greater than the current in 1a or 1b. Adding a bulb in parallel provides a second current pathway, reducing resistance and thereby increasing current flow. The current in 1f should decrease to about the same level as the current in 1a.
9. Student answers will vary depending on the resistances of the bulbs. The resistance should increase from 1a to 1b because electrons are forced to flow through two devices, instead of one, to complete the circuit. The resistance in 1d should be lower than that in 1a because the current now has two pathways to complete the circuit instead of one.

Activity, Page 262   What affects the strength of an electromagnet?

Caution students not to short circuit the battery terminals. The battery will be depleted rapidly and burns can result from the hot wire as well as melting insulation. In addition, caution students not to insert wires into AC outlets.

It is preferable to use the large "ignition-type" cells for this activity because they will last longer and are easier to secure with the wire connections. If you use enameled wire, it is a good idea to wrap the nails with masking tape where the wire will be wound. This avoids slight abrasion, which can cause the wire to short-circuit to the nail. Make sure students disconnect the magnets after each test.

Answers to QUESTIONS AND CONCLUSIONS

1. The strength is measured in paper clips.
2. **a.** The strength increases.
   b. The strength increases.
   c. The strength increases.
3. Powerful motors must have electromagnets with large cores and many turns of large wire.
4. According to Ohm's Law, as the voltage in a circuit increases, so does the current. Therefore, when the voltage was increased, the current increased also.

Skill Inquiry, Page 255

Safety and consumer organizations, fire departments, and electric companies may have booklets, audiovisual materials, or presentations on electrical safety. It may be helpful to relate the reasons for shocks, short circuits, and overloads to the students' study of circuits.

1. Avoid mowing in the rain or when the grass is extremely wet. Also, you should not mow when it is too dark to see well enough to avoid running the mower over its cord.
2. You should patiently teach the child the proper way to remove a plug from the wall socket by grasping the plug itself.
3. Disconnect the toaster immediately before examining or attempting to repair it in any way.
4. Call the police or fire department immediately. Then call the electric company.
5. Remove the plug immediately and have the cleaner examined by a person competent to diagnose and repair it. Make no attempt to use it until you are sure it is safe.

Answers to Review and Reflect

Page 252

1. Most objects have nearly equal numbers of protons and electrons.
2. An object can become positively charged by losing electrons, leaving an excess of protons.
3. Electrons flowing through a conductor are current electricity. Static electric charge stays in one location.
4. Rubber and plastic insulate the wires, preventing unwanted contact with other conductors.
5. At the positive terminal, electrons are being removed by a chemical reaction. At the negative

terminal, the same chemical reaction is adding electrons.
6. The lights are connected in parallel so that if one burns out, the others stay lit.

Page 255

1. The amount of current flowing in a circuit increases as voltage increases and decreases as resistance increases.
2. $I = \dfrac{V}{R}$ therefore, $V = IR$
   $V = (0.2\ A)(75\ \Omega)$
   $V = 15$ volts
3. The current can be reduced by decreasing the voltage or by increasing the resistance in the circuit. The best solution would be to increase the resistance by removing devices (current pathways) from the circuit. It is not practical to reduce the voltage because this is controlled by the power company. Also, electrical devices are designed to operate properly only at one voltage.

Page 259

1. A circuit may become overloaded by having too many devices (current pathways) connected to it. There may also be a short circuit. In both cases, the overload occurs because the resistance becomes too low.
2. The energy used depends on how fast the appliance uses energy and how long it is left on.
3. energy $= Pt$
   energy $= (500\ W) \left(\dfrac{6\ min/day \times 250\ days}{60\ min/hour} \right)$
   $= (500\ W)(25\ h)$
   $= 12\ 500\ Wh$
   $= 12.5\ kWh$
4. energy $= Pt$
   energy $= (4\ W)(8\ h/day \times 365\ days)$
   $= 4\ W \times 2920\ h$
   $= 11\ 680\ Wh$
   $= 11.68\ kWh$
   cost $= 11.68\ kWh \times \$0.07/kWh$
   $= \$0.82$
5. Dryers and ranges can use energy at a rapid rate, permitting large amounts of current to flow through them. Each must be on a separate circuit to avoid current overloads.

Page 263

1. Electromagnets require a continuous supply of electric current in order to maintain their magnetism. Permanent magnets do not.
2. Answers will vary but may include doorbells,

buzzers, auto starters, and solenoids. In all cases, an electric current produces a magnetic field that is concentrated by a core.

3. A commutator switches the direction of current to the electromagnet as an electric motor turns.
4. With direct current, electrons flow continuously in one direction. In alternating current, electrons flow back and forth through a circuit, changing direction many times a second.
5. In a motor, electric current is put in to produce a magnetic field, which causes an electromagnet to turn. The motor produces useful mechanical energy. In a generator, mechanical energy is put in causing a coil of wire to turn in a magnetic field. This results in useful electrical energy.

Page 265

1. Demand is increasing because of population growth and growth of industrial societies. Alternative methods of producing electricity, as well as increased construction of conventional power plants, are current ideas for meeting demand.
2. Problems could include acid rain, thermal pollution, air pollution, nuclear waste disposal, resource depletion, and problems associated with mining, drilling, and transporting fuels.
3. Coal is the most-used fuel.
4. Responses will vary.

Chapter 12 Review, Pages 266–267

Answers to Applications

1. Static charges tend to "leak" off to water molecules in the air.
2. First, use Ohm's Law to determine the amount of current flowing through the bulb.

$$I = \frac{V}{R} = \frac{120 \text{ V}}{240 \text{ }\Omega} = 0.5 \text{ A}$$

Then use the formula for power.
$$P = IV$$
$$P = (0.5 \text{ A})(120 \text{ V})$$
$$P = 60 \text{ watts}$$

3. Energy used $= \dfrac{\$38.48}{\$0.08/\text{kWh}}$

   $= 48/\text{kWh}$

4. Daily energy used $= Pt$

   $= \left(500 \text{ bulbs} \times 40 \dfrac{\text{W}}{\text{bulb}} \right)(16 \text{ hours})$

   $= 320\ 000 \text{ Wh}$

   $= 320 \text{ kWh}$

   Cost per day for 40-watt bulbs
   $= 320 \text{ kWh} \times \$0.09/\text{kWh}$
   $= \$28.80$

   Cost for 250 days for 40-watt bulbs
   $= \$28.80/\text{day} \times 250 \text{ days}$
   $= \$7200$

   Cost for 250 days for 30-watt bulbs
   $= \dfrac{30 \text{ watt}}{40 \text{ watt}} \times \$7200$
   $= \$5400$

   Savings using 30-watt bulbs $= \$7200 - \$5400$
   $= \$1800$

5. The 15-ampere fuse was in the circuit probably because the circuit's wires are too small to carry more than 15 amperes safely. Changing to a 20-ampere fuse could cause the wires to overheat and become a fire hazard.
6. Doubling the voltage should double the current flow provided the resistance did not change.
7. Increasing the voltage five times would tend to increase the current five times. However, increasing the resistance five times will tend to reduce the current to one-fifth its value. The effects offset each other, so the current remains the same.

CHAPTER 13
WAVES AND SOUND

Performance Objectives

GOAL: Students will learn some principles of waves and how they relate to the production and transmission of sound.

OBJECTIVES: When asked to respond after completion of the reading and activities, students will

13:1	K	explain that energy, but not matter, is transferred by waves.
	K	identify and describe the amplitude, wavelength, and frequency of a transverse wave.
	S	calculate the velocity of a wave.
13:2	K	explain the law of reflection.

	K	describe interference.
	K/P	describe characteristics of standing waves.
13:3	K	define refraction.
	K/P	describe how refraction occurs.
	K/P	describe how diffraction occurs.
13:4	K	compare characteristics of compressional and transverse waves.
	K/P	Explain how vibrations of objects are transferred to air.
	K	describe the audible range of sound.
13:5	K	recognize that all sounds are produced by vibrations.
	K	describe two ways that musical sounds are produced.
13:6	K/P	explain the Doppler effect.
	K	relate pitch to frequency.
13:7	K	distinguish fundamental and overtone frequencies.
	S/P	describe factors that vary the qualities of voices and musical instruments.
	P	relate volume, loudness, and energy of a sound wave.
	K/S	describe how the volume of sound is measured.
13:8	A	recognize the need to limit environmental noise.
	K	define acoustics.
	K/P	describe ways that acoustical properties are controlled.
13:9	K	explain why sound must travel through matter.
	P	compare the speed of sound in different materials.
	S	perform calculations using the speed of sound.
13:10	K/P	describe the process by which people hear.
	A/K	identify hazards that may damage hearing.
	K	describe the reason for most high-frequency hearing loss.

Teaching the Chapter

Open section 13:1 by having students imagine they are sitting in a small boat on a lake. The action of the waves causes an up-and-down motion only. The waves do not cause the boat to drift to shore. The drifting of an unanchored boat is caused by water currents and wind. If you have a ripple tank, the instruction booklet with it may describe wave demonstrations that would be instructive in chapters 13 and 14. Many source books describe ripple tank activities and ways of constructing ripple tanks inexpensively. Also, carefully use springs, ropes, clotheslines, or rubber tubing throughout the chapter to demonstrate the properties of waves.

Be sure students can calculate the velocity of a wave. You may wish to demonstrate the process on the chalkboard.

If possible, demonstrate wave interference as shown in Figure 13–3 using a long spring, rope, or rubber tubing. Have an assistant send single pulses toward you as you send pulses in the opposite direction. Send pulses both in phase and out of phase. Proceed to demonstrate standing waves. Most students have experienced firsthand the principle of refraction. Some may know that a track-driven vehicle, such as a bulldozer, is steered by braking the track on one side. Most students are familiar with facilitating turns on a bicycle, motorbike, or sled by dragging a foot on one side or the other.

Compressional waves, discussed in **section 13:4,** are also called longitudinal waves in contrast with transverse waves. You can demonstrate the properties of compressional waves effectively with a Slinky®. Recreate the steps of the activity on page 273, but producing compressional waves.

Beginning **section 13:5,** set up an oscilloscope with a microphone if possible. It will help students realize why sound waves are often depicted as transverse. When discussing overtones in **section 13:7,** have students bring in various musical instruments and observe their overtone patterns.

With **section 13:6,** you could discuss radar speed detectors that work because of the Doppler effect. Radar is reflected from a moving car. The difference in frequency of the reflected wave is analyzed and the velocity of the car is calculated. Perhaps a police officer could demonstrate a radar unit and answer questions about its use.

It is important to note in **section 13:7** that the decibel scale is a logarithmic scale. Each increase of 10 decibels represents a ten-fold increase in intensity.

Activity, Page 273   How do waves behave?

You may want the students to work in groups of four so that two students can observe from the side while two others operate the Slinky®. It is difficult to observe the effects well while also producing waves. After all steps are completed, the two students observing should trade places with those operating the spring. Supply houses sell special extra-length Slinky® springs for this type of activity.

Answers to QUESTIONS AND CONCLUSIONS

1. Students should find that waves reflect from barriers.
2. The tension of the spring had the most effect on the speed of wave travel. Neither the amplitude nor the frequency should have an effect on the speed.
3. The higher the frequency, the shorter the wavelength.
4. They are called standing waves. The frequencies that produce standing waves are the fundamental and overtones.
5. It should seem easier to produce the standing waves that occur at the resonant frequencies of the spring. These should feel like the "natural" frequencies of the spring. At these frequencies, the spring tends to store the added energy of the vibration rather than seeming to work against the vibration source (the student's hand) as it would at nonresonant frequencies.

Activity, Page 285   How can you measure the speed of sound?

If rubber hammers are not available, the tuning forks can be struck against the rubber heel of a shoe. Tuning forks should not be struck against hard objects because they may be damaged. In addition, distracting overtone vibrations may be produced.

If you use glass tubes, caution students not to allow the vibrating tuning fork to touch the edge of the tube. If glass tubes are used, students should wear safety goggles.

If the water is much colder than room temperature, have students take the temperature of the air inside the tube.

The determination of the wavelength suggested in step 8 is an approximation. Actually, this must be corrected for the diameter of the glass tube. The actual wavelength is given by

$$\lambda = 4(L + 0.4d)$$

where d is the diameter and L is the resonant length of the tube.

Answers to QUESTIONS AND CONCLUSIONS

1. Student responses will vary. Possible sources of error include holding the fork too far from the tube opening, difficulty in judging the position at which resonance is loudest, and using tuning forks that are off frequency.
2. Answers will depend on temperature.
3. The measurement would be shorter than the actual resonant length. Because the wavelength would appear shorter than it actually is, the calculated speed of sound would be too low.

Skill Inquiry, Page 282

Point out to students that many instruments have overtones that extend far above the frequency ranges shown.

1. violin
2. clarinet
3. From about 80 Hz to about 1100 Hz
4. The flute, clarinet, trumpet, and violin could play the passage. Only the soprano could sing it.

Answers to Review and Reflect

Page 275
1. energy
2. Student drawings should resemble Figure 13–1 on page 270.
3. The velocity is 120 cm/s.
4. Refraction is caused by the slowing down or speeding up of waves as they pass at an angle from one substance into another.
5. The resonant frequencies of the automobile's springs should be different from frequencies of road vibration usually encountered. Otherwise, the road vibration might set up standing waves that could be destructive to the car. Shock absorbers also help prevent standing waves.

Page 277
1. People can hear sounds having frequencies between 20 and 20 000 hertz.

2. There must be a vibrating object, and there must be matter to carry compressional waves.

3. Ultrasounds have frequencies higher than 20 000 hertz, the upper limit of the human audible range.

4. The vibrations of the strings of an electric guitar are electronically amplified. Therefore, it does not need a hollow body and soundboard to resonate and amplify the sound.

Page 281

1. The Doppler effect is produced whenever waves are produced by a moving object. The waves are pushed together ahead of the object and spread apart behind. The same effect occurs if the observer is moving and the object producing the waves is stationary.

2. The quality of peoples' voices varies because of the variation in shapes and sizes of vocal cords and resonating cavities, such as the mouth and nasal passages.

3. Sound intensity is measured in decibels.

4. Pitch is the way we perceive sound frequency. Volume is the way we perceive sound intensity (energy).

Page 284

1. Loud noise can cause both nervous and physical disorders.

2. Acoustics is the science that deals with sound.

3. Reverberation can be controlled by using sound absorbing materials and by carefully positioning sound absorbing surfaces.

4. 1.3 m/s

5. 750 Hz

Page 287

1. The main parts are the outer, middle, and inner ear.

2. The outer ear serves as a funnel to collect sound waves and direct them into the ear canal.

3. The sound waves cause the eardrum to vibrate. These vibrations are transmitted to the cochlea, which contains hair cells. The vibrations stimulate the hair cells. The movement of the hair cells sends nerve impulses through the auditory nerve to the brain.

4. Hearing loss related to loudness results from destruction of hair cells. The loss may not be noticed because it first occurs at very high frequencies.

Chapter 13 Review, Pages 288–289

Answers to Main Ideas

1. wavelength
2. λ (lambda)
3. 0.5 Hz
4. 1.5 m/s
5. destructive
6. velocity
7. waves passing by the edge of an obstacle or through a narrow opening
8. rarefaction
9. 20 Hz to 20 000 Hz
10. ultrasounds
11. decibels
12. They become shorter.

Answers to Applications

1. work = force × distance
   w = 1000 N × 10 cm
   w = 1000 N × 0.10 m
   w = 100 J
   If the frequency of the waves is 0.5 Hz, one crest occurs every 2 seconds. This means the boat is lifted once every 2 seconds.
   Power = work/time
   P = 100 J/2 s
   P = 50 watts

2. If the car is shaking, you are probably hitting the bumps with a frequency that is the same as some resonant frequency of the suspension system. Either speeding up or slowing down should reduce the shake because either will change the frequency at which the car strikes the bumps. For safety reasons, it is probably best to slow down.

3. When waves strike perpendicular to a boundary, they change velocity uniformly across the whole wave front. At an angle, however, one side of the wave front changes velocity before the other. This causes the waves to refract.

4. There is no matter to transmit compressional waves.

5. d = vt
   d = 344 m/s × 4.5 s
   d = 1548 m

6. Their sounds have different combinations of overtones. This results from their different shapes and different methods of producing sounds.

7. Their vocal cords are smaller, and therefore would vibrate at higher frequencies or pitches.

CHAPTER **14**
LIGHT

Performance Objectives

GOAL: Students will learn some of the properties of the production and control of light.

OBJECTIVES: When asked to respond after completion of the reading and activities, students will

14:1	K	recognize that light exhibits properties of both waves and particles.
	K	state how electromagnetic waves are produced.
	K	state the speed of light.
14:2	K	identify visible light as a type of electromagnetic radiation.
	P/K	compare the properties of the different kinds of electromagnetic radiation.
	K	explain the difference between AM and FM radio.
14:3	K	explain how visible light is produced.
	P/K	compare different devices that produce light.
14:4	K/S	show with diagrams how light is reflected from plane, concave, and convex mirrors.
	K	define real image.
	K	describe practical uses of curved mirrors.
14:5	K	explain how refraction is caused.
	P/K	relate index of refraction to the velocity of light.
	K	define critical angle and total internal reflection.
14:6	K	recognize that white light consists of a spectrum of colors.
	P	explain why objects appear colored.
14:7	K	describe the characteristics of concave and convex lenses.
	P/S	explain how lenses are used to correct sight defects.
14:8	K	describe how light is diffracted.
	P	recognize that diffraction can produce a color spectrum.
	K	define polarized light.
14:9	K	describe the operation of a laser.
	K	discuss uses of lasers.

Teaching the Chapter

The wave theory of light, discussed in **section 14:1,** was first proposed by Robert Hooke and Christian Huygens in the seventeenth century. The work of Planck and others led Einstein to propose the quantum theory of light in 1905. Many physics and chemistry books have detailed information on this subject. If you choose to discuss the particle model of light, point out some of the uses of photoelectric devices in cameras, light meters, electric "eyes," and the sound-track reader on most 16 mm movie projectors.

With **section 14:2,** you may point out that all objects emit some type of electromagnetic radiation. Objects that we consider warm emit a greater proportion of infrared radiation. Photographing the infrared emission of a building during the heating season will show areas of greatest heat loss.

Stress that the electromagnetic spectrum illustrated in Figure 14–1 is shown on an exponential scale. Moving left to right, each successive power of 10 represents a wavelength 10 times shorter or a frequency 10 times greater than the previous one. Because only even-numbered powers are shown, each represents a 100-fold increase or decrease in magnitude.

Interested students may want to learn more about AM and FM broadcasting, including the reasons that AM normally can be heard at a much greater distance than FM. Other topics in connection with **section 14:2** include the production of vitamin D by the skin, the advantages and disadvantages of tanning, the dangers of excess exposure to ultraviolet radiation from the sun, the dangers of excess exposure to X rays, how microwave ovens work, microwave transmission of information, and possible microwave pollution.

The realization that light was produced during

UNIT 3

electron transitions between energy levels was important in understanding the structure of the atom. You may want to review **chapter 6** at this point.

The ripple tank can be used with **section 14:4** (and other sections in this chapter) to model optical effects using water waves. Review the law of reflection in section 13:2.

Kits are available that allow you to demonstrate mirror optics on the chalkboard. A variety of optics can be demonstrated with an aquarium tank filled with water that has been clouded with a few drops of milk or a little calcium hydroxide. Shine the beam from a filmstrip projector into the tank at various angles to show refraction, total internal reflection, and critical angle. Mirrors and lenses that will not be damaged can be placed in the tank to show their optical properties. You may need to narrow the projector beam using a cardboard or foil mask.

With **section 14:5,** you may discuss optical fibers (sometimes called light tubes). Optical fibers are very thin glass or plastic rods in which light undergoes total internal reflection. Light can be made to go around corners by bending the tube.

Apparatus is available for demonstrating additive color, discussed in **section 14:6.** However, a little experimentation with three projectors and some colored cellophane or color filters used in photographic darkrooms or stage lighting can produce equally dramatic results.

It may be helpful to point out in **section 14:7** that light entering a lens tends to be refracted toward the thicker part. Thus, convex lenses cause light to converge, and concave lenses cause light to diverge.

The greatest amount of diffraction (**section 14:8**) is caused if either the opening or obstacle is about the same size as the wavelength of the waves. This is one of the reasons that the amount of magnification of a light microscope is limited, regardless of the quality of the microscope's lenses. As you attempt to look at smaller and smaller objects with a light microscope, the amount of diffraction increases as light passes by the object being observed. The diffraction of light waves passing by the object being viewed causes it to appear more and more blurred.

Activity, Page 299   How is light reflected?

Students will probably have to sight along the right edge of the ruler in order to avoid covering part of line AB. Because of the angle, this edge will not reach the surface of the mirror. Have students draw

a line along the ruler and extend it after the mirror has been removed. The students' eyes must be at the level of the tabletop in order to sight properly. If laboratory mirrors are not available, ordinary mirrors can be used. Attach to a block of wood with a rubber band to provide a support. In question 3, note that more expensive periscopes, binoculars, and reflex cameras use internally reflecting prisms rather than mirrors.

Answers to QUESTIONS AND CONCLUSIONS

1. They should be equal.
2. The image appears as far behind the mirror as the object is in front of the mirror.
3. The mirrors need to be parallel and situated at 45°. This will give a total reflected angle of 90°.
4.

5. These angles are equal also.
6. The mirror needs to be half the person's height. Students may begin by assuming the mirror must start at the floor. After figuring out the solution, you may want to suggest that students note how much of the floor and ceiling they actually see in a "full length" mirror.

Activity, Page 307   How can you make a camera obscura?

The longer tube in this activity should be from a roll of paper towels. The shorter tube should be from a roll of toilet tissue. The shorter tube should be usually slightly larger in diameter, allowing the paper towel tube to fit inside it. The pinhole in the foil can be as much as a millimeter in diameter.

Answers to QUESTIONS AND CONCLUSIONS

1. Student descriptions will vary. Students should mention that the images are dim and inverted. Objects at all distances should be in focus. Light rays from the top of an object pass through the pinhole to the bottom of the image. Light rays from the bottom of the object arrive at the top of the image. The images of distant objects will be small because the distance from the pinhole to the screen is short compared to the distance

from the object to the pinhole.
2. The image moves to the right also.
3.

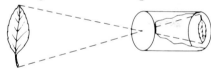

4. Light must travel in straight lines. Otherwise light from a point on the object would travel to different points after passing through the pinhole and an image could not be formed. Refer to the explanation in the answer to question 1.

Skill Inquiry, Page 303

The physiology of how we perceive color is still not well understood. Red and green light mixed together do not "make" yellow light, yet we perceive the result as yellow. Interested students may wish to pursue what is known about this phenomenon.

1. magenta
2. Cyan and yellow pigments could be mixed to produce green paint. Cyan pigment subtracts red from white light, reflecting blue and green light. Yellow pigment subtracts blue, leaving green as the reflected light color.
3. Yellow ink is used on the plate from the blue negative because red and green (yellow) were the light colors that passed through the blue filter. Likewise, magenta ink is used on the plate from the green negative because red and blue light passing through the green filter formed the image.

Answers to Review and Reflect

Page 294
1. Some properties of light can be explained by waves. Other properties require that light be visualized as a stream of particles.
2. High frequency radiation has higher energy.
3. These kinds of radiation are very penetrating and damage living cells.

Page 298
1. Nuclear energy produces sunlight.
2. Much of the radiation given off by the filament is in the infrared region of the spectrum.
3. An electric current passes through mercury vapor. The excited mercury atoms give off ultraviolet light. A special coating on the inside surface of the tube glows when struck by the ultraviolet radiation.

4. A real image is made up of focused points of light and can be projected on a screen. In a virtual image, the light only appears to come from the location of the image. A virtual image is not focused and cannot be projected on a screen.

Page 303
1. Refraction occurs when light waves change speed while passing from one material into another.
2. Diamonds have a high index of refraction. The sparkle is due to total internal reflection. The color is due to refraction spreading light into a spectrum.
3. The white paper reflects all colors nearly equally. The black ink absorbs most of the light striking it. Therefore, no colors are reflected.
4. Red light contains no colors of light that can be reflected by blue or green objects. The objects absorb red light. Therefore, little or no light is reflected.

Page 306
1. The focal point of a lens is the point at which light rays parallel to the principal axis come to a focus.
2. The human eye contains a convex lens.
3. A concave lens cannot bring light rays to a focus.
4. Each chemical element gives off a characteristic mixture of wavelengths.

Page 309
1. LASER stands for light amplification by stimulated emission of radiation.
2. Uses for lasers include cutting and welding metals, communication, recording and reading coded information, surveying, geological studies, and surgery.
3. Laser light is coherent. This means that all the waves are vibrating in the same direction at the same time. Many lasers emit light of only one wavelength (monochromatic light).

Chapter 14 Review, Pages 310–311

Answers to Applications
1. velocity of a wave = wavelength × frequency
$$V = \lambda f$$
$$\lambda = \frac{V}{f}$$
velocity of electromagnetic waves = 3×10^8 m/s
$$\lambda = \frac{3 \times 10^8 \text{ m/s}}{6 \times 10^9 \text{ Hz}}$$
$$\lambda = 0.5 \times 1^{-1} \text{ m}$$
$$\lambda = 5 \times 10^{-2} \text{ m}$$

Electromagnetic radiation of this wavelength is in the microwave region of the spectrum.

2. In AM radio, the amplitude of the carrier wave is modulated or varied by the audio signal. In FM radio, the frequency of the carrier wave is modulated by the audio signal.

3. Because of refraction, the fish will appear shallower and farther away than it actually is. In reality, bears seem to learn to catch fish by jumping straight down at them.

4. When light is refracted, the shorter the wavelength, the more it is refracted. As a result, white light is spread out into a spectrum.

5. Film sensitive to infrared light can detect places where the building is giving off infrared radiation ("heat" loss). Insulation or weatherstripping could be used to reduce heat loss.

6. Upon entering the air, light rays from the bottom of the pool are refracted to a lower angle. This makes it appear the rays are coming from a place closer to the surface of the water.

7. Rain occurs more often in the afternoon. Storms generally move from west to east in most parts of the United States. As a result, we most often see rainbows when the sun is in the west and its rays are striking the "backside" of the rainstorm, which is moving east.

UNIT 4   THE SYSTEMS OF OUR WORLD

Overview

Chapter 15 begins with the Big Bang theory. Types of galaxies are described, and the Milky Way, is highlighted. Other stars are compared with the sun. The H-R Diagram is explained and applied. Stellar evolution is discussed, too. A coordinate system of the celestial sphere is presented in an optional information section at the end of the chapter.

Chapter 16 opens with a discussion of the origin of the solar system. The next section traces the development of ideas about the solar system. The Earth and its moon are considered together. Separate sections are devoted to the features of Mercury and Venus, Mars, Jupiter and Saturn, and Uranus, Neptune, and Pluto. Minor planets, meteoroids, and comets are described. A brief history of space exploration and current major projects is given. An optional issue of funding space exploration is presented.

Chapter 17 deals with nature of the atmosphere, weather processes, and climate. Factors that affect the heating of the atmosphere are considered. A section on water in the air includes relative humidity, dew and frost, clouds, and precipitation. The general circulation of the earth's atmosphere is described; and monsoons, land and sea breezes, and mountain and valley breezes are explained. Air masses, fronts, and weather associated with warm fronts and cold fronts are discussed. Some types of extreme weather are described. Factors that affect climate and examples of climate differences and changes are considered. An optional information section on weather modification closes the chapter.

Chapter 18 describes the nature of minerals and rocks and the rock cycle. The formation of igneous rocks from magma is discussed. Mechanical and chemical weathering and the formation of sedimentary rocks are then considered. A section describes types of metamorphism and the rocks produced by each. Agents of erosion are discussed. Sections cover mass movement, the work of rivers, groundwater, glaciers, and deserts and wind action. Folding and faulting are explained. An optional information discussion of environmental geology is also presented.

Chapter 19 begins with a discussion of the water in oceans. Features of the ocean floor are described. Surface and subsurface ocean currents and the factors that cause them are presented. Sections are devoted to coral reefs, tides, waves, and shorelines. Ocean resources are discussed, also. An optional issue on ocean ownership closes the chapter.

Chapter 20 begins with a discussion of fossils. Principles of superposition and uniformitarianism are presented. Methods of dating rocks are described. Rock formations, correlation, and the Geologic Time Scale are explained. The theory of plate tectonics is presented. Sections describe physical and life events of Precambrian Time, the Paleozoic Era, the Mesozoic Era, and the Cenozoic Era. An optional information section about the Milankovitch theory of ice ages ends the chapter.

Introducing the Unit

Students probably have some previous knowledge about the topics in this unit. Discuss what interests students about space and Earth science topics. Also have students try to think of reasons why the study of these topics is useful.

Students may be familiar with the concept of a space address. Have students imagine that the universe is populated with many people or intelligent beings. Suppose that someone on a distant planet of a distant star of a distant galaxy wishes to send a letter to the student. Ask each student to think of how a letter to him or her should be addressed. What would be printed on a universal address label?

CHAPTER 15
THE UNIVERSE

Performance Objectives

GOAL: Students will learn about a model that describes the origin of the universe and about objects in the universe.

OBJECTIVES: When asked to respond after completion of the reading and activities, students will

15:1	K	describe the stages of the Big Bang and list evidence for the theory.
15:2	P	categorize galaxies as to type, given descriptions or photographs of galaxies.
15:3	K	explain the nature of interstellar matter.
15:4	K	identify solar features and events.
	K	tell how the Earth is affected by certain events.
15:5	P	interpret the conditions of a star from its location on the H-R Diagram.
15:6	P	compare and contrast evolution of stars of different masses.
	K	identify the sources of elements.
15:7	K	describe the celestial sphere.
	S	explain how to use a star chart.

Teaching the Chapter

The Big Bang, discussed in **section 15:1,** is a cosmological model based on observations. About 25 years ago another cosmological model was accepted about equally, a steady-state universe in which there was no Big Bang or beginning. The discovery of microwave radiation in 1965, mentioned in the text, has made the Steady State model unacceptable to most scientists.

The microwave radiation, which serves as important evidence for the Big Bang, has wavelengths between 0.26 cm and 50 cm. It is thought to come from Doppler-shifted (red-shifted) radiation emitted from the universe when it had a temperature of 3000 kelvins. This discovery won a Nobel prize. Students may be interested in using library sources to learn more about the discovery by Bell Telephone Laboratories scientists A. Penzias and R. Wilson.

When **section 15:3** is studied, simulate an interstellar cloud. Fill a large glass container, such as a bell jar, with smoke. Shine a thin beam of white light through the smoke in a darkened room to illustrate how the cloud blocks much of the light and reddens the light that passes through, as do actual interstellar clouds. Also, observe atmospheric clouds and compare them with interstellar clouds. (Atmospheric clouds change quickly and have a very different composition.)

Related to **section 15:4,** compare the rotating sun emitting its particles from coronal holes and flares along force lines to a whirling lawn sprinkler spraying streams of water.

An evening observation session might be held in which class members use star maps to identify stars and constellations of the current evening sky. Look for differences in apparent brightness, also called apparent magnitude.

If a telescope is available, the class or individual students may wish to look at one or more pairs of binary stars that have obvious color differences. One is Albireo at the head of the constellation Cygnus. The smallest telescope will reveal Albireo as one gold star and one light blue star. See "Backyard Astronomy 8: Observing Double Stars," *Sky and Telescope,* November, 1984, pp. 417–419, for other examples and tips for observation.

Many field guides for star and constellation identification exist, including *A Field Guide to the Stars and Planets*, 2d ed., by Donald H. Menzel and Jay M. Pasachoff, Houghton-Mifflin: Boston, 1983. Each month *Astronomy* and *Sky and Telescope* magazines publish fine maps with commentary about the current evening sky.

If possible, arrange for the class to visit a planetarium to learn more about star differences, constellations, the Milky Way, and circles and points of the celestial sphere. Ask for a discussion of how to find the right ascension and declination of a star.

Activity, Page 327   How is absolute brightness found?

Many cameras have built-in photometers that can be used for this activity. Photometers once used for photography also can be obtained at some surplus stores.

Discuss the inverse square law. Note the relationship between distances studied: 100 cm is 2 times 50 cm; 200 cm is 2 times 100 cm. Also note that the 75-watt bulb is 5 times the brightness of the 15-watt bulb. A source of error in this activity can be background light, so try to make the area where photometer readings are taken as dark as possible. An opaque cover over a table works well.

Answers to QUESTIONS AND CONCLUSIONS

1. Absolute brightness is the brightness an object would appear to have at a standard distance from the observer. Absolute brightness can be determined if the star's luminosity and distance are known.
2. The H-R diagram based on apparent magnitude would not be accurate since stars closer to the Earth would appear more luminous than stars farther away, regardless of their size and temperature.
3. The sun is closer to Earth than any other star.
4. A star may appear dim because it has a small diameter or because it is farther away than other stars.
5. In this activity, the light sources could be moved to a standard position to determine the absolute brightness.

Activity, Page 331   What determines the powers of a telescope?

A screen clamp is optional for this activity. Small convex lenses may be obtained singly or in assort-

ments from Edmund Scientific, 101 E. Gloucester Pike, Barrington, NJ, 08007. You may want to review chapter 14, concerning lenses, mirrors, and light.

Answers to QUESTIONS AND CONCLUSIONS

1. The size of the image was changed, but the brightness was not affected.
2. The shorter the eyepiece focal length, the greater the magnification. (Magnification equals focal length of objective divided by focal length of eyepiece.)
3. The brightness increased.
4. Although the magnification increases, light-gathering power remains the same. Objects are still too faint to be seen.
5. It is misleading because the light gathering power determines the faintest objects that can be seen. The ability to see distant objects also depends on the diameter of the lens.

Skill Inquiry, Page 320

There are a number of other ways that astronomers determine star distances, besides parallax. Some are: analysis of radial velocities of stars in clusters, judgment of absolute brightness from a star's spectrum and application of the inverse-square law, analysis of binary stars, and inference from velocities due to galactic rotation. The majority of stars are too distant for their distances to be found by simple parallax measurement.

1. About 8.5 years
2. About 13 years

Answers to Review and Reflect

Page 317

1. A spectral red shift occurs as all galaxies are moving away from the Earth. Also background microwave radiation received from all directions corresponds to the radiation predicted to have been emitted during the Big Bang.
2. Matter at the time of the Big Bang did not exist. According to the model, protons and neutrons were formed as quarks combined about 10^{-6} seconds after the initial explosion.
3. If sufficient matter is present, the universe probably would begin to contract. Gravitational forces between particles of matter could pull the universe together again.

Page 322

1. Galaxies are located in groups called clusters. Groups of clusters are called superclusters.
2. See Figure 15–3 on page 318.
3. **a.** A bright nebula consists mostly of hydrogen gas that fluoresces when it absorbs ultraviolet radiation emitted from a nearby star.
   b. A dark nebula is a collection of dust and gas too far from a star to fluoresce. The concentration of dust may be great enough so that no light can be transmitted through the nebula.
   c. The density of dust and gas is great enough in a giant molecular cloud for stars to form. More than 50 different molecules have been detected within these clouds.
4. 1.2×10^{12} years

Page 326

1. Sunspots are cooler, darker areas on the photosphere. Sunspots seem to be related to the sun's magnetic field and may be responsible for changing Earth's climate and weather.
2. The main features and characteristics of the sun are present on other stars also. These features include sunspots, corona, photosphere, and so on. The sun is different in that it appears to be a single star. Most other stars are binaries. Stars may vary in color, temperature, mass, and size.
3. **a.** The color of a star is directly related to its surface temperature.
   b. The larger a star's mass, the higher the star's surface temperature is.
   c. A star's spectrum depends on its temperature. The atoms of gas within the star will emit light only at certain temperatures. Star spectra vary slightly according to the small differences in chemical compositions.
4. The star's apparent brightness is determined by the distance of the star from Earth and the size of the star.
5. There is lack of sufficient data necessary to show correlation between sunspots and weather on Earth.

Page 330

1. **a.** In a stable star, the outward radiation pressure is balanced by gravitational forces.
   b. Stable stars produce energy by the fusion of hydrogen nuclei in a series of nuclear reactions to form helium nuclei.
2. A star is born when nuclear fusion of hydrogen to helium begins in a shrinking dark globule formed from the breakup of a cloud of gas and dust.
3. The sun will undergo hydrogen fusion until hydrogen is depleted. The sun will contract and become hotter allowing fusion of helium to form carbon. The additional radiation will cause the sun to expand into a red giant. Eventually, all fusion will cease, and the sun will contract to a white dwarf before it finally "dies."
4. A massive star converts H to He more quickly than less massive stars, so its life is shorter.
5. Elements from which the Earth is made were produced by complex nuclear reactions within a red giant and during the explosion of a supernova.

Page 333

1. The celestial sphere describes the sky as a globe or sphere that surrounds the Earth. The position of objects in the sky is determined by its location on this imaginary sphere.
2. Declination and right ascension represent coordinates using the vernal equinox and celestial equator as references. These references do not change as the Earth revolves and rotates.
3. Right ascension is measured in a clockwise direction only from the vernal equinox. Longitude is measured east or west from the prime meridian to the International Date Line at 180°.
4. The horizon is the reference line for a coordinate system, which is based on the observer's position on Earth. The orientation of the horizon may vary with respect to the celestial sphere depending on longitude and latitude as well as the time of year.

Chapter 15 Review, Pages 334–335

Answers to Applications

1. The temperature and the density of the universe both decreased rapidly after the Big Bang.
2. A beam of light (or other radiation) would be pulled into the black hole, never to escape.
3. The charged particles disrupt magnetic force lines. Radio and TV reception depends on movement of electromagnetic waves. The waves are affected by the position of the magnetic force lines.
4. The light emitted at different wavelengths would be shifted toward shorter and bluer wavelengths. (The light is said to be "blue-shifted.")
5. Gas and dust between the stars hide and absorb the light of many distant stars.

CHAPTER **16**
THE SOLAR SYSTEM

Performance Objectives

GOAL: Students will learn the nature of the objects in the solar system and some ways people have learned about them.

OBJECTIVES: When asked to respond after completion of the reading and activities, students will

16:1	K	describe the nebular theory of the origin of the solar system.
	P	differentiate and apply the meaning of revolution and rotation.
16:2	K	list contributions of Ptolemy, Copernicus, Kepler, Newton, and Einstein.
16:3	K	give the time period for each: Earth's rotation, Earth's revolution, the lunar phase cycle.
	K	explain how the Earth became layered.
	P	select all necessary conditions for a lunar or solar eclipse.
16:4	K	describe conditions on Mercury and Venus.
	A	cite ways that learning more about the solar system can help people on Earth.
16:5	K	discuss features of Mars.
16:6	K	list features of Jupiter and Saturn.
	P	compare and contrast Jupiter and Saturn systems with the solar system as a whole.
16:7	K	identify Uranus, Neptune, and Pluto as not visible now or through history with the unaided eye.
16:8	K	describe features of minor planets, meteoroids, and comets.
16:9	K	name the space shuttle as the main space vehicle now used by NASA.
16:10	K	explain differing viewpoints concerning funding of space exploration.
	A	be able to support their own ideas and appreciate other ideas concerning space exploration.

Teaching the Chapter

In **section 16:3**, there is a statement that observations show that the Earth rotates and revolves. There are a number of proofs. One of rotation is the behavior of a Foucault Pendulum. Many students probably have seen these pendulums in museums. The pendulum direction remains fixed in space, while the Earth turns beneath it, knocking down small pegs. One proof of revolution is parallax of stars, discussed in the Skill Inquiry in chapter 15.

To represent the Earth's layers, prepare a set of three materials of different density in a clear container. A very simple model is wood floating on water above a dense solid object.

Mercury and Venus are discussed in **section 16:4.** Both planets change from "morning planet" (morning star is an incorrect term) to "evening planet." Use a sky calendar to learn the current morning/evening positions of these planets. Have students watch for the planets and note changes in position over a two-week period.

With **section 16:5,** compare the appearance of Mars to Earth deserts. Also observe Jupiter and Saturn with a telescope. Note the bands and oblateness of both and the orientation of Saturn's ring system. If possible, take an evening field trip to an observatory with a large telescope to view one or more of the planets. Observe the four brightest (called Galilean because they were first seen by Galileo) moons of Jupiter.

Consider if Uranus, Neptune, and Pluto had been known by early civilizations, is it possible that the week would now have a different number of days?

Use recent sources to learn about spacecraft studies of Halley's Comet done in 1986, the time of its closest approach to the sun and to the Earth. Have students calculate when Halley's Comet passed near the sun and Earth for the last 10 times in history, and use library sources or history texts to learn some event or way of life at the time of each passage. Calculate when Halley's Comet will next arrive, and speculate what life on Earth will be like then.

Related to **section 16:9,** discuss why an astronaut must have such a background. Use recent sources to learn about civilian passengers on the space shuttle. An interesting book or film is *Space* by James A. Michener, Fawcett Crest: New York, 1982. Compare real history with book themes in class discussion.

Activity, Page 343   How do models of the solar system compare?

This activity requires open space, but it should not be done outdoors because a darkened environment is needed to see phases on the ball. A white volleyball or other white sphere may work as well as the Ping-Pong ball. The distance of the ball from the light, light intensity, and size/type of flashlight determine what size of sphere works best. Instruct students to repeat a part of the activity with the same roles if and when a student Earth is unable to judge planet phases. Students may have some trouble maintaining a constant speed while taking roles of moving objects. Instruct teams to practice a short time in each role before recording data. Look for retrograde motion and record it when observed.

Answers to QUESTIONS AND CONCLUSIONS

1. Part A: Copernican Model
   Retrograde motion should be noticed in step 2 by Earth when the planet closer to the sun is between the sun and Earth. Direct motion (apparent eastward motion) is seen by Earth when the planet is beyond the sun in its orbit. Retrograde motion should be noticed in step 3 by Earth when the planet is about opposite the sun (position known as "opposition"). The retrograde motion should begin a little before the time of this arrangement and continue until a little after this time, when Earth has passed by the planet.
   Part B: Ptolemaic Model
   Retrograde motion should be noticed in step 2 by Earth when the planet is on the inside section of its epicycle (small circle). Direct motion is seen by Earth when the planet is on the more distant part of the epicycle. Retrograde motion should be noticed in step 3 by Earth when the planet is on the inside section of its epicycle. (To agree with the observation that retrograde motion is noticed only when the planet and sun are

about opposite, Earth should view this when the sun and the planet are on opposite sides of him or her.)

2. All the phases should be seen for planets in step 2 of the Copernican model. This is the only situation.

3. This observation supports the Copernican theory, or at least it does not disprove it. It disproves the Ptolemaic theory.

Activity, Page 348   How are Jupiter's moons arranged?

Although 18 natural satellites have been identified for Jupiter, data for only 16 are well established. These 16 are included in this activity.

Note that adding machine paper rolls need to be about 47 meters long, or tapes will need to be joined together, for all natural satellites to be drawn.

DATA AND OBSERVATIONS

Object	Scale Diameter (cm)	Scale Distance (cm)	
Metis	.008	11.4	
Adrastea	.005	11.6	
Almalthea	.034	21.8	
Thebe	.016	30.2	
Io	.726	70.2	
Europa	.628	120.0	= 1.20 m
Ganymede	1.052	199.8	= 1.998 m
Callisto	.960	362.8	= 3.628 m
Leda	.003	2207.8	= 22.078 m
Himalia	.037	2279.8	= 22.798 m
Lysithea	.007	2327.8	= 23.278 m
Elara	.015	2333.8	= 23.338 m
Ananke	.006	4125.8	= 41.258 m
Carme	.008	4455.8	= 44.558 m
Pasiphae	.010	4651.8	= 46.518 m
Sinope	.007	4659.8	= 46.598 m

Answers to QUESTIONS AND CONCLUSIONS

1. Approximately 15 000 km

2. The distance between objects varies from about 10 times the diameter to about 300 000 times the diameter of the objects.

3. Since the magnitude of the ratio between distance and diameter is so great, it would be impossible to show the relative sizes and distances on one sheet of paper.

4. Sinope would have the longest period of revolution since it is farthest from the planet.

5. Jupiter consists mostly of gases, similar to the sun. Jupiter's moons revolve around Jupiter like the planets revolve around the sun.

6. Although the distance scale is somewhat accurate, the moons with diameters less than 50 kilometers are difficult to illustrate.

Skill Inquiry, Page 346

An overhead projector is effective in illustrating the projections of a disk, a cylinder, and a sphere, as well as other shapes. Hold the shapes at different orientations, in focus. Have students predict what projection will be seen before the demonstrations. An ovoid could be tried (make one with clay). Ask students how they would be able to tell the Earth is a sphere instead of this shape.

1. Yes, it might produce a linear shadow or a distorted circle shadow.
2. Yes, it might produce a rectangular shadow.
3. No, no matter what position the Earth had between the sun and moon, the shadow would always be a circle or portion of a circle.
4. The Greeks who said the Earth is a sphere were right.

Answers to Review and Reflect

Page 339

1. Revolution is the motion of an object in orbit around another object. Rotation is the spinning of an object on its axis.
2. The solar system was formed about five billion years ago when spinning gases and dust flattened into a disk. The center collapsed to form the sun. Small eddies within the disk contracted to form the planets.
3. The Greek Ptolemy first explained retrograde motion of the planets. Copernicus of Poland presented the sun-centered theory. The Laws of Motion were developed by Newton of England. Kepler and Einstein were German.
4. Saturn would show a shorter retrograde motion because there is less parallax for an object farther away from Earth.

Page 342

1. The barycenter moves in a smooth elliptical orbit about the sun, while the Earth and moon revolve about the barycenter.
2. The moon does not have an atmosphere or liquid

water on its surface. Therefore, erosion due to atmospheric or hydrologic processes does not occur on the surface. Also, there are very few large meteoroids striking the moon.

3. During a solar eclipse, the moon would obscure part or all of the solar disk.

Page 349

1. The high temperatures impart a high kinetic energy to the molecules of gas, which then escape the weak gravitational force of the planet.
2. The cratered surfaces of all three objects suggest heavy meteoroid and asteroid collisions more than three billion years ago.
3. The inner planets consist mostly of rocky material, covered with a relatively thin layer of gases. The outer planets consist mostly of gases such as hydrogen, methane, ammonia, and so on. The outer planets are also much larger, although their densities are lower than that of the inner planets.
4. Neptune and Uranus are further from the sun and so, colder. Also, they may not be generating as much heat internally as Jupiter and Saturn.

Page 353

1. Meteoroids may have been left over from the original solar nebula. Some are fragments resulting from collisions, while others come from material that has broken apart from comets.
2. 1910 + 76 years = 1986
   1986 + 76 years = 2062
   The Earth passed through the tail of Halley's comet in 1910. The comet's period of revolution is 76 years.
3. The Viking mission involved a soft landing on Mars. The Voyager missions were flybys.

Page 355

1. Money paid to workers on space projects is spent on Earth, supporting the economy of a nation.
2. Some general results are given in the text: miniaturized circuits for many things; protective coatings and lubricants for many products; better foam for football equipment; freeze-dried foods, and so on. Students should select three items that they use or affect them.
3. Answers will vary. One student might say space exploration should be funded by the government because it will help the economy or provide perspective that will someday help solve problems on Earth.

Chapter 16 Review, Pages 356–357

Answers to Applications

1. Possibilities may include (1) The water lies frozen now within layers of soil below the surface. (2) The water is frozen along with carbon dioxide and other material in the polar ice caps. (3) The water chemically reacted with material on the surface. (4) The water molecules were blasted into space during meteorite impact.

2. According to studies it is believed that after the moon was formed, it underwent heavy bombardment from meteoroids and asteroids. An impact with a large object resulted in intense heat that melted the original material. The maria formed as the molten material solidified.

3. Water on the Earth, for example, contains most of Earth's carbon dioxide dissolved in solution. Without liquid water on Venus, most of the carbon dioxide remains in the atmosphere.

4. The inner planets consist mostly of more dense material, such as iron and other rocky materials. The other planets consist mostly of lighter gases, such as hydrogen and helium.

5. The Earth's shadow is cast on the moon's surface during a full moon. The curved shadow moving over the moon's surface indicates the spherical shape of Earth.

6. The comet's tail is always opposite the sun. As the comet approaches the sun, the tail is behind the comet. The tail precedes the comet as it moves away from the sun.

7. Large cracks (rifts) on the surface of Mars, as well as the alignment of volcanic formations, indicate large-scale crustal movements. These crustal changes were probably caused by slow fluid movements within the mantle.

CHAPTER 17
WEATHER AND CLIMATE

Performance Objectives

GOAL: Students will learn major properties of the atmosphere and what causes different weather and climates.

OBJECTIVES: When asked to respond after completion of the reading and activities, students will

17:1	K	list characteristics of the troposphere.
17:2	P	make a labeled sketch of the conditions for the seasons.
17:3	K	identify the factors that affect relative humidity.
	K	describe how a cloud is formed.
17:4	P	compare and contrast the general circulation that occurs on earth with rotation to the general circulation that would occur without rotation.
17:5	K	explain how a front forms.
17:6	P	compare and contrast features of midlatitude and tropical cyclones.
17:7	K	describe the work of meteorologists.
17:8	P	compare and contrast climate and weather.
17:9	P	compare results of weather modification experiments.
	A	explain why more research needs to be done about modifying weather.

Teaching the Chapter

In discussing **section 17:1**, review characteristics of gases. Note that the atmosphere is a good example of a mixture.

The seasons are discussed in **section 17:2**. Note, when using Figures 17a and 17b that the earth's axis always points in the same direction as the earth revolves. Use a globe and light to model the seasons.

Water in the atmosphere is discussed in **section 17:3**. Demonstrate the formation of a cloud. A cloud may be formed in a container by saturating the air, providing smoke for condensation nuclei, and then cooling the container. If some water is placed in the bottom of a large, clear bottle at room temperature, with the cap on, the air within the bottle becomes saturated. Holding a blown-out match inside the neck of the bottle introduces the condensation nuclei. Immersing the bottle in a cold tub should cause the appearance of a white cloud (fog) inside the bottle.

When stable and unstable air are discussed in **section 17:3,** note that stable and unstable are terms applied to other things. Discuss the nonscience use and compare the science meaning with it.

With the topic of air circulation, **section 17:4,** demonstrate convection in water, comparing the circulation to convection in the atmosphere. (Both water and the atmospheric gases are fluids.) Heat the bottom of one side of a large beaker of water. Place a crystal of potassium permanganate on the bottom of the inside of the beaker. While heating, the purple-colored water should show upward motion above the heat and downward motion on the cool side of the beaker. The color will diffuse without convection, so place the crystal in the beaker when heating begins.

Demonstrate the Coriolis Force acting on air moving from the North Pole toward the equator using a phonograph record turntable. Put a hole in a disk of cardboard to fit the disk of the spindle, like a record. Draw a straight line from the spindle to the edge freehand, while the disk is stationary. Then have someone turn the turntable slowly in an eastward direction while another person draws from the spindle to the edge. Use different colored markers for the two lines (for comparison), and support the back of the record player so it is angled toward the class for display.

Students could use library sources to prepare a report about El Niño, a disruption in weather over oceans, especially the Pacific Ocean adjacent to South America, that has had major effects on wind patterns and ocean currents.

A tornado is one type of severe weather (topic of **section 17:6**). Usually about the first week of April, the United States recognizes a National Tornado Safety Week. Although tornadoes are most common in the midwest, they can occur almost anywhere. Discuss tornado safety and other weather safety information with the class. Discuss times students have heard the terms watch and warning on television and radio. Locate a windchill chart. Have students use it to prepare a list of recommended clothing for different windchill factors and temperatures.

With **section 17:7,** also discuss folklore sayings about the weather. Locate library sources, such as *Nature's Weather Forecasters* by Helen R. Sattler,

Thomas Nelson, Inc.: New York, 1978. Apply knowledge of weather concepts to give reasons why particular folklore sayings often are correct.

Try to visit a weather station to observe the equipment and procedures used. Have students prepare sets of questions to ask the people on duty about their jobs. Students also can use library materials and sources from the local weather station to prepare reports about careers in meteorology. Some students may be interested in setting up a small weather station at the school and taking regular recordings.

Activity, Page 362   What affects heating of the earth?

The factors investigated in this activity are type of surface, angle of insolation (lamp angle), and time of heating. Students could find the cooling rate of each material right after its heating-rate data is gathered. For the three materials, 60 minutes will be needed, not counting the time for setting up and cleaning up. Therefore, two class periods should be used. When the lamp shines on pans from a 45° angle, it should be directed so that it does not shine directly on thermometers. Radiation will give inaccurate temperatures of materials in the pans.

Answers to QUESTIONS AND CONCLUSIONS
1. Temperature was higher when the lamp was positioned at the vertical angle.
2. The thermometers placed in a horizontal position would receive more energy from the lamp, and so, would record a higher temperature than the actual temperature of the material.
3. Since each material heated at different rates, they would be likely to cool at different rates. Water, the slowest heating substance, would cool more slowly than the others. Soil should cool the fastest.
4. Temperatures at the same latitude may differ because of the different surfaces that are heated by the sun. Ocean surfaces at the equator, for example, would be cooler than land surfaces.
5. The first factor is the low angle at which the sun's energy strikes the earth's surface. The second factor is the highly reflective snow and ice surfaces.

Activity, Page 371   How are clouds related to atmospheric conditions?

Try to plan this activity for a day when clouds will

be present at your location. (Following the weather forecasts should help in planning.) After completing the activity, ask students to check the real weather during the next three hours. Students might look out windows during and between classes and open an outside door briefly between classes. At the end of three hours, remind the students that they have an assignment to write down the weather observed during the period. They should compare it with the forecast they made. Review factors that are part of weather: temperature, air pressure, relative humidity, clouds, precipitation, wind speed. If a barometer is available in the science classroom, air pressure can be recorded periodically during the three hours. Air pressure is a good indicator of weather changes.

Answers to QUESTIONS AND CONCLUSIONS

1. The cumulonimbus cloud indicates the most unstable air. The cloud forms as warm, moist air rises from the surface and continues to rise since it is warmer than the surrounding air.
2. Fog and stratus clouds are very similar. Fog is a stratus cloud that is on or near the earth's surface.
3. Other important factors include wind speed and direction, temperature, relative humidity (dew point), and air pressure.
4. Answers will vary depending on the weather system affecting your area.
5. Wind speed and direction, visibility, temperature, relative humidity (dew point), air pressure, and so on.
6. Answers will vary. Differences will probably be the result of insufficient data on current weather.

Skill Inquiry, Page 370

After completing this brief activity, it is recommended that students spend some time studying current weather maps from local newspapers. Have students note changes for about one week. Have them summarize weather shown by the maps for selected locations.

1. Rain and snow
2. In the center of the continent there is a land-ocean effect, so that during cool seasons the land is colder than the water or land near the water.
3. To the northeast
4. Clear and cold

5. The isotherms curve upward, indicating the warm front.

Answers to Review and Reflect

Page 361

1. The tropopause indicates the boundary between the troposphere and stratosphere, where temperature begins to increase with altitude. The jet streams are also located in the tropopause. Most weather occurs below the tropopause.
2. The earth revolves about the sun tilted at $23\frac{1}{2}°$ with respect to the plane of orbit.
3. Shortwave radiation is absorbed by the earth's surface. The surface then reradiates the energy as longer wavelengths. The long-wave radiation is absorbed by carbon dioxide and water vapor in the air, which increases the kinetic energy of the air.
4. Air pressure is determined by the weight of gas particles due to the attraction of earth's gravity. Gases having the most mass are closest to the earth's surface. Gas particles near the surface are compressed by the weight of overlying gases.

Page 370

1. The amount of water vapor dissolved in air increases as the temperature of the air increases.
2. Cloud heights are determined by a number of factors, such as the rate at which temperature above the surface decreases, and the moisture and temperature properties of the air near the surface.
3. Stable air is usually more dense (cooler and drier) at the lower levels. The air near the surface is, therefore, less buoyant and will only rise if forced upward along a front or mountain range.
4. As air is heated along the equator, it becomes less dense and begins to rise. Decreased pressure is a result of the decreased density.
5. On a nonrotating earth, cold air from the poles would move toward the equator and warm air from the equator would move to higher latitudes. Rotation causes an apparent deflection to the right of the air's line of motion. Prevailing westerlies, trade winds, and polar easterlies develop as a result of this deflection.
6. Warm fronts are associated with the gradual development of clouds and precipitation. Stratus-type clouds usually produce continuous precipitation that may last for several hours. Afterward, warm frontal passage brings warmer temperatures, slight wind shifts, and partial clearing. Cold fronts move more rapidly than warm fronts and produce showery, sometimes intense periods

UNIT 4

of precipitation. Vertically-developed clouds and thunderstorms are associated with cold fronts. Noticeable wind shifts, clearing skies, and cooler, drier air accompany cold frontal passage.

Page 375

1. A hurricane is a tropical cyclone. It has a low pressure center but there are no fronts, as there are with midlatitude cyclones. At a very low pressure center, there is a clear region where air descends. The fastest winds whirl around this "eye." Typically, hurricanes form over an ocean in the tropics.
2. Percent probabilities are given because there are many variables that may affect local weather.
3. An airplane pilot is usually interested in wind speed and direction, cloud cover and heights, visibility, and obstructions to vision such as fog, rain, or snow.
4. Bodies of water help to maintain a small annual temperature range. The specific heat of water does not allow oceans to heat as rapidly as land in the summer and cool as quickly as land in the winter.

Page 377

1. Cloud seeding is the process by which the development of water droplets is promoted artificially by introducing dry ice (which cools the air) or silver iodide (which acts as condensation nuclei).
2. Israeli experiment: A controlled experiment that was done between 1961 and 1975 with exploratory and confirmatory stages. A mixture of silver iodide and sodium iodide was used. There were rainfall increases of 15 percent in the first stage and 46 percent in the second stage, both statistically convincing. Rainfall is judged to have increased in areas downwind of target areas.
   FACE experiment: A recent controlled experiment with inconclusive results due to rainy days as the result of natural causes.
3. Answers will vary. For example:

a. Cloud seeding should be possible by any person over his or her own property.
b. Cloud seeding should be permitted only when it is found that the procedure would bring favorable results to most people involved.
c. Cloud seeding should not be permitted at all now, except for small scientific experiments.

Chapter 17 Review, Pages 378–379

Answers to Applications

1. In summer, land surfaces absorb large amounts of solar radiation and reradiate it quickly. The longer daylight hours and the intense angle of incoming radiation allows the land to maintain a higher temperature. During winter, daylight hours as well as the intensity of solar radiation decrease. More heat is lost than gained in the winter.
2. Warm air is less dense because there are more spaces between the energetic air molecules and atoms. The water molecules that fill the spaces between particles have less mass than the nitrogen and oxygen molecules they replace.
3. Since the lake warms up more slowly than the land, the nearby air also warms more slowly. The bulbs bloom sooner where temperatures are warmer, five kilometers away from the lake.
4. The cool air preceding a thunderstorm is produced by a downdraft that accompanies the falling rain in a mature thunderstorm cell.
5. The increased amount of carbon dioxide would tend to absorb more reradiated long-wave radiation from the surface, thus disrupting the normal heat balance of the atmosphere. Abnormal heating may produce changes in local precipitation and wind patterns.
6. Air over the islands is warmed quickly and begins to rise. The clouds form as parcels or bubbles of rising air are cooled to the dew point.

CHAPTER 18
EARTH'S STRUCTURE

Performance Objectives

GOAL: Students will learn about the materials that make up the earth and the processes that change them.

OBJECTIVES: When asked to respond after completion of the reading and activities, students will

18:1	K	define mineral.
	K	identify the rocks and processes of the rock cycle.

18:2	P	relate rate of cooling of magma to the texture of igneous rocks.
18:3	P	trace the development of sedimentary rocks.
	P	compare and contrast mechanical and chemical weathering.
18:4	P	differentiate between contact and regional metamorphism.
18:5	K	identify agents of erosion.
	K	describe types of mass movement.
18:6	P	relate stream channel profile and gradient to stream development.
	P	relate amount of stream load to the rate of stream flow.
	A	agree that an understanding of watersheds is important.
18:7	P	compare and contrast permeable and impermeable rocks.
	K	identify features in which groundwater has an important role.
18:8	P	compare erosional and depositional features of glaciers.
18:9	K	describe features of erosion and deposition found in a desert.
18:10	K	describe features formed by forces within the earth's crust shifting solid rock.
18:11	K/A	explain the importance of studying the geology of a region before construction is begun.

Teaching the Chapter

When **section 18:1** is discussed, obtain a collection of different minerals. Study their properties, such as density, hardness, luster, and crystal shape. Learn their names. Emphasize that the rock cycle is one of many natural cycles, most of which have different possible sequences or pathways.

With **section 18:2**, obtain a collection of igneous rocks, including granite and basalt. Use a hand lens to study the distribution and sizes of mineral fragments. Learn the names of the rocks.

With a discussion of chemical weathering (**section 18:3**), review the chemical reaction called oxidation.

When metamorphic rocks are discussed in **section 18:4**, simulate the process of contact metamorphism by carefully (wear safety goggles) pouring a little water on anhydrous copper sulfate. The compound turns from white to blue only where the water touches and hydrates it.

Activity, Page 390   How are rocks weathered?

The action of HCl on limestone fragments is the chemical weathering process investigated in this activity. The expansion of the frozen H_2O (ice), which breaks the glass, is the physical or mechanical weathering process. Caution students not to shake the jars of acid with limestone fragments as spillage is more likely to occur. The additional factor of shaking the fragments (a physical process) with the acid could be done as a teacher demonstration only, packing one of the jars with paper or rubber inside a larger container first. Have students predict the outcomes of the procedures before they observe results.

Answers to QUESTIONS AND CONCLUSIONS

1. Chemical weathering was demonstrated in Part A; physical weathering in Part B.
2. The slight acidity of rainwater tends to dissolve carbonate rocks over a period of time.
3. The chemical weathering of rock material increases as the acidity of the rainwater increases.
4. Concrete structures are chemically weathered the same as limestone.
5. Water that freezes within rock pores causes the rock to fragment.
6. Most chemical weathering occurs in humid tropical climates. Chemical and physical weathering also occur in humid temperate climates, which experience periods of winter freezing.

Activity, Page 397   How are earthquakes located?

This activity illustrates the principles of locating the epicenter of an earthquake. Students must use the map scale of the map selected to determine and mark distances. A ruler might help students with this part of the activity.

DATA AND OBSERVATIONS

Seismograph Location	Augusta, GA	Seattle, WA	Santiago, Chile
Time between arrival of P and S waves	4.9 min	2.7 min	10.7 min
Distance from Earthquake	3218 km	1609 km	9654 km

UNIT 4

Answers to QUESTIONS AND CONCLUSIONS

1. The epicenter was located near Los Angeles.
2. Knowing the location of the epicenter will enable geologists to correlate the processes that were responsible for producing the earthquake and may help them forecast the occurrence of the next earthquake.
3. Data from at least three seismographs help geologists to locate the exact position of the epicenter.
4. The additional data helps geologists locate the epicenter more precisely.

Skill Inquiry, Page 396

Students may have heard the Richter scale quoted in television or radio reports, or they may have read about it in newspaper articles about earthquakes. Another scale of earthquake intensity, the Rossi-Forel scale, gives intensities based on personal judgments and observed damage.

1. About 30^5 times, or 24 300 000 times
2. In populated areas, earthquakes cause damage to buildings, roads, dams, and other structures. No such structures were affected during the Nevada earthquake in 1915 since it was in a remote area. Intensity is a measure of damage; magnitude is a measure of energy released.

Answers to Review and Reflect

Page 386

1. The most useful properties include color, density, size, and orientation of mineral grains.
2. Extrusive rocks are formed from lava on the earth's surface. Extrusive rocks usually contain very small mineral grains or no grains at all due to the rapid cooling of the lava. Intrusive rocks form from magma within the earth's crust and generally consist of large mineral grains that can be observed readily.
3. Dark sands are usually formed from extrusive rocks such as basalt. Light-colored sands are usually formed from intrusive rocks such as granite.
4. Regional metamorphism is mostly the result of large-scale compressional forces applied predominantly from one or two directions. Regional metamorphism is associated with mountain building processes.
5. Potholes are the result of physical weathering due to freezing. During winter, New York City experiences periods of freezing and melting.

Page 392

1. Gravity causes weathered rock particles to fall from rocks along slopes. Mass movements are also the direct result of gravity. Gravity causes streams to erode rock surfaces as the water moves to lower elevations.
2. Down-cutting occurs along stream channels at higher elevations forming V-shaped valleys with steep walls. Closer to sea level, lateral erosion produces wide floodplains and meanders within the stream channel.
3. Intrusive rock such as granite is impermeable and therefore tends to elevate the water table.
4. Shale is impermeable and prevents water from percolating deeper underground. During periods of heavy rains, the soil quickly becomes saturated.

Page 396

1. A continental glacier is an ice sheet that covers large portions of land. Valley glaciers form at the top of high mountain ranges and move down, eroding distinctive features within valleys. Continental glaciers generally tend to smooth the land over which they flow.
2. Chemical weathering in deserts is limited because of little rainfall. The lack of moisture in deserts in cooler climates also prevents mechanical weathering resulting from freezing and thawing.
3. Rocks deep in the crust will usually experience folding when forces are gradually exerted. Rocks near the surface usually experience faulting as sudden pressure is applied.

Page 399

1. a. Tunnels may be built at right angles to faults to eliminate groundwater drainage problems.
   b. Tunnels through anticlines require less structural support than tunnels built through synclines.
2. Geologic testing before construction of a skyscraper enables the builders to determine the correct foundations needed to support the building.
3. Factors that should be considered include nature of soil, rock structures, stability of nearby slopes, average depth and variations in the water table, and type and firmness of the bedrock in which the foundation will be built.

Chapter 18 Review, Pages 400–401

Answers to Applications

1. High on volcanic necks, the castles were more safe from attack.

2. Oil is not a mineral since it has an organic origin and is a liquid.

3. Solid crust movements pushed up the ancient sea-floors and they became dry land.

4. A set of large crystals (called phenocrysts) cooled slowly at first. Then the remaining magma cooled quickly. Possibly the magma that started out cooling slowly became exposed at the surface.

5. On earth, agents of erosion such as wind, water, and ice, tend to recycle the older rocks. On the moon, there is no atmosphere or running water or any large-scale internal processes.

6. Slow uplifting of layers tends to maintain down-cutting.

7. Answers will vary. Some examples are given.
   a. Build a home or other structure to withstand lower-level earthquakes; be ready to leave the area if scientific reports give warning of an earthquake; secure a source of power and a source of water that are independent of main lines that could be broken in an earthquake.
   b. Before building or buying in an area subject to landslides, a study of patterns of erosion and landslide flow is advisable.
   c. Develop a plan for flood prevention, such as building levees. Be prepared to evacuate quickly if flooding is predicted.

CHAPTER 19
THE OCEANS

Performance Objectives

GOAL: Students will learn characteristics of ocean water and the seafloor and also about ocean resources.

OBJECTIVES: When asked to respond after completion of the reading and activities, students will

19:1	K	give the probable origin of the oceans' water.
19:2	P	relate seawater density to temperature and salinity.
19:3	K	list major features of the ocean floor and describe the location and nature of each.
19:4	K	describe conditions necessary for coral reefs.
	K	name three types of coral reefs.
19:5	P	compare and contrast surface and subsurface currents.
19:6	K	describe how tides are produced.
19:7	K	explain the origin of most ocean waves, the origin of surf, and the origin of longshore currents.
	P	compare and contrast normal ocean waves and tsunami.
19:8	K	identify shore features of erosion and deposition.
19:9	K	describe ocean resources.
19:10	K	describe the Law of the Sea treaty and its purpose.
	A	cite differing viewpoints concerning the need for laws governing the oceans.

Teaching the Chapter

With **section 19:2,** review the concept of density. An understanding of density is important to comprehension of this section and the activity on page 406. A layered effect, such as exists in oceans, can be illustrated in this way. Pour tinted, cold, salty water into the bottom of a beaker. Next, slowly pour clear, hot, nonsalty water on top. Diffusion and flow due to pouring will cause considerable mixing at the boundary, but students should see some layering. The diffusion, flow (like ocean currents), and layering are similar to processes that occur in oceans.

The food chain based on change of hydrogen sulfide into food (discussed in **section 19:3**) is called chemosynthesis.

Tides are discussed in **section 19:6.** Model the conditions for spring tides. Note the phases of the moon for the two possible positions of the moon (new moon and full moon). Place the moon for positions of first quarter and last (or third) quarter. Ask students how tides at these times would compare with tides at new and full moon. (Highest tides of the day would be lower than at new and full moon.) These tides are called neap tides. Show with a model how the moon's orbit is inclined 5° to the ecliptic, which in turn is inclined 23½° to the earth's equator. This shows why the tidal bulge lies between about 30°N and 30°S.

If your location is near an ocean, look for tide tables in newspapers. Try extrapolating a tide table, noticing its trend. Also, if you are near an ocean, try to visit a tide pool at low tide. Notice the variety of life and the adaptations for the conditions. Be sure to exercise safety precautions as seaweed makes rocks very slippery.

With waves (**section 19:7**), demonstrate the movement of water. Place a few small bits of colored paper or wooden sticks on the surface of a large pan of water. Disturb the water at one place (with a moving finger, for example). Notice the paper bits bob up and down as waves pass. Review wave motion, chapter 13.

With **section 19:9,** discuss what resources students now use that come from the oceans. Seaweed is a good source of the trace element iodine (dietary iodine). About five grams of iodine are found in one kilogram of dry seaweed. In seawater, five grams of iodine is diluted by 100 metric tons of seawater. Seaweed is an important food in some countries. Health-food stores sell a variety of seaweed products. Students may want to taste some. If a fishery exists near you, discuss its existence and impact on the local economy.

Activity, Page 406 What is the relationship between floating and density?

Remind students that no water is to be inside can A or can B when each is submerged. About 100 g of salt is needed to saturate 300 mL of water. Before doing Procedure steps 9 and 10, have students hypothesize how the floating depths of cans A and B in salt water will compare with their floating depths in fresh water.

Answers to QUESTIONS AND CONCLUSIONS

1. The greater the object's density, the deeper it floats in fresh water. It will float proportionately higher in salt water.
2. The greater the fluid's density, the higher the object floats.
3. Seawater has an average density of about 35 g of salt in 1000 mL of water. Since that is about one tenth the density of the salt water made in this activity, the cans should have floated to almost the depths (nine tenths of the difference between depth in fresh water and salt water) of the cans in fresh water.
4. A person would float higher in ocean water since salt water is more dense than fresh water.
5. For a given volume, an object will float if its density is less than the liquid in which it is placed.

Activity, Page 409 How can the ocean floor be mapped?

Review features of the ocean floor before students model a part of the ocean floor with clay. Add dark food coloring to the water, so the clay model seafloor is less observable, to make the situation more realistic. To make the activity even more interesting, students may exchange models before Procedure step 4. Profiles along different lines for the same model can be compared. If colored water is used, have students try to apply understanding of data to sketch the appearance of the seafloor, as seen from above. Make sketches after data is gathered and before water is removed.

Answers to QUESTIONS AND CONCLUSIONS

1. Answers will vary. The accuracy of the model is determined by the distance between the points where measurements were made.
2. The accuracy of the profile would increase as the distance between the points was decreased.
3. The profile may show small scale features not detected using the 1 cm increments.
4. The time needed to make the depth measurements would be increased.
5. Soundings are made at selected locations in the oceans. Features of the ocean floor must be estimated or interpolated between the locations of the known data.

Skill Inquiry, Page 416

One disadvantage of radial symmetry is that it does not permit an animal to concentrate energy in one direction. This Skill Inquiry may be extended to many other organisms, both marine and nonmarine.

Starfish–radial symmetry
Sponge–no symmetry
Bristleworm–bilateral symmetry
Snail–bilateral symmetry
Octopus–bilateral symmetry; some students may say radial because of the eight legs, but point out the two eyes.

Answers to Review and Reflect

Page 413

1. Many of the ions that make up the salts are dissolved by streams as they erode the rocks. The ions are deposited by the streams as they flow into the ocean. When the seawater evaporates, the ions are left behind.

2. Variations in the salinity, temperature, and density of ocean water result in the formation of water layers.

3. Abyssal plains are deep, flat areas in the ocean basins. They average 5 km deep. Rows of submarine volcanoes cross some of the plains. Continental shelves are extensions of the continents. They consist of continental crustal material.

4. For coral to grow, water temperature must be at least 20°C. Coral grow only in shallow water not more than 50 meters deep. Water from which the coral obtain nutrients must freely circulate around the reef.

5. The South Equatorial current, the West Wind drift, and the Peru (or Humboldt) current.

6. The basis for most marine food chains are plants that are restricted to the top few meters of the oceans penetrated by sunlight.

Page 419

1. On the side facing the moon, the water is pulled more than the solid earth below. On the opposite side of the earth, the solid earth is attracted more than the water, which is further away.

2. The size of ocean waves is influenced by the speed and duration of the wind. The size of the wave is also determined by the distance across the water in which the wind blows.

3. Emerging shorelines are recognized by wave-cut cliffs and beaches that are higher than the present shorelines. Submerging shorelines have drowned beaches and wave-cut cliffs. The drowning of river valleys may produce deep bays.

4. Answers will vary. One possible way is to place a device similar to a windmill within the Gulf Stream to make use of the swiftly moving current.

Page 421

1. Today nations recognize the value of ocean resources more than they did in the past. Many nations that were not technologically developed un-til recently now need minerals and oil. There are more people in the world now, which makes fish and other ocean sources more useful.

2. Nations are permitted economic rights to zones up to 320 kilometers from their shores. The high seas are considered the common heritage of people. Resources will be developed by the Seabed Authority and countries will be licensed by the Seabed Authority to develop them. Free passage is permitted in the high seas. A supreme court, the International Tribunal of the Law of the Sea, will settle ocean disputes.

3. Possible answers may include: sanctions such as limiting trade, remove rights within the United Nations, ignore the boundary set by the country for fishing and other economic resources.

Chapter 19 Review, Pages 422–423

Answers to Applications

1. Only the surface layers are at relatively high temperature. The lower layers are near freezing. The ocean's layers resulting from this temperature difference prevent fast mixing.

2. Deep sea vents add minerals. Material from volcanoes and other windblown material is deposited in the oceans.

3. In a region surrounding Antarctica, there is no land at any longitude. The current can flow around the world at this latitude. There is no such region in the Northern Hemisphere.

4. The Gulf Stream brings warm water northeast to Great Britain. The water warms the air above it and brings warmer weather to Great Britain.

5. Platforms for drilling and production must be built and maintained. Over water they are more expensive than on land. Drilling is more difficult and time-consuming, since drill bits must come up through water as well as rock layers.

6. Some animals such as whales might communicate long distances to find mates and food.

UNIT 4

CHAPTER 20
EARTH HISTORY

Performance Objectives

GOAL: Students will learn how the earth has changed and learn a theory that explains many of these changes.

OBJECTIVES: When asked to respond after completion of the reading and activities, students will

20:1   P   compare and contrast different types of fossils.

20:2	K	describe three important principles that help geologists understand the relative ages of rocks.
20:3	P	differentiate between relative age and absolute age.
	K	explain radiometric dating and paleomagnetic dating.
20:4	K	list correlation procedures.
	K	describe the Geologic Time Scale.
20:5	P	explain why particular observations serve as evidence for the theory of plate tectonics.
	K	describe three types of plate boundaries.
20:6	K	list physical and life events of Precambrian time.
20:7	K	list physical and life events of the Paleozoic Era.
20:8	K	list physical and life events of the Mesozoic Era.
20:9	K	list physical and life events of the Cenozoic Era.
20:10	K	explain the Milankovitch theory and its significance.

Teaching the Chapter

With **section 20:1,** note that ice, oil, mud, standing water, sand, and lava can bury animals and plants. Resin from trees also can engulf insects. The dried resin, called amber, is often used in jewelry and displayed in museums. Try to obtain a piece of amber for observation. Make molds and casts using clay or plaster of paris.

Wegener was not the first to notice that coastlines seemed to fit like puzzle pieces. Sir Francis Bacon seems to have been the first to state that the fit was too close to be an accident. Others, before Wegener, repeated this view. However, Wegener worked out a detailed and well-documented theory of continental drift. Wegener first presented his theory in a lecture in 1912. His book, *The Origin of Continents and Oceans,* was published in 1915. Wegener's term Pangaea means "world together."

Formations are discussed in **section 20:4.** Look for formations in your area. They are apt to be seen in fresh roadcuts. Each formation holds clues about the environment in which it formed. Ripple marks, fossils, and types of layering (stratification) can be interpreted to tell much about climates and landscapes long ago.

In discussing **section 20:6,** consider how a time-lapse film of Precambrian and later times would appear. The continents (shields) probably would be seen splitting and joining a number of times, while rotating and changing in other ways.

Activity, Page 430   How can rock ages be determined?

Review the principle of superposition before beginning this activity. Note that crosscutting is an extension of superposition: a feature that cuts across another is younger than the other.

DATA AND OBSERVATIONS
Granite A   3.4–3.7 billion years
Limestone A   590–515 million years
Shale A   515–415 million years
Limestone B   515–415 million years
Coal   325–280 million years
Sandstone   280–240 million years
Limestone C   240–135 million years
Shale B   240–135 million years
Granite B   135–65 million years
Basalt   22–3 million years

Answers to QUESTIONS AND CONCLUSIONS
1. Granite A
2. Between 2.9 and 3.1 billion years
3. Limestone B
4. Between 113 and 62 million years
5. Between 235 and 175 million years
6. The difference in age between the two granite intrusions could be determined by using the concept of crosscutting relationships.

Activity, Page 437   How are rock formations interpreted?

In Part A of this activity, students prepare a geologic model of a sequence of events according to directions and then summarize the sequence of events by examining the concrete model. In Part B, they use a sketch of a side view of a formation to apply principles of superposition and horizontal condition of undisturbed rocks. Point out the need to follow directions carefully.

DATA AND OBSERVATIONS

A	Igneous intrusion	5
B	Sandstone	6
C	Shale	4
D	Sandstone	3
E	Shale	2
F	Limestone	1

Answers to QUESTIONS AND CONCLUSIONS

1. Where no sedimentation occurs, there is no record of the geological processes that occurred at the time of nondeposition. Therefore, there is a gap in the geologic record.
2. Anticlines and synclines are folds resulting from compressional forces, possibly produced by tectonic activity.
3. Faults may occur where brittle surface rocks are subject to sudden tension and compression forces.
4. An intrusion cutting through existing rock layers or deformational features is younger than the layers. An intrusion that is faulted or deformed is older than the time the deformation occurred.
5. Actual cross-sections may be viewed along valley walls or road cuts.

PROCEDURE
Part B
4. Sedimentary layers F, E, were deposited. Folding and uplift of three layers produced anticline. Erosion of anticline followed. Formation was submerged and deposition of layer C occurred. Episode of igneous intrusion (A) cut through layers C, D, E, and F. Uplift resulted in erosion of layer C and igneous intrusion. Finally, deposition of layer B occurred when formation subsided again.

Skill Inquiry, Page 434

Other times shown in the Geologic Time Table, Table 20-2, can be related to the month to expand this activity.

1. Paleozoic: 345 million years; Mesozoic: 160 m.y.; Cenozoic: 65 m.y. (to present)
2. Paleozoic: 7.6%; Mesozoic: 3.6%; Cenozoic: 1.4%
3. Mesozoic: 1.5 days ago; Cenozoic: 0.4 days ago
4. About day 29

Answers to Review and Reflect

Page 429
1. According to the principle of uniformitarianism, all geological processes occurring today have occurred in the past also. Therefore, events in geologic history can be explained in terms of the processes that can be directly observed today.
2. Quick burial may occur as the result of landslides, volcanic eruptions, and so on.

3. Answers will vary. A student's relative age can be described in terms of older and younger brothers and sisters. Absolute age is determined by the student's date of birth.

Page 436
1. A rock formation may consist of one or several kinds of igneous rocks or sedimentary layers. The group of rocks is usually distinct from rocks above or below the formation.
2. In the 1930s, there was no known force or mechanism to push or pull the continents.
3. According to plate tectonics, the earth's crust and upper mantle are composed of rigid sections or plates that move on a pliable zone in the mantle. Seafloor spreading offers the mechanism for producing the movement of the plates. Upwelling of new crustal material occurs at the mid-ocean ridges. The crustal material moves away from the ridges and is eventually pulled into the mantle along subduction zones.

Page 441
1. Continental shields have been enlarged as plates collided and new material along the subduction zone was lifted and folded at shield margins.
2. Collision between Asia and Europe produced the Ural Mountains. Collision between Africa and North America formed the Appalachians.
3. The Atlantic Ocean started to open as Pangaea started to split up during the Jurassic Period of the Cenozoic Era.
4. Answers will vary. See the Geologic Time Scale on page 433.

Page 443
1. There are three cycles that change the amount of solar energy reaching the Northern Hemisphere: axial tilt in a cycle of 41 000 years; precession in a cycle of 22 000 years; and shape of the earth's orbit (eccentricity) in a cycle of 100 000 years. Acting in combination, they caused the Pleistocene ice ages.
2. Studies of ocean sediments show that there are changes in the amount of ice over the Northern Hemisphere during the last 500 000 years. The changes show cycles of about 40 000 years, 20 000 years, and 100 000 years.
3. Other factors apparently affect the amount of solar radiation reaching the earth's surface. They include carbon dioxide concentration of the atmosphere, which is increasing.

Chapter 20 Review, Pages 444–445

Answers to Main Ideas

1. plate tectonics
2. Cenozoic
3. Cenozoic
4. existence of hard parts
5. mold
6. there was no explanation of what caused the motion to occur
7. using methods of relative dating
8. the trilobite
9. correlation
10. eras
11. convection
12. 570 million years ago

Answers to Applications

1. Plants might fall on uncooled lava. Animals might walk on uncooled lava. It is necessary that the lava not be too hot, or the material would burn or decompose quickly. The lava would have to be covered soon after the organisms made imprints.

2. Geologists had to study rock formations in many places and correlate them to find a relative scale.

Then formations of known relative age throughout the scale had to be absolutely dated by radiometric and paleomagnetic methods.

3. Early observations, by Wegener and others, resulted in the hypothesis of continental drift. Additional data confirmed the hypothesis and extended it with ideas about how it could have happened. Now scientists make further predictions about the earth, based on the theory of plate tectonics.

4. The half-life is too short. All the carbon-14 would be gone in about 50 000 years.

5. Salt is precipitated in ocean floor deposits as more salt is added by rivers emptying into the ocean. Thus, the percentage of salt (salinity) in ocean water is relatively constant.

6. 50 000 years (2 cm = 1/50 meter; 1000 meters ÷ 1/50 meter = 50 000); 5 000 000 years (100 × 50 000) It is assumed that the rate of separation is continuous and constant.

UNIT 5   PATTERNS OF LIFE

Overview

In chapter 21, students observe and consider differences between living and nonliving things. The parts and functions of cells are emphasized throughout this chapter. Homeostasis, transport through the cell membrane, photosynthesis, cell respiration, and enzyme activity are discussed. An optional information section on cryobiology ends the chapter.

In chapter 22, students learn how forms of life are classified. The five kingdom system of animals, plants, fungi, protists, and monerans is described. Eukaryote and prokaryote cells are compared, and scientific naming is explained. Viruses are described briefly, and the theory of evolution by natural selection is presented. The chapter closes with an optional section concerning endangered species.

Chapter 23 features a systems approach to the human body. After the section on body homeostasis, sections are devoted to the parts and functions of the digestive, cardiovascular, immune response, respiratory, urinary, nervous, endocrine, and reproductive systems. Proper health management is considered, followed by an optional discussion of organ transplant programs.

Chapter 24 concerns heredity. The application of genetics to crop production and the understanding of genetic disease opens the chapter. DNA as the location of genetic information is discussed. The processes of mitosis and meiosis are explained. The mechanisms of trait inheritance, including sex-linkage, are discussed. Mutations and mutagens are described. The chapter ends with an optional section on the uses of a genetically-changed bacteria.

Chapter 25 closes the unit with a study of ecology. Cycles in ecosystems, including the carbon dioxide-oxygen and nitrogen cycles are described. Major world biomes are presented, and habitat and niche are defined. Succession, community relationships, and limiting factors are discussed. Concerns relating to the human population are considered. The chapter closes with an optional section considering Antarctica as an ecosystem.

Introducing the Unit

Direct students' attention to the unit opening photograph. Have them list the visible forms of life as well as those they think might have been present but unseen in the environment at the time the photograph was made. Using the list, you may want to have students consider several possible relationships and interdependencies among the organisms as well as between the organisms and the nonliving part of their environment.

It may be useful to have students consider and list possible answers to the first unit opening question before proceeding to chapter 21. Discuss the remaining questions at this time. Although intended to be motivational, the questions may be used as an assessment of students' prior knowledge of the subjects to be discussed.

CHAPTER **21**
CELLS

Performance Objectives

GOAL: Students will learn what is found within cells and how each main part functions.

OBJECTIVES: When asked to respond after completion of the reading and activities, students will

21:1	P	differentiate between living and nonliving things.
21:2	K	describe tools scientists use to learn about cells.
21:3	K	identify major parts of cells shown in drawings or photographs.
	K	describe the functions of major parts of cells.
21:4	K	describe homeostasis.
	K	state an example of feedback.
	A/K	recognize the importance of feedback loops in homeostasis.
21:5	P/K	explain the importance of a selectively permeable cell membrane in cell function.
	K	compare the processes of diffusion and active transport.
21:6	K	explain why cells need energy.
	P/K	recognize the importance of ATP in cell processes.
	P/K	compare photosynthesis with cell respiration.
21:7	K	explain how enzymes function.
	K	describe the role of coenzymes.
21:8	K	explain why freezing may damage cells.
	A/P	appreciate the contributions of cryobiology to medicine.

Teaching the Chapter

Homeostasis, discussed in **section 21:4,** is a major concept of life science. Homeostasis is maintained by

feedback loops in cell parts, in cells, and in entire organisms, as well as in stable ecosystems. Describing how simple physical feedback loops work can help students understand biological feedback loops. Examples include thermostats and float valve assemblies in toilets.

Students may be able to better visualize the processes of photosynthesis and respiration by manipulating models of the molecules. If ball and stick models are not available, you can cut out circles of three different colors of posterboard to represent carbon, hydrogen, and oxygen atoms. Apply a small square of stick-on magnetic tape to the back of each circle. The circles can be attached to the chalkboard to represent molecules of glucose, oxygen, carbon dioxide, and water. To demonstrate respiration, form a glucose molecule and then disassemble it using six oxygen molecules to form six carbon dioxide and six water molecules.

You may want to have students research the biochemical function of the common vitamins. They will discover that the exact activity of some vitamins is not yet understood. This may surprise some students who think everything in science is known.

Students may better appreciate the problems discussed in **section 21:8** if they can actually observe the effects of the expansion of water during freezing. Place equal masses of water in two similar paper or thin plastic containers. Freeze one of the containers and exhibit the obvious expansion of the frozen water. You may want to have students freeze small samples of vegetables and fruits to observe the effects of freezing on cells.

Activity, Page 456   What can you learn from a feedback loop?

Even adults who try this activity the first time find it difficult to produce a correct tracing. Practice should improve the tracing, but rarely can one become proficient with only the amount of practice allowed by doing this activity once. Interested students may wish to practice until they can trace smoothly over lines or do other tasks while only looking at the mirror. The entire procedure may be repeated using the other hand. There is some evidence that the left hand may perform better than the right hand. The right brain hemisphere, which controls the left hand, has been found to be a locus of spatial ability.

Answers to QUESTIONS AND CONCLUSIONS

1. Students probably had difficulty tracing shape A since it was their first try.
2. Students may or may not note improvement.
3. Answers will vary. Comparison of the second group of tracings to the first group should provide information.
4. Students trace the drawings normally at first to make sure they can trace without a mirror. The variable, then, is the use of a mirror.
5. Students' drawings should be similar to Figure 21–5 on page 454.

Activity, Page 459   What can pass through a membrane?

The dialysis tubing must be soaked for about a minute in order to make it pliable. The relationship between this activity and concepts discussed in section 21:5 should be pointed out. To prepare Lugol's iodine solution, dissolve 12 g of potassium iodide in 50 mL of distilled water. Add 3 g of iodine crystals and stir until dissolved. Add enough distilled water to make one liter. For each liter of starch solution needed, mix 4 g of soluble starch (corn or potato starch) with 10 mL of cold, distilled water to form a paste. Add the mixture to 1 L of boiling distilled water. Continue to stir and boil for two to three minutes. It is recommended that ready-made Benedict's solution be purchased from supply houses. Review Appendix B before beginning this activity.

Answers to QUESTIONS AND CONCLUSIONS

1. Corn syrup moved out of the bag. When Benedict's solution was added and the mixture heated, it changed color. Starch did not move out of the bag. A dark blue color formed when Lugol's solution was added to the tube's contents. Water moved into the bag. The bag became swollen by the increased amount of water.

2. The materials moved by diffusion and osmosis, a special case of diffusion.
3. Some materials pass through and some do not.

Skill Inquiry, Page 451

This math-related skill inquiry allows students to evaluate magnifications of cells, to appreciate the actual sizes of cells, and to show how sizes of cells can be determined given certain data. This process can be generalized to allow students to compare or calculate the sizes of objects shown in photographs, drawings, and maps.

1. $160\times$
2. .005 cm
3. a. Figure a is five times larger than Figure b.
   b. Figure b is 10 times larger than Figure a.
4. Student's height in cm $\div$ 0.025 cm

Answers to Review and Reflect

Page 453

1. a. Mitochondria—oxidize food, providing energy
   b. Cell membrane—controls ingoing and outgoing material
   c. Nucleus—the control center for the cell
2. Answers will vary. Students may say they would check to see if the object responds to conditions around it, like touch or light. They might look for use of energy, offspring, or other features of living things mentioned in section 21:1.

Page 458

1. Systems of control within the organism make adjustments according to environmental changes.
2. Only certain materials pass in and out of the cell membrane.
3. Diffusion: material in greater concentration on one side of the cell membrane moves with no added energy through the membrane to the other side. (Osmosis is a form of diffusion.) Active transport: certain molecules act as carriers to move materials through the cell membrane; energy is required.
4. Answers should be based on ventilation.

Page 463

1. Most cells obtain energy by breaking down food molecules in the process of respiration. In some organisms, the food molecules are manufactured by the organism itself in the process of photosynthesis.

2. Photosynthesis: $6H_2O + 6CO_2 + \text{light energy} \rightarrow C_6H_{12}O_6 + 6O_2$

Respiration: $C_6H_{12}O_6 + 6O_2 \rightarrow \text{energy} + 6H_2O + 6CO_2$

Viewed as overall reactions, photosynthesis and respiration are the reverse of one another.

3. Enzymes allow reactions to take place at lower temperatures.

4. Students should indicate any fruits and juices, tomatoes, cabbage, potatoes, or leafy green vegetables they have eaten.

Page 465

1. **a.** Red blood cells are separated from the rest of the blood by spinning. Then they are mixed with water, glycerol, and sodium chloride. The mixture is carefully frozen and stored at $-85°C$.

   b. Some diseases are not passed on to people receiving frozen blood. Frozen blood can be stored for 10 years or more. Also, frozen blood can be shipped easily to hospitals.

2. Cryosurgery is surgery in which low temperatures are used to kill unwanted cells by instant freezing. Tumors are less likely to grow back and recoveries are faster.

3. **a.** a blunt instrument used to apply cold to tissues in surgery

   b. protecting from freezing

   c. therapeutic use of cold

Chapter 21 Review, Pages 466–467

Answers to Applications

1. An atomic nucleus contains atomic particles, rather than complex molecules. An atomic nucleus shows no life properties.

2. Answers will vary. Students may say that they would explore the nucleus because, as the cell's control center, it must be complex and interesting.

3. The eyes see the pencil; the hand aims in the direction of the pencil; the eyes see that the action is nearly correct; the hand adjusts its aim toward the pencil; the fingers curl to grasp the pencil; the eyes see that the action is nearly correct; the hand adjusts its fingers to grasp perfectly. The eyes see that the action is correct; the hand moves the pencil; the eyes see that movement is far enough in a particular direction; the hand stops movement in that direction and starts movement in another direction.

4. Chlorophyll absorbs red, orange, most yellow, blue, and violet light in the visible spectrum of white light. It does not absorb green and some yellow. The green is reflected, which makes chlorophyll appear green. (Note: sometimes other pigments mask the green color of chlorophyll.)

5. Photosynthesis, as we know it, cannot be taking place on the other planets because oxygen is needed for photosynthesis to occur.

CHAPTER **22**

CLASSIFICATION

Performance Objectives

GOAL: Students will investigate the main properties of different forms of life and how organisms are classified.

OBJECTIVES: When asked to respond after completion of the reading and activities, students will

22:1	P/K	contrast eukaryotes and prokaryotes.
22:2	K	give an example of an organism in each of the five kingdoms.
	A/P	appreciate the need to identify organisms by scientific names.
22:3	K	state the characteristics of organisms in the animal kingdom.
	K/P	classify an animal as a vertebrate or an invertebrate.
	K	give an example of an invertebrate in each of the major phyla.
22:4	K	state the characteristics of organisms in the plant kingdom.
	K/P	classify a plant as vascular or nonvascular.
	K/P	compare the methods of reproduction in ferns and seed plants.
22:5	K	state the characteristics of organisms in the fungi kingdom.

22:6	K	state characteristics of protists.
22:7	K	identify monerans as prokaryotes.
	K	state the two main groups of monerans.
	K	identify both useful and harmful activities of bacteria.
	A/K	appreciate the need to inspect food for evidence of bacterial spoilage.
22:8	K	describe how viruses reproduce.
	K	explain how fungi can be both helpful and harmful.
	P	relate viral reproductive methods to cell damage.
22:9	K	list observations on which the theory of evolution by natural selection is based.
22:10	K	identify human activities that have caused species to become endangered.
	A	appreciate the need for an objective evaluation of risks versus benefits in human activities that may affect species.

Teaching the Chapter

The five kingdom system of classification discussed in **section 22:2** is currently accepted by most scientists. However, a sixth kingdom, known as archaebacteria, has been proposed recently. Scientists increasingly are considering biochemical relationships in determining how organisms should be classified. Help students to understand biological classification by discussing other hierarchical classification systems, such as mail sorting, office or library filing systems, and organized packing to move household goods.

When **section 22:4** is studied, samples of nonvascular plants and different types of vascular plants might be examined. To understand the transport structures in vascular plants, cross-sections and longitudinal sections of stems can be examined.

With **section 22:6**, give students an opportunity to observe live protists in pond water or in cultures.

Students may be interested in learning symptoms and phases of development in botulism, discussed in **section 22:7**. Library sources or information from local health authorities may be used.

While studying **section 22:10**, you may want to have students research specific cases of human activ-

ities affecting endangered species or causing species to become endangered. Perhaps students could prepare a risk-benefit analysis or propose arguments from both points of view. It may be instructive for students to find out why humans need or want to pursue these activities. Interested students could research and suggest solutions that would accommodate both sides of the issue.

Activity, Page 475   How do flowering plants differ?

Flowering plants are classified in two groups, monocots and dicots. Monocot and dicot are shortened names for monocotyledons and dicotyledons. Make certain that students exercise safe procedures in the handling and use of the scalpel and any other sharp tool, such as scissors, that might be used for examination of plant parts. Review Appendix B with the class before beginning the activity.

Answers to QUESTIONS AND CONCLUSIONS

1. Oat and barley grew like the corn. Pea, peanut, and squash grew like the bean. Students should note the presence of one or two cotyledons.
2. Monocots: one cotyledon, vascular bundles in stem are scattered, leaves have parallel veins, flowers have petals and sepals in multiples of 3. Dicots: two cotyledons, vascular bundles in stem are in rings, leaves have net or branched veins, flowers have petals and sepals in multiples of 4 or 5.
3. Oat and barley are monocots. Pea, peanut, and squash are dicots.
4. Answers will vary.

Activity, Page 477   How are fungi different from plants?

Proper handling, use, and care of microscopes should be reviewed with students before beginning this activity. The Basic Skills master in the Teacher Resource Book about the microscope may be helpful. If available, a microscope having a $45\times$ objective and a $20\times$ zoom eyepiece is quite effective for showing the difference between algae cells and yeast cells.

Answers to QUESTIONS AND CONCLUSIONS

1. In beaker B the "foaming" indicates growth of yeast.
2. The sugar is the source of energy.
3. Yeast are fungi. They do not have chloroplasts or chlorophyll. Yeast cannot grow without food

(sugar in this activity) from another source. Green algae are plants. They have chloroplasts that contain chlorophyll. Green algae can make their own food.

4. Yeast and algae are microorganisms. They have eukaryotic cells.

5. Green algae have chloroplasts and can make their own food.

6. Yeast have no chloroplasts and cannot make their own food. They get food from other sources.

Skill Inquiry, Page 481

The skill improved by this inquiry has many applications. The ability to interpret and/or draw cross-sectional sketches or photographs is essential to a number of everyday activities and special tasks, such as understanding illustrations in books and periodicals, reading maps, putting together kits, assembling products, or following pattern and needlework directions. Discuss the importance of the interpretation skill with students.

1.

2.

3. (image)

4. c. tree trunk
   d. seed (dicot)
   e. pencil

Answers to Review and Reflect

Page 472

1. Eukaryotes have nuclei and distinct structures, such as mitochondria and inside cell membranes. Prokaryotes have no nuclei or distinct structures.

2. Biologists use data about kinds of cells, body structures, body chemistry, reproduction and development, complexity, and behavior.

3. Unless biologists understand exactly what organism is being discussed, information about a species might be misinterpreted.

Page 476

1. A vertebrate has a backbone and an internal skeleton. An invertebrate does not. Examples will vary, such as vertebrates: fish, frog, human; invertebrates: sponge, worm, ant.

2. Reptiles have scaly skins, lay eggs on land, and have young that look much like their parents. Amphibians have smooth skins, lay eggs in water, and have young with gills and tails.

3. In seed plants, pollen grains are transferred from male structures by wind, water, or insects to female reproductive structures. In the ovule, eggs and male sex cells unite forming a fertilized egg. A seed is a fertilized egg with its protective covering. In ferns, spores are released from spore cases, distributed by wind, and form new fern plants in moist places.

4. They periodically lose their exoskeletons and grow new ones. This process is called molting.

5. Harmful crop diseases and mildews would be gone. Soil would not form as fast without lichens. Without important *Penicillium notatum,* which is used to make penicillin, many people would die of infections. Most importantly, the recycling of organic matter by decay would be reduced.

Page 480

1. Both have eukaryotic cells. Like fungi, many protists have no chlorophyll. There are both helpful and harmful forms of both. Protists are single cells, but most fungi are many-celled. Fungi have no chlorophyll.

2. The protists that do not contain chlorophyll move and seek food like animals. Some protists contain chlorophyll and make their own food.

3. Helpful: Blue-green algae is believed to have produced almost all the oxygen, O_2, in the earth's atmosphere, making animal life possible. Bacteria cause decay. Different bacteria are used to make cheeses, butter, vinegar, yogurt, sour cream, and solvents for industry. Harmful: Some bacteria cause diseases such as botulism.

Page 483

1. Evolution by natural selection.

2. Viruses do not have most features of life. They can reproduce only inside living cells.

3. Giraffes with longer necks had more food available to them because they could eat leaves from the tops as well as the lower branches of trees. When food was in short supply, the long-necked giraffes were more likely to survive. The long neck characteristic was passed on to offspring when these organisms reproduced.

Page 485

1. An extinct species has no living members. An endangered species is in danger of becoming extinct.

2. Many desert animals, such as birds, depend on cacti for survival. If the cacti are removed, many animals will die.

3. **a.** Answers will vary. Problems may include cost, environmental destruction, and displaced human populations. Benefits include flood control, hydroelectric power, recreational uses, and so on.

   b. Answers will vary. Problems may include cost and public opinion. Benefits include preserving the natural order, since the species role may not be fully recognized. Also, the species may be a source of medicine or other items. The aesthetic value of the organism is benefit.

4. Solutions will vary. Encourage students to think of compromises such as relocating the highway or the plant to another area if possible.

Chapter 22 Review, Pages 486–487

Answers to Main Ideas

1. They have living and nonliving characteristics.
2. nuclei
3. arthropods
4. animal, plant, fungus, protist, moneran
5. Parasites
6. viruses
7. internal skeletons, backbones
8. Organisms produce many offspring. Offspring compete for food, places to live, and mates. Organisms pass on their traits to offspring, but there are slight differences in the many offspring of a species. The offspring with differences that help them get food, places to live, and mates are the ones most likely to survive and reproduce.
9. lichen
10. chloroplasts or chlorophyll
11. protists
12. kingdom, phylum, class, order, family, genus, species

Answers to Applications

1. There are more different kinds of environments on land than in oceans. Water may vary in temperature, pressure, amount of sunlight penetration, and dissolved chemicals. However, a water environment is much more uniform than the land environments found at different latitudes and altitudes.

2. **a.** In a many-celled organism, cells are specialized for different activities or functions. More functions are possible.

   b. An efficient system of getting raw materials (water, nutrients) and products of photosynthesis (glucose) circulated inside a plant enables the plant to function faster and grow taller. Taller growth improves ability to compete for sunlight.

   c. Animals can grow larger because they have a frame to support large amounts of body tissue. An exoskeleton, which would need to be shed and regrown periodically, would not support tissue during periods of regrowth. Size can help in competing for food and avoiding predators.

   d. Animals with lungs could live on land. As a lake or pond dried up, the creature could survive.

   e. Eggs like these do not need to be laid in water. Adults need not find water to reproduce.

3. A sponge contains no chlorophyll. Also, its reproduction is more like that of animals.

4. Answers will vary. Students should note that if the organism is tiny, some cells would be examined first to determine if its cells are prokaryotic or eukaryotic. Microscope examination also could help to specifically relate a one-celled organism to other known organisms. If the organism was large and complex, a study of body structures and reproduction could relate the organism to known forms of life.

5. Nonflowering plants, such as pine trees, grow quite slowly in comparison with flowering plants. Fast growth and reproduction are an important aid in competition for space.

CHAPTER 23
THE HUMAN BODY

Performance Objectives

GOAL: Students will learn the major systems of the human body and relate their functions to good health.

OBJECTIVES: When asked to respond after completion of the reading and activities, students will

| 23:1 | K | explain why body homeostasis is essential to good health. |

	P/K	give an example of a feedback loop in body homeostasis.
23:2	K	list the components of a balanced diet.
	K	relate Calorie consumption to weight maintenance.
	A	use information about diet to maintain and improve health.
23:3	K	trace food as it passes through the digestive system.
23:4	K	list the parts and functions of the blood.
	A	recognize the importance of maintaining the health of the cardiovascular system.
	P	trace the flow of blood through the cardiovascular system.
23:5	K	describe the body's lines of defense against disease.
	K	explain how immunization may prevent disease.
	A	ask to know what immunizations they have had.
23:6	K	describe processes that take place in the lungs during breathing.
	A/P	ask about the effect of smoking on the body.
23:7	K	list the various functions of the urinary system.
	K	describe how a nephron works.
	A/K	recognize that the urinary system has vital homeostatic as well as excretory functions.
23:8	K	describe the functions of the major parts of the nervous system.
	K	explain how a nerve impulse travels.
	K	describe the effects of major drugs on the nervous system.
	A	act responsibly in regard to drug usage.
23:9	K	list the major glands of the endocrine system.
	P/K	discuss thyroid fuction as an example of the action of hormones.
23:10	K	describe the major events of the female reproductive cycle both with and without fertilization.
23:11	A/P	recognize that many practices contribute to health maintenance.

23:12	A	recognize the importance of the availability of transplants.
	P	discuss the reasons for controversy over transplant programs.

Teaching the Chapter

An activity related to **section 23:2** is the study of nutrition labels. Collect nutrition labels from many different kinds of food. List the specific nutrition and Calorie information found on each. Plan a balanced diet for a day or longer using this information. Obtain nutrition information from reference books.

Most students will know the major parts of the digestive system, **section 23:3,** from earlier study. It is, therefore, recommended that teaching/learning concentrate on topics such as the need for digestive processes and how increased surface area makes absorption and enzyme action more efficient. To illustrate this concept, make a cubical stack of blocks and calculate the surface area exposed. Break up the stack. Then calculate the total surface area of all the individual blocks.

The cardiovascular system is discussed in **section 23:4.** If blood cells were not examined with a microscope when cells were studied in chapter 21, they might be studied now. Use either commercially-prepared slides or isotonic solutions of blood cells. It is suggested that students do NOT obtain their own samples.

As **section 23:5** is studied, it is hoped that students will try to find out which immunizations they have had. Parents and family physicians are the best sources of information.

In **section 23:7** students are invited to consider the urinary system as a mechanism for maintaining homeostasis. This aspect should be emphasized. If available, use a large model of the nephron to show the three-dimensional relationship of the tubules and capillaries.

Activity, Page 496   How does blood pressure vary?

The school nurse or a paramedic can be asked to help students learn to use a sphygmomanometer. It is recommended that student participation be optional, as a student could have a medical problem that he or she does not want revealed.

Aneroid sphygmomanometers with stethoscopes bound into the cuff are recommended because they

UNIT 5

are relatively inexpensive and less subject to damage. One set of materials to a maximum of four students is recommended, as student attention may wander while waiting. The room must be relatively quiet, or sounds will not be heard well. Check equipment for leaks and smooth functioning before use. Have students listen to a record, if available, of the normal sounds heard while taking blood pressure.

Answers to QUESTIONS AND CONCLUSIONS

1. The cuff must be able to compress the artery to shut off the flow of blood. You must be able to hear the rush of blood through the artery as the pressure in the cuff is released.
2. When the ventricles contract, blood is forced into the arteries and the pressure increases. When the ventricles relax, arterial pressure decreases.
3. Blood pressure is read in mm of mercury.
4. The systolic pressure is written first followed by a slash mark and then the diastolic value. This is often read as systolic over diastolic value.
5. Yes. Students should find that lying down lowers blood pressure. Students should find that exercise raises blood pressure. A sustained exercise program may, however, lower resting blood pressure.
6. Student answers will vary. Other factors that affect blood pressure include weight, age, smoking, drug use, illness, emotional state, and diet.

Activity, Page 499   How much gas passes in and out of your lungs?

The diameter of the tubing and that of the straws should be such that a straw can be inserted securely into the tubing. If glass bottles are used, instruct students to use caution. If students share an apparatus, a clean straw should be used by each student.

Answers to QUESTIONS AND CONCLUSIONS

1. A person may inhale and exhale differently from one breath to the next, especially when breathing under conscious control.
2. For most people, the tidal volume after sitting will be less than the tidal volume after mild exercise. When the oxygen need increases, the mechanisms of homeostasis cause one to breathe more deeply.
3. The tidal volume should increase with more vigorous exercise.
4. There may be a difference.

5. Student answers will vary. Factors could include smoking, air pollution, physical size, illness, and inherited differences.

Skill Inquiry, Page 495

The skill, which gives practice in judging term meanings from previous information, can be extended. From a high school or college biology book or a medical book, prepare a list of additional terms for students. Have students use dictionaries to find the meanings of terms and their roots. Student answers may vary. Equivalent meanings taken from the word list in the student's text are given below.

1. dermatitis = skin inflammation
   photosensitive = sensitive to light
2. osteoporosis = bones with small holes
   cardiovascular = heart and blood vessels
3. gastritis = stomach inflammation
   renal = kidney
4. hypothermia = low temperature
5. hemostat = stop blood (flow)
   leukocyte = white blood cell

Answers to Review and Reflect

Page 492

1. A balanced diet should include adequate amounts of carbohydrates, fats, proteins, vitamins, minerals, and water.
2. In the mouth, chewing increases the surface area of food, while water and an enzyme in saliva begin hydrolysis. In the stomach, peristalsis churns food with enzymes, water, and hydrochloric acid. Some protein is digested. In the small intestine, food is further digested by more enzymes along with alkaline juices from the liver and pancreas. Food droplets enter the blood through the villi. In the large intestine, water and other materials diffuse into the blood leaving solid waste.
3. On the average, males are larger than females, so they need more energy for movement and body processes.

Page 498

1. When the ventricles contract, the valves to the atria must remain closed to prevent backflow and to get the most efficient pumping of blood into the arteries. When the ventricles relax, the valves to the arteries remain closed to prevent blood from rushing back into the heart from the arteries.
2. Immunizations help the body resist diseases by

causing the production of antibodies that destroy the pathogens that cause those diseases. Recommended immunizations may include polio, rubella, diphtheria, whooping cough, smallpox, measles, tetanus, and mumps.

3. The cardiovascular system pumps blood through the capillaries of the lungs where carbon dioxide is released and oxygen is taken up. The respiratory system provides a moist membrane of large surface area for this exchange to take place. In addition, the rate and depth of breathing is controlled in response to feedback from the cardiovascular system.

Page 505

1. In the kidney nephrons, filtrate collected from the blood is reabsorbed into the blood, leaving wastes that are excreted as urine.
2. At a synapse, an impulse from one neuron causes a chemical to be released. The chemical stimulates an impulse in the neuron on the outer side of the gap.
3. The thyroid gland controls the rate of chemical reactions in the body.
4. a. Although sometimes considered to be an organ of the digestive system, the liver participates in the activity of many body systems.
   b. The liver secretes bile.
   c. Bile is transported to the gallbladder and then pumped into the small intestine.
   d. Bile is used to digest food in the small intestine.

Page 507

1. The uterus develops a thick lining in preparation for the fertilized egg. Ovulation occurs and the egg moves into the oviduct. If fertilization does not occur, the lining of the uterus begins to break down. Menstruation begins. Another egg matures in the ovary and the cycle repeats.
2. Fertilization is the uniting of a sperm and an egg. It occurs in the oviduct.
3. Preventive medicine refers to all the practices that help prevent or minimize health problems. These practices include maintaining a proper diet, exercising regularly, reducing stress, getting regular checkups, promptly seeking help for a health problem, obtaining proper immunizations, and avoiding tobacco and alcohol.
4. Yes. The antibodies in the mother's blood do not cross the placental barrier and enter the bloodstream of the fetus. Generally, only small molecules and ions can diffuse across the membranes that separate the two blood supplies.

Page 509

1. cornea, heart, heart-lung, kidney, lung, bone marrow, liver, pancreas
2. Student answers may vary. Answers should take into account the need to quickly and efficiently find matches between donors and recipients. Perhaps the media could be used to better inform the public of the need for donations.
3. Students' opinions will vary. Students may want to discuss the advantages and disadvantages of having a program controlled by government.

Chapter 23 Review, Pages 510–511

Answers to Applications

1. (1) Eat a balanced diet in proper amounts. (2) Get regular medical and dental checkups. (3) Get all needed immunizations. (4) Avoid drugs such as tobacco and alcohol, as well as illegal drugs. (5) Find ways to reduce stress. Many other answers are possible.
2. Immunizations help keep people from getting contagious diseases. Disease pathogens are parasites. When we prevent the disease, we are preventing the pathogens from using people as hosts in order to reproduce. Without reproduction, the pathogen species may die and the disease be eliminated.
3. Pathogens might be able to get through a wound in the skin in sufficient numbers that the white blood cells could not get rid of them fast enough. The body's first lines of defense may not be effective against some pathogens, especially viruses that are ingested or inhaled. The body's defenses may be weakened because of stress, lack of sleep, illness, and so on. Other answers are possible.
4. Colds and flu are caused by a variety of viruses. Antibodies produced for one type of virus will probably not be effective against a different type.
5. Without sufficient water, the body cannot eliminate enough wastes in urine. Excess salt intake may cause the kidneys to reabsorb too much water into the blood while attempting to maintain salt balance. This, in turn, may cause the blood volume to remain too large causing high blood pressure and fluid accumulation in the tissues.
6. The movement of an impulse along a neuron is electrical. The movement of an impulse across a synapse is chemical.

CHAPTER 24
HEREDITY

Performance Objectives

GOAL: Students will learn the nature of DNA, how DNA is passed to new cells, and the ways that DNA can change.

OBJECTIVES: When asked to respond after completion of the reading and activities, students will

24:1	K	describe genetics and genes.
	A	show interest in learning more about human genetics.
24:2	K	explain how DNA forms the genetic code.
24:3	K	describe the process of mitosis.
24:4	K	describe the process of meiosis.
	P/K	explain the purpose of meiosis.
24:5	K	explain how dominant and recessive genes affect traits.
	P/S	use Punnett squares to predict probable outcomes of simple genetic crosses.
24:6	K	explain how sex of offspring is determined.
	P/K	compare the occurrence of ordinary traits with sex-linked traits.
24:7	K	define mutation.
	P/K	explain how mutations could be beneficial.
	A/K	recognize the importance of minimizing exposure to mutagenic agents.
24:8	A/P	discuss the need for precautions in the use of genetically modified organisms.

Teaching the Chapter

You may wish to purchase a kit for staining root tips to show DNA. Probably some cells will be seen in the midst of mitosis, discussed in **section 24:3.** Follow the instructions provided with the kit. As an alternative, use prepared slides of root tip cells showing mitosis. Likewise, prepared slides showing cells in meiosis may be used with **section 24:4.** Both mitosis and meiosis may be easily modeled using colored pipe cleaners or construction-paper cutouts.

Have students identify whether they have traits noted in Table 24–2. Skill in calculating ratios can be practiced by finding the ratio of those who have a dominant trait to those who have the corresponding recessive trait for each trait in the table for the class.

When discussing the Punnett square shown in the text, substitute other symbols for other pure dominant and pure recessive traits. Have students "solve" Punnett squares for all possible crosses.

Activity, Page 517, How are proteins made in cells?

Four different colors of paper pieces, 12 each, improve the appearance of the model and result in quicker identification of matched base pairs. The process of copying and encoding the information in DNA to mRNA is called transcription. The process of copying and encoding the information in mRNA into amino acid sequences in proteins is called translation.

Answers to QUESTIONS AND CONCLUSIONS

1. Thymine pairs with adenine, and guanine pairs with cytosine in DNA. Uracil pairs with adenine, and guanine pairs with cytosine in mRNA.
2. Because of the many possible combinations of proteins synthesized with DNA's guidance, many different traits are possible.
3. A DNA molecule "unzips." An mRNA molecule forms by base pairing. The mRNA unzips and the DNA molecule is reconstructed. The exposed bases of the mRNA molecule pair with bases of tRNA molecules that have amino acids attached. The chain of amino acids that is formed breaks away from the mRNA and tRNA. The chain of amino acids is a protein. Although there are only four bases, the codes for amino acids are formed of groups of three bases. Many combinations of amino acids are possible. Because DNA molecules are so large, huge varieties of base combinations are possible.

Activity, Page 526 Is red-green color blindness a sex-linked trait?

Before each student carries out assigned interviews, discuss how to make the experiment as controlled as possible. Discuss possible effects of lack of controls. Display each student's tabulated totals for the entire class. You may want to have students compile data from all classes doing the activity.

Answers to QUESTIONS AND CONCLUSIONS

1. Answers will vary according to the sample population. Ideally, about 8% of males and less than 0.5% of females are color blind.
2. Yes. The data should show that males with the trait outnumber females with the trait.
3. Yes. It must be on the X chromosome only. If it were also on the Y chromosome, it would be expressed in the same way as any nonsex-linked trait since every person would have a pair of genes controlling the trait, regardless of sex.
4. Color blindness in males is inherited from the mother. Color-blind females would have to receive one gene from each parent.
5. Answers will vary. Most people who are color blind know that they are.

Skill Inquiry, Page 516

See "The Persistence of Memory," pp. 269–290, of *Cosmos,* by Carl Sagan, Random House, 1980, for further examples of bits of information. For example, the world's libraries together contain perhaps 10^{14} bits of information in words, 10^{15} bits in pictures. Sagan estimates that this is 10^4 times more than the information stored in a set of human genes and 10 times more than in a human brain.

1. 2^{16} or 65 536; $2^{32} = (2^{16})^2$, about 4 295 000 000 or 4.295×10^9
2. About 125 000 bytes or 1.25×10^5 bytes in scientific notation.
$$\frac{1 \times 10^6 \text{ bits}}{8 \text{ bits/byte}} \text{ or } \frac{1\,000\,000}{8} \text{ bytes} = \frac{125\,000}{\text{bytes}}$$
About 625 000 000 bytes or 6.25×10^8 bytes in scientific notation.
$$\frac{5.0 \times 10^9 \text{ bits}}{8 \text{ bits/byte}} \text{ or } \frac{5\,000\,000\,000}{8} \text{ bytes} =$$
625 000 000 bytes
3. The DNA in each human cell has about 62.5 times the information storage capacity of a large computer.
$$\frac{625\,000\,000 \text{ bytes}}{10\,000\,000 \text{ bytes}} = \frac{62.5 \times 10^8}{1 \times 10^7} = 62.5$$

Answers to Review and Reflect

Page 516
1. Student answers will vary. See Table 24-1 on page 514.
2. DNA is a complex spiral-shaped molecule having a long series of base pairs. The bases are adenine, guanine, cytosine, and thymine. The order of these base pairs in each gene forms the code for the manufacture of one protein. In this way, DNA forms the genetic code for an organism's traits.
3. The bases can be arranged in many different orders. In addition, many DNA molecules are hundreds or thousands of base pairs in length. You may want to make an analogy with the letters of the alphabet or the notes of the musical scale being able to form an almost infinite variety of words or music.

Page 521
1. Cells produced by mitosis have the same number of chromosomes and all the kinds of structures contained in the original cell. Cells produced by meiosis have the kinds of structures in the original cell but have only half the chromosomes.
2. The number of chromosomes in each sperm and egg has been reduced to 23 by meiosis. When a sperm fertilizes an egg to form a zygote, the zygote has 46 chromosomes.
3. Genes contain DNA needed to make proteins. Chromosomes are the cell structures that contain the cell's genes.

Page 527
1. In a pair of genes, a dominant gene is one that is always expressed if it is present. A recessive gene is one that is not expressed if a dominant gene is present. Recessive genes are expressed only if both genes of a pair are recessive.
2. Sex is determined by the combination of sex chromosomes. The father can produce sperm with either an X or a Y chromosome. A mother produces eggs with only an X chromosome. Thus, the sex depends on which type of sperm fertilizes the egg.
3. Since the ratio of male to female offspring is about 1:1, males must produce about the same number of X- and Y-chromosome sperm.
4. As a result of a beneficial mutation the organism may be better able to survive environmental conditions, find food, reproduce, or avoid getting killed. A harmful mutation may result in genetic disease or the death of the organism.

Page 529

1. Answers may vary. Students may mention that crop damage could be reduced if Ice Minus is effective, thus providing more food and saving billions of dollars. Ice Minus is not likely to cause environmental damage according to scientists who have studied this possibility. It may make plants healthier. Testing Ice Minus may be the only way to answer the questions about its use.

2. Answers may vary. Students may mention possible destruction of frost-resistant plants and insects, changes in weather and climate, and spread of the bacteria throughout the environment.

3. Answers will vary. Be sure students support their choices with information and logical conclusions.

Chapter 24 Review, Pages 530–531

Answers to Applications

1. The color-blind man would be X_cY. The color-blind woman would be X_cX_c. Therefore, all the children would be color blind regardless of sex.

2. One would expect the number of genetic diseases to increase. Species would change at a greater rate because there would be a greater range of variation.

3. Organisms would be able to adapt to changing environments only within the range of genetic variation that exists now. Without mutation, no new variations would be introduced. This could lead to a reduction in the number of species present on earth. Life might cease to exist.

4.

	H_1	H_2
H_1	$H_1\,H_1$	$H_1\,H_2$
H_2	$H_1\,H_2$	$H_2\,H_2$

The genes that control the hemoglobin development show incomplete dominance. As a result, 25% of the children will be normal, 50% will have the sickling trait—some sickled cells in the blood—and 25% will have the disease in the severe form.

CHAPTER **25**

ECOLOGY

Performance Objectives

GOAL: Students will learn the nature of ecosystems, how they change, and how organisms interact within them.

OBJECTIVES: When asked to respond after completion of the reading and activities, students will

25:1	K	identify features of an ecosystem.
25:2	K	state the characteristics of the major biomes.
	P/K	differentiate between habitat and niche.
25:3	K	describe the general process of succession.
	P/K	differentiate between primary and secondary succession.
25:4	K/S	identify the role of organisms in a food web.
	P	trace the flow of energy through an ecosystem.
25:5	K	describe and name the ways that organisms get food.

25:6	K	list limiting factors for populations.
25:7	K	state reasons for the increase in the human population.
	A/P	discuss the possible problems of continuing growth of the human population.
25:8	K	describe the Antarctic ecosystem.

Teaching the Chapter

Biomes are listed in **section 25:2**. Ecologists do not agree about the exact total number of biomes since biomes have vague boundaries where climates and communities overlap. These blended regions are called ecotones. It is suggested that students be asked to find and list the features of the major biomes shown in Figure 25–2.

Habitats and niches are also discussed in **section 25:2**. It is often said that a habitat is an organism's address while a niche is the organism's profession. After students read the definitions of habitat and niche, ask them why this analogy is used. Students can use library sources to prepare a report on the niche and habitat of an animal that interests them.

Energy transitions within a community are discussed in **section 25:4.** It may be helpful to discuss other systems besides food webs in which useful energy is lost in transformations. Examples can include any simple or complex machine.

Behaviors that aid in an organism's survival are part of the species' niche. They include chemical defense, chemical recognition by animals, chemical defense by plants, mating rituals and patterns, sexual dimorphism (the different appearance of the two sexes). In addition to daily and seasonal biological clocks, some organisms, such as fiddler crabs, have internal clocks in step with lunar phases. Jet lag is evidence of the daily (also called circadian) biological clock in humans. Discuss jet lag, which is a tiredness that occurs in people who travel quickly across a number of time zones. Also discuss the effect of changing at work from a day to a night shift.

Activity, Page 535   What is the density of a population?

Make certain that students first obtain permission to enter areas of study for this activity. Instruct students about proper behavior in outdoor environments. Take proper precautions if there are students who have allergies to pollen and insect bites. If space is limited, students might share ecosystem rectangles and select different trees or shrubs within them. A plot with approximately the area of a classroom floor may be appropriate for shrubs, while a plot several times this size would be best for trees. Discuss sources of error in measuring length and in counting all the members of a population within the plot.

Answers to QUESTIONS AND CONCLUSIONS

1. Population density is the number of organisms in a species living in a given area.
2. Answers may vary. Students may mention rainfall, paved areas, structures, sunlight, etc.
3. Students may mention any rocks, gravel, statues in the aquarium plus the glass walls, temperature, lighting, and so on.
4. The glass walls of the aquarium form the most clear-cut boundaries.
5. Microorganisms exist in both ecosystems.
6. Answers will vary. For example, population density is useful information when changes in environments occur or are planned. Ecologists can determine the environmental effects of the changes and may be able to suggest ways to minimize harmful effects.

7. Architects and city planners can use this information. Population density in a school affects the number of restrooms, size of the cafeteria, number of classrooms, and so on. Population density in cities may affect zoning for residential dwellings, shopping centers, or hospitals.

Activity, Page 541   How does energy flow in ecosystems?

Some students may wish to select an ocean region, such as a continental shelf, abyssal plain, or deep-sea vent region. A deep-sea food web is very different from those most students are familiar with. You could have students research and list the natural limiting factors in the ecosystem they choose. How human activities are affecting the ecosystem could also be considered.

Answers to QUESTIONS AND CONCLUSIONS

1. Answers will vary. Students may mention light, water, and so on.
2. Answers will vary. Higher order consumers require the most organisms to support them.
3. Answers will vary. First-order consumers require the least.
4. Higher-order consumers would be affected since their food supply would be decreased. Producers that were a food source for the first-order consumers may be affected also. Overpopulation may result.
5. Answers will vary. People may be first-, second-, or third-order consumers.

Skill Inquiry, Page 544

The skill table and calculations probably will lead to questions by students on why there are differences in birthrate and death rate. Recent library sources can be used to learn the nature of conditions in the different world areas. After such reading, a class discussion can be worthwhile. Students should defend their opinions and assumptions with evidence.

1. Africa
2. North America, Central and South America
3. Central and South America
4. 8 percent
5. highest—Africa; lowest—Europe
6. 1.6 percent

Answers to Review and Reflect

Page 539

1. Answers may vary. Possible answers include

physical environment: soil, sidewalks, benches; community: grass, squirrels, birds, people.

2. Natural cycles help maintain homeostasis in an ecosystem.

3.

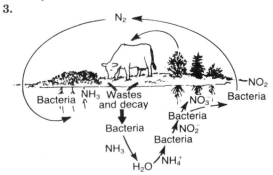

4. The habitat of a squirrel may be a tree. The niche of a squirrel may be as a plant eater.

5. **a.** desert   **c.** grassland
   b. taiga   **d.** tundra

Page 542

1. Answers will vary. Examples are producer—plant; first-order consumer—insect, second-order consumer—bird, third-order consumer—fox, decomposer—bacteria.

2. Predation, scavenging, parasitism

3. More energy is lost when food is transferred from a producer to a second-order consumer than to a first-order consumer. In the corn—people example, people are first-order consumers.

4. Decomposers might perform a larger role in food webs, breaking down all dead things.

5. All three orders of consumers include people. People eat plants, they eat plant-eating animals, and animal-eating animals. As a result, people have more available food sources.

Page 545

1. Answers may vary. For example:
   a. food, water, number of predators
   b. temperature, soil nutrients, sunlight
   c. food, water, space

2. Answers will vary. Examples of mimicry include walking sticks, wasp orchids, and chameleons.

3. People, like other animals, have food, water, and space needs. Unlike other populations, people use their intelligence to adapt the environment to meet their needs.

Page 547

1. There are more than five. Antarctica is the only polar continent. It is covered with a large, thick glacier. Temperatures are very low. Winds blow constantly. The relatively few types of life include lichens, mosses, insects, and penguins.

2. Answers will vary. A study of the currents surrounding Antarctica and past climate records held in ice cores can reveal details about the earth's climate.

3. Answers will vary. Students may say no change because the present situation appears to preserve the ecosystem and provide important scientific information about the earth. Students may say that nations should have some measure of control because it is unfair for only 16 nations to make all the decisions. Students may say that all nations should help control Antarctica, and some of the resources should be used with care because food, energy, and mineral resources are badly needed by people in other parts of the world.

Chapter 25 Review, Pages 548–549

Answers to Applications

1. **a.** rain forest   **b.** tundra
   More energy is available near the equator than at other latitudes. Less energy is available at latitudes near poles than at other latitudes. There are many levels, including deep ground, in which food webs occur in rain forests. There is a very limited surface area for food-web action in the tundra.

2. Blue-green algae, some protists like euglena, and chemosynthetic bacteria such as are found in deep-sea vents are also producers.

3. The garden's other populations eventually would die out. Decomposers are needed to break down dead materials and supply elements and compounds (for example, nitrates) from them to the producers. The nitrogen cycle would be broken.

4. More energy is needed to feed people with meat than with plants. When people eat meat, they are second-order consumers rather than first-order consumers. Ten times as much energy is used by complete meat eaters as by complete vegetarians, if the meat is from animals that only eat plants.

5. Birds mistake the viceroy for a monarch and so avoid it.

UNIT 6   THE INFLUENCE OF SCIENCE

Overview

In chapter 26, students study energy resources and problems associated with their use. Some resources are noted to be nonrenewable, including fossil fuels and nuclear fission sources. Others are noted to be continuous flow, including solar, wind, geothermal, tidal, and hydroelectric. The concept of conserved energy by improved efficiency is discussed. Other methods of conserving energy are described as well. An optional information section considers use of plants to produce energy.

In chapter 27, the problem of wastes is related to growth of technology and increased population. Three general categories of pollution are presented: land pollution, water pollution, and air pollution. Eutrophication, both natural and pollution-caused, is described, noting that pollutant-accelerated eutrophication may be reversed. The concept of pollution chains is introduced and examples are given. Problems with toxic chemicals and hazardous wastes are considered. A major point is made that technology can be used to help solve pollution problems, even though there is no simple solution to pollution. Risk-benefit analysis, marginal cost, and environmental ethics are topics in the closing sections. An optional issue on disposable containers is presented at the end of the chapter.

Chapter 28 opens with the positive and negative effects of technology and urbanization. Natural resources discussed in the sections include minerals, forests, soil, open space, and wildlife. Methods for preserving and conserving these resources are given. The importance of resource management is stressed. An optional information section on tropical rain forests closes the chapter.

Introducing the Unit

Call students' attention to the unit opening photograph, which compares urban and rural areas. Encourage discussion with the following questions. What are some ways that people change the environment? What resources have people used in order to change their environment? How can urban and rural environments be managed so that they do not deteriorate?

It is suggested that the concept of an ecosystem be reviewed, together with conditions that maintain an ecosystem (chapter 25). Discuss how people disrupt and change natural ecosystems. Some questions for discussion are, Do all societies disrupt ecosystems to the same extent? Which societies disrupt ecosystems most? Does technology necessarily mean that an ecosystem deteriorates?

Use the unit opening paragraph and questions to preview the unit and assess students' current knowledge of the concepts that will be presented.

CHAPTER 26
ENERGY RESOURCES

Performance Objectives

GOAL: Students will learn different sources of energy and some problems related to energy use.

OBJECTIVES: When asked to respond after completion of the reading and activities, students will

26:1	A	reflect on ways they use energy.
	K	describe the relationships between standard of living, energy use, and population growth.
26:2	K	identify problems with the use of fossil fuels.
26:3	P	differentiate between nuclear fission and nuclear fusion and the problems/advantages of each.
26:4	K/P	compare and contrast use of solar energy by passive and active methods.
26:5	K	explain how wind energy can be used to produce power.
26:6	K	describe geothermal energy; explain where and how geothermal energy is used.
26:7	K	explain how power is produced

		from falling water and tides; describe problems with hydroelectric and tidal power plants.
26:8	K	define efficiency.
	K	explain how family size affects population increase.
26:9	K	list ways in which energy can be conserved.
	A	take steps to conserve energy when possible.
26:10	K	explain possible uses of plants as energy resources.

Teaching the Chapter

In **section 26:2,** the energy crisis of the 1970s is discussed. Have interested students research newspapers and magazines to find articles describing this energy crisis. Even though the term energy crisis is generally reserved for the period of critical shortages in the 1970s that the text mentions, consider the long-term significance of the energy crisis. You may want to have some students prepare a time line showing events that led to public awareness of an energy crisis in 1973. Additionally, have students continue the time line to include more recent events by researching articles about the energy situation since 1973.

While the class is doing **sections 26:2 and 26:3,** you may want to arrange field trips to local power plants or have representatives visit your class. The safety of nuclear power plants has been a topic of media interest, especially since the Three Mile Island incident. You may want to have students prepare reports or have a debate concerning the pros and cons of nuclear power.

Section 26:9, the energy section, briefly surveys some of the many possibilities for energy conservation. Students could prepare reports using library sources and local government and environmental sources on some aspect of energy conservation, such as transportation or building construction. An additional student activity concerning energy conservation is listing places at school where low-cost retrofitting would save energy. Practical benefit from student analysis may be realized if a composite report about possible conservation measures for the school is submitted to the administration.

Activity, Page 562   What factors affect passive solar heating?

Other variables might also be explored, such as exterior colors (different colors of construction paper), angle of lamplight, design of overhang, and presence of a roof window (use plastic wrap first, then colored cellophane). Make sure that the thermometer is not in direct light when light shines through the window of the model house.

Answers to QUESTIONS AND CONCLUSIONS
1. a. Heating should be greatest with the window side facing the lamp.
   b. Heating should be greatest with the black house.
   c. The overhang should cause heating to be less.
   d. Heating should be reduced with the plant. Buildings may be landscaped with deciduous trees so that in summer heating is reduced and in winter heating is unaffected since the trees lose their leaves.
2. This made the investigation controlled. If one color were tested with the window facing the lamp, while another color was tested with the long nonwindow side facing the lamp, one could not decide whether color or orientation caused the result.
3. Colors other than black and white, oblong orientation, and draperies are other factors students may mention.
4. Sketches will vary. The students should include features studied in this activity and apply them in some way. For instance, large windows in a south direction may be shown.

Activity, Page 569   How does insulation affect the flow of heat?

If the shoe boxes used for the activity on page 562 are used for this activity, it is suggested that the window be covered completely with insulation material. If time permits, the activity could be repeated with students cutting and taping insulation material around the window. As with the first activity, the lamp should not be allowed to shine directly on a thermometer.

Answers to QUESTIONS AND CONCLUSIONS
1. Answers will vary. The material with the highest R-value should be the best insulator. The

lowest temperature inside the house after 10 minutes is the experimental evidence for the conclusion.

2. Results should agree with R-values. If not, look for sources of error, such as the lamp at different distances or shining from different angles.

3. Cost, difficulty/ease of installation, possible hazards in handling or breathing.

4. Tight seals around windows and doors.

5. Answers will vary. If a student says no, the conclusion should be backed up with the evidence that the difference in the two thermometer values in part B was less than 2.5°C. If a student says yes, the conclusion should be backed up with the evidence that the difference in the two thermometer values was more than 2.5°C.

Skill Inquiry, Page 567

Students could use library and government sources to learn ways that different countries' economies are reacting to large population increases and ways that governments of some countries have tried to cope with rapidly increasing populations. If population (on the y axis) is graphed versus time (years on the x axis), students will see an exponential curve, an important illustration.

1. 70/1.7 = 41 years from now (Students should add this to present year date.)

2. 70/3.5 = 20 years (Students should add this to present year date.)

3. For 1: increased or decreased birthrate, increased or decreased death rate
   For 2: increased or decreased population growth rate, increase or decrease in the rate that people use energy

4. The greater the average number of children per family, the less the doubling time is.

5. Since population grows exponentially, it may be compared to an explosion.

Answers to Review and Reflect

Page 556

1. In 1973, OPEC stopped supplying oil to the United States and other countries for a short time. As a result, gasoline became scarce and expensive.

2. Oil, natural gas, and coal are fossil fuels. Fossil fuels are being used up at a rapid rate. Their use has some negative effects on the environment.

3. Removing oil from oil shale and tar sands is costly, requires a lot of energy, and is harmful to the environment. However, in some situations, use of these energy resources may be desirable because these problems are outweighed by other advantages.

4. Students should note that, in addition to use of oil for energy, oil is used to make paving materials for roads, building materials, cosmetics, plastics, fertilizers, medicines, and so on. Answers should reflect this understanding.

Page 561

1. Currently, only nuclear fission produces power. (It is hoped that nuclear fusion will become possible.) A chain reaction splits uranium 235 into neutrons and energy. A loop of pressurized water transfers heat to a steam line that runs a turbine.

2. a. Combustion is incomplete. Sulfur oxides from coal and nitrogen oxides produce acid rain. Smoke and other particles affect breathing and make things dirty.

   b. They produce radioactive wastes. High-level radioactive wastes are particularly dangerous. A meltdown is possible.

   c. A plasma must be kept at a temperature of 40 000 000 K, long enough and in a dense enough state for fusion to occur.

3. Nuclear fission is nonrenewable. There is a limited (finite) amount of uranium 235 in the earth. (Note: uranium 235 can be produced from thorium 232 in special breeder reactors. Other fissionable nuclides can also be bred.) There is an almost unlimited supply of isotopes of hydrogen in oceans and other water for nuclear fusion.

4. Passive does not utilize special collectors, storage units, and circulation systems, while active does.

5. Sketches will vary. Probably the student's home was not designed with passive solar heating in mind. The student may suggest a large window in a south direction or other factors.

Page 565

1. Advantages: All are continuous flow, produce relatively little pollution, are generally efficient. Disadvantages: Cost, geographic limitations, storage.

2. Solar energy would be eliminated. Wind and hydroelectric energy would cease soon after the sun stopped shining. Tidal energy, geothermal energy, fossil fuels, and nuclear energy would still be present.

3. Answers will vary since all energy alternatives have some advantages and disadvantages. Students should support their answers with logical thought.

4. Answers may vary. Students may mention costs, environmental and health hazards, available resources and technology.

Page 568

1. No. The efficiency of any system is always less than 100 percent.

2. The material with the higher R-value has more resistance to heat flow and is a better insulator.

3. Answers will vary. Examples are turning down thermostats, walking, riding with others in a car pool, or turning off lights and appliances when they are not being used.

Page 571

1. Answers may vary. Students should mention the abundance of solid wastes and plant matter. Liquid fuels are emphasized because transportation is a major use of fuels. Methane is also important because natural gas is mostly methane.

2. So that use of nonagricultural land for fuel production by plants will not affect food production

Chapter 26 Review, Pages 572–573

Answers to Applications

1. The long-range reason was the very large rate of increase in energy use—mostly oil, while oil production did not increase as much.

2. Land would need to be flooded. Other environmental considerations may prevent construction of dams. Also, dams of sufficient height to produce power may not be possible. The cost in a certain area might make hydroelectric power unfeasible.

3. Answers may include convincing people to use the system instead of private vehicles, securing investment money to pay for the system (special rails and construction through tunnels and across bridges, as well as the vehicles themselves), obtaining rights-of-way, keeping equipment repaired so service is not interrupted, training safe and courteous operators, preventing crime in vehicles and waiting areas.

4. Since there is more friction near the ground, winds move at a greater speed above ground.

5. According to the Law of Conservation of Energy, energy is not destroyed. However, some energy is always lost as heat and is not usable.

6. Probably small amounts of coal, oil, and natural gas are being made. However, it takes millions of years for the materials to turn into usable fossil fuels.

7. One fission produces more than one neutron. As more fission occurs, the number of neutrons rises rapidly. This causes many more fission reactions.

8. In a fossil fuel power plant, much heat is lost in the gases released to the atmosphere. There is no such heat loss in a hydroelectric plant. Efficiency is a comparison between the energy of the fuel used in a system and the total energy output. Efficiency does not take the cost of a plant and its equipment into account.

CHAPTER 27
ENVIRONMENTAL QUALITY

Performance Objectives

GOAL: Students will learn how the natural environment is being changed by human activities and what can be done to offset the negative effects of changes.

OBJECTIVES: When asked to respond after completion of the reading and activities, students will

27:1	K	identify three major categories of pollution and identify types of each.
27:2	P	compare and contrast natural eutrophication and eutrophication caused by pollutants.
27:3	P	trace the effects in a pollution chain.
27:4	A	adopt a positive approach to pollution problems, recognizing that a variety of technical measures can be used to curb pollution.
	K	describe methods for reducing pollution problems.
27:5	P	apply the meaning of a risk-benefit analysis to a situation in daily

27:6   K   life; apply the meaning of acceptable risk to a nontext example.

list two categories of issues involved in environmental ethics.

P/A   apply the concept of environmental ethics to describe specific ways people can help solve some environmental problems.

27:7   P   compare and contrast different viewpoints concerning deposit legislation.

Teaching the Chapter

Eutrophication is discussed in **section 27:2.** There are different reasons for the death of fish in a polluted lake. Eutrophication is one; acidity and toxic chemicals are others. Encourage students to research magazines and newspapers for information about current issues of water quality. If possible, arrange to visit a water purification plant to find out how area water quality problems are handled.

Many other issues of environmental quality, some of which are mentioned in **section 27:3,** are topics of media interest. Have students make a collection of articles on a particular subject. Try to detect biases in the articles and have a class debate presenting various viewpoints.

Sewage treatment (**section 27:4**) may have several levels of removal and purification. Primary treatment means removal of solids by screening, grinding, flocculation, and sedimentation. Secondary treatment uses biological processes (microorganisms) to degrade and assimilate wastes. Tertiary treatment refers to chemicals added to purify the water. Primary and secondary treatments together remove up to 90 percent of the hazardous organic material. Arrange to tour a local sewage treatment plant. Have students prepare questions in advance to ask the guide.

Some students may enjoy gardening. Have them prepare a chart showing some natural methods of pest control for home gardeners. Many resources are available in local libraries and from the agricultural cooperative extension service in your area. A recommended reference is *Ranger Rick Nature Magazine,* January, 1978. Reprints of the article are available from the National Wildlife Federation, 1412 16th St. NW, Washington, DC 20036.

With **section 27:6,** Environmental Ethics, discuss other issues that involve private versus public benefit. Psychology, political science, anthropology, and economics have been suggested as valuable subjects for environmental decision making. Thus, environmental ethics unite physical, biological, and social sciences.

Activity, Page 580   How do water samples vary?

Water samples for this activity may come from faucets, puddles, streams, oceans, rainwater, distilled or bottled sources, and from known polluted sources. Use appropriate safety measures when gathering the samples and caution students about handling polluted samples. If possible, let a tap water sample stand overnight, loosely covered, to eliminate some of the dissolved oxygen present as it leaves the faucet. Purchase methylene blue solution.

A term not used with this activity, although an important indicator of water quality, is biological oxygen demand, BOD. BOD is the amount of oxygen required for biological decomposition by bacteria in water. It is measured in milligrams per liter of oxygen consumed over five days at 20°C.

Answers to QUESTIONS AND CONCLUSIONS

1. Students should recognize the relationship between oxygen content and dead organic matter. If a sample remained blue for many days, it contained more oxygen than was needed for decay processes. If the oxygen was depleted quickly, the dead organic matter content was high. This high content may be the result of pollution.
2. This prevents oxygen from being absorbed from the air into the methylene blue solution.
3. Any photosynthetic organisms would add oxygen to the water, obscuring the result due to decomposing organisms.
4. Because sewage is organic, the oxygen content would decrease rapidly.
5. The rate of oxygen depletion in the water samples is an indication of the organic nutrient content of the water.
6. Oxygen content is an indication of the health of a waterway. If oxygen content is low, pollution may be a problem.

Activity, Page 586   How should clothes be washed?

Rags are fine for the light-colored cloth if they have not been stained previously. Pieces should be the same size and the same type of material. An extension of this activity is to try different types of material each time activity procedures are followed. Old clothing with composition labels from secondhand stores is an inexpensive source for many types of material. Discuss why the same type of material must be used each time the activity is done as a control so that washing materials can be compared. Remind students that to find the cost per gram of a material, divide the price of a box by the number of grams in it.

Answers to QUESTIONS AND CONCLUSIONS

1. Answers will vary. It is expected that two spoonfuls of phosphate detergent will work best.
2. Answers will vary. It is expected that the more used, the greater the cleaning ability for each material. However, students should notice progressively less improvement in cleaning ability as more of a cleaning material is added.
3. Answers will vary. It is expected that the washing soda will improve the cleaning ability of soap flakes.
4. Disposal of wastewater containing soap might cause rivers, ponds, and oceans to develop foamy surfaces, which is unsightly. Also, soap would promote growth of harmful bacteria in the water.
5. Phosphate detergents might cause unnatural eutrophication in rivers, ponds, and oceans. Fish could die due to depleted oxygen as algae decompose.
6. They clean well, often better than low-phosphate detergents.
7. Answers will vary. A typical answer is the use of low-phosphate or no-phosphate detergent, depending on the cleaning job.

Skill Inquiry, Page 578

Glyphs are often used for medical data, although they also are used in a variety of other professions. If too much information is incorporated into a glyph, the representation becomes too confusing. One recommendation is to use not more than four types of information for a data point on a glyph. Students may wish to apply glyphs to some creative projects. For instance, glyphs could be used to represent the wins or losses of a sports team.

Meanings of weather symbols (left to right): no clouds, cloud cover one tenth or less of sky, two tenths or three tenths, four tenths, five tenths, six tenths, seven tenths or eight tenths, nine tenths or overcast with openings, completely overcast, sky obscured.

1. No noticeable effect at low concentrations of particulates; a noticeable rise in frequency and severity of illness at high (600 micrograms/m^3) concentrations.
2. No noticeable effect at low concentrations of particulates; a sharp rise in illness rates at 500 micrograms/m^3 of SO$_2$; a sharp rise in deaths at 750 micrograms/m^3 of SO$_2$.
3. There is a greater harmful effect on respiratory systems. The two data values at about 50 micrograms/m^3 of SO$_2$ support this answer. The three data values at about 750 micrograms/m^3 of SO$_2$ do not differentiate, as they all show increased deaths.
4. There is a greater harmful effect on respiratory systems. The 4 values for about 100 micrograms/m^3 of particulates support this answer.
5. Student answers will vary. Have students explain how they developed their glyphs.

Answers to Review and Reflect

Page 577

1. More people create more waste.
2. Answers may vary. Major sources of land pollution include garbage and refuse, sludge, mining by-products, industry, and agriculture. Major sources of air pollution include motor vehicles, mining, and industry. Major sources of water pollution include industries, power plants, agriculture, and sewage.
3. Thermal pollution raises the temperature of waterways, creating conditions in which certain moneran populations increase. As a result, decay activity in the water decreases and dissolved oxygen content is lowered. Fewer organisms can survive.

Page 582

1. Eutrophication is the process of adding nutrients to a body of water. Natural eutrophication takes place slowly, over many thousands of years. Pollution-caused eutrophication occurs quickly, possibly within decades; algae populations decompose in vast numbers, lowering the oxygen content of water; fish die.
2. Answers will vary. One example is the production of sulfur oxides and nitrogen oxides by burning fossil fuels. Tall smokestacks scatter the pollutants widely. They combine with water and produce acid rain. Acid rain causes damage to forests, crops, and buildings, and decreases the pH of lakes. Life in lakes is harmed or destroyed.

3. Some food products eaten by people in the United States are imported. Other countries that produce these foods still use DDT. Wildlife in the United States, such as migratory waterfowl, may be affected by DDT use in other countries.

Page 585
1. A catalytic converter is a device on a car that removes a large portion of harmful exhaust gases. Carbon monoxide and hydrocarbons are changed into carbon dioxide and water.
2. Answers will vary. For example, toxic chemicals may leak out of dumps and reach water supplies.
3. Answers will vary. For example, point—smokestacks, dumps; nonpoint—pesticides, fertilizers.
4. Answers should indicate the need for finding out about common insect pests in a locale and effective methods used to reduce problems.

Page 589
1. Using resources while caring for the environment
2. Student answers will vary. Encourage creative thinking. For example, a numerical index rating environmental aesthetics could be used.
3. Many times the acceptable risk in a risk-benefit analysis depends on human attitudes and values. Whether or not a measure or policy will work may depend on how society and politics operate. Other subjects, such as the social sciences, give guidance in these areas.

Page 591
1. a. People should have a free choice; recycling would be more economically effective; antilitter laws would be more effective in stopping litter; many jobs would be lost if a change were made; the consumer would pay more since there would be a need to change equipment; it would take more energy since the bottles have to be washed and trucks use gasoline to return the bottles.

b. Answers will vary. Make sure students support their opinions with logic or data.
2. Litter and garbage costs should be everyone's concern. They cost everyone money in terms of cleanup costs. People still would have a choice based on cost and convenience factors of disposing or returning a container for deposit. Raw materials and energy for manufacturing containers would be conserved.
3. Answers will vary. Students may say yes, because past data show that it would probably reduce pollution. Point out the private versus public benefit.

Chapter Review, Pages 592–593
Answers to Applications
1. Answers will vary. Students may suggest paying people for recycled products or offer other incentives, such as prizes or trips.
2. Answers will vary. Students might name smokestacks and dumps as point sources and pesticides and fertilizers as nonpoint sources. They should be as specific as possible. Students should discuss ways to reduce pollution discussed in the text, being specific wherever possible.
3. First, the nutrients (pollutants) are reduced. Second, the algae population is reduced. Third, the oxygen level goes up. As a result, more fish can live in the water.
4. Answers will vary. One example is to use products longer. Another is to walk more, use public transportation, or ride in car pools.
5. Answers will vary. Lists of benefits should derive from the high salary. Lists of risks should include the likelihood of hazards to health. Many students may consider doing something to dispose of hazardous wastes as a benefit for themselves and all of society.
6. Answers will vary. Possibly students will be critical of present management. Have them suggest alternatives.

CHAPTER 28
RESOURCE MANAGEMENT

Performance Objectives
GOAL: Students will learn the nature and importance of some natural resources and problems of their use.

OBJECTIVES: When asked to respond after completion of the reading and activities, students will

28:1   K   identify the meaning and effects of urbanization.

28:2	K	list features of the environmental impact of using mineral resources; list solutions to some of these problems.
28:3	K	describe forest management techniques that help to produce a sustained yield.
28:4	K	explain why open spaces have value.
	A	avoid abuse of recreational areas and other open spaces.
28:5	P	compare and contrast soil types and soil uses.
	P	select the best soil conservation method(s) for a given purpose.
28:6	K	describe active strategies of wildlife management.
28:7	S	prepare a resource management plan that uses a variety of procedures to minimize environmental damage.

Teaching the Chapter

When **section 28:2,** Mineral Resources, is studied, review the concepts of activity at plate boundaries, the formation of igneous and sedimentary rocks, and the meaning of weather and erosion (unit 4). Also, review some of the elements in seawater that become mineral resources.

When **section 28:3** is studied, invite a forestry person to discuss forest management techniques with the class, and include some forestry career.

With **section 28:4,** discuss parks the students may have visited. Ask when they went and if conditions were crowded or uncrowded. Have them tell about any evidence of pollution they experienced.

If you live in a rural area, invite a farmer or agricultural extension agent to visit your class and talk about soil conservation methods when **section 28:5** is studied. Or, arrange for the class to visit a farm where several soil conservation methods are in use. You might also want to include information about pest control (chapter 27).

In relation to **section 28:7,** students could interview government or industry resource management workers, preparing reports about management techniques and specific problems. Management of the earth as a whole could be considered.

Activity, Page 596   How can stress be reduced?

If a stressful event has ever affected the people of your area (tornado, flood, earthquake), add it to the list of situations in Procedure step 1. Be attentive to students' reactions to the list of stressful situations. Discuss being tactful in the interviewing process since this activity deals with some sensitive issues. Advise students to use only willing subjects and to make certain that questions and answers are rendered in a serious manner. Advise students to use numbers instead of names on records of subject data. The *Teacher Resource Book* contains interview forms that can be copied, ten for each student.

Answers to QUESTIONS AND CONCLUSIONS

1. Answers will vary.
2. No. Some situations may cause "happy stress," perhaps traveling for a vacation.
3. Some causes of stress today, such as automobile accidents, did not exist in the past. Conversely, some causes of stress in the past do not exist today. For example, fears of children getting polio have been nearly eliminated.
4. Some stress, such as the death of a close friend, might have occurred in the past as well as in the present.
5. Answers will vary. Bicycles or exercise equipment may be used.
6. People often use the natural environment—open spaces and scenic places—as a respite from the pressures of their daily routine.
7. When a person recognizes that there is or is not a way to affect the situation, this is the first step in adapting to the stress. Next, the person can devote energy to accepting or changing the situation, less hampered by feelings of guilt for something he/she could not control.
8. Answers will vary. A student might say that the plan would be discussing a way to avoid as much stress as possible by taking particular actions and recognizing control or lack of control.

Activity, Page 608   How can resources be managed?

Before 1906, deer of the Kaibab Plateau were hunted by native Americans of the area. Pioneers did a small amount of hunting as well. In the late 1800s, at least 200 000 sheep, 20 000 cattle, and some horses purposely were grazed on the Kaibab, depleting vegetation. By 1906, restrictions had greatly reduced numbers. It is thought, however, that more animals were grazing on the Kaibab than those officially permitted. As the deer population rose, the grazing animals were an additional burden to the Kaibab ecosystem. Sheep grazing finally was eliminated within the National Forest boundary in 1945. Reports for this activity may be written or oral. If oral, discussion by the entire class may accompany presentations.

Answers to QUESTIONS AND CONCLUSIONS

1. The predator-prey relationships among the deer and coyotes, mountain lions, bobcats, and wolves
2. Killing the region's predators—coyotes, mountain lions, bobcats, and wolves; hunting beginning in 1929; building fences; building access roads; raising livestock on the range.
3. In this project, the natural controls for the deer, the predators, were eliminated without regard to where the increased number of deer would get food. The amount of vegetation required per deer and the number of deer killed by predators were key factors in the outcome.
4. Starvation, malnutrition, disease, and hunting
5. Although some people object to hunting deer as cruel, hunting in season is an important limiting factor when predators have been eliminated.
6. Answers will vary. Students should recognize that once people interfere in some way, they must keep interfering in order to maintain some populations.

Skill Inquiry, Page 611

Students may be confused by the terms qualitative and quantitative. Review the meanings of the terms as described in chapter 2. Remembering that quantitative refers to "quantities" is sometimes helpful. Discuss examples of qualitative and quantitative data gathered in activities done throughout the text.

1. Figure a is qualitative. Figure b is quantitative.
2. Figure a shows that, overall, between 1970 and 1985, wildlife, soil, open space, minerals, and forests are declining in terms of environmental quality. Air and water quality are improving. Figure b shows that in 1978, about 16 billion dollars were spent for air pollution control, 18 billion dollars for water pollution control, and

10.5 billion for solid waste pollution control.
3. Qualitative diagrams are useful when quantitative data is not available or one only wants to show trends, and exact values are not needed. A quantitative graph is preferred when exact values are needed.

Answers to Review and Reflect

Page 600

1. Many natural cycles have been stressed to their limit.
2. Increases in population with accompanying advances in technology have led to greater demands on these resources.
3. The mass of the pollutants is reduced. The pollution resulting from processing the materials from their original sources is reduced also.
4. Tree farms usually contain just one or a limited species of trees. Pests that begin affecting the trees can easily spread to other trees of the same species. In this way, most of the tree farm is affected. In a natural forest, other tree species that are not affected by the pests separate the trees that pests affect. The spread of the problem may be reduced.

Page 605

1. Open spaces contain timber, minerals, and fossil fuels. Many of these places are national parks, wildlife refuges, and wilderness areas. Natural beauty found in open spaces is important to human nature. Soil is the source of nutrients for land plants, such as crops, grasses, and trees. Farmlands supply food for people. Forests provide additional resources.
2. a. By wind and precipitation. Sheet wash by rain occurs over flat as well as sloped land. Gullying takes place on sloped land when it rains.
   b. Contour farming, strip cropping, planting with crop rotation, damming gullies, and using windbreaks can prevent soil erosion.
3. Answers will vary. Examples might be limiting entry to a first-come basis, charging a fee to enter as well as other fees for specific uses, or increasing the supervision of park use.
4. Earthworms break up soil by burrowing through it (physical change). They add organic compounds as they pass the soil through their bodies (chemical change). The texture, porosity, permeability, and pH can change with much earthworm action.

5. Leaching

Page 611

1. Habitats have been destroyed. Pesticides contaminate the air, water, and food needed by wildlife. People have killed animals for food, in sport, and as pests.

2. Answers will vary. Some things to be considered include how the land was used before strip mining, whether the land could be returned to its original use, what the cost of reclamation would be, the value of the coal to be removed, the habitats of plants and animals that would be affected and how severely.

3. Answers will vary for both a and b. Possibilities for a are contour farming, strip cropping, crop rotation, windbreaks. Possibilities for b are how to handle vegetation along roadways or construction of the Trans-Alaska oil pipeline.

4. Answers will vary. One answer might be that there are trees, grass, birds, and small mammals (squirrels, rabbits, groundhogs).

Page 613

1. Tropical forest trees have roots that protect (hold) soil and help prevent floods. Once destroyed, the tropical forest trees and wildlife will disappear for a very long time.

2. Better use of cut wood for cooking and heating; preservation of wood used for homes; new ways to use different species of trees, such as in papermaking; promoting the environment that aids a species or raising a species; using previously unused species for food and planting crops in optimum amounts and patterns adjacent to and within the forests

3. Answers will vary. Students might point out the need for educating the public, for example.

Chapter 28 Review, Pages 614–615

Answers to Applications

1. Sometimes one procedure alone cannot accomplish as much as the use of a combination of procedures.

2. Samples of water from the ground at the site of the strip mine could be compared with polluted water to see if the pollutants are the same. If they are, water that flows between the mine and the site of the water in question could be checked at various points. The water should show a greater dilution the farther it is from the mine. Water in directions not draining from the mine should be checked also to show that no mine pollutants are present. If they are, it is probably that another source is polluting the water.

3. In Europe, the land has been farmed for thousands of years. Small-scale soil conservation methods are practiced on small plots of land. All farmland in Canada and the United States has come into production within the last few hundred years. Too often soil conservation methods have not been practiced.

4. Cattle are first-order consumers, eating grasses, which are producers. There is a reduction of about 10 times the food value for this one step in the food chain.

5. A soil survey will provide information about how well the ground will support a house. The survey will show the range of heights of the water table and the soil permeability, which indicates whether the land is subject to flooding. The slope of the land will show how fast and which way rain and melting snow will run off. If the family wants a garden, features of humus in topsoil, certain minerals, and a clay with sand texture will be sought. Depth of soil to bedrock is important in deciding a location if a basement and/or swimming pool is desired.

6. If the environment and resources are conserved through resource management, everyone has a better environment and more resources potentially available than if poor decisions are made. The beneficial effect may be felt even more by people in the future than by people living now.

7. Answers will vary. Students might say that they would accept the clearcutting first because they want more money. They might say they would accept selective cutting each time because selective cutting would preserve more habitats for wildlife.

Teacher Questionnaire

Perhaps one of the best ways to ensure that effective educational materials are produced is to let authors and publishers know how you feel concerning the ones you are using. Please help us in our planning of revisions and new programs by completing and returning the form found on the next page. After removing the questionnaire from the book, fold and staple it so that the address label shows. We would certainly appreciate hearing from you.

MERRILL GENERAL SCIENCE

Circle the number which corresponds most nearly to your opinion of each of the following items of this general science program. Please also star (*) three factors which most influence your choice of a text.

	Excellent	Very Good	Satisfactory	Fair	Poor	Comments
Pupil's Edition						
1. Format	1	2	3	4	5	_____
2. Readability	1	2	3	4	5	_____
3. Approach	1	2	3	4	5	_____
4. Organization	1	2	3	4	5	_____
5. Factual accuracy	1	2	3	4	5	_____
6. Coverage of science principles	1	2	3	4	5	_____
7. Concept development	1	2	3	4	5	_____
8. Visual impact	1	2	3	4	5	_____
9. Margin notes	1	2	3	4	5	_____
10. Treatment of new terms	1	2	3	4	5	_____
11. Activities	1	2	3	4	5	_____
12. Problems	1	2	3	4	5	_____
13. Tables	1	2	3	4	5	_____
14. Illustrations	1	2	3	4	5	_____
15. Review and Reflect	1	2	3	4	5	_____
16. Career Profiles	1	2	3	4	5	_____
17. Skill Inquiries	1	2	3	4	5	_____
18. Information/Choices sections	1	2	3	4	5	_____
19. Appendixes	1	2	3	4	5	_____
20. Glossary	1	2	3	4	5	_____
21. Index	1	2	3	4	5	_____
Teacher's Annotated Edition						
1. Teachability	1	2	3	4	5	_____
2. Planning Guide	1	2	3	4	5	_____
3. Equipment and Supplies Information	1	2	3	4	5	_____
4. Laboratory Safety section	1	2	3	4	5	_____
5. Performance Objectives	1	2	3	4	5	_____
6. Computer Software information	1	2	3	4	5	_____
7. Audiovisual information	1	2	3	4	5	_____
8. Career information	1	2	3	4	5	_____
9. Unit-by-unit materials	1	2	3	4	5	_____
10. Chapter-by-chapter materials	1	2	3	4	5	_____
11. Annotations	1	2	3	4	5	_____
12. Tint block answers	1	2	3	4	5	_____
Teacher Resource Book						
1. Basic Skills masters	1	2	3	4	5	_____
2. Teaching masters	1	2	3	4	5	_____
3. Activity Worksheets	1	2	3	4	5	_____
4. Challenge masters	1	2	3	4	5	_____
5. Science and Society masters	1	2	3	4	5	_____
6. Evaluation materials (reviews, tests, evaluations)	1	2	3	4	5	_____

School Information

1. Grade level of students	9		10	11	12
2. Total number of students enrolled in general science	1–50		51–100	101–200	200+
3. Average class size	25 or less	26–30	31–35	36–40	41 or more
4. Total school enrollment	1–200		201–500	501–1000	1000+
5. Locale of school	rural		small town	suburban	large city
6. Ability level of class	below average		average		above average
7. Appropriateness of text for your class	easy		about right		difficult
8. Number of years text used	0	1	2	3	4
9. May we quote you?	yes				no

Please feel free to enclose an additional sheet to make further comments.

Name _____ Date _____

School _____ City _____ State _____ Zip _____

- -

Fold

- -

Fold

MERRILL
GENERAL SCIENCE

TEACHER'S ANNOTATED EDITION

AUTHORS

Richard H. Moyer
University of Michigan–Dearborn, Michigan
Jeanne E. Bishop
Westlake Public Schools–Westlake, Ohio

Content Consultants

Dr. Philip E. Barnhart, Associate Professor of Physics and Astronomy
    Otterbein College, Westerville, Ohio
Dr. Orin G. Gelderloos, Professor of Biology and Environmental Studies
    University of Michigan–Dearborn, Michigan
Robert C. Smoot, Science Department Chairman and Chemistry Teacher
    McDonogh School, McDonogh, Maryland
Dr. Sidney E. White, Professor of Geology
    The Ohio State University, Columbus, Ohio

CHARLES E. MERRILL PUBLISHING COMPANY
A Bell & Howell Company
Columbus, Ohio
Toronto   London   Sydney

A MERRILL SCIENCE PROGRAM

MERRILL GENERAL SCIENCE
MERRILL GENERAL SCIENCE: Teacher's Annotated Edition
MERRILL GENERAL SCIENCE: Teacher Resource Book

Dr. Richard H. Moyer is Associate Professor of Science Education at the University of Michigan–Dearborn. He received a B.S. in Chemistry and Physics Education and an M.S. in Curriculum and Instruction from the University of Wisconsin, and an Ed.D in Science Education from the University of Northern Colorado. With more than 16 years of elementary, secondary, and college teaching experience, he is currently involved in teacher training and environmental education. In 1983, he received the University of Michigan–Dearborn Distinguished Faculty Award. He is a member of the State Superintendent's Study Committee for Science Education and general editor of the Michigan Educational Assessment Program (MEAP) in Science. Dr. Moyer conducts numerous workshops and inservice training programs for teachers and is a coauthor of Merrill's *Accent on Science* program.

Dr. Jeanne E. Bishop is Planetarium Director and Science Teacher for Westlake Public Schools, Westlake Ohio. She received a B.S. in Comprehensive Science and Mathematics Education from Kent State University, an M.S. in Secondary Education from the University of Pittsburgh, and a Ph.D in Secondary Education from the University of Akron. She has taught science for 20 years and has received first-place STAR and Ohaus Awards of the National Science Teachers Association, the Distinguished Service Award of the Mid-Atlantic Planetarium Society, and the Master Teacher Award of the Martha Holden Jennings Foundation. In 1984–85, Dr. Bishop served as President of the International Planetarium Society. She is a consultant for other Merrill science programs and is coauthor of Merrill's *Focus on Earth Science Review and Reinforcement Guide.*

Reading Consultants
Dr. Judith Doyle, Physics Teacher, Newark High School, Newark, Ohio
David R. Urbanski, Assistant Head–Business and Technology Division, Public Library of Columbus and Franklin County, Columbus, Ohio

Safety Consultant
Franklin D. Kizer, Council of State Science Supervisors, Lancaster, Virginia

Reviewers
Betty S. Abernathy, Chemistry and Physics Teacher, Fike High School, Wilson, North Carolina
Gerald J. Garner, Secondary Science Specialist, Los Angeles Unified School District–Science Materials Center, Van Nuys, California

Larry E. Hess, Science Department Chairman, Ephrata High School, Ephrata, Pennsylvania
Richard V. Knapik, Science Supervisor, Milwaukee Public Schools, Milwaukee, Wisconsin
Dr. James H. Luckey, Jr., Science Consultant, Memphis City Schools, Memphis, Tennessee
William J. Mandara, Science Coordinator (Grades 7–12), Clifton Schools, Clifton, New Jersey
Dr. Donald E. Michel, Supervisor of Science, Math, and Social Studies (7–12), Muncie Community Schools, Muncie, Indiana
Dr. Iraj M. Nuban, Science Department Chairperson, McClatchy High School, Chemistry and Physics Instructor, Sacramento City College, Sacramento, California
Marianne Kay Wilson, Secondary Science Coordinator (7–12), Pulaski County Special School District, Little Rock, Arkansas

Project Editor: Michele J. Wigginton; *Editors:* Francis R. Alessi, Jr., Mary Beth Gallant, Robert Davisson; *Project Designer:* Joan Shaull; *Illustrators:* Intergraphics, Tasa Graphic Arts, Inc., Vantage Art, Inc.; *Photo Editor:* Elaine Comer Shay; *Production Editor:* Janice Wagner

Cover photo: Comstock
The cover photograph represents the interrelationship of physical, earth, and life science. General science encompasses knowledge of life, the earth, and physical processes of the universe. Yet, science is a dynamic process, not a static body of knowledge. The search for understanding continues.

ISBN 0-675-07687-0
Published by
CHARLES E. MERRILL PUBLISHING COMPANY
A BELL & HOWELL COMPANY
Columbus, Ohio 43216
Copyright 1986 by Bell & Howell Company

Printed in the United States of America

Preface

MERRILL *GENERAL SCIENCE* is designed to meet the needs of today's high school students. The text emphasizes practical applications of science to an ever-increasing technological society. It helps make students aware of some of the ways in which science and technology influence their daily lives as well as their future careers.

Recently, the Conference on Goals for Science and Technology Education of the National Science Foundation published a report in which it recommends that science curricula in grades 9 through 11 should emphasize "the application of science and technology to the improvement of community, local and national." MERRILL *GENERAL SCIENCE* has been developed to help further this goal in science education.

MERRILL *GENERAL SCIENCE* is interdisciplinary, covering concepts of physical science, space and earth science, and life science. Students are introduced to an overview of science and technology in Unit One. The use of the processes of science by the scientist as well as the nonscientist is presented. Units Two through Five are devoted to the study of chemistry, physics, space and earth science, and life science, respectively. Within each unit, the interrelationships among these sciences are reinforced, especially in terms of practical applications. Unit Six, the last unit of MERRILL *GENERAL SCIENCE*, integrates many of the concepts presented in earlier units with a study of our relationship to the environment.

Many student aids to learning appear throughout MERRILL *GENERAL SCIENCE*. Each unit begins with a photograph, brief overview, and questions designed to motivate student interest in the chapters that follow. A chapter-opening photograph and introductory paragraph help students relate familiar experiences to the content of the chapter. A goal statement identifies the major objective of each chapter. Margin notes throughout the chapter and Review and Reflect questions at the ends of sections improve reading comprehension.

Two activities in each chapter provide experiences that emphasize scientific processes and improve students' understanding of concepts. Career Profiles help students understand the importance of studying science in preparation for a variety of technical and nontechnical careers. Skill Inquiries present the application of science skills beyond the classroom. The Information or Choices section at the end of each chapter provides optional material for study of an additional science concept of a current event.

Each Chapter Review includes a summary, vocabulary list with a related exercise, and questions for self-assessment of understanding. Student investigations and reading material are suggested for further study. At the end of the textbook, the Appendices, Glossary, and Index complete the many learning aids.

To The Student

MERRILL *GENERAL SCIENCE* is designed to prepare you to live in a world in which science and technology are becoming increasingly important. At no other time in history has it been more important to understand basic concepts of science and how they relate to technology and society. Whether you plan a career in a science-related field or not, understanding science and its applications is vitally important as well as interesting.

Knowing how to use your text will help you in your study of science. Each unit begins with a photograph, a discussion, and questions that preview what you will study in the chapters that follow. Each chapter begins with a photograph and brief paragraph that will show you the importance of science in your world. A GOAL statement at the beginning of each chapter lets you know what you are expected to learn from the chapter. Throughout a chapter, vocabulary words appear in boldface type. Blue margin notes highlight the main points in each section. REVIEW AND REFLECT questions will help you to check your understanding of the previous sections.

In the CHAPTER REVIEW, a SUMMARY provides a list of the main points in the chapter. Listed in blue is the number of the section in which each point was discussed. The boldface words in the chapter are listed as VOCABULARY. A vocabulary exercise helps you check your knowledge of the meanings of the terms. The Chapter Review also includes QUESTIONS. MAIN IDEAS questions check how well you recall the main points of the chapter. APPLICATIONS questions require you to apply what you learned in practical ways. FURTHER STUDY provides ideas for INVESTIGATIONS and READINGS that you might do on your own or for extra class credit.

The APPENDICES provide information to help you understand science. Safety and first aid guidelines are presented in Appendix B. The GLOSSARY lists definitions of all the boldface words in the text. The INDEX is useful for locating information on specific topics.

Contents

Activities

THE TOOLS OF SCIENCE

Unit One focuses on the tools that scientists use to learn about the world. For example, measurement is an important tool. People use measurements to compare objects, assign values, and so on. All of the heads of lettuce in a market may be the same price. You probably would buy the largest one you could find. Oranges may be sold by the kilogram. So, a ten kilogram bag of oranges would be priced higher than a five kilogram bag of oranges. In this unit, you will learn how scientists use measurements and other tools of science.

1. How did different systems of measurement originate?
2. What system of measurement do scientists use?
3. What is scientific notation?
4. What methods do scientists use to solve problems?
5. How do scientists design experiments?
6. How are laws and theories developed?

3

HAVE you ever worked on a group project? If you have you know how important organization is. Building a parade float requires the organization and measurement of supplies. Organization and measurement are required in many daily activities and in scientific activities as well. What are the methods of scientific measurement? How do scientists organize information?

MEASUREMENT IN SCIENCE

INTRODUCING THE CHAPTER   Call students' attention to the chapter opening photograph. Some students may have helped build a parade float. Let students suggest other group projects they have worked on in which measurement and organization were important. Relate these skills to activities of daily living. Have students list as many ways that they regularly use measurement as they can think of.

1:1 Studying Science

What is science and why should you study it? The word science comes from the Latin word, *scire*, which means to know. What is known about the universe is called science. The methods of obtaining knowledge about the universe are called science, too. What is known about the universe often changes as new information is obtained. Science is an ongoing process.

One reason to study science is because it is so interesting! Since early times, people have been curious about the universe. They have sought answers to their questions. People are still asking questions. Perhaps you have wondered why the sky is blue. Or, why does the sun set in the west? How do birds know when to fly south for the winter, and how do they find their way? Is there life elsewhere in the universe? Keep in mind that science is an organized method of answering questions.

The application of science to everyday situations is called **technology**. Sometimes technology is called applied science. Technology greatly affects people's lives. The influence of technology in our lives has been increasing rapidly in recent years. This influence is another important reason to study science.

GOAL   You will learn how scientists quantify the properties of objects and use standardized methods of measurement.

What are science and technology?

b
d

FIGURE 1–1. Vacuum tubes (a) were once used in computers (b). The development of integrated circuits (c) has led to the use of much smaller and faster micro-computers (d).

BACKGROUND In about 10 years, the cost of common calculators has dropped by about a factor of 10.

Why is studying science and technology important?

The rapid change in technology can be seen in many examples, such as the growth in the computer industry. The first electronic computer was developed in the 1940s. It had vacuum tubes, was very large, and was quite slow by today's standards. The development of the transistor in the 1950s made much smaller computers possible. More recently, scientists have produced integrated circuits, tiny silicon chips containing many electronic parts. Compare the sizes of the vacuum tube and the integrated circuit in Figure 1-1.

Often as technology advances, costs are reduced. The first computers were quite expensive and only a few large companies had them. Today, calculators, video games, and home computers are quite common and inexpensive.

Everyone needs to have a general understanding of how science and technology affect our lives. People are being asked to make more and more decisions on issues relating to science and technology. As a consumer, you are faced with decisions about which brand of product to buy. For example, you may decide to buy organic shampoos even though they may cost more than other shampoos. As a future homeowner, you may have to decide between the expense of adding more insulation or paying high heating bills. As citizens, people are asked to vote on issues such as nuclear waste disposal and wildlife preservation. With an understanding of science, you will be able to make intelligent decisions on issues such as these.

See Teacher's Guide.

Career Profile

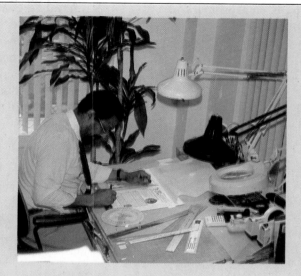

In a hallway near the lunchroom of Champion Junior High School in Columbus, Ohio, hangs a photograph of William Frost. This "Hallway of Champions" as it is called, honors those graduates who have gone on to great career achievement. Bill Frost has been the president of Dimensions and Directions Limited for 13 years. It is a service organization for publishers in New York City.

As a high school student Bill recognized his talent for drawing realistic art. After graduation he entered what is now the Columbus College of Art and Design. Later in the military service he took correspondence courses in art. When his tour of duty was completed, Bill entered The Ohio State University as a commercial art major. For about 10 years after earning his degree, Bill worked as a graphic designer for several publishing companies. During this period he also moved to New York City, got married, and began Dimensions in his apartment. Today, Bill employs nine people in a building near Park Avenue. Recently, Bill began Frost Publishing Group Limited, which has allowed him to develop his own products.

Bill must be very careful about using measurement tools in his work. To draw a line illustration, he uses a regular ruler. When measuring type size or deciding how many lines of type will fit in a space, a special ruler marked in tiny units called points is needed. The width and depth of the type page are measured with a ruler marked in pica units. If a photograph or piece of art needs to be reduced, Bill uses a proportion wheel to measure the percentage of reduction necessary. Though his design work is very creative, none of Bill's creations would be useful if they did not fit on the page.

1:2 Why Measure?

Measurements are an important part of many decisions you make. For example, most items you buy are measured. What size shoe do you wear? What size are your blue jeans? Many food products come in different size containers and sell at different prices. The largest container usually is most economical, but not always. Unit pricing in supermarkets helps people determine which size is actually the most economical.

Why is measurement important?

Almost everything you use and everything you do involves some kind of measurement. Your science class is measured in several ways. It probably meets at the same time each day and for the same length of time. Time is a form of measurement. Life would be very confusing if we did not measure things. No advances in science and technology could be made without accurate, precise measurements.

See Teacher's Guide.

REVIEW AND REFLECT

1. How is technology different from science?
2. List three ways technology has changed travel in the past 100 years.
3. Why use measurement?

ACTIVITY   Have students measure various objects in the classroom using the units in Figure 1–2.

Why are standards of measurement developed?

FIGURE 1–2. Some early units of measurement have interesting origins.

1 cubit = length of forearm

1 inch = 3 barley corns end-to-end

1 yard = distance from king's nose to fingertips

1:3 Standards of Measurement

In order for measurements to have meaning, standards are developed. **Standards** of measurement are the basis of evaluating objects in terms of length, mass, weight, and other properties. Units are names that describe standards. For example, meter is the unit that describes a standard length.

Making units of measurement uniform is very important. In other words, everyone must use the same size unit to measure an item. For example, if you wear a size 8 shoe, you expect that most size 8 shoes will fit you. Shoe manufacturers have a uniform system of measuring shoes. Shoes are measured in units different from the units used to measure soft drinks. You cannot mix different units of measurement.

In early times, people made measurements with objects that were handy. The foot was useful for measuring distance. The cubit was a unit of length based on the forearm. Some early units of measure are shown in Figure 1–2.

One problem with these early units of measurement was that they were not uniform. While everyone's forearm was likely to be longer than their foot, not everyone had the same size forearms or feet! Another problem was that these early units do not relate to one another. How many feet are in a cubit? Converting from one unit to another was difficult, if not impossible.

Today, most countries in the world have agreed on a standard system of measurement. This system is known as the International System of Units. It is usually abbreviated as **SI**. This abbreviation stands for the French name, le d'Unités Système International. SI is based on the **metric** system, which began in France in the 1790s. Most, but not all, metric units and SI units are the same. In some cases, different units are used. For example, units for temperature in SI and the metric system are different.

1:4 Linear Measurement

Linear measurement is the measurement of length. The standard unit for linear measurement in SI is the meter, m. The word meter comes from the Greek word, *metron,* which means a measure. The French intended for the meter to be one ten-millionth of the distance from the North Pole to the equator. Problems developed with this early calculation of the meter. So, a bar of a platinum alloy was made to be the length of a standard meter. The original bar is kept in France at the International Bureau of Weights and Measures. A similar bar is kept in the United States at the National Bureau of Weights and Measures. Since the meter bars are affected by changes in the environment, a new standard for the meter has been developed. The length of the meter is now based on the distance traveled by light in a vacuum during $1/2.997\,924\,58 \times 10^8$ second. This standard is not affected by environmental changes.

In order to become familiar with SI measurement, think in terms of metric units. To give you an idea of the size of a meter, most doorknobs are about one meter above the floor. Most people are less than two meters tall.

In order to measure smaller lengths, the meter is subdivided into smaller units. One major advantage of the metric system is that all of the units measuring the same property are related to each other by a factor of 10. The relationships can be seen in Table 1–1. A meter can be

FIGURE 1–3. Many businesses in the United States are converting all of their measurements to SI units. For example, most new automobiles are designed with metric-sized parts. This conversion will help American industries sell their goods worldwide. The Common Market in Europe will import only goods that are measured in SI units.

What is linear measurement and what is its standard unit in SI?

BACKGROUND   More than 95% of the people in the world use SI units for measurement. Appendix A summarizes SI units.

How many dm are in one m?

divided into 10 equal parts called decimeters, dm. The prefix *deci-* means one tenth. A decimeter is one tenth of a meter.

TABLE 1–1.   LINEAR METRIC UNITS
1 meter, m = 0.001 kilometer, km
1 meter, m = 10 decimeter, dm
1 meter, m = 100 centimeters, cm
1 meter, m = 1000 millimeters, mm

How many cm are in one m?

A centimeter is obtained by dividing the decimeter into ten equal parts. The prefix *centi-* means one-hundredth. One hundred centimeters are in a meter. The centimeter is a very common metric unit. The width of your smallest fingernail is about one centimeter. The pages in this book are about 18 centimeters wide.

How are the prefixes *milli-* and *kilo-* different?

The smallest unit on most metric rulers is the millimeter, mm. The prefix *milli-* means one thousandth. One thousand millimeters are in one meter. A dime is about one millimeter thick.

The kilometer, km, is used to measure long distances. The prefix *kilo-* means one thousand. A kilometer contains one thousand meters.

ACTIVITY   You may wish to have students measure their heights in SI units. It is very important *not* to have students convert between metric and English units of measure at this time.

You may already be somewhat familiar with SI measurement from other science classes. You may have used SI in other situations, too. For example, some cameras use

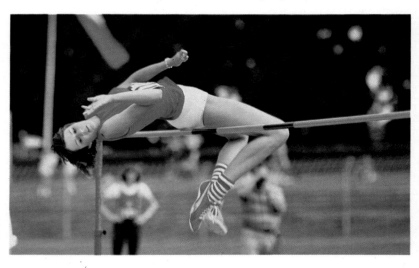

FIGURE 1–4.   Precise linear measurements are important in determining the winners in Olympic competition.

35 mm film. This type film is 35 mm wide. Skis are usually measured in centimeters. International sporting events, like the Olympic Games, are conducted using SI measurements. The prefixes commonly used in SI and metric measurement are listed in Table 1–2. These prefixes are not only applicable to linear measurement. They are used when measuring volume, area, mass, and other units as well.

All of the units used to measure length in SI are related by a factor of ten. Therefore, changing from one unit to another is quite simple. Suppose you want to change from a larger unit to a smaller unit. You *multiply* the number of larger units by the number of smaller units in one of the larger units. If you want to change from smaller units to larger units, you *divide* the number of smaller units by the number of smaller units in one of the larger units.

TABLE 1–2. COMMON SI PREFIXES	
milli	1/1000
centi	1/100
deci	1/10
deka	10
hecto	100
kilo	1000

How are all SI units related to each other?

EXAMPLES: Metric Conversions

Problem: An object is 3 cm long. How many millimeters long is it?

Solution: Since 10 mm (small unit) are in 1 cm (larger unit), multiply the number of centimeters by 10.

$$1 \text{ cm} = 10 \text{ mm}$$
$$3 \text{ cm} \times 10 \text{ mm/cm} = 30 \text{ mm}$$

Problem: How many meters are in 700 cm?

Solution: Since 100 cm are in 1 m, divide the number of centimeters by 100.

$$1 \text{ m} = 100 \text{ cm}$$
$$\frac{700 \text{ cm}}{100 \text{ cm/m}} = 7 \text{ m}$$

See Teacher's Guide.

REVIEW AND REFLECT

1. How many millimeters are in 6.5 dm?
2. How many kilometers are in 3800 m?
3. What do you think the problems were with using one ten-millionth of the distance from the North Pole to the equator as the standard meter?
4. Why should people use standard units of measurement?
5. What problems might you encounter if you bought carpeting in cubit units?

Activity: Why are units made uniform?

See Teacher's Guide.

MATERIALS

metric ruler
meter stick

PROCEDURE

1. Work in a group with three other students.
2. Measure the height of each student in your group in hands. Use the width of your hand as shown in Figure 1–5. Record the heights in a data table.
3. Compare your measurements with your partners' measurements.
4. Using a metric ruler, determine the width of your hand in centimeters. Record your hand width. Record the hand widths of your partners also.
5. Determine the average hand width for your group (divide the sum of your group's hand widths by the number of people in your group). Record this value.
6. Use the average value to convert your measurement of each person's height from hands to centimeters.
7. Measure the actual height in cm of each person with a meter stick. Record these measurements.

FIGURE 1–5.

DATA AND OBSERVATIONS

Student				
Measured Height (hands)				
Calculated Height (cm)				
Measured Height (cm)				

QUESTIONS AND CONCLUSIONS

1. Were your measurements of your partners' heights the same as the measurements made by others in your group?
2. If the measurements in your group varied, explain why.
3. What is the average hand width for your group?
4. How did your calculated measurements of your partners' heights compare with your actual measurements with a meter stick?
5. The heights of horses commonly are measured in hands. A hand is a unit that describes a standard linear measure, 10 cm, which is the average width of a man's hand. Why do you think the unit, one hand, was made uniform?
6. Change your partners' measured heights in centimeters to uniform units of hands.

1:5   Area

The SI units for measuring area are derived from the units for linear measure. To measure area, you must determine the number of square units covered by the area. A square unit has the same linear measure on each side. For example, a square meter, m^2, measures one meter on each side.

$$\text{square meter} = \text{meter} \times \text{meter}$$
$$m^2 = m \times m$$

Small areas may be measured in square centimeters, cm^2, or square millimeters, mm^2.

The area of any rectangular object can be found by multiplying its length times its width.

$$\text{area} = \text{length} \times \text{width}$$
$$A = L_1 \times L_2$$

How is the area of a rectangle determined?

EXAMPLE: Calculating Area of a Rectangle

Problem: What is the area of a room that measures 4 m by 3 m?

Solution: The area of the room is its length times its width.

$$A = L_1 \times L_2$$
$$A = 4 \text{ m} \times 3 \text{ m}$$
$$A = 12 \text{ m}^2$$

The area of a circle is calculated by multiplying the square of the radius times pi, π. Pi is a constant with a value of about 3.14. The radius of a circle is one half its diameter.

$$\text{area} = \text{pi} \times \text{radius squared}$$
$$A = \pi r^2$$

EXAMPLE: Calculating Area of a Circle

Problem: What is the area of a round tabletop that measures 1.2 m in diameter?

Solution: The area of the tabletop is pi times the radius squared. The radius is one-half of the diameter.

$$A = \pi r^2$$
$$A = 3.14 \times (0.6 \text{ m})^2$$
$$A = 3.14 \times 0.36 \text{ m}^2$$
$$A = 1.13 \text{ m}^2$$

FIGURE 1–6. Conversions of SI volume units are based on cubed powers of ten, $(100 \text{ cm})^3 = 1 \text{ m}^3$.

What is the SI unit for measuring volume?

$\underline{1:6}$ Volume

Volume is a measure of how much space an object occupies. The volume of a cube is the product of its length times its width times its height.

$$\text{volume} = \text{length} \times \text{width} \times \text{height}$$
$$V = L_1 \times L_2 \times L_3$$

The SI unit for measuring volume is the cubic meter, m^3. Notice that in SI the unit for measuring volume also is derived from the linear unit, the meter. A cubic meter is the volume of a cube that measures one meter on each side.

$$\text{cubic meter} = \text{meter} \times \text{meter} \times \text{meter}$$
$$m^3 = m \times m \times m$$

Figure 1–6 shows a trunk that has a volume of one cubic meter. The cubic meter is a relatively large volume. For this reason, we often use cubic centimeters to measure smaller volumes. A cubic centimeter, cm^3, is the volume of a cube that measures one centimeter on each side.

EXAMPLE: Calculating Volume

Problem: How much cereal will a box hold that is 30 cm high, 20 cm long, and 4 cm wide?

Solution: The volume of cereal that the box will hold is the product of the length times the width times the height.

$$V = L_1 \times L_2 \times L_3$$
$$V = 30 \text{ cm} \times 20 \text{ cm} \times 4 \text{ cm}$$
$$V = 2400 \text{ cm}^3$$

Sometimes the unit liter is used to measure volume. Liquids and gases commonly are measured in liters. The liter is a metric unit, but it is not an SI unit. In SI, volumes of solids, liquids, and gases are measured in cubic meters, cubic centimeters, or cubic decimeters. A liter has the same volume as a cubic decimeter. A cubic decimeter measures one decimeter on each side.

Scientists often measure liquids with a graduated cylinder. A graduated cylinder usually is marked off in cubic centimeters or milliliters. A milliliter is 1/1000 of a liter and has the same volume as a cubic centimeter.

1:7 Mass

The **mass** of an object is a measure of the amount of matter it contains. The SI unit for measuring mass is the kilogram, kg. The standard kilogram mass is made of a platinum alloy and is kept at the International Bureau of Standards. The unit used for measuring smaller masses is the gram, g. A gram is one thousandth of a kilogram.

The mass of a cubic decimeter of pure water is about one kilogram. In other words, if you had a cube measuring one decimeter on each side and filled it with water, the mass of the water would be about one kilogram. Likewise, the mass of water filling a cubic centimeter would be about one gram. Since a liter is the same volume as a cubic decimeter, the mass of a liter of water is about one kilogram. A milliliter of water has a mass of about one gram.

A paper clip has a mass of about one gram. A nickel has a mass of about five grams. The average adult male has a mass of about 75 kilograms. Some common objects and their masses are shown in Figure 1–7.

Recall the SI prefixes listed in Table 1–2. A milligram, mg, is one thousandth of a gram. This unit is used for measuring relatively small masses. You may be familiar with 250 milligram or 500 milligram vitamin capsules. The ingredients in most medicines are measured in milligrams. Also, the nutritional information on many food packages is listed using milligrams.

How is mass measured in SI?

What substances are commonly measured in milligrams?

FIGURE 1–7. The kilogram is the SI standard unit for mass. Smaller objects may be measured in grams.

Like SI and metric units of linear measure, the units of area, volume, and mass are based on multiples of ten. You can easily convert from one unit to another.

EXAMPLE: Calculating Mass

Problem: A bottle contains 50 vitamin pills that have a mass of 250 mg each. What is the total mass of the vitamin pills in grams?

Solution: First, calculate the total mass of the vitamin pills in milligrams. Then convert milligrams to grams. Since you are changing from a smaller unit to a larger unit, you will divide.

$$50 \times 250 \text{ mg} = 12\,500 \text{ mg}$$
$$1 \text{ g} = 1000 \text{ mg}$$
$$\frac{12\,500 \text{ mg}}{1000 \text{ mg/g}} = 12.50 \text{ g}$$

EXAMPLE: Calculating Volume and Mass

Problem: An aquarium measures 50 cm long, 30 cm high, and 30 cm wide. How many liters of water does the aquarium contain when full? What is the mass of the water?

Solution: First, calculate the volume of the aquarium in liters. Then, since you know that one liter of water has a mass of one kilogram, you can calculate the mass.

$$V = L_1 \times L_2 \times L_3$$
$$V = 50 \text{ cm} \times 30 \text{ cm} \times 30 \text{ cm}$$
$$V = 45\,000 \text{ cm}^3 = 45\,000 \text{ mL}$$
$$\frac{45\,000 \text{ mL}}{1000 \text{ mL/L}} = 45 \text{ L}$$

45 L of water has a mass of 45 kg.

See Teacher's Guide.

REVIEW AND REFLECT

1. What are the SI units of area, volume, and mass?
2. What is the surface area of a pool that is 5 m $\times$ 3 m?
3. If the volume of the pool is 15 m^3, how deep is it?
4. What is the mass of the water in the pool?
5. How many square centimeters are in a square meter? cubic centimeters in a cubic meter?

Activity: How well can you estimate?

MATERIALS

metric ruler
3 different size bottles
graduated cylinder
balance

objects to measure
labels

PROCEDURE

Part A

1. Estimate in centimeters the length and width of this book. Record your estimate in a data table. Be sure to include the units.
2. Select three objects. Estimate the length and width of each. Record your estimates.
3. With the ruler, measure the book and the other objects. Record the measurements.

Part B

1. Label three bottles A, B, and C.
2. Estimate in milliliters the volume of each bottle. Record your estimates in a data table. Include the units.

FIGURE 1–8.

3. Determine the volume of each bottle using the graduated cylinder. Record the measurements.

Part C

1. Select three objects. Estimate their mass in grams. Record your estimates in a data table. Include the units.
2. Using the balance, determine the mass of each object. Record the measurements.

DATA AND OBSERVATIONS

Object	Actual Measure	Estimated Measure

QUESTIONS AND CONCLUSIONS

1. How well did your estimates compare with the measurements you made?
2. What is the area of the cover of this book?
3. How well do your measurements compare with those made by other students in your class?
4. Convert your answers in Part B to liters.
5. How could you use the graduated cylinder to find the volume of irregularly-shaped solid objects?
6. What units would you use to measure the following?
   a. the area of your classroom
   b. the volume of a can of soup
   c. a person's height

See Teacher's Guide.

Skill Inquiry

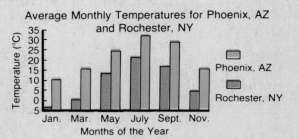

Average Monthly Temperatures for Phoenix, AZ and Rochester, NY

Phoenix, AZ

Rochester, NY

Scientists make many measurements. They use this information to study and explain events and ideas. Measurement information may be hard to understand and take up a lot of space if it is not presented in an organized way. Scientists often use graphs to organize measurement information. Refer to the graphs throughout this book to help you understand what you read. Practice reading a graph by answering the following questions about the graph shown.

1. What is the average monthly temperature for each city in January? March? September?

2. What is the coldest month shown for each city? the warmest?

How can you find the average monthly temperature for June? Since there is no measurement for the month of June, but there are measurements for the months of May and July, you can estimate for June. Locate the position you think the measurement for the average June temperature should occupy on the graph. This method of estimating is called interpolation (IN tur puh lay zhun). Use interpolation to answer the following questions.

3. In which month is the difference in temperature between the two cities the greatest? the least?

4. What is the average monthly temperature in each city during the summer (June, July, and August)?

1:8 Time and Temperature

Time is an important measurement in science. For example, the time that an event is observed or how long an event takes are data that may be recorded in an experiment. The units for measuring time in the SI system are the second, s, and the hour, h. A second is 1/86 400 of a day. An hour is 1/24 of a day or 3600 seconds. This definition of time is referred to as solar time. Solar time is based on the time of rotation of the earth. Around the turn of the century, scientists realized that the period of the earth's rotation varied. For this reason, a different standard for the measurement of time has been developed. This newer standard is based on the frequency of vibration of electron transfers within certain atoms.

The SI unit for measuring temperature is the **kelvin, K.** You are probably more familiar with the metric unit for measuring temperature, the Celsius degree, °C. The Kel-

What are the SI units for measuring time and temperature?

vin and Celsius temperature scales are related to each other. The Kelvin temperature can be determined by adding 273 to the Celsius temperature.

$$K = °C + 273$$

Table 1-3 lists some common temperatures in Celsius degrees and kelvins.

TABLE 1–3. SOME COMMON TEMPERATURES		
Example	**K**	**°C**
Water freezes	273	0
Water boils	373	100
Comfortable room	293	20
Human body	310	37
Cold day	258	−15
Hot day	303	30

1:9 Force

A force is a push or a pull on an object. There are many types of forces. A force is exerted on a ball when it is thrown. The wind exerts a force on the sail of a boat. A magnet exerts a pulling force on a paper clip. The force of the wind can vary greatly. The force of the wind on a kite is small compared to the force of a hurricane.

The SI unit for measuring force is the **newton,** N. The newton was named in honor of Sir Isaac Newton. In 1686, he was the first scientist to explain the relationship between forces and motion. The weight of an object is one type of force that is measured in newtons.

Many people confuse the ideas of weight and mass. Remember that mass is a measure of the amount of matter in an object. An object's mass is not affected by the location at which it is measured. The **weight** of an object is a measure of the force of gravity between that object and another object. Your weight is a measure of the force of gravity between your body and the earth. Weight does depend on the location of the object. The force of gravity is reduced as the distance between the two objects is increased. For example, your weight is less if you are standing on top of a mountain than if you are on a beach. The distance between you and the center of the earth is greater on the mountaintop. However, your mass is the same in both places.

How is weight different from mass?

FIGURE 1–9. Mountain climbers must work to overcome the force of gravity that pulls them toward the earth.

See Teacher's Guide.

REVIEW AND REFLECT

1. What is the SI unit for measuring temperature?
2. Would you go water skiing or snow skiing if the temperature was 25°C?
3. What is the SI unit for measuring weight?
4. What is the mass of a 65 kg person on the moon?

1:10 Scientific Notation

Scientists often work with very small or very large objects. For example, note the actual sizes of the objects shown in Figure 1–10. Scientists represent very small or very large numbers with scientific notation. In **scientific notation,** any number can be represented by a number multiplied by some multiple of 10. For example, the number 1560 is the same as 1.56×1000. Since 1000 is the same as 10 times 10 times 10, or 10 to the third power (10^3), in scientific notation 1560 becomes 1.56×10^3. The number 3 in this example is called an **exponent.**

$$10^3 = 10 \times 10 \times 10 = 1000$$
$$10^{-3} = \frac{1}{10^3} = \frac{1}{10 \times 10 \times 10} = \frac{1}{1000} \text{ or } 0.001$$

For what purposes is scientific notation used?

Table 1–4 shows some powers of ten and their equivalents.

EXAMPLES: Writing Numbers in Scientific Notation

Problem: Write 149 600 000 in scientific notation.
Solution: To write 149 600 000 as 1.496 you must move the decimal point to the left 8 places. In order to represent the same number, 1.496 must be multiplied by 10^8 or 100 000 000.

$$149\ 600\ 000 = 1.496 \times 10^8$$

Problem: Write 0.001 293 in scientific notation.
Solution: To write 0.001 293 as 1.293 you must move the decimal point to the right 3 places. In order to represent the same number, 1.293 must be divided by 1000. Dividing by 1000 is the same as multiplying by the inverse of 1000, or 10^{-3}

$$0.001\ 293 = 1.293 \times 1000$$
$$= 1.293 \times 10^{-3}$$

You can change a number from scientific notation back to standard form easily. If the exponent is positive, it indicates the number of places to the right you need to move the decimal point. For example, 1.56×10^2 becomes 156 if you move the decimal point to the right two places.

When the exponent is negative, move the decimal point to the left to change from scientific notation to standard form. For example, 7.5×10^{-2} is 0.075. Notice that the decimal was moved to the left two places. While 10^2 means

TABLE 1–4. POWERS OF TEN		
10^2	$= 10 \times 10 =$	100
10^1	$=$	10
10^0	$=$	1
10^{-1}	$= \dfrac{1}{10} \qquad =$	0.1
10^{-2}	$= \dfrac{1}{10} \times \dfrac{1}{10} =$	0.01

10 times 10, 10^{-2} means one divided by 10 times 10 which is 0.01. In the above example, if you multiply 7.5 times 0.01, you get 0.075.

Suppose you want to add two numbers written in scientific notation. If the exponents are the same, simply add the numbers together and keep the same exponent.

What if the exponents of the numbers to be added are different? Then you need to rewrite the numbers in scientific notation until the exponents are the same. Subtraction is done similarly.

EXAMPLE: Subtracting Using Scientific Notation

Problem: Subtract 4.0×10^6 from 3.5×10^7

Solution: Since the exponents of the two numbers are different, rewrite one of the numbers to make the exponents the same. In this case, rewrite 4.0×10^6 so that it is expressed as a multiple of 10^7. Then subtract.

$$4.0 \times 10^6 = 0.4 \times 10^7$$
$$(3.5 \times 10^7) - (0.4 \times 10^7) = 3.1 \times 10^7$$

To multiply numbers using scientific notation, multiply the numbers and add the exponents. For division problems, divide the numbers and subtract the exponents.

EXAMPLE: Dividing Using Scientific Notation

Problem: Divide 6×10^9 by 4.8×10^5

Solution: Since the problem is division, you need not make the exponents the same. Just divide the numbers and subtract the exponents.

$$\frac{6 \times 10^9}{4.8 \times 10^5} = \frac{6}{4.8} \times 10^{(9-5)}$$
$$= 1.25 \times 10^4$$

See Teacher's Guide.

a

b

FIGURE 1–10. Scientific notation is useful when comparing very small and large objects. The actual diameter of a pollen grain is about 1.5×10^{-5} meter (a). The actual diameter of the earth is about 1.27×10^7 meters (b).

REVIEW AND REFLECT

1. Write 4.5×10^{-9} in standard form.
2. Write 42 000 000 000 000 in scientific notation.
3. What is the total volume of two suitcases with the following measurements?
   1.2×10^2 cm long, 8.0×10^1 cm wide, 2.5×10^1 cm high
   1.2×10^2 cm long, 1.0×10^2 cm wide, 2.0×10^1 cm high

1:11 Information: Solving Problems

Knowing how to solve mathematical problems is important to doing well in science. To solve a problem, carefully read it. Then determine what information is given to you and what you are trying to find out.

A helpful way to solve problems is the factor-label method. The factor-label method of problem solving uses the labels of the units as mathematical factors. Thus, the units can be manipulated in an equation. The result of these manipulations yields a "units" answer as well as a numerical answer. The units then can be checked against the expected to be sure they are appropriate. For example, if you expect an answer to be the mass of an object, the units of the answer must be in kilograms or some other mass unit.

To use the factor-label method, include all of the units with each numerical value when you solve a problem. When you multiply or divide the numerical values, multiply or divide the units as well. When you add or subtract numerical values, the units do not change. Remember, that you cannot add or subtract units that measure different properties.

What is the factor-label method?

SUGGESTION You may need to remind students that when a number is multiplied by a factor equal to one, the number remains unchanged.

EXAMPLES: Using the Factor-Label Method

Problem: How many millimeters are in six kilometers?
Solution: Since you are changing from a larger unit to a smaller unit, you multiply.

$$1 \text{ km} = 1000 \text{ m}, \ 1 \text{ m} = 1000 \text{ mm}$$

$$6 \text{ km} = 6 \text{ km} \times \frac{1000 \text{ m}}{1 \text{ km}} \times \frac{1000 \text{ mm}}{1 \text{ m}}$$

$$= 6 \ 000 \ 000 \text{ mm or } 6.0 \times 10^6 \text{ mm}$$

Problem: How many seconds are in 30 days?
Solution: Since you are changing from a larger unit to a smaller unit, you multiply.

$$1 \text{ day} = 24 \text{ h}, \ 1 \text{ h} = 60 \text{ min}, \ 1 \text{ min} = 60 \text{ s}$$

$$\text{number of seconds} = 30 \text{ days} \times \frac{24 \text{ h}}{1 \text{ day}} \times \frac{60 \text{ min}}{1 \text{ h}} \times \frac{60 \text{ s}}{1 \text{ min}}$$

$$= 2 \ 592 \ 000 \text{ s}$$

It is also important to consider which digits in your measurements are significant when solving problems. A student measures the top of a school desk with a meter stick. It can be seen from Figure 1–11 that the width of the desk is closer to 71 than to 72 centimeters. The student measures the desk width to be 71.2 centimeters. It is not possible to measure the width with any more precision using the meter stick. Similarly, the desk is found to be 53.7 centimeters deep. Both measures contain three significant digits. The significant digits in a measurement are those digits known to be correct and one estimated digit. The desk is known to be at least 71 centimeters wide and 53 centimeters deep. The 0.2 and 0.7 are estimated.

When the two measures are multiplied together to find the area of the desk, the calculated product appears to contain six significant digits.

FIGURE 1–11. The desk measures 71.2 centimeters wide. The last significant digit is estimated.

$$A = 71.2 \text{ cm} \times 53.7 \text{ cm}$$
$$A = 3823.44 \text{ cm}^2$$

However, the measurement of the desk's area cannot be more precise than the linear measures. When two measures are multiplied or divided, the answer can have no more significant digits than the least number of significant digits in the original measurements. Therefore, the area of the desk is 3820 cm^2.

The rules for determining the number of significant digits are listed below.

1. Digits other than zero are always significant.
2. Any final zeroes after the decimal point are significant.
3. Zeroes between two other significant digits are always significant.
4. Zeroes used solely for spacing the decimal point are not significant.

What are the rules for determining significant digits?

See Teacher's Guide.

REVIEW AND REFLECT

1. What should you do first when solving a problem?
2. Use the factor-label method to help solve the following:
   a. How many centimeters in 47.5 km?
   b. How many days is 1 209 600 s?
3. How many significant digits in each of the following?
   a. 71.6   c. 31.6
   b. 0.004   d. 100 036
4. Calculate the answer in the correct number of significant figures.
   a. 6.3 × 8.6   c. 15.3 × 10 005
   b. 4.0 ÷ 6.15   d. 0.15 ÷ 0.62

CHAPTER 1 REVIEW

SUMMARY

1. The application of science to everyday situations is called technology. 1:1
2. Measurement is important in science and technology. 1:2
3. The International System of Units, SI, has been accepted worldwide as a standard of measurement. 1:3
4. The meter, m, is the SI linear unit. 1:4
5. Area is usually measured in square meters, m^2, or square centimeters, cm^2. 1:5
6. Volume is measured in cubic centimeters, cm^3, milliliters, mL, or liters, L. 1:6
7. Mass is the measure of the amount of matter in an object. It is measured in kilograms, kg, and grams, g. 1:7
8. The second, s, and hour, h, are SI units used to measure time. 1:8
9. The SI unit for measuring temperature is the kelvin, K. 1:8
10. Weight is the measure of gravitational force of attraction between two objects. Weight is measured in newtons, N. 1:9
11. Scientific notation is useful when manipulating very large or small numbers. 1:10

VOCABULARY

exponent 10	newton 4	standard 8
kelvin 5	scientific notation 6	technology 1
mass 3	SI 2	weight 7
metric 9		

Match each definition with the correct word from the list.

1. Applying science to everyday matters
2. An internationally agreed upon measurement system
3. The amount of matter in an object
4. SI unit for measuring force
5. SI unit for measuring temperature
6. A method of expressing very large and very small numbers
7. A measure of the force of gravity between an object and the earth
8. The basis for evaluating the properties of objects
9. A commonly used system of measurement in which many, but not all, units are the same as SI units
10. A superscript that appears with a number and indicates the power to which the number is raised

QUESTIONS

MAIN IDEAS

Choose the correct answer to each question.

1. What is the force of gravity between the earth and an object called? *(mass, newton, weight, force)*
2. What is a measure of the amount of matter an object contains? *(newton, weight, force, mass)*
3. What is the basic SI unit of length? *(centimeter, meter, milliliter, kilo)*

4. What is the SI unit of weight? *(newton, kilogram, ounce, liter)*

5. What is the standard SI unit of mass? *(gram, kilogram, milligram, centigram)*

6. Which is not warm summer temperature? *(25°C, 298 K, 315 K, 10°C)*

7. What has the same volume as a cubic centimeter? *(mL, dm³, kg, m²)*

8. Which prefix stands for one thousand? *(milli, kilo, deci, centi)*

9. In the number 4.08×10^{12}, what is 12 called? *(factor label, SI, prefix, exponent)*

10. How many milligrams are in 6.5 g? *(65 mg, 650 mg, 6500 mg, 6.5 × 10² mg)*

See Teacher's Guide.

APPLICATIONS

Answer each question in one or more paragraphs. Show how to solve each problem.

1. Name three examples of technology that affect you. Use the examples to explain why you need to study science.

2. If you heard some scientists talking about "standards of measurement," what kinds of things would they be discussing?

3. How are metric and SI units different?

4. Make a table listing the basic SI units of linear measure, area, volume, mass, force, time, and temperature.

5. A can of paint indicates that it will cover an area of 40 m². You want to paint a floor that is 5.5 m wide and 6.5 m long. How many cans of paint should you buy?

6. Astronauts in space are said to be "weightless." If this is so, are they also massless? Explain.

7. Why do you think scientific notation was developed?

8. What would you use to measure the following?
   a. a baby's birth weight
   b. the mass of a desk
   c. the volume of a soft drink can
   d. the dimensions of a house
   e. the area of a lawn
   f. the volume of snow that falls on a driveway in North Dakota

9. If the distance from New York to Chicago is about 1200 km, what is the distance in meters?

10. What is the volume of a swimming pool that is 10 m long, 5 m wide, and 3 m deep?

FURTHER STUDY

INVESTIGATIONS

1. Keep a record of daily temperatures in your locale. Determine monthly high and low average temperatures.

2. Report on consumer products that have been developed, or "spun off," from the NASA space program's technology.

3. Read and report on the history of the development of the metric system during the French Revolution.

4. Investigate early attempts at measurements. Find out how early standards were developed.

READINGS

− Baird, Eva-Lee, and Rose Wyler. *Going Metric the Fun Way.* Doubleday: Garden City, NY, 1980.

0 Humphrey, Henry, and Deidre O'Meara-Humphrey. *When Is Now?* Doubleday: Garden City, NY, 1980.

+ Janos, Leo. "Timekeepers of the Solar System." *Science 80.* May/June, 1980. pp. 44-55.

− Schefter, Jim. "Rendezvous with a Comet." *Popular Science.* October, 1983. pp. 102-105.

+ Shallis, Michael. *On Time.* Schocken Books: New York, 1982.

SUPPOSE you are going to buy a used car. In order to decide which car to buy, you need information. You might ask a salesperson about the age and general condition of several cars. You might look at the cars carefully and take a test drive in some of them. Scientific information is gained in a way similar to the way any information is gained. What methods do scientists use to get information?

SCIENCE PROCESSES

INTRODUCING THE CHAPTER   Initiate a discussion of the processes consumers use to decide which purchases to make. For example, people view ads, read labels, try alternative products. You may want to bring some consumer testing magazines to class or compare ads and labels of competitive products. Ask students about the importance of measurement in purchase decisions (in terms of unit pricing) to review the concepts of chapter 1. Relate these processes to scientific methods of answering questions and solving problems.

2:1   Scientific Methods

A primary way of getting information is asking questions. Everyday people ask many questions to get information. People ask directions, what time it is, and how things work. People also get information by making observations and trying things out. For example, you can look out a window if you want to know if it is raining. You know what kinds of soft drinks you like because you have tasted several different ones.

Scientists get information by asking questions, making observations, and trying things out in a systematic way. They use processes called **scientific methods.** In this chapter, a general model of scientific methods is presented. Figure 2–1 illustrates the major parts of this model. While you are reading this chapter, think of ways you might vary from this model if you were to do the tests described.

Scientific methods are not limited to use by scientists only. They can be applied to everyday situations. For example, the makers of most dishwashing detergents claim that their product is best. Obviously they cannot all be best. The question is, which one really is best? You can use scientific methods to find the answer to this question.

GOAL   You will learn about the methods scientists use to answer questions and solve problems.

How do scientists get information?

QUESTION
1. Decide what you want to know.
2. Do some research.
3. Design a test: identify and define the variables.
4. State a hypothesis.

TEST
1. Select a representative sample.
2. Determine how variables will be controlled and measured.
3. Conduct experiment and observe.
4. Record results.

CONCLUDE
1. Draw inferences from data and observations.
2. Form conclusions about original hypothesis.
3. Identify limitations and sources of error.
4. Re-evaluate original questions.

ANALYZE
1. Organize data using graphs, tables, and charts.
2. Make necessary calculations.

FIGURE 2–1. Scientific methods are processes that generate information as well as more questions.

SUGGESTION   Do not require students to memorize a specific list of steps in the scientific method. There are many different approaches to problem-solving. For this reason, the text refers to scientific methods (plural).

What affects the methods a scientist uses?

SUGGESTION   Students may want to consider some of the ideas mentioned in sections 2:1 and 2:2 as topics for science fair projects.

Assume that a certain amount of the best detergent will clean more greasy dishes than any other detergent. You might think that the most expensive detergent is best, so you decide to test three of the most expensive brands. After washing stacks of greasy dishes with each detergent and analyzing the results, you may conclude which detergent among those tested is best.

However, your experiment probably generates some additional questions. For example, did the most expensive detergent clean enough better to justify the extra expense? What other questions might you have?

Remember, there are many different ways to conduct an experiment. For example, the way you choose a pain reliever is different from the way a hospital's staff determines what type of pain reliever to give to patients. The experimental design may be very simple and compare only two factors. Some experimental designs are quite elaborate and test as many as one hundred or more factors. The methods a scientist uses change depending on the questions being asked and the conditions for testing. Such conditions as the amount of time to do the experiment, funding, type of equipment, and the number of people or objects to be tested all influence the way in which an experiment will be designed.

2:2 Questioning

In order to use scientific methods to get information, we first need to decide what we want to know. For example, suppose we want some information about flashlight batteries. We already know that there are several different types. Our question is, which type of battery lasts the longest?

Next we need to do some research about the question. We may go to a store and make a list of how many types of flashlight batteries there are. We might compare the information on the battery packages. We might ask a sales clerk which battery usually lasts the longest.

Now we need to design a test or an experiment that will provide information to help us answer our question. Some factors to consider are

1. What types of batteries will be used?
2. For what purpose will the batteries be used?
3. How long will the batteries be used?
4. How often will the batteries be used?
5. How much time will elapse between uses?

Changeable factors such as these are called the **variables** in an experiment. What other variables can you think of?

It is important to identify as many variables as possible when planning an experiment. However, it usually is not possible to test the effects of all variables in one experiment. In the simplest type of experiment, the effects of only two variables are investigated. Our battery experiment will be limited to an investigation of how long certain types of batteries will continuously light a flashlight. One variable is the type of battery used. The other variable is how long the battery can continuously light a flashlight.

Once the variables to be studied have been identified, they need to be defined. Based on the research that we did at the store, suppose we define the type of battery used as regular, heavy-duty, or alkaline, Figure 2–2. We shall define the other variable in terms of how it will be measured. For this experiment, we will measure how long a battery continuously lights a flashlight by how long it can project a one-meter flashlight beam. After a period of time, a battery still may be able to light the bulb in a flashlight,

What is the first step in a scientific investigation?

BACKGROUND Technically, what is generally referred to as a "battery" is actually a cell. A battery is formed by the combination of 2 or more cells.

BACKGROUND The December, 1983, issue of *Consumer Reports* includes an extensive report on flashlight batteries.

What are variables?

FIGURE 2–2. In order to make a good decision when purchasing batteries, you should know which batteries work best for your needs.

What is an operational
definition?

What is a hypothesis?

but only to a faint glow. Assume a battery has ceased lighting a flashlight when it can no longer project a beam of light a distance of one meter and light an area of one square meter. Defining a variable in terms of how it will be measured is an **operational definition.**

Now that the variables have been defined, a hypothesis (hi PAHTH uh sus) can be stated. The **hypothesis** is what we think the answer to the question is. A hypothesis should be stated in terms of the variables. A reasonable hypothesis for this experiment is that an alkaline battery will light a flashlight continuously for the longest time.

See Teacher's Guide.

Career Profile

Dr. Linda James Myers is a wife, mother, and Associate Professor of Black Studies, Psychology, and Psychiatry at The Ohio State University. Her early morning hours are spent with her family. By 10 A.M. she is teaching students at the university. Linda spends her afternoons writing, doing research, reading, preparing for classes, and attending faculty meetings. The early evening hours are spent preparing the family dinner and enjoying the company of her

family. Some evenings Linda works in her home office with adult clients in need of psychotherapy.

After Linda earned a master's degree in school psychology, she became an instructor of psychology at the University of Nebraska. From there she was invited to organize the psychology curriculum in the Black Studies Department at The Ohio State University. While at Ohio State, Linda completed her Ph.D in clinical psychology and later acquired her license to practice psychotherapy.

Linda has always enjoyed her teaching experiences, but recently her private practice has become meaningful as well. Her clients struggle with a variety of problems that include identity crises, family problems, depression, anxiety, and eating disorders. After questioning her clients, Linda forms an impression and develops a hypothesis about the nature and cause of their problems. She then sets about testing her hypothesis through further inquiry and analysis. The feedback from her clients strengthens or weakens her hypothesis. Once Linda reaches a conclusion, she can focus her efforts on helping the clients deal with their problems.

2:3 Testing

After the variables in the experiment have been defined and the hypothesis stated, the actual testing or experiment itself must be planned. This step is important. If the experiment is not carefully thought out, it may not provide any useful information.

The first step in planning an experiment is choosing a sample. A sample is a small group that represents a larger group. For example, we cannot test all batteries in our experiment. We will choose a few batteries as a sample to test.

To ensure that a sample is representative of the larger group, it must be chosen at random. In our battery experiment, we will select three batteries of each type to be our sample. We should purchase one of each type of battery at three different stores. This sampling process will help us be sure that any differences in battery performance are due to the type of battery. We will not wonder if differences are because one particular battery is faulty or that one particular type has been on a store shelf for a longer time than others.

Some types of experiments have two sample groups. One group is called the experimental group, and the other is called the control group. The characteristics of both of these groups are very similar. The experimental group receives some type of treatment while the control group does not. The results obtained with the experimental group are

What is a sample?

Why are random samples chosen?

FIGURE 2–3. The control group of rats (a) were fed a normal diet. The experimental group (b) were given a diet supplement, too.

a

b

FIGURE 2–4. The variables in an experiment must be carefully controlled. Here, the flashlight is exactly one meter from the cardboard.

What is the purpose of a control group?

then compared to the control group to determine if the treatment made any difference. Figure 2–3 shows an example of a research investigation that involved experimental and control groups of mice. The experimental group, Figure 2–3a, received a diet supplement. To determine the effect of the diet supplement, a control group of mice, Figure 2–3b, were fed a normal diet. The only difference between the experimental and control groups was the variable that was being tested, a diet supplement.

During an experiment, the variable being tested is changed by the experimenter. The variable that the experimenter changes is called the **independent variable.** In the battery experiment, we will change the battery in the flashlight since we are testing three different types.

What are independent and dependent variables?

The variable being measured in an experiment is the **dependent variable.** It "depends" on the changes in the independent variable. In the battery experiment, we will measure how long a continuous beam of light projected a distance of one meter from a flashlight will light a one square meter area. That time will depend on the type of battery that is in the flashlight.

The experimenter needs to control, or keep constant, all other variables in an experiment to ensure that it is a fair test. For example, we should not test the regular battery in a flashlight, the heavy-duty battery in a radio, and the alkaline battery in a cassette recorder. If the alkaline battery lasts the longest, we will not be sure why. It might be because batteries last longer in cassette recorders than they do in radios or flashlights. To be fair, each battery must be tested under exactly the same conditions.

The details for carrying out an experiment must be planned carefully. Exactly how will each variable be controlled and measured? In the battery experiment, we must be sure that each type of battery will project a one-meter beam of light on an area of one square meter. We must also decide how to measure the light beam. In this experiment, we have decided to measure the beam in a darkened room using a sheet of white cardboard with a one square meter area outlined as a screen. See Figure 2–4.

As an experiment is conducted, the experimenter observes the results. Some observations involve measurement and some do not. Observations that are based on careful measurements that provide numbers and units are **quantitative.** In quantitative observations, some quantity is being measured. Observations that do not involve exact measurements are **qualitative.** Qualitative observations are evaluations of characteristics. Observe again in Figure 2–3 that the mice in the experimental group are larger and appear to be more healthy than the control group. This observation is qualitative. To make quantitative observations, we might weigh the mice in each group or count the number of offspring from each group.

A data table is a useful tool for recording observations. Figure 2–6 shows a record of the observations that were made in the battery experiment. Notice that the independent and dependent variables are at the head of each column in the data table. A data table shows how the dependent variable was affected each time the experimenter changed the independent variable. Not all data collection consists of recording observations in data tables however. Many other methods of recording data exist.

FIGURE 2–5. A CAT (Computerized Axial-Tomography) scanner produces images that provide a meaningful record that doctors can use to make a diagnosis.

How are quantitative and qualitative measurements different?

Type of Battery	Time Lasted (Hours)		
	Battery 1	Battery 2	Battery 3
Regular	5.1	5.8	5.5
Heavy-duty	6.1	6.3	6.1
Alkaline	10.4	10.2	10.1

FIGURE 2–6. A data table is a good way to organize and display test results.

REVIEW AND REFLECT

1. What are scientific methods?
2. Identify the independent and dependent variables in the battery experiment. Name at least three other variables that are controlled in the battery experiment.
3. Some students conducted a survey and found that three quarters of high school students preferred rock music to other types of music. If their survey is accurate, why do fewer than three fourths of the radio stations in their town play rock music?
4. Name three ways that data can be recorded.
5. Are the observations listed in Figure 2–6 quantitative or qualitative?

2:4 Analyzing

After an experiment has been done and the observations and data recorded, the results must be analyzed. Conclusions can be made when the analysis is completed. When data is organized in a table, it is easier to analyze than when it is recorded randomly. Organization is most important in experiments that provide large amounts of data.

Displaying the results of experiments in charts or graphs is often helpful. A bar graph, or histogram, is a good way to represent data comparing two or more groups in terms of a single characteristic. For example, in the battery experiment, we compared three types of batteries in terms of how long they last in flashlights.

Another type of graph is a circle, or pie graph. Pie graphs are useful in representing fractions or percentages. Suppose that we asked a group of people their age. The results could be represented with the pie graph like the one shown in Figure 2–7.

One of the most common types of graphs is an x-y graph. This type of graph shows how two or more variables change with respect to one another. In order to make x-y graphs easier to interpret, the dependent variable always is represented on the vertical, or y-axis. The independent variable always is represented on the horizontal, or x-axis. Bar graphs usually are set up this way, too.

How can data be organized?

FIGURE 2–7. Pie graphs show the percent each group is of the total sample.

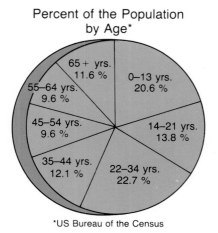

Percent of the Population by Age*

*US Bureau of the Census

The x-y graph in the Skill Inquiry on page 18 shows how average temperature varies on a monthly basis for two cities. For this graph, the time of year is plotted on the x-axis. It is the independent variable. Temperature is the dependent variable. (The average temperature in each city depends on the time of year.) The temperatures are plotted on the y-axis. Note in this graph that time of year is measured in months. Temperature is measured in degrees Celsius. Labeling each axis of a graph with the units used to measure the variables is important. A graph also should have a title. What is the title of the graph on page 18?

Sometimes you need to make calculations when you analyze the results of an experiment. You may need to know a total or the difference between two values. An average value often is useful to know. An average is calculated by first finding the sum of all the data for a sample. This sum is divided by the total number in the sample. The Greek letter sigma, Σ, is used in mathematics to represent a sum.

$$\text{Average} = \frac{\text{sum of data}}{\text{number in sample}}$$

$$\text{Average} = \frac{\Sigma\, x}{N}$$

EXAMPLE: Finding An Average

Problem: In the battery experiment, three batteries of each type were tested. Using the data in Figure 2–6 on page 33, calculate the average time that the regular batteries lasted.

Solution: Add the times that each regular battery lasted. Divide the sum by three, since three regular batteries were tested.

$$\text{Average} = \frac{\Sigma\, x}{N}$$

$$\text{Average} = \frac{5.1 + 5.8 + 5.5}{3}$$

$$\text{Average} = \frac{16.4}{3}$$

$$\text{Average} = 5.5$$

SUGGESTION Stress that when making an x-y graph, students should not merely connect the x-y points in a dot-to-dot manner. Rather, a smooth (best fit) line should be drawn through the points.

How is an average calculated?

BACKGROUND Average also is called mean.

FIGURE 2–8. Correct data on the cost-effectiveness of different soaps could help this restaurant save money.

Activity: How do selected variables affect a pendulum?

See Teacher's Guide.

MATERIALS

100 cm string
watch with second
  hand or stopwatch
large paper clip
4 large steel washers
goggles

metric ruler
  with three holes
protractor
felt-tip pen
graph paper

PROCEDURE

Part A

1. Tie a paper clip to the end of a 100 cm length of string. Place one washer on the paper clip as shown.
2. Mark off 50 cm of string, including the paper clip and washer.
3. Pull the string through one of the end holes. Hold the string against the top of the ruler so that the 50 cm mark is at the hole. Place the ruler on the edge of a table or desk. Pull the string back to a 60° angle as shown to start its swing. Use a protractor to measure the angle.
4. Carefully time 10 periods of the pendulum. The period of a pendulum is the time it takes to complete one back-and-forth swing and return to its starting place. Record this time.
5. Determine the average period.
6. Repeat steps 3–5 with two, three, and four washers on the paper clip.
7. Make a graph of the data.

Part B

1. Place one washer on the paper clip again and hold the string at the 50 cm mark.
2. Let the string go from a 60° angle.
3. Time 10 periods. Figure the average.
4. Repeat steps 2 and 3 using 50°, 40°, and 30° angles.
5. Graph the data.

Part C

1. Mark off 20 cm of string, including the paper clip. Put one washer on the paper clip. Hold the string at the 20 cm mark.
2. Swing the pendulum from a 60° angle.
3. Time 10 periods. Figure the average.
4. Repeat steps 2 and 3 holding the string at 40 cm, 60 cm, and 80 cm lengths.
5. Graph the data.

DATA AND OBSERVATIONS

Length of String	Number of Washers	Angle	Time of Ten Periods	Average Period

QUESTIONS AND CONCLUSIONS

1. Identify the independent and dependent variables in each part of the experiment.
2. What variables were controlled in each part of the experiment?
3. Why was it necessary to conduct the experiment in three parts?
4. What can you conclude from each graph about the relationship between the period and the mass of the pendulum, the angle, or its length?

FIGURE 2–9.

2:5 Concluding

The final step after conducting an experiment and analyzing the data is forming conclusions. You form conclusions by making inferences from your experimental observations and data. An inference is a logical conclusion based on observations and data. More than one inference may be based on the same observations and data. For example, if you phone a friend and no one answers, you might infer that your friend is not home. You also might infer that no one else is home either. These are logical conclusions. However, perhaps you dialed the wrong number. Or, perhaps your friend is outside and did not hear the phone ring. Although your conclusions may be logical, they also may not be true. How could you find out if your conclusions are true?

Before making any conclusions about the results of an experiment, consider the limitations of the methods used. The limitations of an experiment are related to its design and restrict the conclusions that can be made. From our data in the battery experiment, we can conclude that alkaline batteries last longer than regular or heavy-duty batteries in flashlights. However, other research indicates that alkaline batteries cost more than the other types. We would need more data to form any true conclusions about which type of battery is most economical to use.

In addition, all of the variables that are controlled in an experiment limit the conclusions that can be made. The type of device in which the batteries were tested was controlled. The same flashlight was used in each case. Testing each variable under the same conditions is important. However, it does limit the conclusions that can be made. The data observed in this experiment tend to indicate that alkaline batteries, when used continuously, last about twice as long in flashlights as regular batteries. As is usually the case, this experiment provided some information, but at the same time leads to additional questions. For example, it cannot be concluded from this experiment that alkaline batteries would last twice as long as regular batteries in a radio. Because this experiment tested only continuous use, no conclusions can be made about how long the batteries would last with on and off use.

What is an inference?

What is meant by an experiment's limitations?

SUGGESTION Discuss with students other possible limitations to this experiment, such as temperature, other uses, and so on.

REVIEW AND REFLECT

1. What must be done with data collected in an experiment before conclusions can be made?
2. A study was done to find out which political candidate was preferred by most people. What kind of graph could be best used to display the results?
3. Why must the limitations of an experiment be considered when making conclusions?
4. What is the average number of days in a month during leap year?

Skill Inquiry

After plotting the individual data points on an x-y graph, a line may be drawn through the points. The relationship between the variables is shown by the shape of the graph. For example, Graph A shows the distance traveled and the driving time required for a trip. Notice that as the independent variable, distance, increases, there is a proportional increase in the dependent variable, time. This type of relationship is known as a direct proportion. The graph of the relationship has a positive slope.

The graphs of some directly proportional variables have negative slopes, as shown in Graph B. Assume you need to know how much farther you can drive if your car continues to use fuel at its current rate. As the amount of fuel used increases, the distance you can travel decreases.

You also may want to know how a change in your speed will affect the time required to reach your destination. You determine that as you increase your speed, driving time will decrease. This relationship is called an inverse proportion. In an inverse relationship, one variable increases as the other variable decreases. As shown in Graph C, the shape of the graph for an inverse proportion is different from a direct proportion. Notice that the graph never reaches zero. Because the car is in motion, the speed always will be greater than zero. Also, some period of time will elapse no matter how fast you travel.

1. What are the independent and dependent variables in the following graphs?
   a. Figure 2–13 on page 42
   b. Figure 9–5 on page 189
   c. Figure 26–1 on page 554
2. Which of the graphs listed above shows a positive direct proportion? a negative direct proportion?
3. Do any of the graphs in question 1 show an inverse proportion?

2:6 Laws and Theories

As information about the universe is gained, scientific laws and theories are developed. A scientific **law** is a description of a natural occurrence that has been observed many times. A scientific **theory** is a reasonable explanation of a scientific law. A theory is derived from a hypothesis that has been supported by repeated testing.

Consider the following example. In 1865, Gregor Mendel discovered a pattern in the inheritance of certain traits. Mendel crossbred tall and short pea plants in a series of experiments. From his data, he inferred that some tall offspring must have carried a trait for shortness since they produced some short offspring. Mendel concluded that the short trait must not affect the growth of pea plants when the tall trait is present. In other words, when both traits are present in the offspring, only one trait, called the dominant trait, is observed. This occurrence is called the Law of Dominance. Since Mendel's time, the Law of Dominance has been observed in countless experiments.

The gene theory helps explain the Law of Dominance. Genes are units of inheritance that occur in pairs in cells. In sexual reproduction, one gene in each pair comes from one parent. The second gene comes from the other parent. Some genes are dominant over other genes. For each gene pair containing a dominant gene, only the dominant gene is expressed as a trait.

Scientific laws and theories cannot be proven. They are maintained as long as all observations support them. When observations are made that do not agree with a law or cannot be explained by a theory, then the law or the theory may be changed. Science is always changing. As more information is gained, new laws may be stated and new theories proposed to explain them.

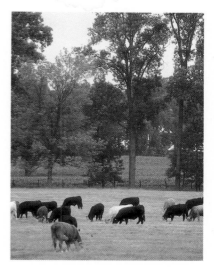

FIGURE 2–10. Understanding the gene theory has helped scientists develop new and healthier varieties of crops and livestock.

What are scientific laws and theories?

How are scientific laws or theories changed?

SUGGESTION You may wish to discuss how the Law of Definite Proportions led Dalton to propose, in an attempt to explain the law, his theory of the structure of an atom. While information gained since 1803 has resulted in many changes, some of Dalton's ideas exist today in modern atomic theory.

2:7 Models

Mendel made direct observations of the offspring in his pea plant experiments. Observations made when his experiments are repeated support the Law of Dominance and the gene theory. Many laws and theories are supported by direct observations. Sometimes only indirect observations

When do scientists use models?

can be made. For example, what did dinosaurs look like? No one knows for sure because no one has ever seen a dinosaur. However, scientists have found fossils of dinosaurs, and with their knowledge of the anatomy of reptiles, have developed models of them.

Models can help us visualize things that we cannot observe directly. Scientists use indirect observations to develop models. A **model** is what scientists think would be observed if direct observations could be made.

Models are useful in many situations, such as in the auto industry. Suppose an automobile manufacturer wants to make a new car that is more fuel efficient than any other car. It would be costly to build a lot of different cars and directly observe their performance until the most fuel efficient one was built. Instead, engineers compile what they know about the design of other fuel efficient cars. A model car is designed and then built based on those observations.

See Teacher's Guide.

REVIEW AND REFLECT

1. How are scientific laws different from theories?
2. Are scientific theories true? Explain.
3. How could you use a model to find the best arrangement of furniture in your classroom?
4. How are models helpful in space travel?

FIGURE 2–11. The designers of these structures were actually making a model of what they think future buildings will be like (a). Blueprints are helpful models to engineers and builders (b).

a

b

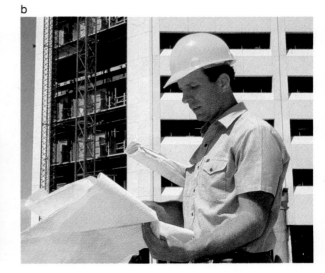

Activity: How can you use scientific methods?

See Teacher's Guide.

MATERIALS

400 mL beaker   stirring rod
water   graduated cylinder
table salt   balance
4 hard boiled eggs   tongs
   (in shell)   apron

PROCEDURE

Part A

1. Put 300 mL of water in the beaker. The water should be at room temperature. Determine the mass of the beaker and water. Record your data.
2. Carefully put a hard boiled egg into the water. Determine the mass of the beaker, water, and egg.
3. Slowly add salt to the water, stirring carefully. Add only enough salt to make the egg float. Determine the mass of the beaker, salt water, and egg.
4. Carefully remove the egg from the salt water. Place a different egg in the salt water. Does it float? Determine the mass of the beaker, salt water, and egg.
5. Repeat step 4 with two other eggs.

Part B

1. Clean your beaker from Part A. Using the same equipment from Part A, determine a way to get an egg to float in the middle of the beaker. See Figure 2–12.

FIGURE 2-12.

2. Write a hypothesis for your method and then test it by trying to float the egg according to your plan. Record your observations carefully.
3. Revise your hypothesis and method until you find a way to float the egg that supports your hypothesis.

DATA AND OBSERVATIONS

Mass	Trial			
	1	2	3	4
Beaker + water				
Beaker + water + egg				
Egg				
Beaker + salt water + egg				
Salt				
Egg floats?				

QUESTIONS AND CONCLUSIONS

1. Why did an egg float when salt was added to the water in Part A?
2. What could you have done to make all the eggs float?
3. State your hypothesis and describe your procedure for Part B.
4. What other techniques did you try that did not work in Part B? What variables might affect whether the egg floats in salt water?
5. Based on your observations, state a law that describes how an egg floats in the middle of the beaker. Write a theory that explains this law.
6. Why is it easier to float in the ocean than in most lakes?

2:8 Information: Statistics

Presenting numerical information in a graph can be very helpful. The general relationship between two variables can be determined by glancing at a graph. However, depending on how they are constructed, graphs for the same data may lead to different conclusions. Look at Figure 2–13a below. The line on this graph represents the results of a student's monthly test scores in science class. As you can see, the graph is rather flat because the student's scores did not change much during the school year. The scores increased from about 80 to 90 as the year progressed.

Now study Figure 2–13b. It is a graph of the same student's weekly test scores. As before, the increase is from about 80 to 90 for the school year. This graph shows a steep positive increase in test scores. The shape of the graph has been drastically altered by simply changing the scales on the y-axis. The impression one gets from looking at these two graphs is quite different. In this case, it appears as though a very large increase has taken place.

The dotted line on Figure 2–13a shows a second student's weekly test scores. This student's scores improved from about 68 to 91. Why do you think this student would

FIGURE 2-13. Changing the scale on the y-axis can make the data in (a) and (b) seem quite different. The change in average quiz grades in (a) and (c) appear similar even though the actual difference is relatively large.

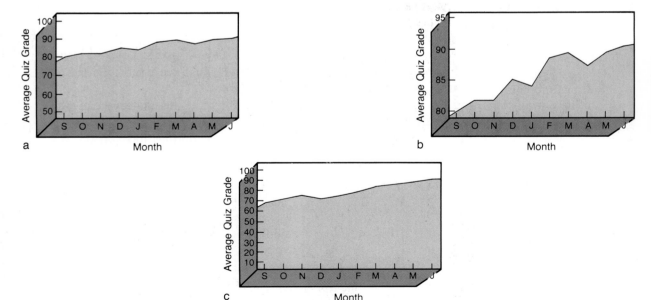

be disappointed if the test scores were represented using Figure 2–13c?

Occasionally advertisers make use of statistics to convince consumers of a product's value. An advertisement may use a bar graph like the one in Figure 2–14a to show that a car is more fuel efficient than other cars. The actual differences may be slight, but the impression you get by looking at the graph would indicate otherwise.

Figure 2–14b shows another way graphs can be misleading. The amount of protein in an average serving of two breakfast cereals is compared in this graph. As you can see, one cereal contains three times more protein than the other. You may think this difference is quite impressive. However, the recommended daily amount of protein is 50 grams. If the actual amount of protein in each cereal is analyzed, you find that neither provides much protein.

See Teacher's Guide.

REVIEW AND REFLECT

1. How are graphs useful in presenting information?
2. How can data be misrepresented with graphs?
3. Redraw the graph in Figure 2–14b to give a more accurate representation of the amount of protein provided by these cereals.

FIGURE 2–14. Advertisers may try to emphasize some qualities of their products or disguise others by using misleading scales on graphs.

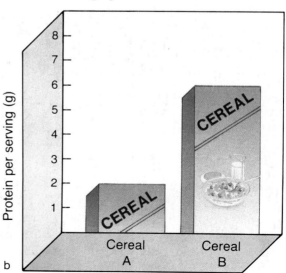

CHAPTER 2 REVIEW

SUMMARY

1. Scientific methods are systematic processes of gaining information. 2:1
2. Scientific methods involve questioning, testing, analyzing, and concluding. 2:1
3. Identifying and defining variables are important parts of planning an experiment. 2:2
4. It is important to control variables in order to test hypotheses. 2:3
5. Graphs and tables are useful ways to record and interpret observations. 2:4
6. What we can conclude from the results of an experiment is likely to be limited by the experimental design. 2:5
7. Scientific theories are developed to explain natural occurrences. 2:6
8. Models are useful to help explain things that cannot be observed directly. 2:7

VOCABULARY

dependent variable 3
hypothesis 8
independent variable 2
inference 10

law 4
model 6
operational definition 12
qualitative 9

quantitative 11
scientific methods 1
theory 5
variable 7

Match each definition with the correct word from the list.

1. Organized ways of gaining information
2. Variable changed by the experimenter
3. What responds to the variable that is changed in an experiment
4. A description of a repeatable natural occurrence
5. Reasonable explanation of natural occurrences
6. Used to help visualize occurrences and objects that cannot be observed directly
7. Changeable factor that may affect outcomes
8. Possible answer to a question or problem
9. Nonnumerical observations
10. A logical conclusion that can be drawn from an observation
11. Careful numerical measurements
12. An explanation in terms of how something will be measured

QUESTIONS

See Teacher's Guide.
MAIN IDEAS

Complete each sentence with the correct word or phrase.

1. Asking questions, making observations, and trying things out are ways used to gain _____.
2. The results of many experiments may lead to new _____.
3. A(n) _____ is a diagram of the relationship between two or more variables.
4. A variable that is held constant is said to be _____.
5. The _____ variable is manipulated by the experimenter.
6. When scientists cannot make a direct observation, they often create a(n) _____.

7. In order to explain observed natural occurrences, _____ are developed.

8. The _____ variable in an experiment responds to changes in the manipulated variable.

9. Before designing an experiment, it is important to gather information by doing some _____.

10. In many experiments, an experimental group receives a treatment. The results are compared to results of a(n) _____ group that receives no treatment.

11. In experiments in which a lot of data are recorded, it is important to have a way to _____ the data.

12. In science, laws and theories cannot be _____.

See Teacher's Guide.

APPLICATIONS

Answer each question in one or more paragraphs.

1. Why have scientists developed a model about the inner structure of the earth?

2. What variables would have to be controlled in an experiment designed to measure how much air to put in the tires of a racing bike?

3. Why is it important to repeat an experiment many times?

4. Suppose you have decided to buy a used car. Write a step-by-step procedure, based on scientific methods, that you might use to decide which car to buy.

5. The atomic theory states that all matter is made up of tiny particles called atoms. Some people, upon hearing the word "theory," would think that the atomic theory must be only an unproved belief or a poor idea about the structure of matter. What would you tell them to help them understand what the word theory means when used in science?

6. Assume you are in charge of a charity organization that grants money for scientists to do medical research. A scientist has applied for a grant to study the effects of a certain new chemical on cancer. What questions would you want to ask the scientist before granting money for the research?

FURTHER STUDY

INVESTIGATIONS

1. Read an article in a consumer magazine on a test of some household product(s). Describe how the scientific method was used. What are some limitations to the report?

2. Select a simple experiment that you can design and conduct at home. Some ideas are
Absorbency of paper towels
Strength of paper towels
Sogginess of cold cereals
Durability of nail polishes
Effectiveness of stain removers

3. Write a report about "bloodletting", once an important treatment of disease. What is bloodletting and how have theories about its uses and benefits changed?

4. Suppose two different employers offer you a job. How can you use scientific methods to help you decide which job offer to accept? Write an account of your plan.

READINGS

– Beller, Joel. *So You Want to Do a Science Project?* Arco: New York, 1982.

+ Goldstein, Martin, and Inge F. Goldstein. *How We Know.* Plenum Press: New York, 1978.

0 McCain, Garvin, and Erwin M. Segal. *The Game of Science.* 4th ed. Brooks/Cole Publishing Company: Monterey, CA, 1982.

+ Zinder, Norton D., and Alfred Meyer. "Fraud in Science." *Science 83.* January/February, 1983. pp. 94–96.

THE STRUCTURE OF MATTER

UNIT 2

Unit Two focuses on the structure of the objects around us. Every object is made up of smaller parts arranged in different ways. For example, a building may be made of glass and steel. Plants are made of cells. Glass, steel, and cells contain elements made of atoms. Atoms are made of even smaller particles. In this unit, you will learn about the arrangements of these and other particles in the structure of matter.

1. How is matter classified?
2. What patterns are found in the structure of matter?
3. What particles make up atoms?
4. How do scientists organize information about the elements?
5. In what ways do particles of matter combine?
6. Why is knowing about the structure of matter important in today's world?

THINK of all the different types of items for sale in a shopping area. Different kinds of stores sell different types of items. This specialization of stores is a classification system. Scientists have developed a classification system for the millions of different types of matter. Why do scientists classify matter? How are types of matter different?

MATTER

INTRODUCING THE CHAPTER   Discuss with students the many ways they classify the materials in which they come in contact daily. Without classification, they would not be able to find things in their homes. Clothing is in closets, food and cooking utensils in the kitchen, and so on. Ask students to think of other classification systems used commonly, such as in the school library.

3:1   Defining Matter

The differences in materials allow people to use them for many purposes. All materials are alike in some ways, too. All materials are made of matter. **Matter is anything that resists a change in motion.** What is meant by a change in motion? The chair on which you are sitting will not move unless some force is applied to it. If a sufficient force is applied to the chair, it will move. The state of motion of the chair has been changed. Likewise, a force is necessary to stop matter that is in motion. When a football player is tackled, the motion of the player is changed. Generally, the player will resist this change.

Resistance to change in motion is called **inertia** (ihn UR shuh). Objects maintain their state of motion unless some force acts on them to overcome their inertia. Inertia is a property of all matter. It is related to the mass of an object. The greater the mass of an object, the more inertia it has. More force is required to change the motion of large, massive objects than small objects.

Matter is also defined as anything that has mass and takes up space. This book and you are matter. The air you

GOAL   You will learn about the properties of matter and how it is classified.

Define matter.

How is inertia related to mass?

SUGGESTION   Review Newton's laws of motion, presented in chapter 9, if you wish.

49

breathe and the food you eat are matter. You cannot directly see all matter. For example, although air is invisible it has mass and takes up space. Air is matter. Not everything that you can see is matter. If you shine a flashlight beam on a screen, you can see the reflection of the light. Light, however, is not matter. It does not have mass and it does not take up space. Light does not exhibit the property of inertia.

Why is air classified as matter, but light is not?

3:2 Classification of Matter

In order to avoid confusion, some method is needed to classify the millions of different types of matter. A classification system is an organized way of putting similar objects into groups. People make use of classification systems every day. Telephone books are a common example of a classification system. How are names and numbers classified in telephone books? Imagine trying to locate a phone number without this classification system!

What is a classification system?

DEMONSTRATION Point out that two pieces of matter cannot occupy the same space at the same time. Fill a glass with water. Point out that once it is full of water, no more water can be added.

Many classification systems for matter have been proposed. Aristotle (384–322 B.C.) suggested that all matter could be classified into four groups: earth, air, fire, and water. He thought that a fifth type of matter might exist. He called it the "perfect substance."

Today, scientists classify matter as homogeneous or heterogeneous, Figure 3–2. Homogeneous matter is the same throughout. Heterogeneous matter can be separated into two or more types of homogeneous matter.

All heterogeneous materials are mixtures. When you make a tossed salad at a salad bar, you make a heterogeneous mixture. You start with some lettuce on your plate. Maybe you like a lot of cheese on top and a few mushrooms. Your salad is not the same throughout. Each bite is slightly different. At first you taste a lot of cheese and an occasional mushroom. At the end you taste mostly lettuce. Heterogeneous matter is not the same throughout.

Some types of homogeneous matter are mixtures. Mixtures that are homogeneous are called **solutions.** Suppose you order a cup of tea with your salad. You may stir sweetener into the tea, making a solution of tea and sweetener. The tea tastes sweet when you start drinking it and it

FIGURE 3–1. A library card catalog is a classification system that provides organized information on the title, author, and subject of books and periodicals.

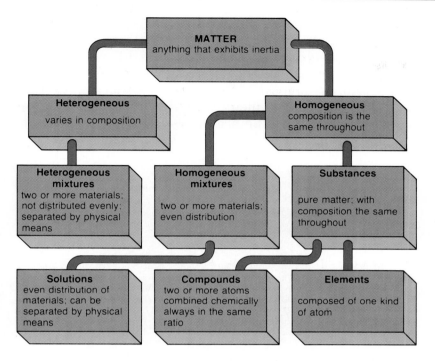

FIGURE 3-2. Matter can be classified as homogeneous or heterogeneous.

BACKGROUND Elements 1–107 and 109 have been discovered and verified. At the time of printing, element 108 had been discovered but not verified.

tastes sweet when you finish. The amount of sweetener is the same throughout the tea. Homogeneous matter is the same throughout.

Not all solutions are liquids. Deep-sea divers breathe a gaseous solution of oxygen and helium while they are under water. The alloy sterling silver is a solid solution of silver and copper. An alloy is a combination of two or more metals or a metal and one or more nonmetals. Alloys can be heterogeneous mixtures, solid solutions, or compounds.

Substances are another type of homogeneous matter. A **substance** is homogeneous matter that always has the same composition. Water is a homogeneous substance. The composition of water, H_2O, is always the same—two atoms of hydrogen and one atom of oxygen.

Substances are divided into two classes: elements and compounds. The simplest substances are elements. An element is composed of only one type of atom. Scientists have discovered 109 elements. Ninety elements occur naturally in the earth. The remaining elements have been produced in laboratories. Most of the elements are quite rare. Some of the most common elements are listed in Table 3–1.

What is the difference between homogeneous and heterogeneous matter?

SUGGESTION It may be helpful to reinforce the idea that mixtures are not necessarily liquids.

TABLE 3–1. COMMON ELEMENTS	
Element	**Percent of Earth's Crust**
Oxygen	46.6
Silicon	27.7
Aluminum	8.1
Iron	5.0
Calcium	3.6
Sodium	2.8
Potassium	2.6
Magnesium	2.1

What is a compound?

When two or more different elements combine chemically, a compound is formed. Compounds are a more complex class of substances. Compounds are different from the elements from which they were formed. Rust is a compound that is composed of the elements iron and oxygen. The element iron is a metallic solid while oxygen is a colorless, odorless gas. The properties of these two elements are quite different from the properties of rust.

See Teacher's Guide.

Skill Inquiry

The labels on many packaged foods contain useful information. Reading food labels can help you make informed decisions about which product to buy. In the United States, the Food and Drug Administration (FDA) requires that all food labels list the name and net weight of the product. The name and address of the manufacturer must be listed as well. In addition, a list of ingredients and nutritional information must be provided for many foods.

The ingredients must be listed in order of the amount by weight that the product contains. The ingredient that the product contains the most of by weight is listed first. The second most common ingredient, by weight, is listed next, and so on. The least common ingredient is listed last. Look at the food labels shown.

1. What is the most common ingredient in each of the products shown? the least common?

2. Which product probably contains more carrots? Why can you not be sure?

3. If both products are the same price, which do you think is a better value? Explain.

a   b

Included in the label's nutritional information are the number of Calories and the amount of protein, carbohydrates, fat, and sodium per serving. The nutritional information also lists the percentage of the U.S. Recommended Daily Allowance (RDA) of protein and important vitamins and minerals that the product supplies per serving.

4. If your doctor told you to limit your intake of sodium, which product would be your better choice?

5. If you are dieting to lose weight, which product would you buy?

3:3 Properties of Matter

A property is some quality or trait of an object. Matter has both chemical and physical properties. Chemical properties are descriptions of how matter interacts. For example, the flammability of a substance is a measure of how readily it burns. Flammability is a chemical property. When a substance is burned, one or more new substances are formed. Chemical changes take place when substances are changed to new substances with different chemical and physical properties.

Physical properties can be observed without chemically changing matter. Suppose you wanted to describe a piece of chalk. You might say it is white, long and slender, and powdery. Your description of the color, shape, and texture is a list of some of the physical properties of the chalk. If you break a piece of chalk, you change its physical property of shape, but it is still chalk. Physical changes in matter do not cause new substances to form.

What are chemical properties?

What are some physical properties?

TABLE 3–2. SOME PROPERTIES OF MATTER		
Physical		**Chemical**
Shape	Freezing point	Flammability
Size	Boiling point	Reactivity
Texture	Conductivity	Combustibility
Hardness	Malleability	Acidic or basic
Odor	Ductility	Tendency to ionize
Mass	Solubility	in solution
Color	Density	Electronegativity
State		

Some properties of matter are listed in Table 3–2. Scientists use properties to describe and identify matter. Properties are also important in determining how to use matter. Think about your school desk. The top is probably made of wood or plastic. Two very important physical properties for the material used in desk tops are hardness and texture. In order to write on a desk, it should be hard and smooth. Imagine trying to write on a surface like cotton that did not have these properties!

How do scientists use their knowledge of the properties of matter?

a

b

FIGURE 3–3. When engineers design buildings and bridges, they must know about the properties of matter. Wood, plaster, and plastic are important homebuilding materials (a). Bridges are constructed mainly of steel and cement (b).

Boiling point and freezing point are important physical properties to consider when selecting a material for automobile radiator antifreeze and coolant. Methanol was once used as antifreeze because it has a freezing point of −97.8°C. However, it had to be replaced in summer because its boiling point is only 64.7°C, and it is very flammable. Today, ethylene glycol is used year-round as antifreeze/coolant. The freezing point of ethylene glycol is −15.6°C, and its boiling point is 197.9°C.

See Teacher's Guide.

REVIEW AND REFLECT

1. How are elements, compounds, and solutions similar? different?
2. Name three properties that describe all types of matter.
3. Consider your school's sports program. How are the athletes in the program classified?
4. How are physical properties different from chemical properties?
5. What are some physical properties of a rose?

3:4   States of Matter

The state of matter is also a physical property. You are familiar with matter in the solid, liquid, and gaseous states. A fourth state of matter known as plasma also exists. Of the 90 naturally occurring elements, 77 are in the solid state at room temperature. Solids have a definite volume and shape. The elements copper, sulfur, and aluminum are solids at room temperature.

True solids have a crystalline structure. The atoms in a crystal are arranged in regular, repeating patterns, Figure 3–4. This crystalline structure makes the solid rigid. Some materials exist without a definite crystalline structure but appear to be solids. These materials are called amorphous. Amorphous is from the Greek word, *amorphos,* which means without form. Most plastics are amorphous. Glass is also amorphous since it has no crystalline structure. Perhaps you have noticed that the windows in a very old building are thicker at the bottom than at the top. The

What are the four states of matter?

Describe a true solid.

ACTIVITY   Have students investigate the properties of an amorphous solid that can be made by mixing about five parts cornstarch and three parts water.

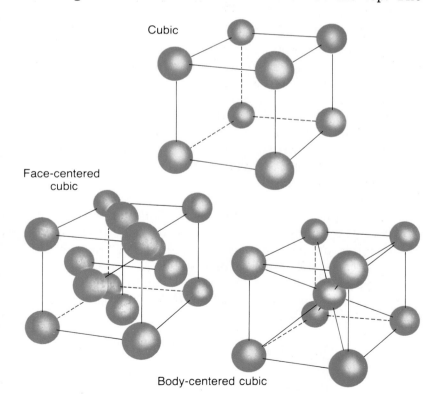

Cubic

Face-centered cubic

Body-centered cubic

FIGURE 3–4. The atoms in these three types of cubic crystals are arranged in a regular pattern.

difference in thickness occurs as the glass flows downward. This process is so slow that it takes many years for the flow to be noticed.

Only two of the 90 natural elements, mercury and bromine, are in the liquid state at room temperature. Liquids have a definite volume but no definite shape. Liquids conform to the shape of their container.

The remaining 11 natural elements are in the gaseous state at room temperature. Air is a mixture of gases, mostly nitrogen and oxygen. Gases have neither a definite volume nor a definite shape. Gases conform to both the shape and volume of their container.

What is the plasma state of matter?

Matter exists in the **plasma** state at extremely high temperatures. In the plasma state, electrons are separated from atoms. When this occurs, the matter consists of charged particles. You know that water changes from a liquid to a gas at about 100°C. Matter changes to the plasma state at much higher temperatures. The temperature on the surface of the sun is about 6000°C. Hydrogen, one of the elements in water, is found in the plasma state on the sun. Matter in the plasma state also is used in some types of nuclear reactions.

What kind of change occurs when matter changes state?

A physical change occurs when matter changes from one state to another. A change of state does not form chemically different matter, even though some of the physical properties of the material change. When you boil water, it changes from the liquid to the gaseous state. However, in either state, it is still H_2O.

The temperature at which matter changes from the liquid to the gaseous state is called the boiling point. The freezing point is the temperature at which matter changes from the liquid to the solid state. The temperature at which matter changes from the solid to the liquid state is the melting point. The freezing point and the melting point are the same temperature.

Boiling points, freezing points, and melting points are physical properties that describe physical changes in matter. The relationship between these physical changes is

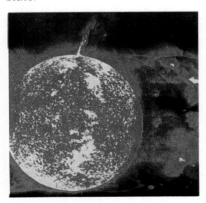

FIGURE 3–5. The sun's intense thermal energy causes much of its matter to exist in the plasma state.

solid $\xrightleftharpoons[\text{melting}]{\text{freezing}}$ liquid $\xrightleftharpoons[\text{boiling}]{\text{condensing}}$ gas

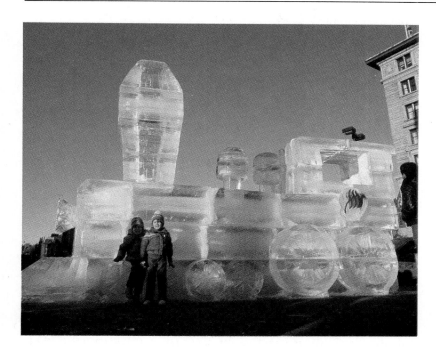

FIGURE 3–6. An ice sculpture will begin to melt in temperatures above the freezing point of water.

3:5   Other Physical Properties

Some physical properties are characteristic of certain types of matter. The melting point of ice is 0°C no matter what its shape. Boiling points, freezing points, and melting points are some examples of characteristic physical properties.

Another characteristic physical property of matter is conductivity. Conductivity is the ability to transmit heat or electricity. Materials that readily transmit heat or electricity are **conductors.** Materials that resist the flow of heat or electricity are **insulators** (IHN suh layt urz). Some elements, like silicon and germanium, are called **semiconductors.** Semiconductors do not conduct heat or electricity under normal conditions. Special treatment of these elements can cause them to conduct. Semiconductors are of great importance in the field of electronics. Semiconductors are used to make transistors and integrated circuits, ICs. These devices can be used in electronic applications in place of vacuum tubes. ICs and transistors are smaller, operate without producing great amounts of heat, and use much less power than vacuum tubes.

What is conductivity?

How do conductors, insulators, and semiconductors differ?

FIGURE 3–7. Metals are good conductors of heat, which is an important property for pots and pans.

Generally, most metals are conductors and most nonmetals are insulators. Conductivity is an important physical property in determining how materials are used. Copper and aluminum are both good conductors of heat and electricity. Both metals are used to make wire. Rubber and plastic are both insulators. They are often used to insulate wire.

Malleability and ductility are physical properties that relate to how readily a material's shape can be changed. Most metals are malleable and ductile. Nonmetals are generally brittle. **Malleability** (mal ee uh BIHL uh tee) refers to the ease with which a material can be pressed, rolled, or hammered into thin sheets. Steel is used for car bodies because it is strong but malleable. **Ductility** is the ease with which a material can be drawn into wires.

Solubility (sahl yuh BIHL uh tee) is a physical property that describes how readily a substance dissolves in another substance. Salt is dissolved in ocean water, but this solution can be separated into salt and water. On some cruise ships, ocean water is used to supply fresh water on the ship. Thousands of liters of ocean water are heated to the boiling point. The escaping steam is collected and cooled. It condenses, leaving the salt. This process, known as distillation, is a physical change.

Describe malleability and ductility.

Define solubility.

See Teacher's Guide.

Career Profile

"No two days are ever alike," says Dale Jones, a tool and die maker who owns his own business in Bowling Green, Ohio. Dale designs and makes the tooling (cutting devices) and dies (molds) needed to produce a variety of manufactured goods. "You'd be surprised how many common, everyday items are molded using dies. Everything from soft drink cans to silverware, from plastic toys to machine parts." Dale specializes in making dies that are used to manufacture small automobile parts.

A great deal of training is needed to become a tool and die maker. Dale served as an apprentice for four years. As an apprentice, he worked with an experienced tool and die maker. Dale completed 8000 hours of on-the-job experience in addition to classroom training at a technical school. Dale also elected to take some metallurgical engineering classes at the University of Toledo. These courses taught him more about the basic properties of metals and alloys. The materials that can be made from alloys can vary greatly as the metal composition changes. "We usually think of aluminum as

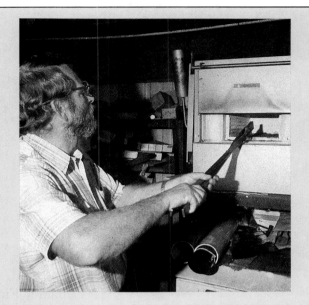

being lightweight, but soft and not very strong," says Dale. "But some alloys of aluminum are extremely strong and rigid."

Dale advises anyone who wants to become a tool and die maker to acquire a good understanding of basic science. He emphasizes a strong knowledge of mathematics and the properties of materials. Learning about computers is also important in today's business world.

3:6 Density

Another characteristic physical property of matter is density. **Density** is a measure of the amount of matter contained in a given volume.

$$\text{density} = \frac{\text{mass}}{\text{volume}}$$

$$D = \frac{m}{V}$$

How is density calculated?

Density usually is measured in grams per cubic centimeter, g/cm^3.

a
b

FIGURE 3–8. The mass of the items in each suitcase is the same. The volume of (a) is less than (b), which means the density of the items in (a) is greater than in (b).

switch a b

SUGGESTION Explain that for this example, the masses of the suitcases, which might not be the same, are being ignored.

Consider Figure 3–8. A student is preparing for a vacation. He has two suitcases, but he only wants to take one. One of the suitcases is a little larger than the other. First he packs his clothes into the smaller suitcase. The suitcase becomes too full. So he decides to take the larger suitcase instead. He repacks his clothes into the larger suitcase. The mass of the clothes is the same in each suitcase, but the volumes of the suitcases are different. If you calculate the density of each suitcase, you will see that the densities are different, too.

EXAMPLE: Calculating Density

Problem: The volume of the small suitcase is 65 000 cm³. The volume of the large suitcase is 75 000 cm³. What is the density of each suitcase filled with 26 000 g of clothing?

Solution: The density of each suitcase is the mass of the clothing divided by the volume of the suitcase.

$$D = \frac{m}{V}$$

$$D_{small} = \frac{26\ 000\ g}{65\ 000\ cm^3}$$

$$D_{small} = 0.40\ g/cm^3$$

$$D_{large} = \frac{26\ 000\ g}{75\ 000\ cm^3}$$
$$D_{large} = 0.35\ g/cm^3$$

At the last minute, the student decides to put a few more clothes in the suitcase. The volume of the suitcase does not change, but the mass of the clothing does. Stuffing more and more matter into the same volume increases the density.

The density of a material is a practical piece of information. Objects with a density less than water will float. An oceanliner has an overall density less than water.

DEMONSTRATION Place an ice cube in methanol (or ditto fluid, D = 0.87) and another ice cube in water. Discuss what students observe in terms of density.

TABLE 3–3. DENSITIES OF COMMON MATERIALS			
Material	**Density**	**Material**	**Density**
Iron	7.9 g/cm^3	White pine	about 0.40 g/cm^3
Aluminum	2.7 g/cm^3	Oak	about 0.75 g/cm^3
Lead	11.3 g/cm^3	Ice	about 0.92 g/cm^3
Sugar	1.6 g/cm^3	Leather	0.86 g/cm^3
Concrete	2.4 g/cm^3	Butter	0.87 g/cm^3
Glass	2.5 g/cm^3	Cardboard	0.69 g/cm^3
Nylon	1.2 g/cm^3	Charcoal	0.57 g/cm^3
Water	1.00 g/cm^3	Limestone	about 2.72 g/cm^3

See Teacher's Guide.

REVIEW AND REFLECT

1. Why do we generally not observe the plasma state of matter?
2. Why are cooking and baking pans often made of aluminum and copper?
3. Which would be easier to move, an oak antique desk or a white pine reproduction of it? Why?
4. A block of wood is 30 cm long, 10 cm wide, and 5 cm thick. It has a mass of 600 g. What kind of wood is it? Will it float in water? How do you know?
5. A piece of metal is almost eight times as dense as water. What kind of metal might it be?

Activity: What are some properties of matter?

See Teacher's Guide.

MATERIALS

graduated cylinder
2 wooden clothespins
flashlight bulb
and holder
2 150-mL beakers
various samples of
matter supplied by your teacher

metric ruler
dry cell
3 30-cm wires
apron
goggles
balance

PROCEDURE

1. Observe as many physical properties of each sample as you can and record in the data table. **CAUTION:** *Always handle unknown materials with care.*

2. Using the flashlight bulb, wire, and dry cell, determine which samples are conductors of electricity as shown in Figure 3–9. **CAUTION:** *Work only on a dry surface.* Connect one wire to the dry cell. Connect another wire from the dry cell to the light bulb. Connect the third wire to the light bulb. Pick up the free wires from the dry cell and the light bulb with clothespins. Touch these two wires to your sample.

3. Determine the mass of each sample.

FIGURE 3–9.

4. If the sample is a regular shape, carefully measure the length, height, and width with the ruler.

5. If the sample is a liquid, determine its volume using the graduated cylinder.

6. If the sample has an irregular shape, determine its volume using the graduated cylinder. Add water to the graduated cylinder and record the volume. Place the sample in the graduated cylinder and again record the volume. The difference is the volume of the sample.

7. Calculate the density of each sample.

DATA AND OBSERVATIONS

Sample				
General Observations				
Electrical Conductivity				
Volume				
Mass				
Density				

QUESTIONS AND CONCLUSIONS

1. What physical properties would be most helpful in identifying the samples?

2. Which samples conduct electricity?

3. Which samples will float in water? Which will not? Check your predictions. Using the table of densities on page 61, try to identify each sample.

4. If water is an insulator, why is it necessary to take precautions using electrical devices near a bathtub?

3:7 Chemical Properties

The science of chemistry focuses on the chemical properties and chemical changes of matter. The chemical properties of matter are descriptions of how a substance interacts with other substances. Some chemical properties are listed in Table 3–2. Like physical properties, the chemical properties of matter are closely related to how materials are used.

One chemical property is **reactivity.** Some substances readily interact chemically with other substances. Many metals are highly reactive and tend to combine with other substances to form compounds. Corrosion is a common example of the reactivity of metals. Iron, copper, and most other metals tend to corrode when exposed to the atmosphere. For this reason, iron and copper often are painted or coated with a metal, such as zinc, which is less likely to corrode. Galvanized steel has been coated with zinc. Aluminum and some other metals do not readily corrode. They react with oxygen in the air to form a thin oxide film. This film protects the metal from further corrosion.

Why are some metals painted or galvanized?

FIGURE 3–10. Electroplating is a process that can be used to coat objects with a metal such as zinc or chromium to prevent the objects from corroding (a). Gold is an excellent conductor and resists corrosion. These properties make gold very useful in wiring sensitive computer parts (b).

a

b

Why should you never taste an unknown substance to determine its physical properties?

What are combustible and flammable materials?

ACTIVITY   Have students check labels of food and other home products to determine if they contain acids or bases. Acids and bases are discussed in chapter 6.

BACKGROUND   Some common flame retardants contain ammonium bromide, boric acid, borax, sodium phosphate, and some phosphorous compounds.

Another chemical property is the reactivity of a substance with an acid or base. Whether a substance is acidic, basic, or neutral is also a chemical property. Many household products are acids or bases. Many foods contain acids. Acids generally taste sour. Vinegar is a weak solution of acetic acid in water. Oranges, lemons, and limes all contain citric acid.

Bases, the chemical opposites of acids, are generally slippery. Ammonia and lye are two common bases used in the home. Ammonia is an ingredient in many household and window cleaners. Lye is sometimes used as a cleaner for clogged drains. It also can be used as a starting material for making soap. Both acids and bases can be harmful and must be used with care.

Two other chemical properties are flammability and combustibility. When a material burns, it combines with oxygen to form a new material with different properties. A substance is **combustible** if it will burn. **Flammable** materials are ignited easily and burn vigorously. In this sense, we would classify wood as combustible and gasoline as both combustible and flammable. Some substances tend not to be combustible. These substances can be used to treat paper as well as fabrics used for clothing and upholstery to protect them from burning.

The various properties of matter are important to scientists as they develop new materials. For example, rubber is a natural product that is obtained from treating the sap of rubber trees. Rubber is used to produce a wide variety of products including electrical insulation, footwear, toys, and tires. The uses of rubber were limited until an American, Charles Goodyear (1800–1860), invented the process known as vulcanization which greatly strengthens natural rubber. Vulcanized rubber is about ten times stronger than nonvulcanized rubber. By varying the amount of vulcanization, rubber products with different properties can be produced.

See Teacher's Guide.

REVIEW AND REFLECT

1. Name at least five chemical properties.
2. Since aluminum is resistant to corrosion, why do you think aluminum is not always used instead of steel?

Activity: What are chemical changes?

See Teacher's Guide.

MATERIALS

12 test tubes
droppers
iodine solution
vinegar
water
cornstarch

baking powder
baking soda
talc
unknown powders
goggles
apron

PROCEDURE

1. Place a small amount of cornstarch in each of three test tubes. Add a dropper of water to one test tube. Record your observations.

2. Add a dropper of iodine solution to the second test tube. **CAUTION:** *Iodine solution is poisonous, stains, and causes burns. Rinse spills with plenty of water.* Record your observations.

3. Add a dropper of vinegar to the third test tube. Record your observations.

4. Repeat steps 1 to 3 substituting baking powder, baking soda, and talc for cornstarch.

5. Obtain unknown powders from your teacher. **CAUTION:** *Handle all unknown materials with care. Never taste any unknown materials!* Using iodine solution, vinegar, and water, identify the unknown powders.

FIGURE 3–11.

DATA AND OBSERVATIONS

Known Samples	Water	Vinegar	Iodine
Cornstarch			
Baking powder			
Baking soda			
Talc			

Unknown Samples	Water	Vinegar	Iodine
1			
2			
3			
4			
5			
6			

QUESTIONS AND CONCLUSIONS

1. What did you observe when you added water to each known sample?

2. What did you observe when you added water to each unknown sample?

3. What did you observe when you added iodine solution to each known sample?

4. What did you observe when you added iodine solution to each unknown sample?

5. What did you observe when you added vinegar to each known sample?

6. What did you observe when you added vinegar to each unknown sample?

7. What chemical changes did you observe?

8. Identify each of your unknown powders. Explain how you obtained your answers.

9. What physical characteristics helped you identify the unknown powders?

3:8 Information: Photography

Before this century, pictures were taken mainly by professionals. Cameras were expensive and photographers had to develop film themselves. In 1888, George Eastman invented a camera for amateur use. The camera was lightweight, easy to use, and relatively inexpensive. People could take about 100 pictures with one roll of film. Then they sent the camera with the film inside to one of Eastman's developing plants. Black-and-white photographs, called "prints," were made and returned to the owner along with the camera containing a new roll of film. The rolls of film with which you are familiar, that can be removed from a camera without exposing them, were developed later. What happens to your film when you take it to a photo lab?

Black-and-white photographic film is a thin sheet of plastic material coated with a light-sensitive chemical. This coating contains many small particles of a silver compound. When a picture is taken, the film is exposed to light. The silver compound undergoes a chemical change. Metallic silver is formed on the developed film, called a negative. Bright areas in the subject reflect more light than dark areas. So they cause more formation of metallic silver on the negative. The metallic silver is dark. The

Briefly describe the history of amateur photography.

BACKGROUND The most common silver compounds used in black-and-white film are AgBr, AgCl, and AgI.

FIGURE 3–12. The steps in film and photo development are shown in this illustration. This process involves chemical changes in the silver compound that coats the film and photographic paper.

Film coated with silver compound is exposed to light

Developing—metallic silver formed on areas exposed to light

Fixing—excess silver compound removed

Washing—extra chemicals removed

Developed negatives ready for use

Paper coated with silver compound is exposed to light filtered through negative

Developing—metallic silver formed on areas exposed to light

Fixing—excess silver compound removed

Washing—excess chemicals removed

Finished print

bright areas show up as dark portions of the negative. The dark areas show up as lighter portions of the negative.

The development process of the film must be performed in darkness. If the film were exposed to light, it would turn completely dark upon development since all of the silver compound would be changed to metallic silver. After the film has been developed, the excess silver compound that has not been changed to metallic silver is removed from the film. This process is called fixing. Without fixing, the film would gradually turn dark when exposed to light.

When a negative is used to make a black-and-white print, the entire process is repeated. The negative image is projected on light-sensitive photographic paper. The dark areas of the negative, which represent the brighter areas of the subject photographed, become the bright areas of the finished print. The lighter portions of the negative, which represent the darker areas of the subject, allow the paper to be exposed to more light. So the light areas of the negative become the dark areas of the print. After the paper is developed, it too must be fixed to remove excess silver compound. The silver used in photographic films can be recovered and recycled. As the price of silver increases, this process is becoming more important. Large amounts of silver are recovered from unneeded X-ray photographs in hospitals and clinics each year.

Color film became available in 1935. The same basic process is used to develop it. Color film has three layers of chemical coatings. Each layer is sensitive to one of the three primary colors of light (blue, green, red). All of the colors you see are formed from the combination of these three colors. When color film is exposed, the blue light in the subject forms an image on one layer, the green light on another, and the red light on a third layer. Negatives are formed with complementary colors that produce the original colors of the subject when the prints are made.

See Teacher's Guide.

FIGURE 3–13.   Many people enjoy developing their own film as a hobby.

How is color film developed?

REVIEW AND REFLECT

1. What is a negative?
2. Why must films and prints be fixed?
3. If a person taking a picture allows too much light to enter the camera, the picture will be overexposed. What will the negative look like?

CHAPTER 3 REVIEW

SUMMARY

1. Matter exhibits inertia. 3:1
2. Homogeneous matter is the same throughout. Heterogeneous matter is a mixture that can be separated into homogeneous matter. 3:2
3. Homogeneous mixtures are solutions. 3:2
4. A substance is homogeneous matter that always has the same composition. 3:2
5. Compounds and elements are substances. 3:2
6. Matter has chemical and physical properties. 3:3
7. A physical change does not result in a different substance. 3:3
8. When a substance undergoes a chemical change, new substances are formed. 3:3
9. Matter exists in four physical states. 3:4
10. Some physical properties are characteristic of certain types of matter. 3:5
11. Density is a measure of the amount of mass per unit volume. 3:6
12. The physical and chemical properties of matter help determine how it will be used. 3:7

VOCABULARY

combustible 7	inertia 2	reactivity 8
conductor 4	insulator 10	semiconductor 11
density 6	malleability 1	solubility 3
ductility 13	matter 12	solution 9
flammable 15	plasma 5	substance 14

Match each definition with the correct word from the list.

1. Ability to be formed into thin sheets
2. Resistance to change in motion
3. Ability of one substance to dissolve in another substance
4. Readily transmits heat or electricity
5. State of matter consisting of charged particles
6. Amount of matter in a given volume
7. Ability to burn
8. The ability to combine readily
9. Homogeneous matter with same composition throughout
10. Resists the flow of heat and electricity
11. Widely used in electronics
12. Anything that resists a change in motion
13. Ability to be drawn into wire
14. A homogeneous mixture
15. Ignites and burns readily

QUESTIONS

MAIN IDEAS

Choose the correct answer to each question.

1. Which of the following is not an example of matter? *(wood, air, light, ice)*

2. What properties can be observed without chemically changing matter? *(chemical, physical, both chemical and physical, neither chemical or physical)*

3. Which of the following is an example of heterogeneous matter? *(solution, element, compound, mixture)*

4. What is a homogeneous mixture called? *(solution, element, compound, substance)*

5. Of what are elements and compounds both examples? *(substances, mixtures, solutions, heterogeneous matter)*

6. Of what are elements made? *(compounds, atoms, substances, mixtures)*

7. In what state do most elements occur naturally? *(solid, liquid, plasma, gas)*

8. What is matter that resists the transfer of heat or electricity called? *(conductor, insulator, semiconductor, ductile)*

9. Of what is density a measure? *(volume per unit mass, mass per unit volume, mass that will dissolve in a given volume)*

10. What is defined as a mixture of two or more metals? *(conductor, alloy, insulator, semiconductor)*

11. In how many states can matter exist? *(one, two, three, four)*

12. What process would not form a new substance with different properties? *(cutting, burning, rusting, decomposing)*

See Teacher's Guide.

APPLICATIONS

Answer each question in one or more paragraphs. Show how to solve each problem.

1. Which of the substances in Table 3–3 on page 61 will float in water?

2. What conditions exist on stars that result in matter being in the plasma state?

3. What properties are necessary for materials used to construct airplanes for passenger travel?

4. Using Table 3–3 on page 61, calculate the mass of a block of ice measuring 20 cm × 10 cm × 5 cm.

5. Will an ice cube (D = 0.92) float in methanol (D = 0.87)? Explain.

6. What is the density of an object that occupies 125 cm^3 and has a mass of 150 g?

FURTHER STUDY

INVESTIGATIONS

1. Find out what a metallurgist does. How are the properties of matter important to a metallurgist? How does the training metallurgists receive help them understand the properties of matter? Give an oral report about your findings.

2. Investigate the properties of materials used in cookware. What are some properties of Teflon®? Report on the history and use of Teflon® in cookware.

3. Report on the contributions of Aristotle to our understanding of matter today.

4. Investigate how scientists analyzed the properties of moon rocks. Prepare posters explaining the procedures.

READINGS

+ March, Robert H. "Catching Nature's Vanishing Act." *Science Year, 1983*. 1982. pp. 196–207.

+ Meyer, Alfred. "Stirrings in Glass." *Science 81*. May, 1981. pp. 34–43.

0 Schechter, Bruce. "Bubbles That Bend the Mind." *Science 84*. March, 1984. pp. 44–51.

+ Sagan, Carl. *Cosmos*. Random House: New York, 1980.

0 Verbit, Lawrence P. "Chemistry's Speedy Servants." *Science Year, 1982*. 1981. pp. 194–205.

+ Walters, Derek. *Chemistry*. Franklin Watts: New York, 1982.

THE pyramid structure in this picture is made up of individual cheerleaders arranged in a definite pattern. All matter is made up of atoms. The atoms are arranged in definite ways. Atoms are made up of smaller particles that are arranged in definite ways, too. How are atoms arranged in matter? How are the particles arranged?

ATOMIC STRUCTURE

INTRODUCING THE CHAPTER   While there are millions of different materials that are known, students should realize that there is order and structure in how elements combine. The approximately 100 elements combine in orderly ways to form many different materials. Compare this to the way thousands of words are formed from 26 letters.

4:1   Early Atomic Theories

About 2300 years ago, the Greek philosopher Democritus proposed the idea that matter is composed of atoms. Democritus reasoned that an apple could be cut into smaller and smaller pieces. Eventually he would have particles that could no longer be cut and still be apple. He called these small particles atoms, which is Greek for unable to be cut.

Democritus never saw an atom. Atoms are too small for anyone to observe directly. For example, one drop of water contains millions of atoms. Scientists often propose models to help them visualize things that cannot be observed directly. The models are based on scientific theories. Much of the early work on the atomic theory was done in England. The Cavendish Laboratory at the University of Cambridge was the site of many important discoveries about atomic structure. Table 4–1 summarizes some major steps that led to the modern atomic theory. As more information was gathered by scientists about atoms, the atomic theory was revised. Scientists are still learning about atoms and atomic structure.

GOAL   You will learn how theories of atomic structure have developed and changed.

BACKGROUND   The Greek derivative of the word atoms is *atomos*, which means indivisible.

Why do scientists propose theories?

TABLE 4–1. DEVELOPMENT OF ATOMIC THEORY

Scientist	Theory	Model
John Dalton 1803 Manchester, England	All matter is composed of atoms. Atoms are solid spheres. Each element has a unique type of atom.	
J.J. Thomson 1897–1903 Cavendish Laboratory Cambridge, England	Electrons are negatively-charged particles. Electrons are located in a ball of positively-charged matter.	
Ernest Rutherford, Niels Bohr 1913 Cavendish Laboratory Cambridge, England	The nucleus of an atom is small, dense, and positively charged. The electrons travel in "orbits" around the nucleus.	

4:2 Current Atomic Theory

Of what does an atom consist mostly?

According to current atomic theory, an atom consists of a small, dense nucleus surrounded by mostly empty space in which electrons move at high speeds. Most of an atom's volume is empty space. The average diameter of a nucleus is about 5×10^{-13} centimeters. The average diameter of an atom is about 2×10^{-8} centimeters. The difference in these two sizes means an atom is about 40 000 times larger than its nucleus. Consider an example of this relative difference. If the nucleus were the size of an orange, the whole atom would measure about 24 city blocks across.

What makes up most of an atom's mass?

Even though an atomic nucleus is relatively small, it makes up over 99.9% of an atom's mass. The nucleus of an atom contains protons. A **proton** is a relatively massive particle with a positive electric charge. The nucleus of a helium atom contains two protons. The mass of a helium nucleus is about twice the mass of two protons. The additional mass is due to neutrons found in the nuclei of helium atoms. A **neutron** is a nuclear particle that has no electric charge. A neutron has about the same mass as a proton. Most atomic nuclei contain neutrons.

a

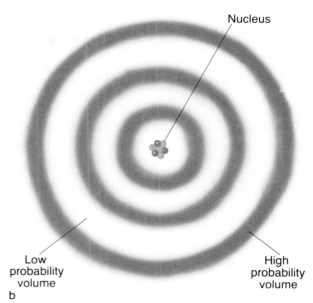

b

Nucleus

Low probability volume

High probability volume

Current atomic theory suggests that electrons move rapidly around an atomic nucleus forming an electron "cloud." An **electron** is a negatively-charged particle with very little mass. According to the electron cloud model, an electron may be anywhere within the cloud at any given moment. Scientists have developed mathematical ways to predict the probability of where an electron will be in a given area at any specific time.

Atoms are electrically neutral, which means they have no net electric charge. The sum of negative charges of the electrons equals the sum of positive charges of the protons. (Remember, neutrons have no electric charge.) The nucleus of the simplest element, hydrogen, has one proton. One electron moves in the electron cloud about its nucleus. All atoms of hydrogen are alike in that they have one proton and one electron. The charge of an electron is -1, which balances the $+1$ charge of a proton, resulting in a neutral atom.

A helium nucleus has two protons, so the charge on the helium nucleus is $+2$. Since all atoms are neutral, helium must have two electrons (a charge of -2) in its electron cloud. A lithium nucleus contains three protons. What is the charge on a lithium nucleus? How many electrons are in the electron cloud of a lithium atom?

FIGURE 4–1. The spokes of a moving bicycle wheel create a blurred or cloudy image (a). The spokes appear to fill the entire volume of space. Electrons moving rapidly around a nucleus form an electron cloud (b).

Where are electrons found?

See Teacher's Guide.

Skill Inquiry

The ideas of probability have many applications to everyday life. Weather predictions help us plan for picnics, traffic congestion, and space flights. Statistics are used to help decide how much food a restaurant is likely to need on a given day.

Insurance companies use probabilities to help determine the rates they charge for insurance policies. For example, rates for auto insurance usually decrease as a person gets older. Statistics show that people older than 25 years have fewer accidents than younger people.

1. Why do you think auto insurance rates for women may be less than for men?
2. How do you think the number of accidents or traffic violations people have may affect their auto insurance rates?

Younger people have a greater probability of living longer than older people. For this reason, the rates people must pay for life insurance vary depending on their age when they apply for the insurance. The probabilities used by insurance companies are organized in actuary tables. The table shown is an example of an actuary table that may be used by a life insurance company in the United States.

TABLE OF AVERAGE FUTURE LIFETIME IN THE U.S. (YEARS)

Age	Average Life Expectancy	Average Remaining Lifetime	
		Male	Female
15-20	57.9	52.0	59.5
20-25	53.2	47.5	54.8
25-30	48.6	43.2	50.0
30-35	43.9	38.8	45.3
35-40	39.3	34.4	40.8
40-45	34.7	30.2	36.4
45-50	30.3	26.2	32.0
50-55	26.1	22.4	27.8
55-60	22.2	18.9	23.9
60-65	18.5	15.6	20.0
65-70	15.2	13.0	16.6
70-75	12.1	10.7	13.6

3. If a woman and a man, both 40 years old with similar lifestyles and health, applied for life insurance, who probably would be charged a higher rate?
4. Why must people pay more for life insurance if they are older when they apply for it?
5. If you were designing an application form for life insurance policies, what questions would you ask the applicants?

4:3 Energy Levels

What are energy levels?

Electrons have a high probability of being located in the electron cloud at predictable distances from the nucleus. These areas are called energy levels. Energy levels are like the floors of a building. In a building, people cannot occupy the area between floors. They can occupy only specific floors of the building. Electrons cannot occupy the area between energy levels in atoms.

There are seven energy levels known for electrons of stable atoms. Electrons with a greater amount of energy are found in the outermost levels. Those electrons with less energy occupy the levels nearest the nucleus. Each energy level can hold only a certain number of electrons. For example, the lowest or first energy level can hold only two electrons.

The reactivity of an atom is related to its electron arrangement. The maximum number of electrons in most atoms' outermost energy level is eight. According to the octet rule, atoms with a complete set of eight electrons in their outermost energy level tend to be very stable. Certain gases, called the noble gases, contain the most stable atoms. These atoms have filled outer energy levels and do not react easily. Atoms with outer energy levels that are not completely filled tend to react until their outer energy levels are completely filled.

See Teacher's Guide.

Where are electrons with the greatest energy located?

Describe the octet rule.

BACKGROUND The maximum number of electrons an energy level can hold is $2n^2$, where n is the number of the energy level. For example, the maximum number of electrons in the third energy level is $2(3)^2 = 18$.

REVIEW AND REFLECT

1. What did each of these people contribute to modern atomic theory?
   a. Dalton
   b. Thomson
   c. Bohr
2. Why are scientists unable to determine the exact location of an electron in an atom?
3. The element radon is a relatively unreactive gaseous element. What type of electron arrangement would you expect radon to have?

4:4 Other Subatomic Particles

As more has been learned about the structure of atoms, scientists have altered their models. For example, scientists have found that atoms are made up of smaller particles. These particles are called subatomic particles. Thus, early models of atoms as hard spheres were replaced with the electron cloud model. Since the early 1930s, scientists have found or predicted the existence of more than 200 subatomic particles. Some subatomic particles exist for only short periods of time.

What are subatomic particles?

TABLE 4–2. SOME SUBATOMIC PARTICLES

Particle	Charge	Antiparticle	Average Lifetime
LEPTONS			
Electron	−	Positron (+)	infinite
Neutrino	0	Antineutrino	infinite
Muon	−	Antimuon (+)	2.2×10^{-6} s
Muon neutrino	0	Antimuonneutrino	infinite
HADRONS			
Proton	+	Antiproton	10^{31} y
Neutron	0	Antineutron	925 s
Lambda	0	Antilambda	2.6×10^{-10} s
Sigma	+	Antisigma (−)	8.0×10^{-11} s
Sigma	−	Antisigma (+)	1.48×10^{-10} s
Sigma	0	Antisigma (0)	5.8×10^{-20} s
Pion	+	Pion (−)	2.6×10^{-8} s
Pion	−	Pion (+)	2.6×10^{-8} s
Pion	0	Same particle	8.3×10^{-17} s
J-PSI	0	Same particle	3.3×10^{-20} s
Upsilon	0	Same particle	4.9×10^{-20} s

How are subatomic particles classified?

BACKGROUND   The average lifetime of protons has always been thought to be infinite. Current theory of the structure of matter suggests that the average lifetime of protons is not infinite, but has a lower limit of about 10^{31} years. Experiments are being conducted to detect the decay of a proton. To date, none have been observed.

Subatomic particles are far too small to be observed directly. They measure about 10^{-13} centimeters across. In order to detect these particles, scientists use devices called accelerators. These devices make particles move at very high speeds. When these accelerated particles collide with each other, they may be broken up into smaller, subatomic particles.

Scientists classify subatomic particles into two groups, leptons and hadrons. Table 4–2 summarizes some of the types of leptons and hadrons. **Leptons** have relatively small masses and do not exhibit strong nuclear interactions. The electron is an example of a lepton. **Hadrons** are particles that respond to strong nuclear forces. Both protons and neutrons are examples of hadrons.

In 1969, the American physicist Murray Gell-Mann predicted that hadrons are composed of even smaller particles he called **quarks**. Several different kinds of quarks have been suggested. Gell-Mann postulated that quarks interact with each other by exchanging massless particles called gluons.

Each subatomic particle is believed to have an antiparticle. Particles and antiparticles are identical to one another except they possess opposite electric charges. The first antiparticle, the positron, was discovered in 1932. The positron has the same mass and other characteristics as an electron except it has a positive electrical charge. **Antiparticles** are produced in nuclear reactions, but do not exist for long. When a particle and its antiparticle collide, they cancel each other. Energy is given off as their masses are converted to energy. Antimatter or antiparticles do not exist in great amounts near us in the universe.

What are antiparticles?

BACKGROUND   The collision of a particle and its antiparticle is an example of Einstein's equation, $E = mc^2$.

See Teacher's Guide.

Career Profile

In the late 1800s the small community of Moab, Utah, was founded because of uranium mining. Then, uranium was used chiefly as a pigment in glass manufacturing. By the late 1940s, uranium was being used to fuel nuclear reactors. Since that time, the use of this valuable substance has increased.

Louis Nicol grew up in the uranium mining business. Each summer as a youth, he and his brothers worked with their father in the mines. Today, Louis is a foreman of an uranium mine. Louis supervises about 20 miners.

Uranium deposits are usually found in sandstone. To detect the location of uranium deposits, an instrument called a gamma ray recorder is used. A hole about 15 centimeters deep is drilled into the sandstone. The recorder is lowered into the hole. It detects the radiation given off by the uranium. The information indicates how deep uranium lies below the earth's surface. Once the miners begin digging the uranium, Louis must assume some very important responsibilities.

One of Louis' primary concerns is the safety of his miners. He must be sure his miners are properly equipped before they enter the mine. They must wear heavy clothing, rubber boots, hard hats with lights, mining belts with batteries, safety glasses, respirators, and gloves. Louis must also monitor the amount of radiation exposure the miners receive. A technician measures the radiation levels of each mining area. The technician provides Louis with a report on the miners' radiation levels. Louis is careful not to exceed maximum radiation levels for his miners. He regularly rotates them from areas of high radiation to areas of low radiation.

Activity: How can you make predictions?

MATERIALS

10 coins   2 dice
1 plastic foam cup

PROCEDURE

1. Place the coins in a cup and gently shake them onto a table. Record the number of heads. Repeat 24 more times.
2. Using your data, predict how many heads will turn up if you flip the 10 coins. Test your prediction five times. Record your results.
3. Place the dice in the cup. Gently roll the dice onto the table. Record whether the numbers on the dice are the same or different. Repeat 24 times.
4. Predict how many times you would have to roll the dice to get the same number on each die. Test your prediction five times. Record your results.

DATA AND OBSERVATIONS

Number of Heads	Frequency
0	
1	
2	
3	
4	
5	
6	
7	
8	
9	
10	

FIGURE 4–2.

Dice Rolling	Frequency
Same	
Different	

QUESTIONS AND CONCLUSIONS

1. Which is more likely, to get three or eight heads when flipping ten coins? Explain.
2. Is it possible to get ten heads when flipping ten coins? Would you predict that ten heads would occur if you flipped ten coins? Explain.
3. Are you more likely to get heads or tails when you flip a coin? Explain your answer based on your results.
4. Are you more likely to get the same numbers or different numbers when you roll two dice? Why?
5. Which is more likely, to get two heads when two coins are flipped or to get the same number on each die when two dice are rolled? Explain.
6. How are probabilities used to determine atomic structure?

4:5 Isotopes

The 109 elements known to scientists are listed in Table 4–3 along with the symbols scientists use to represent them. Each element has a characteristic number of protons. Scientists have assigned each element a number according to the number of protons in the nuclei of its atoms. Hydrogen, with one proton, is number one. Helium, with two protons, is number two. The number assigned to an element is called its **atomic number.** The atomic number of tin is 50; tin atoms have 50 protons. Uranium atoms have 92 protons; the atomic number of uranium is 92. The atomic numbers of the elements also are listed in Table 4–3.

While the number of protons found in the nucleus of each atom is always the same, the number of neutrons sometimes varies. In its most common form, the hydrogen nucleus contains only one proton and no neutrons. However, two other forms of hydrogen exist. One form of hydrogen, known as deuterium, has one proton and one neutron. Another form of hydrogen, called tritium, has one proton and two neutrons in the nucleus. It is important to remember that each of these alternate forms are hydrogen atoms. All three forms have the same number of protons and therefore the same atomic number. Atoms of an element that each have different numbers of neutrons are called **isotopes.**

BACKGROUND Element 108 had been produced but not verified at the time of printing.

How are numbers assigned to the elements?

BACKGROUND The most common isotope of hydrogen is the only atomic nucleus with no neutrons.

BACKGROUND Deuterium is from the Greek word meaning second. Tritium is from the Greek word meaning third.

FIGURE 4–3. Before 1940, uranium had the highest atomic number known. Using particle accelerators, like the one at Fermilab (a), scientists bombarded the nuclei of atoms with other subatomic particles to produce elements with higher atomic numbers. Large generators (b) provide the energy required by this process.

a

b

TABLE 4–3.   ATOMIC NUMBER AND MASS OF ELEMENTS

Element	Symbol	Atomic Number	Average Atomic Mass	Element	Symbol	Atomic Number	Average Atomic Mass
Actinium	Ac	89	227.02779*	Neodymium	Nd	60	144.24
Aluminum	Al	13	26.98154	Neon	Ne	10	20.179
Americium	Am	95	243.06139*	Neptunium	Np	93	237.0482
Antimony	Sb	51	121.75	Nickel	Ni	28	58.71
Argon	Ar	18	39.948	Niobium	Nb	41	92.9064
Arsenic	As	33	74.9216	Nitrogen	N	7	14.0067
Astatine	At	85	209.98704*	Nobelium	No	102	255.093*
Barium	Ba	56	137.33	Osmium	Os	76	190.2
Berkelium	Bk	97	247.07032*	Oxygen	O	8	15.9994
Beryllium	Be	4	9.01218	Palladium	Pd	46	106.4
Bismuth	Bi	83	208.9808	Phosphorus	P	15	30.97376
Boron	B	5	10.81	Platinum	Pt	78	195.09
Bromine	Br	35	79.904	Plutonium	Pu	94	244.06424*
Cadmium	Cd	48	112.41	Polonium	Po	84	208.98244*
Calcium	Ca	20	40.08	Potassium	K	19	39.0983
Californium	Cf	98	251.07961*	Praseodymium	Pr	59	140.9077
Carbon	C	6	12.011 −	Promethium	Pm	61	144.91279*
Cerium	Ce	58	140.12	Protactinium	Pa	91	231.0359*
Cesium	Cs	55	132.9054	Radium	Ra	88	226.0254
Chlorine	Cl	17	35.453	Radon	Rn	86	222*
Chromium	Cr	24	51.996	Rhenium	Re	75	186.2
Cobalt	Co	27	58.9332	Rhodium	Rh	45	102.9055
Copper	Cu	29	63.546	Rubidium	Rb	37	85.4678
Curium	Cm	96	247.07038*	Ruthenium	Ru	44	101.07
Dysprosium	Dy	66	162.50	Samarium	Sm	62	150.4
Einsteinium	Es	99	254.08805*	Scandium	Sc	21	44.9559
Erbium	Er	68	167.26	Selenium	Se	34	78.96
Europium	Eu	63	151.96	Silicon	Si	14	28.0855
Fermium	Fm	100	257.09515*	Silver	Ag	47	107.868
Fluorine	F	9	18.998403	Sodium	Na	11	22.9898
Francium	Fr	87	223.01976*	Strontium	Sr	38	87.62
Gadolinium	Gd	64	157.25	Sulfur	S	16	32.06
Gallium	Ga	31	69.737	Tantalum	Ta	73	180.9479
Germanium	Ge	32	72.59	Technetium	Tc	43	96.9062*
Gold	Au	79	196.9665	Tellurium	Te	52	127.60
Hafnium	Hf	72	178.49	Terbium	Tb	65	158.9254
Helium	He	2	4.00260	Thallium	Tl	81	204.37
Holmium	Ho	67	164.9304	Thorium	Th	90	232.0381
Hydrogen	H	1	1.0079	Thulium	Tm	69	168.9342
Indium	In	49	114.82	Tin	Sn	50	118.69
Iodine	I	53	126.9045	Titanium	Ti	22	47.90
Iridium	Ir	77	192.22	Tungsten	W	74	183.85
Iron	Fe	26	55.847	Uranium	U	92	238.029
Krypton	Kr	36	83.80	Vanadium	V	23	50.9415
Lanthanum	La	57	138.9055	Xenon	Xe	54	131.30
Lawrencium	Lr	103	256.099*	Ytterbium	Yb	70	173.04
Lead	Pb	82	207.2	Yttrium	Y	39	88.9059
Lithium	Li	3	6.941	Zinc	Zn	30	65.38
Lutetium	Lu	71	174.967	Zirconium	Zr	40	91.22
Magnesium	Mg	12	24.305	Element 104†		104	257*
Manganese	Mn	25	54.9380	Element 105†		105	260*
Mendelevium	Md	101	258*	Element 106†		106	263*
Mercury	Hg	80	200.59	Element 107†		107	258*
Molybdenum	Mo	42	95.94	Element 108†		108	265*
				Element 109†		109	266*

*The mass of the isotope with the longest known half-life.

†Names for elements 104–109 have not yet been approved by the IUPAC. The USSR has proposed Kurchatovium (Ku) for element 104, and Bohrium (Bh) for element 105. The United States has proposed Rutherfordium (Rf) for element 104, and Hahnium (Ha) for element 105.

Of the 109 elements listed in Table 4–3, 90 occur naturally and the others have been produced in laboratories. All but 20 of the naturally-occurring elements exist as mixtures of two or more isotopes. Three isotopes are known to exist for oxygen, seven for mercury, and ten for tin. Scientists haved identified over 1500 different isotopes. Keep in mind that the isotopes for any given element all have the same atomic number and therefore the same number of protons and electrons. Only the number of neutrons varies.

Compare the number of isotopes and elements known.

4:6 Atomic Mass

Scientists have derived a unit for measuring the mass of an atom. This unit is known as the atomic mass unit, amu. The amu is based on the mass of an atom of the element carbon. One isotope of carbon contains six protons and six neutrons. This isotope of carbon is said to have a mass of exactly 12 amu. The mass of an electron is very small compared to the mass of a proton or neutron. Protons and neutrons are nearly equal in mass. The mass of a proton or neutron is about 1/12 the mass of a carbon-12 atom. Therefore, one **atomic mass unit** is about equal to the mass of a proton or a neutron. Because the mass of an electron is so small, the **atomic mass** of an atom is very nearly equal to the sum of the protons and neutrons.

Isotopes of elements are identified by their atomic masses. For example, all carbon isotopes have six protons. The carbon isotope that also has six neutrons is carbon-12. The carbon isotope with eight neutrons is carbon-14. Its atomic mass is 14 amu.

Scientists use a shorthand notation to distinguish the isotopes of an element. Carbon-12 is written $^{12}_{6}$C. C is the symbol for carbon. The 12 at the upper left is the mass number. The mass number of an isotope is the sum of the protons and neutrons in one atom. The 6 at the lower left is the atomic number of carbon.

If you subtract the atomic number from the mass number, you find the number of neutrons in an isotope.

mass number − atomic number = number of neutrons

BACKGROUND The mass of a hydrogen atom (1 proton + 1 electron) is 1.007 825 2 amu. The mass of a neutron is 1.008 665 2 amu. The difference in the predicted mass, 12.078 624 amu, and the actual mass, 12 amu, is called the mass defect. This amount of mass is converted to energy when the carbon-12 nucleus is formed.

How is an amu determined?

FIGURE 4–4. Radioactive isotopes are used to test water levels in soil. Cesium-137 is used at this watershed to test soil moisture near the surface.

EXAMPLE: Determining the Number of Neutrons in an Isotope

Problem: How many neutrons are in an atom of tin-118?

Solution: The mass number for this isotope of tin is 118. The atomic number of tin is 50.

mass number − atomic number = number of neutrons

118 − 50 = 68 neutrons

As you know, most of the natural elements are found as mixtures of isotopes in nature. The atomic mass of an element is an average number based on the percentage of each isotope occurring naturally. The average atomic masses of the elements are shown in Table 4–3.

See Teacher's Guide.

What is the atomic mass of an element?

REVIEW AND REFLECT

1. What are the two main classes of subatomic particles?
2. What is the difference between a subatomic particle and its antiparticle?
3. The atomic number of gold is 79. How many electrons do gold atoms have?
4. The number of protons in an atom of any carbon isotope is six. Explain why.
5. An isotope of chlorine has an atomic mass of 35 amu. Write the shorthand notation for this isotope of chlorine. How many electrons, protons, and neutrons are in this isotope?

4:7 Radioactivity

What are radioactive elements?

Radioactive elements are ones in which the atoms' nuclei disintegrate and emit energy, called radiation. Certain elements, such as uranium, tend to decay naturally and emit radiation. This process continues, perhaps for thousands of years, until the radioactive element is changed into a substance with a more stable nucleus.

Name the three types of natural radiation.

Three types of radiation are emitted by naturally-occurring radioactive material. They are alpha particles (α), beta particles (β), and gamma rays (γ). The symbols for each type of radiation are shown in parentheses. **Gamma rays** are a form of energy similar to X rays. They are more penetrating than alpha or beta particles, Figure 4–5.

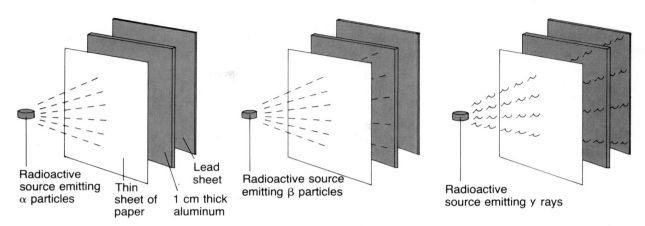

Radioactive source emitting α particles — Thin sheet of paper — Lead sheet — 1 cm thick aluminum

Radioactive source emitting β particles

Radioactive source emitting γ rays

FIGURE 4–5. Gamma rays have more penetrating ability than either alpha or beta particles.

BACKGROUND   Actually, beta particles may have either a positive or a negative charge. In some rare instances of beta decay (from a proton-rich nucleus), a positron (the antiparticle of an electron) is emitted.

An **alpha particle** is two protons and two neutrons. You may remember that a helium nucleus is two protons and two neutrons. The shorthand notation for an alpha particle is $^4_2$ He. A **beta particle** is an electron. Its electric charge is -1. When a beta particle is emitted from a radioactive atom, no protons or neutrons are emitted. Therefore, the mass number of a beta particle is 0. In shorthand notation, a beta particle is written as $^0_{-1}$ e.

When an atom emits radiation, the atom may change into an atom of another element. For example, if an atom emits an alpha particle, its charge is reduced by the charge of a helium nucleus. This loss leads to a change in that atom's nuclear charge, and thus its atomic number.

For example, an isotope of thorium, $^{232}_{90}$ Th, is a naturally radioactive element. The mass number of thorium is 232, and its atomic number is 90. Remember that the mass number is the sum of the protons and neutrons. Thorium, $^{232}_{90}$ Th, decays by radiating an alpha particle, $^4_2$ He. Two protons and two neutrons are lost, so the mass of the atom is reduced by 4. The new mass number is 228. ($232 - 4 = 228$) Two positive electric charges are lost, so the new electric charge is 88. ($90 - (+2) = 88$) The new atom has only 88 protons in its nucleus, which means its atomic number is 88. The atom with atomic number 88 is radium, Ra. Therefore, when thorium undergoes radioactive decay, it is changed into radium, $^{228}_{88}$ Ra.

The change caused by radioactive decay of one element into another is called a **transmutation.** Making use of shorthand notation, an equation can be written to represent this transmutation.

Define transmutation.

The equation shows that thorium, $^{232}_{90}$ Th, gives off an alpha particle, $^4_2$ He, as it decays into radium, $^{228}_{88}$ Ra. The resulting radium, $^{228}_{88}$ Ra, is another radioactive isotope. It decays by emitting a beta particle, $^0_{-1}$ e. Since the mass of a beta particle is considered to be zero, the atomic mass of the atom does not change ($228 - 0 = 228$). During beta decay, a neutron is changed to a proton yielding a net increase of one in the electric charge ($88 + 1 = 89$). There is no net change in the mass number. The new element formed with atomic number 89 is actinium, $^{228}_{89}$ Ac. Actinium is also radioactive and undergoes further nuclear decay. This process continues until a stable nucleus is formed. The stable nucleus that would be formed in this example is lead, $^{208}_{82}$ Pb. A series of transmutations is called a disintegration series.

What is a disintegration series?

See Teacher's Guide.

REVIEW AND REFLECT

1. What are the symbols for alpha and beta particles and gamma rays?
2. Which type of radiation has the greatest penetrating power?
3. What isotope is formed by the emission of an alpha particle from polonium, $^{212}_{84}$ Po? Write the transmutation equation.

FIGURE 4–6. The transmutation of thorium-232 leads to the formation of the stable isotope lead-208.

Activity: How are theories developed?

See Teacher's Guide.

MATERIALS

black box supplied by your teacher
balance
metric ruler

PROCEDURE

1. Work with a partner.
2. Record a qualitative description of the properties of the black box your teacher supplies.
3. Measure and record the mass of the black box.
4. Measure and record the size of the black box.
5. With your partner, develop a hypothesis about the internal structure of the black box. Record your hypothesis. NOTE: You may not be able to discover the exact contents of the box since you cannot actually open it and look inside. However, you should try to test your hypothesis about its internal structure.
6. Record the observations that support the hypothesis.

DATA AND OBSERVATIONS

Properties	Measurements and Observations
Mass	
Size	

FIGURE 4–7.

QUESTIONS AND CONCLUSIONS

1. What was your hypothesis about the internal structure of the black box?
2. How did you develop a hypothesis about the internal structure of the black box?
3. What observations supported your hypothesis?
4. How did your observations and hypothesis compare to the observations and hypotheses of other students in your class?
5. State your theory about the contents of your black box.
6. Do you think the structure inside all of the black boxes in your class is the same?
7. Can your theory be proven? Can scientists' theories about atomic structure be proven? Explain.
8. How are your experiments with the black box similar to a scientist's experiments with atomic structure?
9. What are some advantages of working with a partner in this activity?
10. What are some theories people have developed about why they catch colds? What are some other things people develop theories about?

4:8   Information: Radioactivity

Radioactive substances decay at different rates. Some decay in fractions of a second and others take thousands of years. A half-life is the amount of time it takes for one half of a radioactive substance to decay. If a radioactive substance has a half-life of one year, it means that half of that substance will decay in one year. After another year, half of the remaining half will decay. Only one fourth (1/2 × 1/2 = 1/4) of the original radioactive substance will remain.

How do scientists use radioactive decay and half-life information?

Scientists use radioactive decay and half-lives to determine the age of many materials. About one out of every 100 million carbon atoms is the radioactive isotope, $^{14}_{6}C$, instead of stable carbon, $^{12}_{6}C$. When organisms are alive, they constantly exchange carbon with the atmosphere. However, when they die, they no longer exchange carbon. The amount of $^{14}_{6}C$ the once-living organism had begins to decrease as the isotope decays. The half-life of $^{14}_{6}C$ is about 5730 years. The ratio of radioactive $^{14}_{6}C$ to nonradioactive $^{12}_{6}C$ in living organisms can be measured. The age of ancient animal bones can be estimated by comparing the ratio of $^{14}_{6}C$ to $^{12}_{6}C$.

In industry, beams of radioactivity are used to continuously keep track of the thickness of materials such as plastic wrap, paper, and aluminum foil. Thickness is measured by the amount of radiation absorbed by a material as it is produced at high speeds. Computers analyze the readings and adjust the machines automatically to keep a standard thickness.

FIGURE 4–8. Carbon-14 dating is a method used by scientists to determine when an animal died.

Instead of being heat-sterilized and sealed in cans, many foods can be sterilized in sealed plastic pouches by radiation. The food may then have a fresher, less overcooked quality. Scientists have found that treating some foods, such as beans, with radiation makes them easier to digest.

Radioactivity also is useful in the medical fields. Plastic syringes, tubing, bandages, and other heat-sensitive medical materials can also be sterilized by radiation.

Radioactive isotopes of many common elements can be incorporated into molecules. This process is called radioactive tagging. Scientists can follow these tagged molecules through an industrial process or even a living organism. For example, cancer cells use food molecules faster than surrounding cells. Tagged food molecules are especially useful in detecting and treating certain cancers. Radioactive tagging may help scientists design new drugs that will travel only to specific disease locations. Radioactive iodine travels mainly to the thyroid gland, which makes it useful for treating thyroid cancer.

Scientists can use tagged fertilizers and pesticides to study how these materials are used by plants. Tagging can be used to discover pesticides that accumulate in animal tissues.

Gases containing radioactive molecules can be passed at high pressure through new pipe assemblies. Engineers can then discover dangerous cracks, leaks, or faulty connections before natural gas, chemicals, or other hazardous materials are allowed to flow through them. X rays as well as other radioactive materials can be used to find invisible cracks and flaws in metal parts. These parts could include aircraft landing gear and building support beams.

See Teacher's Guide.

a

b

FIGURE 4–9. Industrial materials are tested for flaws using radioactive isotopes such as cobalt-60 (a). An isotope of technetium is tagged to phosphorus to provide a clearer view of bone structure (b).

REVIEW AND REFLECT

1. What is meant by the half-life of a radioactive substance?

2. If you start with 1000 kg of a radioactive substance with a half-life of 2 years, how much will remain after 4 years? after 10 years?

3. Carbon dating is not considered to be reliable beyond 40 000 years. Why do you think this statement is true?

4. What is meant by radioactive tagging?

SUMMARY

1. Theories about the structure of atoms have changed many times. 4:1
2. Current atomic theory suggests that an atom is composed of a densely packed nucleus surrounded by an electron cloud. 4:2
3. The nucleus contains protons and neutrons, which are relatively massive particles. 4:2
4. Atoms are electrically neutral. Neutrons have no electric charge. The positive charge of the protons equals the negative charge of the electrons. 4:2
5. Electrons occupy energy levels in the electron cloud of an atom. 4:3
6. Atoms with eight electrons in their outermost energy level tend to be stable. 4:3
7. The nucleus of an atom contains many subatomic particles and antiparticles. 4:4
8. The number of protons in the atoms of an element is always the same, but the number of neutrons may vary. 4:5
9. Each element has a unique atomic number and is represented by a symbol. 4:5
10. The mass of an atom is measured in atomic mass units. 4:6
11. Radioactive atoms emit particles or energy, resulting in the decay of their nuclei. 4:7

VOCABULARY

alpha particle 12	beta particle 13	leptons 14
antiparticles 8	electrons 5	neutron 15
atomic mass 11	gamma rays 1	proton 9
atomic mass unit 3	hadrons 10	quark 2
atomic number 4	isotopes 7	transmutation 6

Choose a word from the list to complete each sentence correctly.

1. _____ are a form of natural radiation similar to X rays.
2. A subatomic particle thought to make up other subatomic particles is a(n) _____.
3. A(n) _____ is approximately the mass of a proton or neutron.
4. An element's _____ indicates its number of protons.
5. _____ are particles with little mass and a negative charge.
6. A radioactive element decays into another more stable element by the process called _____.
7. Alternate forms of an element with different numbers of neutrons are called _____.

8. Subatomic particles that are identical in mass with electrons, protons, and neutrons but opposite in charge are _____.
9. A massive subatomic particle with a positive electric charge is a(n) _____.
10. _____ are a class of subatomic particles that react to strong nuclear forces.
11. The sum of an atom's protons and neutrons is about equal to its _____.
12. A(n) _____ is a helium nucleus.
13. A(n) _____ is a product of radioactive decay with little mass and a negative electric charge.
14. _____ are the class of subatomic particles that includes electrons.
15. A massive subatomic particle with no electric charge is a(n) _____.

QUESTIONS

MAIN IDEAS

Choose the correct answer to complete each sentence.

1. Most of an atom's volume is *(electrons, empty space, protons, the nucleus).*
2. Most of the mass of an atom is the *(electrons, nucleus, neutrons, beta particles).*
3. The number of electrons in an atom is equal to the number of *(protons, neutrons, protons + neutrons, protons − neutrons).*
4. The number of neutrons in the nucleus of potassium, $^{40}_{19}$ K, is *(40, 19, 21, 59).*
5. Na is the symbol for the element *(chlorine, sodium, nitrogen, tin).*
6. The radiation with the least penetrating power is *(alpha particles, beta particles, gamma rays, electrons).*
7. The octet rule states the maximum number of electrons in an atom's outermost energy level is *(7, 2, 4, 8).*
8. The electric charge on an electron is *(negative, positive, neutral, either positive or negative).*
9. $^{122}_{50}$ Sn and $^{118}_{50}$ Sn are both *(isotopes, antiparticles, compounds, subatomic particles)* of tin.
10. Protons and neutrons are both examples of *(leptons, hadrons, gluons, mesons).*
11. The antiparticle of an electron is the *(beta particle, proton, alpha particle, positron).*
12. Quarks combine to form *(electrons, leptons, hadrons, positrons).*

See Teacher's Guide.

APPLICATIONS

Answer each question in one or more paragraphs.

1. Determine the element formed when $^{226}_{88}$ Ra decays by emitting an alpha particle.
2. Why were Democritus' ideas about the structure of matter not an example of the scientific method?
3. Describe the current atomic theory.
4. What must scientists do when their observations do not fit their theoretical model?
5. Describe how an accelerator is used to discover subatomic particles.
6. What happens when antiparticles collide?
7. Why are the atomic masses listed in Table 4–3 not whole numbers? (Atomic mass units are whole numbers.)

FURTHER STUDY

INVESTIGATIONS

1. Find out who Millikan was and how his research contributed to modern atomic theory.
2. Report on the work of early alchemists and their attempts to make precious metals.
3. Construct a model of the structure of an atom.
4. Write a report on how radioactive isotopes are used in medicine.
5. Research news magazines for the past year and determine if any additional discoveries have been made regarding atomic structure.

READINGS

0 Ardley, Neil. *Atoms and Energy.* Warwick Press: New York, 1982.

0 Dettling, J. Ray. "Quest for the Ultimate Particle." *Science Digest.* December, 1982. pp 78–81.

+ Ecker, Martin D., and Norton J. Bramesco. *Radiation.* Vintage Books: New York, 1981.

0 Pagels, Heinz R. *The Cosmic Code.* Simon and Schuster: New York, 1982.

+ Wolkomir, Richard. "Quark City." *Omni.* February, 1984. pp. 40–44, 80–83.

HAVE you ever noticed colorful stones or grains of sand in a stream? Did you ever think you found gold? The students are panning for gold, one of the more than 100 elements scientists have discovered. Scientists organize the elements into groups or families with similar properties in the periodic table. Which elements are metals? How are elements named?

THE PERIODIC TABLE

INTRODUCING THE CHAPTER   Ask students to name some of the materials with which they are most familiar. Identify those that are elements. Locate these familiar elements on the periodic table and note, for future reference, their positions and symbols.

5:1   Classifying the Elements

In chapter 4, you used Table 4–3, on page 80 to answer several questions. The elements are listed with their data in alphabetical order in Table 4–3. You may have found that this arrangement was not very helpful for answering questions about atomic number, atomic mass, and the number of electrons for different elements.

About 100 years ago, scientists discovered a more useful way to organize the elements. In 1869, the Russian chemist Dmitri Mendeleev published a periodic table of the elements. Periodic means repeating at regular intervals. Mendeleev arranged the 57 elements known at that time according to increasing atomic mass. However, in this arrangement, several differences in properties of elements expected to be similar could not be explained.

In 1913, Henry Moseley arranged the elements in order of increasing atomic number. In this arrangement, the properties of the elements follow a regular repeating pattern. Moseley's arrangement is based on the periodic law. According to the **periodic law,** the properties of the elements are periodic functions of their atomic numbers. In other words, the properties of elements repeat at regular intervals if the elements are arranged by increasing atomic number. Recall that the number of electrons equals the atomic number of a neutral atom. Today, the elements are organized in the modern periodic table, pages 96–97, according to electron structure.

GOAL   You will learn how the elements are organized into the periodic table and how people use the properties of elements to develop useful products.

What does periodic mean?

How did Moseley's arrangement of the elements differ from Mendeleev's?

Each horizontal row of the periodic table is called a **period.** The properties of the elements repeat in each period. For example, as you move from left to right in any period, the elements change from metals to nonmetals. Note in the periodic table that aluminum (element 13) in period 3 is a metal. Tin (element 50) in period 5 is a metal, too. Sulfur (element 16) and iodine (element 53), elements farther to the right in periods 3 and 5, are nonmetals.

The vertical columns in the periodic table are called **groups** or families. The elements within each group have similar properties. For example, the elements in the first group are all highly reactive metals. The elements in the last group are stable nonmetals.

In many ways, the periodic table is like a calendar. The days of the month have periodic properties. The days are arranged in seven-day periods on a calendar. Several characteristics repeat within each period. For example, as you move from left to right in any period, you move from the beginning to the end of a week. The groups or families on a calendar share many similar properties. The Monday family usually represents the first day of the school or work week. What other things have periodic properties?

See Teacher's Guide.

REVIEW AND REFLECT

1. In chapter 4, you used Table 4–3 to answer questions similar to the ones below. Find answers to the following questions using the periodic table.
   a. What is the atomic mass of Al?
   b. What element has the atomic number 79?
   c. How many electrons do atoms of the element with an average atomic mass of 55.847 amu have?
2. Name three advantages of using the periodic table instead of Table 4–3 to find information about the elements.

5:2 Atomic Structure and the Periodic Table

The periodic relationships among the elements are related to atomic structure. Recall from chapter 4 that electrons can exist in one of seven energy levels. The seven

Where are metallic and nonmetallic elements in the periodic table?

How is the periodic table like a calendar?

periods of the periodic table correspond to these energy levels.

Except for helium in period 1, the last element in each period has eight electrons in its outer energy level. This group of eight electrons is called an octet. When an atom's outer energy level is completely filled with eight electrons, the atom is very stable. The elements in Group VIIIA have an octet, and they do not combine readily with other atoms. Elements with either a few outer electrons or nearly-filled outer energy levels are generally the most reactive.

For elements in the A groups on the periodic table, the group number represents the number of electrons in the outer energy level. Most elements in the B groups have one or two outer energy level electrons.

5:3   Naming the Elements

Scientists use symbols to represent the elements. The use of symbols makes writing the names of elements and the compounds they form easier. Often, the symbol for an element is the first letter of the element's name. Sometimes two letters are used to represent an element. The letter C is used as a symbol for carbon. The symbol for calcium is Ca and the symbol for chlorine is Cl.

The symbols for some elements seem unusual. For example, the symbol for sodium is Na. The symbol Na comes from the Latin word for sodium, *natrium*. Table 5–1 lists other symbols for elements that are based on Latin words.

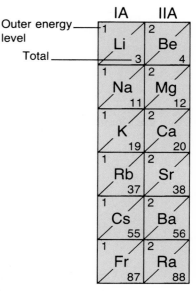

FIGURE 5–1. Group IA elements have one outer energy level electron; Group IIA elements have two. The total number of electrons increases across a period and down a group.

Why do scientists use symbols to represent the elements?

SUGGESTION Discuss words that come from Latin or Greek. For example, consider medical terms and scientific classifications of organisms. Explain to students how to use a dictionary to find the origin of a word.

TABLE 5–1. SYMBOLS OF ELEMENTS FROM LATIN NAMES		
Element	**Symbol**	**Latin Name**
Copper	Cu	*cuprum*
Gold	Au	*aurum*
Iron	Fe	*ferrum*
Lead	Pb	*plumbum*
Mercury	Hg	*hydrargyrum*
Potassium	K	*kalium*
Silver	Ag	*argentum*
Sodium	Na	*natrium*
Tin	Sn	*stannum*

Many of the names of the elements have interesting histories. Elements have been named to honor famous scientists or mythological characters. Some elements were named for the discoverer's native country, state, or town, and the place where the element was discovered. Properties of the elements or compounds of the element have also been sources for names of the elements. Table 5–2 lists some elements and the origin of their names.

How are elements named?

BACKGROUND Mendelevium was named in honor of Mendeleev and his work on the early periodic table. Other elements have been named after Einstein, Fermi, Lawrence, and Nobel. Some elements have been named in honor of the place where they were first discovered or produced. Berkelium was first synthesized at the University of California at Berkeley. Additional elements that have been named in honor of a country or a place include europium, francium, americium, californium, germanium, lutetium, and polonium. Mercury, uranium, neptunium, and plutonium were all named after planets. Other elements were named after other heavenly bodies. Many elements have been named because of their color or the color of common compounds they form or the color of the minerals in which they are found.

TABLE 5–2.	ORIGIN OF SOME ELEMENTS' NAMES
Element	**Origin of Name**
Bromine	From the Greek word *bromos,* which means stench, because it has a strong odor
Calcium	From the Latin word *calx,* which means lime, because it is found in limestone
Cerium	For the asteroid, Ceres, discovered two years before the element
Chlorine	From the Greek word *chloros,* which means greenish-yellow, because of its color
Curium	To honor the famous scientists Marie and Pierre Curie
Gallium	From the Latin word *Gallia*, which means France, the place where it was discovered
Helium	From the Greek word *helios,* which means sun, because it was first discovered in a solar eclipse
Iridium	From the Latin word *iris*, which means rainbow, because it produces brightly colored salts
Manganese	For its magnetic properties
Promethium	For the mythological character Prometheus
Rubidium	For the deep red color of its flame test
Strontium	For a town in Scotland where minerals containing it are found

In recent years, the naming of newly discovered elements has caused some disagreement among scientists. There is no agreement for the names of elements with atomic numbers greater than 103. For example, scientists in both the Soviet Union and the United States claim to have produced element 104 during the mid-1960s. The Soviet scientists have suggested element 104 be called kurchatovium, while the American scientists have suggested the name rutherfordium. Disputes over the names of elements cause many problems when the element or its compounds are discussed in scientific journals. It is confusing to readers when the same substance has more than one name.

In an effort to settle such disputes, the International Union of Pure and Applied Chemistry (IUPAC) has suggested a naming system for elements 104 and above. Using the IUPAC system, elements would be named based on their atomic number using the roots shown in Table 5–3.

Using the IUPAC system, element 104 would be named unnilquadium. In a similar manner, elements 105 and 106 would become unnilpentium and unnilhexium. Currently, the use of this system is being debated by scientists.

TABLE 5–3. IUPAC NUMERICAL ROOTS	
Number	**Root**
0	nil
1	un
2	bi
3	tri
4	quad
5	pent
6	hex
7	sept
8	oct
9	enn

See Teacher's Guide.

REVIEW AND REFLECT

1. The element calcium is in period 4 on the periodic table. In which energy level are its outermost electrons?
2. Chlorine has seven outer energy level electrons and argon has eight. What is the difference in the reactivity of these two elements?
3. Use the periodic table to determine the symbols and names for the elements named after Fermi, Lawrence, and Nobel.
4. Using the proposed IUPAC system, write the name for element 107.
5. What would mendelevium and nobelium be called if the IUPAC system had been used to name them?
6. What is your opinion of the IUPAC naming system? How might you suggest that disputes over the naming of new elements be handled?

The Periodic Table

(Based on Carbon 12 = 12.0000)

Solids—cream, Liquids—orange, Gases—blue, Synthetics—green

Noble Gases

VIIIA

						VIIIA
						2 / 2 **He** Helium 4.00260

Nonmetals

IIIA	IVA	VA	VIA	VIIA	
5 / 2,3 **B** Boron 10.81	6 / 2,4 **C** Carbon 12.011	7 / 2,5 **N** Nitrogen 14.0067	8 / 2,6 **O** Oxygen 15.9994	9 / 2,7 **F** Fluorine 18.998403	10 / 2,8 **Ne** Neon 20.179
13 / 2,8,3 **Al** Aluminum 26.98154	14 / 2,8,4 **Si** Silicon 28.0855	15 / 2,8,5 **P** Phosphorus 30.97376	16 / 2,8,6 **S** Sulfur 32.06	17 / 2,8,7 **Cl** Chlorine 35.453	18 / 2,8,8 **Ar** Argon 39.948

IB	IIB	IIIA	IVA	VA	VIA	VIIA	
28 / 2,8,16,2 **Ni** Nickel 58.71	29 / 2,8,18,1 **Cu** Copper 63.546	30 / 2,8,18,2 **Zn** Zinc 65.38	31 / 2,8,18,3 **Ga** Gallium 69.737	32 / 2,8,18,4 **Ge** Germanium 72.59	33 / 2,8,18,5 **As** Arsenic 74.9216	34 / 2,8,18,6 **Se** Selenium 78.96	35 / 2,8,18,7 **Br** Bromine 79.904	36 / 2,8,18,8 **Kr** Krypton 83.80
46 / 2,8,18,18,0 **Pd** Palladium 106.4	47 / 2,8,18,18,1 **Ag** Silver 107.868	48 / 2,8,18,18,2 **Cd** Cadmium 112.41	49 / 2,8,18,18,3 **In** Indium 114.82	50 / 2,8,18,18,4 **Sn** Tin 118.69	51 / 2,8,18,18,5 **Sb** Antimony 121.75	52 / 2,8,18,18,6 **Te** Tellurium 127.60	53 / 2,8,18,18,7 **I** Iodine 126.9045	54 / 2,8,18,18,8 **Xe** Xenon 131.30
78 / 2,8,18,32,17,1 **Pt** Platinum 195.09	79 / 2,8,18,32,18,1 **Au** Gold 196.9665	80 / 2,8,18,32,18,2 **Hg** Mercury 200.59	81 / 2,8,18,32,18,3 **Tl** Thallium 204.37	82 / 2,8,18,32,18,4 **Pb** Lead 207.2	83 / 2,8,18,32,18,5 **Bi** Bismuth 208.9808	84 / 2,8,18,32,18,6 **Po** Polonium 208.98244*	85 / 2,8,18,32,18,7 **At** Astatine 209.98704*	86 / 2,8,18,32,18,8 **Rn** Radon 222*

The annotations show the number of electrons in each principal energy level.

63 / 2,8,18,25,8,2 **Eu** Europium 151.96	64 / 2,8,18,25,9,2 **Gd** Gadolinium 157.25	65 / 2,8,18,27,8,2 **Tb** Terbium 158.9254	66 / 2,8,18,28,8,2 **Dy** Dysprosium 162.50	67 / 2,8,18,29,8,2 **Ho** Holmium 164.9304	68 / 2,8,18,30,8,2 **Er** Erbium 167.26	69 / 2,8,18,31,8,2 **Tm** Thulium 168.9342	70 / 2,8,18,32,8,2 **Yb** Ytterbium 173.04
95 / 2,8,18,32,25,8,2 **Am** Americium 243.06139*	96 / 2,8,18,32,25,9,2 **Cm** Curium 247.07038*	97 / 2,8,18,32,26,9,2 **Bk** Berkelium 247.07032*	98 / 2,8,18,32,28,8,2 **Cf** Californium 251.07961*	99 / 2,8,18,32,29,8,2 **Es** Einsteinium 254.08805*	100 / 2,8,18,32,30,8,2 **Fm** Fermium 257.09515*	101 / 2,8,18,32,31,8,2 **Md** Mendelevium 258*	102 / 2,8,18,32,32,8,2 **No** Nobelium 255.093*

*The mass of the isotope with the longest known half-life.

5:4 A Group Metals

The elements in Groups IA through IIIA and some of the elements in Groups IVA through VIA are metals. In section 5:2, you learned that the group numbers for these metals indicate the number of electrons in the outermost energy level. In general, reactivity of the metals decreases as more electrons are added to the outer energy level. For example, the Group IA metals react violently with oxygen and moisture in the air. They may be stored under oil to prevent such reactions. Aluminum, tin (Group IIIA), and lead (Group IVA) are much less reactive than the Group IA and IIA metals.

The properties of A group metals are summarized in Table 5–4. These properties make the A group metals suitable for a wide variety of uses. Some uses of these metals and compounds containing these metals are listed in Table 5–4 also.

The elements in Group IA are called the **alkali metals.** They are the most reactive of all the metals and have one electron in the outer energy level. They form compounds that are used in such diverse products as pharmaceuticals and explosives. Sodium is one of the most useful of the alkali metals. Vast quantities of sodium are used each

Which metals are most reactive?

BACKGROUND   Most compounds formed by the Group IA elements have the properties of bases. For this reason, they are called the alkali metals.

FIGURE 5–2. Most of the A group metals occur in a combined form as minerals or salts. Mining of mineral ores (a) and processing of ocean water (b) are two methods of obtaining minerals and salts.

a

b

year in the form of sodium chloride, NaCl, which is common table salt. Baking soda is the common name for sodium hydrogen carbonate, $NaHCO_3$. Sodium hydroxide, NaOH, commonly referred to as lye, causes severe chemical burns. Lye is sometimes called caustic soda. Caustic means being able to destroy by chemical action. Because of this caustic property, sodium hydroxide is the chief ingredient in most household drain cleaners. Sodium compounds also are important in the glass-making industry. Most common glass is made by melting together soda ash (sodium carbonate), salt cake (sodium sulfate), sand (silicon dioxide), and lime (calcium oxide).

Group IIA elements are known as the **alkaline earth elements.** They have importance in industry as well as for living systems. For example, plasterboard, marble, and cement contain calcium compounds. In addition, milk contains calcium, which is important for the healthy development of bones and teeth. Large amounts of calcium chloride are used to melt ice and snow from roadways in winter. Calcium chloride is also used in rural areas to control dust on unpaved roads.

Aluminum is the most abundant element in Group IIIA. Aluminum alloys are very strong but less dense than steel. This property makes them useful in a wide variety of products. For example, alloys of aluminum are used to make cooking utensils, car and airplane body parts, and foil packaging.

Tin is in Group IVA, the carbon family. Compared to the alkali and alkaline earth elements, tin is relatively stable. For example, it does not combine readily with oxygen in the air, so it is often used to coat other metals to prevent rust. Tin also is replacing more harmful elements in some weed killers.

FIGURE 5–3. Vitamin and mineral supplements contain compounds of A group metals. These compounds are important to good health.

SUGGESTION Caution students of the danger of handling strong bases such as sodium hydroxide (NaOH) and products containing strong alkalines.

Describe the elements in Groups IA, IIA, IIIA, and IVA.

5:5 B Group Metals

Remember from section 5:2 that the elements in the B groups of the periodic table have one or two electrons in their outer energy level. These elements are known as the **transition metals.** Electrons are added to different energy levels of the transition metals as their atomic numbers increase. In general, the transition metals are less reactive

What elements are transition metals?

BACKGROUND   As a general rule, metals have one to three outer energy level electrons. However, the metals tin and lead have four and bismuth has five.

Why are copper, silver, and gold used to mint coins?

What is galvanizing?

BACKGROUND   Two common topical antiseptics, merthiolate and mercurochrome are mercury compounds.

What elements are in the lanthanide and actinide series?

than the Group IA and IIA metals. Some properties and uses of transition metals and their compounds are summarized in Table 5–4.

Recall that elements within a group tend to have similar properties. The transition metals in Group IB (copper, silver, and gold) have an important property in common. They resist corrosion. Corrosion is the gradual wearing away of metals that occurs when a metal interacts chemically with its environment. Resistance to corrosion makes the Group IB elements quite suitable for use as coins. These elements are often referred to as the coinage metals.

The zinc family includes zinc, cadmium, and mercury. Less reactive than iron, zinc is often used to coat steel to prevent it from rusting. This process is known as galvanizing. Mercury has many uses, particularly in dentistry. Alloys of mercury, called amalgams, are used to make fillings for teeth. Cadmium is used in batteries. Having properties similar to zinc and mercury, cadmium is sometimes used to coat steel and in dental amalgams.

The elements with atomic numbers 57 through 70 are known as the lanthanide series. Just below them in the periodic table is the actinide series, which includes elements with atomic numbers 89 through 102. In order to print the periodic table more easily, these two series are usually listed at the bottom of the table. Many of the lanthanide metals are used to make specialized alloys. The actinide series includes several common nuclear fuels including thorium, plutonium, and uranium. At one time the lanthanides were referred to as the rare earth elements.

See Teacher's Guide.

REVIEW AND REFLECT

1. Which groups of metals are the most reactive?
2. What are other, more common names for the metals of Groups IA and IIA?
3. Use Table 5–4 and the periodic table to list some of the properties of A Group metals.
4. Name one way that B Group metals differ from A Group metals.

TABLE 5–4. SOME PROPERTIES AND USES OF METALS AND METALLIC COMPOUNDS

Physical Properties	Good conductors of heat and electricity
	Solids are malleable and ductile
	High density
	Metallic luster
Chemical Properties	One to three electrons in the outermost energy level
	Form compounds by losing or sharing electrons

Sodium	Fertilizer, glassmaking, soap
Potassium	Fertilizer, gunpowder, glassmaking
Magnesium	Found in chlorophyll, structural parts for planes and cars
Tin	Canning, fertilizer, pesticides
Titanium	Lightweight alloys for plane parts, paint pigment
Molybdenum	Stainless steel, pen points, spark plug points
Iron	Structural and stainless steel, paint pigments
Copper	Electrical wiring, plumbing, cooking utensils
Zinc	Deodorant, plating metal car parts, galvanizing steel

Lithium	Tranquilizers
Potassium	Pharmaceuticals
Rubidium, Cesium, Gallium	Photoelectric cells in medical equipment and elevators
Beryllium	Electrical switches
Titanium	Artificial joints, tooth replacement, heart valve replacement

Activity: How can you identify some metals?

See Teacher's Guide.

MATERIALS

platinum or nichrome wire loop
known metallic ion solutions
unknown metallic ion solutions
laboratory burner
dilute hydrochloric acid solution
goggles
apron
piece of cobalt glass

PROCEDURE

1. Obtain samples of known solutions from your teacher.

2. Clean your wire loop by dipping it into the dilute hydrochloric acid. Carefully heat the wire in the burner flame, Figure 5–4. **CAUTION:** *Hydrochloric acid causes severe burns. Avoid skin contact. Wash spills with plenty of water.* Repeat the cleaning process each time you use a wire loop.

3. After you clean the loop, dip it into the first sample. Then place it into the flame and note the color produced. Record the name of the metal ion and your observations in your data table. Use the cobalt glass filter to observe the flame.

FIGURE 5–4.

4. Repeat this procedure with each of the known samples provided by your teacher.

5. Obtain several unknown solutions from your teacher. Examine the flames produced by each of the unknown solutions and record your observations. **CAUTION:** *Handle all unknowns with care.*

DATA AND OBSERVATIONS

Metal Ion		Flame Color	Flame Color Through Cobalt Glass
Known			
Unknown			

QUESTIONS AND CONCLUSIONS

1. What colors were produced by each of the metals in your known sample?

2. How did the colors of the flames change when you observed them through the glass filter?

3. What was the purpose of the cobalt glass filter?

4. What metallic elements were present in each of your unknown samples?

5. The yellow flame of sodium is intense and often masks other colors. A small amount of sodium contamination can cause problems. What are some possible sources of this contamination?

See Teacher's Guide.

Career Profile

Anne Albers is an industrial hygienist for the National Institute for Occupational Safety and Health (NIOSH). When Anne visits one of the deep, metal mines in the Colorado mountains, she does so at the request of an employee or an employer. Anne's job is to test the health conditions of the workplace.

Anne's work at the mining site may take from two days to two weeks, depending on the problem. She collects samples of the air at different locations in the mine and also takes samples from workers' hair, skin, and clothing. Throughout the mine, Anne records temperature, humidity, and air pressure. She also writes down her observations of the miners' behavior. She looks for signs of stress or discomfort. Back in her office, she prepares the samples she collected for laboratory analysis. When the results come back from the lab, she writes a detailed report about her procedures, findings, conclusions, and recommendations.

Anne could not perform her job without a strong background in chemistry. For example, she must know what physical form each hazard will take—liquid, particulate, gas, or solvent. She has to know how the chemists should test each chemical. And, when the chemists' reports come back, she must be able to understand what they mean.

Though Anne's work can at times be physically demanding, she loves the variety each day brings. Using science to solve problems is Anne's idea of a real challenge.

5:6   Metalloids

Some elements have properties of both metals and nonmetals. Thus, they cannot be classified as either metals or nonmetals. These elements are referred to as **metalloids** (MET ul oydz). The metalloids are listed in Table 5–5. The metalloids are located toward the right of the periodic table and separate the metallic from the nonmetallic elements.

Define metalloids.

During the past two decades, metalloids have become more important for their use as semiconductors. Depending on their purity, the conductivity of metalloids varies. This property makes metalloids valuable in electronics as transistors and integrated circuits. (See section 1:1.)

BACKGROUND Semiconductors are usually pure crystals of germanium and silicon that are doped with arsenic or gallium to increase their conductivity.

TABLE 5–5. SOME PROPERTIES AND USES OF METALLOIDS AND THEIR COMPOUNDS

Physical Properties	Solids similar to metals
	Semiconductors
Chemical Properties	Three to six outer energy level electrons
	Similar to metals and nonmetals

Boron	Ceramics, heat resistant glassware, delayed action fuses, specialized fuels, shields and control rods in nuclear reactors
Silicon	Alloys for telephone wires, transistors, photocells, solar batteries, laboratory glassware
Germanium	Transistors, vacuum tubes
Arsenic	Diodes and semiconductors, solder
Tellurium	Stainless steel

Boron	Insecticides
Silicon	Caulking, Carborundum® grinding wheels, glass cookware, cosmetics, lubricants
Germanium	Dental alloys
Arsenic	Insecticides, heart worm preventive for dogs, crabgrass control
Tellurium	Vulcanizing agent for rubber, coloring agent for glass and ceramics, antiseptics

5:7 Nonmetals

The elements on the right side of the periodic table are classified as nonmetals. They have distinctly different properties from metals. For example, they are not conductors. Some properties and uses of nonmetals are summarized in Table 5–6. Many of the nonmetals are gases at room temperature. A nonmetal generally has four or more electrons in its outer energy level.

The elements in Group IVA are the carbon family. All elements in this family have four electrons in their outer energy level. While they share some properties, the elements of the carbon family vary more than any other group on the periodic table. Carbon is a nonmetal, silicon and germanium are metalloids, and tin and lead are distinctly metallic.

Carbon is an extremely important element. There are several different forms of carbon. Pencil "lead" is actually graphite, a form of carbon. Diamonds are another form of carbon. More than three fourths of all known compounds contain carbon. Carbon compounds are present in all living organisms. At one time, scientists theorized that only living organisms could produce carbon compounds. For this reason, carbon compounds are often referred to as organic compounds.

The elements in Group VA are known as the nitrogen family. The properties of the elements within this group vary considerably. Like the elements in the carbon family, those at the top have nonmetallic properties while those at the bottom of the group tend to be more metallic. Each element in this group has five electrons in the outer energy level. The elements in the nitrogen family are not very reactive. They must either gain three or lose five electrons to form an octet.

Nitrogen comprises almost 80 percent of the earth's atmosphere. In its pure elemental form, nitrogen is very stable. Because of this property, it is used in the processing of foods to prevent oxidation or spoilage.

While elemental nitrogen is stable, most nitrogen compounds are not. This property makes some nitrogen compounds useful for making explosives. Common explosives that are made from nitrogen compounds include gunpowder, nitroglycerin, dynamite, and TNT (trinitrotoluene).

How are nonmetals different from metals?

What are some uses for carbon?

BACKGROUND Coal and charcoal are mainly carbon.

SUGGESTION Compare the properties of different forms of carbon.

What is the most common element in the earth's atmosphere?

SUGGESTION Caution students about the dangers of unstable nitrogen compounds. Do not provide information about how these compounds are made.

TABLE 5–6. SOME PROPERTIES AND USES OF NONMETALS AND NONMETALLIC COMPOUNDS

Physical Properties	Poor conductors of heat and electricity
	Solids are brittle and nonductile
	Low density
Chemical Properties	Four to eight electrons in the outermost energy level
	Form compounds by gaining or sharing electrons except Group VIIIA

Nitrogen	Fertilizer, cleansers, food processing
Oxygen	Basic component in most foods, welding
Fluorine	Etching glass, refrigerant
Chlorine	Bleaching clothes and paper pulp, disinfectant
Iodine	Dye
Sulfur	Sulfuric acid, matches
Selenium	Red glass, photometers, vulcanizing rubber
Phosphorus	Fertilizer, matches, detergent
Helium	Support for weather balloons
Neon	Lighted signs
Argon	Welding
Krypton	Lighted signs
Xenon	Lighted signs

Nitrogen	Medication, essential for life
Oxygen	Essential for life
Sulfur	Sulfa drugs for bacterial infection, control dandruff
Fluorine	Prevent tooth decay
Chlorine	Disinfectant
Bromine	Photographic film
Iodine	Medicines to prevent goiter, radioactive tracers
Selenium	Photoelectric cells in light meters

The elements in Group VIA are referred to as the oxygen family. An element in the oxygen family has six electrons in its outer energy level. By gaining two electrons, these elements form an octet. Except for oxygen, all are solids at room temperatures. The properties of Group VIA elements vary from nonmetallic at the top (oxygen) to metallic at the bottom of the group (tellurium and polonium). Polonium is a radioactive element.

Most of the earth's crust is composed of oxygen. In its natural uncombined state, oxygen is an odorless, colorless, and tasteless gas. Air, a mixture of gases, is approximately 20 percent oxygen. Oxygen is an essential element. Almost all living organisms need oxygen to survive. People suffering from respiratory ailments are unable to get enough oxygen from the air. They are often given oxygen to help them breathe easier.

The elements in Group VIIA are known as the **halogens.** The word halogen means salt former. All of the halogens, except astatine, are nonmetals. Astatine is a radioactive metalloid. The halogens have seven electrons in their outer energy levels. They are the most chemically active nonmetals. This reactivity is due to a nearly-filled outer energy level. Only one electron is needed to form an octet. Fluorine, chlorine, and iodine are halogens that are probably familiar to you. They have many common uses. For example, a fluorine compound, stannous fluoride, is added to drinking water in some cities and to toothpaste to reduce tooth decay. Other fluorine compounds are used to cool air in air conditioners and refrigerators. Halogens are never found uncombined in nature because of their high reactivity. Halogens form compounds with all of the other elements, except for some of the Group VIIIA elements.

The elements in Group VIIIA, at the far right of the periodic table, are the **noble gases.** They are very stable and do not combine readily with other atoms. Neon is used in neon signs for advertising. Tubes filled with the gas display a distinctive orange-red color when an electric current is passed through them. Krypton, xenon, and argon also are used in signs. Krypton and xenon produce blue-colored light. Argon produces a purple-colored light.

What is the oxygen family?

What is the most common element in the earth's crust?

Why are the halogens chemically active?

BACKGROUND Halogens form many compounds among themselves, including ClF, BrF, IF, IF_7, BrCl, and ICl_3.

What are some uses for the noble gases?

BACKGROUND The first compound of the noble gas family was produced in 1962, xenon hexafluoroplatinate, $XePtF_6$.

See Teacher's Guide.

REVIEW AND REFLECT

1. What are some properties of metalloids?
2. How do nonmetals differ from metals?
3. What is the minimum number of electrons in the outer energy level of nonmetals?
4. Explain why the elements in Group VIIIA are relatively unreactive.

See Teacher's Guide.

Skill Inquiry

Look at Figure 5–5 on page 111. Compare the atomic radii of the elements. Graph a on this page shows the atomic radii of some elements plotted in relation to their atomic numbers. The regular repeating pattern shows that atomic radii are a periodic property. Note that lithium, sodium, potassium, rubidium, cesium, and francium have the largest atomic radii. Also, they form Group IA on the periodic table. Graph a indicates that the atomic radii of the elements decrease from left to right on the periodic table. This information is a statistical trend. You may not have noticed the trend by simply looking at the atomic radii values listed in Figure 5–5. Graphs are helpful in determining statistical trends. Trends are useful for making predictions. Refer to Graph a.

1. Which atoms are larger?
    a. magnesium or aluminum
    b. carbon or chlorine
    c. sodium or potassium
2. The farther electrons are from the nucleus of an atom, the more reactive the atom tends to be. Which element in Group IA is most reactive?
3. How large would you expect element 108 to be compared to francium? to element 109?

Graph b shows the incidence of some childhood diseases from 1970 to 1980 that can be prevented by vaccinations.

4. What statistical trends does Graph b show?
5. How might the trend in incidence of childhood diseases during the late 1970s be explained?

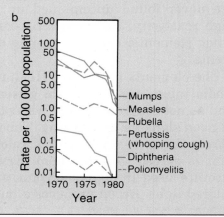

Activity: How can you make soap?

MATERIALS

bowl
hot plate
thermometer
wooden spoon
newspaper
large pan, not aluminum
150 mL sodium
   hydroxide (NaOH)
   solution in a
   250-mL beaker
150 g rendered beef tallow
300 g vegetable shortening
ladle, not aluminum
cardboard egg carton
3 test tubes with stoppers
distilled water
hard water
soft water
goggles and apron

PROCEDURE

Part A

1. Put warm tap water in the bowl to make a water bath. **CAUTION:** *NaOH causes severe burns. Avoid skin contact. Rinse spills with plenty of water.* The NaOH solution needs to be 35–37°C, so make the water bath this temperature. Then place the beaker of NaOH solution in the water bath.

2. Put the tallow and vegetable shortening in the pan. Place the pan on the hot plate over low heat. Remove the pan from the heat when the fats are melted. Do not allow the temperature of the melted fats to exceed 50°C.

3. Let the melted fats cool to 35–37°C. Make sure the fats and the NaOH solution are within this temperature range before you go on to the next step.

4. While stirring the fats constantly with a wooden spoon, slowly pour the NaOH solution in a thin stream into the pan.

5. Continue stirring gently for 20 to 30 minutes until the mixture thickens.

6. Carefully ladle the thickened mixture into an egg carton. Close the carton and cover it with newspaper to retain heat. Do not disturb for at least 24 hours.

7. Age the soap for at least two weeks before going on to Part B.

Part B

1. Label three test tubes hard, soft, and distilled. Then fill each test tube half full of the appropriate type of water.

2. Put a small amount of soap in each of the three test tubes. Use the same amount of soap in each test tube. Stopper the test tubes.

3. Shake each test tube and record your observations of the suds.

DATA AND OBSERVATIONS

Water	Amount of Suds
Hard	
Soft	
Distilled	

QUESTIONS AND CONCLUSIONS

1. In which type of water did you obtain the most suds?

2. How can you account for the differences in the amounts of suds?

3. What kind of water is best for washing dishes and clothing? Explain.

4. Why is the NaOH added to the fat?

5:8 Information: Periodic Trends

One of the values of the periodic table is that elements with similar properties are grouped together. In addition, there are several patterns or trends that exist among the elements on the periodic table. We have already discussed some of these trends in this chapter. For example, as we move across any row of the periodic table from left to right, the number of electrons in the outer energy level increases. The most reactive elements must gain or lose only one electron to have an octet. For this reason, the elements in Groups IA and VIIA tend to be the most reactive. For the same reason, the elements in Group VIIIA, the noble gases, with completely filled outer energy levels, are very unreactive. The metals with partially filled outer energy levels tend to be good conductors, while the nonmetals at the right of the table are not readily conductive.

What are periodic trends?

The periodic table is a useful guide to relative atomic size. However, atomic size changes in a predictable way. Each successive horizontal row in the periodic table represents the filling of another energy level by electrons. Therefore, as we move down any column on the periodic table, the atomic radii tend to become larger. The size of atoms also exhibits a trend as we move across the periodic table from left to right. Moving across any row of the periodic table, the atomic number increases. Recall that this increase in atomic number represents an additional proton in the nucleus of each successive element. Consider potassium, K, in the fourth period. It has 19 protons while bromine, Br, at the right of the table has 35 protons. The bromine nucleus has a greater positive charge and attracts the outer electrons more closely than the potassium nucleus. The atomic radius of potassium is about twice as large as the atomic radius of bromine. In general, the size of atomic radii decreases as we move from left to right across any period. (See Figure 5–5.)

BACKGROUND The atomic radius is the average distance from the center or nucleus to the outermost energy level of electrons.

What is electronegativity?

The tendency of the nuclei to attract electrons when atoms combine is known as electronegativity. The smaller atoms, because of the greater positive charge of their nuclei, tend to be the most electronegative. For large atoms, the outer electrons are relatively far away from the nucleus. Generally, large atoms have lower electronegativity

ELECTRONEGATIVITY VALUES AND ATOMIC RADII

1	2	3	4	5	6	7	8	9	10	11	12	13	14	15	16	17	18
2.20 **H** 0.053																	**He** 0.122
0.96 **Li** 0.152	1.50 **Be** 0.111											2.02 **B** 0.083	2.56 **C** 0.077	2.81 **N** 0.070	3.37 **O** 0.066	4.00 **F** 0.072	**Ne** 0.160
0.96 **Na** 0.192	1.29 **Mg** 0.160											1.63 **Al** 0.143	1.94 **Si** 0.117	2.04 **P** 0.115	2.46 **S** 0.104	3.00 **Cl** 0.099	**Ar** 0.191
0.84 **K** 0.227	1.02 **Ca** 0.197	1.28 **Sc** 0.161	1.44 **Ti** 0.145	1.54 **V** 0.132	1.61 **Cr** 0.125	1.57 **Mn** 0.124	1.74 **Fe** 0.124	1.79 **Co** 0.125	1.83 **Ni** 0.125	1.67 **Cu** 0.128	1.60 **Zn** 0.133	1.86 **Ga** 0.122	1.93 **Ge** 0.123	2.12 **As** 0.125	2.45 **Se** 0.114	2.82 **Br** 0.111	**Kr** 0.198
0.85 **Rb** 0.248	0.97 **Sr** 0.215	1.16 **Y** 0.181	1.27 **Zr** 0.160	1.23 **Nb** 0.143	1.73 **Mo** 0.136	1.36 **Tc** 0.136	1.42 **Ru** 0.133	1.87 **Rh** 0.135	1.78 **Pd** 0.138	1.57 **Ag** 0.144	1.52 **Cd** 0.149	1.69 **In** 0.163	1.84 **Sn** 0.141	1.83 **Sb** 0.136	2.03 **Te** 0.143	2.48 **I** 0.128	**Xe** 0.218
0.82 **Cs** 0.265	0.93 **Ba** 0.217	1.20 ***Lu** 0.173	1.23 **Hf** 0.156	1.33 **Ta** 0.143	1.88 **W** 0.137	1.46 **Re** 0.137	1.52 **Os** 0.134	1.88 **Ir** 0.136	1.86 **Pt** 0.138	1.98 **Au** 0.144	1.72 **Hg** 0.160	1.74 **Tl** 0.170	1.87 **Pb** 0.175	1.76 **Bi** 0.155	1.76 **Po** 0.167	1.96 **At** 0.14	**Rn** 0.22
0.86 ****Fr** 0.27	0.97 **Ra** 0.220																

1.09 ***La** 0.188	1.09 **Ce** 0.183	1.10 **Pr** 0.183	1.10 **Nd** 0.182	1.07 **Pm** 0.181	1.12 **Sm** 0.180	1.01 **Eu** 0.204	1.15 **Gd** 0.180	1.10 **Tb** 0.178	1.16 **Dy** 0.177	1.16 **Ho** 0.177	1.17 **Er** 0.176	1.18 **Tm** 0.175	1.06 **Yb** 0.194
1.00 ****Ac** 0.188	1.11 **Th** 0.180	1.14 **Pa** 0.161	1.30 **U** 0.139	1.29 **Np** 0.131	1.25 **Pu** 0.157	1.2 **Am** 0.184	**Cm**	**Bk**	**Cf**	**Es**	**Fm**	**Md** 1.2	

(←— estimated —→ across Am to Md)

values than small atoms. Therefore, electronegativity trends tend to be just the opposite of trends of the size of atomic radii. Electronegativity decreases as we move down a column and increases from left to right in any period.

FIGURE 5–5. The electronegativity values (red) and average atomic radii (blue) for the elements show periodic trends.

See Teacher's Guide.

REVIEW AND REFLECT

1. State whether each value increases or decreases as you move across the periodic table from left to right.
   a. number of electrons   c. electronegativity
   b. size of atomic radii
2. State whether each value increases or decreases as you move from top to bottom of the periodic table.
   a. number of electrons   c. electronegativity
   b. size of atomic radii
3. Which element is more reactive, cesium or tin? Explain using your knowledge of periodic trends.

SUMMARY

1. In the modern periodic table, the elements are arranged according to electron arrangement. 5:1

2. The properties of the elements repeat in each period of the periodic table. The elements within each group have similar properties. 5:1

3. Elements toward the left on the periodic table have metallic properties. Elements toward the right on the periodic table have nonmetallic properties. 5:1

4. Elements with nearly-filled outer energy levels tend to be the most reactive. Elements with completely filled outer energy levels tend to be stable. 5:2

5. The periodic relationships among the elements are related to atomic structure. 5:2

6. Many elements have been named after scientists, geographic locations, and for specific properties of the elements. 5:3

7. A Group metals include the alkali metals, alkaline earth elements, and Groups IIIA and IVA metals. 5:4

8. B Group elements are transition metals. 5:5

9. Metalloids have become important for their use in the field of electronics. 5:6

10. Nonmetals include elements in the carbon, nitrogen, and oxygen families, the halogens, and the noble gases. 5:7

VOCABULARY

alkali metals 4	halogens 3	period 1
alkaline earth elements 5	metalloid 6	periodic law 9
group 2	noble gases 8	transition metals 7

Choose the correct word from the list to answer each question.

1. What is a horizontal row in the periodic table called?

2. What is a vertical column, or family of elements, in the periodic table called?

3. How are A Group elements with seven electrons in the outer energy level classified?

4. How are A Group elements with one electron in the outer energy level classified?

5. What are A Group elements with two electrons in the outer energy level called?

6. What has some properties of a metal and some properties of a nonmetal?

7. How are elements in the B Group of the periodic table classified?

8. How are elements with an octet classified?

9. What states that the properties of elements are periodic functions of their atomic numbers?

QUESTIONS

See Teacher's Guide.
MAIN IDEAS

Complete each sentence with the correct word or phrase.

1. K is the symbol for _____.

2. The nonmetallic elements are located _____ on the periodic table.

3. The first periodic table was published by _____.

4. The elements in Group VIIIA have _____ electrons in their outer energy level.

5. The symbol for hydrogen is _____.

6. The symbol for iron is Fe and not I because _____.

7. The symbol for chlorine is _____.

8. The atomic number of oxygen is _____.

9. Tin is a metal in the _____ family.

10. An element with three outer energy level electrons would most likely be a(n) _____.

11. _____ are malleable and ductile.

12. _____ first stated the periodic law.

13. The most reactive elements are in Groups _____ and _____.

14. Gold, zinc, and manganese are all _____ metals.

15. Elements in period 5 have their outer electrons in the _____ energy level.

See Teacher's Guide.

APPLICATIONS

Answer each question in one or more paragraphs.

1. Why is the periodic table important?

2. Why are groups in the periodic table often referred to as families?

3. Why are the elements in Group VIIIA (the noble gases) so stable?

4. Why are the elements in Groups IA and VIIA (the alkali metals and the halogens) so chemically reactive?

5. What properties of aluminum allow it to have such widespread use?

6. Explain possible origins of the symbols and names of the following elements.
   a. californium   d. neptunium
   b. chlorine   e. rubidium
   c. mendelevium   f. unnilennium

7. What is the difference between groups and periods on the periodic table?

FURTHER STUDY

INVESTIGATIONS

1. Select a group from the periodic table. Find out more about how each element or its compounds is commonly used. Prepare a poster with the information for display in your classroom.

2. Pick an element from the periodic table and discover when it was first identified (or synthesized). What is its major industrial use? household use? Report your findings to your class.

3. Write a report about the work of early alchemists and their attempts to make precious metals.

4. Research on boron compounds has received two Nobel prizes in recent years. Find out why these compounds are so important. Prepare a news bulletin with the information.

5. Obtain permission from your teacher and school officials to paint a mural of the periodic table on a science classroom wall.

READINGS

+ Asimov, Isaac. *A Short History of Chemistry*. Greenwood Press: Westport, CT, 1979.

+ Firsching, F. H. "Anomalies in the Periodic Table." *Journal of Chemical Education*. June, 1981. pp. 478–479.

+ March, Robert H. "Atom." *Science Year, 1983*. 1982. pp. 370–376.

0 Sherman, Alan, and Sharon J. Sherman. *Chemistry and Our Changing World*. Prentice-Hall: Englewood Cliffs, NJ, 1983.

0 Standen, Anthony. "The Periodic Table." *The New Book of Popular Science*. 1982. v.3, pp. 29–45.

MANY people think of chemical reactions taking place only in test tubes, beakers, and flasks in laboratories. However, chemical reactions are a part of everyday life and natural processes. Chemical reactions take place when wood is burned and food is cooked. When people eat food, chemical reactions occur within their bodies. How do chemical reactions occur? What are the results of chemical reactions?

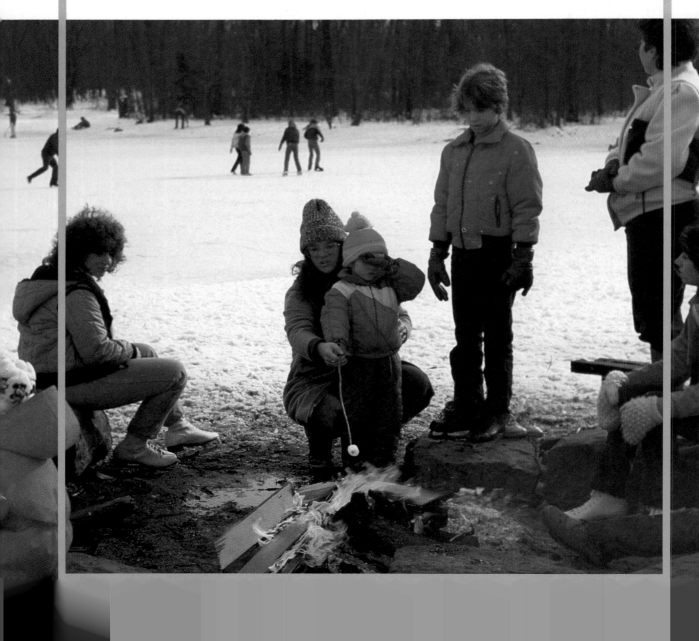

BONDING AND REACTIONS

INTRODUCING THE CHAPTER   Point out to students that chemical reactions take place literally everywhere around them. The wood in the bonfire is undergoing a chemical reaction with the air. When food is cooked, a reaction takes place. Metals, such as iron, undergo reactions as they rust. Within the human body, countless chemical reactions take place constantly.
  Place some vinegar and baking soda in a tall glass container. (A large graduated cylinder works well). Add a handful of raisins. The reaction produces CO_2. It sticks to the raisins causing them to rise to the surface. At the surface, the CO_2 bubbles burst and the raisins fall. This process will continue for 20–30 minutes.

6:1 Formation of Compounds

Most of the materials you use are compounds or mixtures of compounds. Other materials familiar to you are elements. Some of these elements, such as oxygen and nitrogen, occur in a combined form of two or more atoms of the element. For example, air contains oxygen molecules that each consist of two oxygen atoms. Only the noble gas elements are found in nature as individual atoms.

The food you eat, the clothes you wear, and the chair on which you sit are made of compounds. Even you are made of compounds. Compounds are formed from elements in chemical reactions. Without chemical reactions many processes, both simple and complex, could not take place. Dangerous forest fires would not occur, but you could not warm up in front of a fireplace on a cold evening either. You could not survive if chemical reactions did not occur in your body.

The forces that hold atoms together in compounds are called bonds. Atoms form bonds in two main ways. Atoms bond with one another either by transferring electrons or by sharing electrons.

GOAL   You will learn how elements combine chemically and form compounds.

How are compounds formed?

SUGGESTION   Review from chapter 3 that a compound is the chemical combination of two or more different elements.

What are bonds?

115

6:2 Ionic Bonding

The elements in Groups IA and VIIA are chemically active and readily bond with one another. The bonding activity of these elements can be explained by examining their atomic structure. The alkali metals, Group IA, all have one electron in their outer energy level. The halogens, Group VIIA, all have seven outer energy level electrons. By losing or gaining one electron, these elements have a new arrangement of electrons with a filled outer energy level. For example, the loss of one electron from a sodium atom results in an electron arrangement similar to that of neon, the element with the next lower atomic number. When a chlorine atom gains an electron, it has an electron arrangement similar to argon, the element with the next higher atomic number.

$$Na^x + .\ddot{C}l: \rightarrow Na^+ + {}^x\ddot{C}l:^-$$

What is an ion?

Remember that an atom is electrically neutral. The number of protons in the nucleus equals the number of electrons in the electron cloud. When an atom loses or gains an electron, it no longer has an equal number of positive and negative charges. When one electron is lost, the atom is left with a net charge of $1+$. This charged particle is called an ion. An **ion** is an atom that has a positive or negative charge as a result of losing or gaining one or more electrons. For example, the atomic number of sodium is 11. A sodium atom has 11 protons and 11 electrons. The positive and negative charges are equal. When an electron is lost, there are still 11 positively charged protons but only 10 negatively charged electrons. The resulting sodium ion has a net charge of $1+$ and is written Na^+. All the elements in Group IA form ions with $1+$ charges by losing an electron.

In a similar manner, when an atom in Group VIIA gains an electron, an ion with a $1-$ charge is formed. For example, chlorine has 17 protons and 17 electrons. When a chlorine atom gains an electron, it has 17 protons and 18 electrons. The resulting chloride ion has a $1-$ charge and is written Cl^-. All the elements in the halogen family form ions with $1-$ charges by gaining an electron.

FIGURE 6–1. The ionic compound calcium carbonate is needed for the healthy development of bones and teeth. Pregnant women are often given calcium carbonate as a dietary supplement.

Elements in Groups IA and VIIA combine with each other by a process called ionic bonding. **Ionic bonding results from a transfer of one or more electrons between atoms. As electrons are transferred, oppositely charged ions are formed and attracted to each other, resulting in an ionic compound.** Sodium and chlorine atoms transfer an electron, and the resulting ions form the ionic compound sodium chloride.

In general, only outer energy level electrons are used in bonding. The elements in other groups form ionic bonds in a way similar to Groups IA and VIIA. Magnesium oxide is formed when Mg^{2+} ions bond with O^{2-} ions. Magnesium, a Group IIA element, bonds with oxygen, a Group VIA element, to form the ionic compound magnesium oxide, MgO. Magnesium transfers two electrons to oxygen and the resulting ions bond.

$$Mg_x^x + \cdot \ddot{O} \colon \rightarrow Mg^{2+} + {}_x^{}\ddot{O}\colon^{2-}$$

Note that magnesium bromide, $MgBr_2$, is formed when magnesium atoms transfer their two outer electrons to bromine atoms. Bromine, a Group VIIA element, forms $1-$ ions. Two bromine ions bond with each magnesium ion.

$$Mg_x^x + 2 \cdot \ddot{Br} \colon \rightarrow Mg^{2+} + 2\ {}^x\ddot{Br}\colon^{-}$$

6:3 Covalent Bonding

Atoms also may combine by sharing electrons. **Bonds formed by electron sharing are called covalent bonds.** When atoms combine by sharing electrons, molecules are formed. Water, H_2O, is an example of a molecule formed by covalent bonds. The covalent bonds between two hydrogen atoms and one oxygen atom result in a filled outer energy level for each of the three atoms in the molecule.

Covalent bonds that involve one pair of shared electrons between two atoms are single bonds. A double bond is a covalent bond that involves two pairs of shared electrons. A triple bond involves three pairs of shared electrons. Structural formulas indicate the type of bond in a molecule. Each line between the symbols of the elements in the molecule represents a pair of shared electrons, Figure 6–2.

Define ionic bonding.

What electrons usually are involved in bonding?

BACKGROUND   The forces of attraction between ions are electrostatic forces.

BACKGROUND   Covalent is based on the root word valence derived from the Latin *valere,* meaning to be strong. Loosely translated, covalent means of equal strength, or sharing.

What are covalent bonds?

FIGURE 6–2.   1-Pentol (3-methyl-2-penten-4-yn-1-ol) is used in vitamin A synthesis. Molecules of this compound contain single, double, and triple bonds.

BACKGROUND   Covalent network compounds such as diamond have very high melting points. Network bonding is an exception.

How are the properties of covalent and ionic compounds different?

Many covalent compounds are gases or liquids at room temperature. Covalent solids are generally soft and have low melting points. Covalent compounds do not conduct electricity. Most ionic compounds are hard, brittle solids with high melting points. The solids do not conduct electricity, but when melted or dissolved, the fluid ionic compounds are conductors.

See Teacher's Guide.

REVIEW AND REFLECT

1. How are compounds formed from elements?
2. Name and explain the two ways in which atoms bond.
3. Draw a dot diagram representing the ionic compound potassium iodide, KI.

6:4 Chemical Formulas

In the previous sections, symbols and numbers were used to represent compounds, such as H_2O to represent a water molecule. H_2O is the chemical formula for water. A **chemical formula** is a shorthand way of indicating the types and relative proportions of the elements in a compound. The chemical formula for an oxygen molecule is O_2. The 2 is called a subscript. It indicates that each oxygen molecule is made up of two oxygen atoms. The chemical formula for water, H_2O, indicates that each molecule of water is composed of two hydrogen atoms and one oxygen atom. The subscript 1 is not used.

What are chemical formulas?

SUGGESTION   You may wish to discuss the ideas of John Dalton at this time. Be sure students recognize the relationship between atomic theory and the Law of Definite Proportions.

FIGURE 6–3.   Pharmacists must have a thorough understanding of the names and chemical formulas of medications.

Formulas also can be written for ionic compounds. The formula for table salt, sodium chloride, is NaCl. This formula shows that sodium chloride crystals are made up of an equal proportion of sodium and chloride ions. What is the chemical formula for potassium bromide?

The number of electrons an atom shares, gains, or loses is related to its combining ability with other atoms. The combining ability of an element is described by its **oxidation number.** Oxidation numbers may be positive or negative. An element that tends to give up electrons has a positive oxidation number. For example, sodium has an oxidation number of $1+$ since it gives up one electron. Chlorine, which readily gains one electron, has an oxidation number of $1-$. The oxidation numbers of some common elements are listed in Table 6–1.

TABLE 6–1.   OXIDATION NUMBERS OF SOME COMMON ELEMENTS

1+	2+	3+	4+
Copper(I), Cu^+	Calcium, Ca^{2+}	Aluminum, Al^{3+}	Lead(IV), Pb^{4+}
Hydrogen, H^+	Copper(II), Cu^{2+}	Chromium(III), Cr^{3+}	Silicon(IV), Si^{4+}
Potassium, K^+	Iron(II), Fe^{2+}	Iron(III), Fe^{3+}	Tin(IV), Sn^{4+}
Silver, Ag^+	Lead(II), Pb^{2+}		
Sodium, Na^+	Magnesium, Mg^{2+}		
	Tin(II), Sn^{2+}		
	Zinc, Zn^{2+}		

1–	2–	3–	4–
Bromine, Br^-	Oxygen, O^{2-}	Nitrogen, N^{3-}	Carbon, C^{4-}
Chlorine, Cl^-	Sulfur, S^{2-}	Phosphorus, P^{3-}	
Fluorine, F^-			
Iodine, I^-			

When naming a compound, the name of the element with the positive oxidation number usually is given first. The element with the negative oxidation number is given last. The ending of the negative element is also changed to -*ide*. For example, sodium has a positive oxidation number and chlorine has a negative oxidation number. The compound formed by these two elements is called sodium chloride.

As you can see in Table 6–1, some elements have more than one oxidation number. Copper has two oxidation numbers, 1+ and 2+. In compounds where copper tends to lose or share one electron, its oxidation number is 1+ and it is called copper(I). Similarly, when copper loses or shares two electrons, it is called copper(II). The Roman numeral in parentheses following the name of an element distinguishes the combining abilities of elements with more than one oxidation number.

You may have noticed in Table 6–1 that the oxidation numbers for the elements listed are the same as the charges on ions of these elements. Oxygen forms ions that have a 2– charge, and the oxidation number for oxygen is 2–. There is no net electric charge on a compound. Therefore, the sum of the oxidation numbers for a compound must be zero. The formula for copper(I) chloride is CuCl. The oxidation number for chlorine is 1– and for copper(I) it is 1+. These two elements must be in a one-to-one ratio for the net charge on the compound to be zero.

BACKGROUND   Some compounds are known by trade names or other common terms. In addition, nonbinary compounds are named differently. For example, compounds containing polyatomic ions have the same ending as the ion, $CuSO_4$, copper sulfate. These rules do not apply to naming acids.

What does a Roman numeral following an element's name indicate?

What is the net charge on a compound?

EXAMPLE: Writing Chemical Formulas

Problem: What is the chemical formula for iron(III) oxide?

Solution: Refer to Table 6–1 for the oxidation numbers of iron(III) and oxygen.

$$\text{iron(III)} = 3+ \qquad \text{oxygen} = 2-$$

In order to have a net charge of zero, two iron(III) atoms must combine with three oxygen atoms.

$$2Fe^{3+} + 3O^{2-} = Fe_2O_3$$

The formula for iron(III) oxide is Fe_2O_3. Use subscripts to indicate the relative proportions of each type of atom.

See Teacher's Guide.

Skill Inquiry

Many household products contain chemicals that can be dangerous if not handled properly. Products that contain these chemicals are labeled with safety information. For example, the label of a laundry bleach is shown.

When you purchase a product, you should read the label to find out if the product has special storage requirements. Any potentially dangerous chemical should be stored out of the reach of children. Mr. Yuk® labels and child-proof caps are also useful in protecting children.

When you use a product, you should read the label to find out what precautions you should take. Some product labels also include information about proper disposal of the container when it is empty.

1. How should bleach be stored?
2. What should you avoid when using bleach? Why?

Occasionally accidents happen and someone is burned, poisoned, or otherwise harmed with a household product. Most products contain emergency information. Follow the directions on the label for minor accidents, such as a spill. For more serious accidents, always contact the Poison Control Center in your area, a paramedic, or a doctor immediately. Post the numbers near your phone. When you call, know the product that caused the harm and the approximate amount involved.

3. If you spilled a little bleach on your hands and clothing accidentally while doing laundry, what should you do?
4. If a child accidentally has swallowed some bleach, what should you do?
5. What is the phone number of your local Poison Control Center?

Activity: What are properties of mixtures and compounds?

MATERIALS

iron filings	powdered sulfur
balance	test tube and holder
hand lens	laboratory burner
magnet	sheet of white paper
forceps	hammer (one per class)
stirring rod	test tube clamp
paper towels	goggles and apron

PROCEDURE

1. Measure 4 g of iron filings and 2 g of sulfur. Find the mass of your test tube.

2. Place a small amount of each element on a sheet of white paper and observe with a hand lens. Record your observations in the data table.

3. Place a magnet under the sheet of paper and note the effect on each element.

4. Using a stirring rod, carefully mix the two substances together. Again, observe with the hand lens. Try to separate the two elements using the magnet, again under the paper.

5. Place the mixture in a test tube and heat. **CAUTION:** *This mixture should be heated in a fume hood.* Remove the test tube from the heat when the contents begin to glow.

6. Allow the test tube and contents to cool. Find the total mass.

7. Wrap the test tube in several paper towels. Tap with a hammer to break open the test tube so the contents can be removed. **CAUTION:** *Handle contents and broken test tube with forceps. Dispose of broken test tube as directed by your teacher.*

8. Spread the contents on a sheet of paper and observe with a hand lens. Place a magnet under the sheet of paper and observe the effect. Record the properties.

FIGURE 6–4.

DATA AND OBSERVATIONS

Substance	Color	Magne-tism	Other
Iron			
Sulfur			
Sulfur & iron before heating			
Sulfur & iron after heating			

QUESTIONS AND CONCLUSIONS

1. Was there any evidence of a chemical change when the iron and sulfur were mixed together? Explain.

2. Was there any evidence of a chemical change when the iron and sulfur were heated together? Explain.

3. What do you think was formed when the two elements were mixed together and heated?

4. What can you conclude about the properties of compounds and the properties of the elements from which they are formed?

5. How did the mass of the products compare to the mass of the reactants?

6:5 Polyatomic Ions

Some ions are composed of more than one atom. These groups of atoms are known as polyatomic ions. One common polyatomic ion is the hydroxide ion, OH^-. Oxygen has six electrons in its outer energy level and hydrogen has one. One additional electron gives both atoms filled outer energy levels and together they have a net charge of $1-$. The hydroxide ion bonds with a sodium ion forming the compound sodium hydroxide, NaOH. The $1+$ charge of the sodium ion balances the $1-$ charge of the hydroxide ion yielding an electrically neutral compound. Table 6–2 lists the oxidation numbers of some common polyatomic ions.

TABLE 6–2. OXIDATION NUMBERS OF SOME POLYATOMIC IONS

1+	1−	2−	3−
Ammonium, NH_4^+	Acetate, $C_2H_3O_2^-$	Carbonate, CO_3^{2-}	Arsenate, AsO_4^{3-}
	Chlorate, ClO_3^-	Silicate, SiO_3^{2-}	Phosphate, PO_4^{3-}
	Hydroxide, OH^-	Sulfate, SO_4^{2-}	Citrate, $C_6H_5O_7^{3-}$
	Nitrate, NO_3^-	Chromate, CrO_4^{2-}	
	Nitrite, NO_2^-	Peroxide, O_2^{2-}	

Magnesium bonds with the nitrate ion, NO_3^- to form the compound magnesium nitrate. Notice that the name of the polyatomic ion does not change in the name of the compound. Magnesium has an oxidation number of $2+$ and nitrate has an oxidation number of $1-$. Two nitrate ions are needed to bond with one magnesium ion in order for an electrically neutral compound to be formed. This ratio is indicated in the formula for magnesium nitrate. Parentheses are placed around the formula for the nitrate ion and a subscript 2 is placed after the parentheses, $Mg(NO_3)_2$.

EXAMPLE: Writing Formulas for Compounds Containing Polyatomic Ions

Problem: What is the chemical formula for aluminum hydroxide?

Solution: Refer to Tables 6–1 and 6–2 for the oxidation numbers of the two ions.

aluminum $= +3$ hydroxide $= -1$

Three hydroxide ions must combine with each aluminum ion in order to form an electrically neutral compound. Aluminum is written first since it is positive. Place parentheses around the hydroxide ion before adding the subscript 3. The formula for aluminum hydroxide is $Al(OH)_3$.

$$(1)Al^{3+} + 3OH^- = Al(OH)_3^0$$

See Teacher's Guide.

REVIEW AND REFLECT

1. Name the following compounds.
   a. KBr c. NH_4NO_3
   b. Ag_3PO_4 d. SiC
2. Write the chemical formulas for the following compounds.
   a. iron(III) sulfate   c. ammonium phosphate
   b. copper(I) oxide   d. sodium acetate
3. Why are parentheses important when writing the formula for a compound that contains more than one polyatomic ion? How is $Al(OH)_3$ different from $AlOH_3$?

FIGURE 6–5. Fertilizers are generally a mixture of various compounds that contain phosphate and nitrate ions.

6:6   Acids and Bases

Scientists classify compounds into several groups. Two important groups of compounds are acids and bases. Many ordinary substances contain acids and bases. Soaps and cleansers often contain bases. Many fruits and juices contain acids. Acids and bases can be thought of as chemical opposites. Some properties of acids and bases are compared in Table 6–3.

What are two important classifications of compounds?

TABLE 6–3. PROPERTIES OF ACIDS AND BASES

Property	Acids	Bases
Type of ion formed in water	H_3O^+	OH^-
Taste	Sour	Bitter
Tactile	Not slippery	Slippery
Effect on litmus	Turn blue litmus red	Turn red litmus blue
Conductivity of solutions	Conduct electricity	Conduct electricity
Chemical activity	Proton donor	Proton acceptor

SUGGESTION   Caution students about the safety hazards of acids and bases. Point out that unknown substances should never be tasted as a test of properties, nor should they be touched. Strong acids and bases are toxic and cause chemical burns. However, weak acids give many foods a characteristic sour taste, for example lemons, tomatoes, and milk.

a

b

FIGURE 6–6.   Universal indicator paper is a special paper that has been treated with chemicals. It can be used to determine the pH of a solution over a wide pH range (a). A pH meter automatically measures pH and is generally more precise than indicators (b).

How are the strengths of acids and bases measured?

DEMONSTRATION   Prepare an indicator by boiling shredded red cabbage for about five minutes. Then strain the liquid. Use red cabbage juice as an indicator to test common substances such as vinegar, tea, lemon juice, baking soda solution, and ammonia. Red cabbage juice turns pink in acids and blue-green in bases.

For what purpose are indicators used?

An acid is a substance that gives up a proton. A proton can be thought of as a hydrogen atom stripped of its electron. Without an electron, a hydrogen atom becomes an ion with a $1+$ charge, H^+. When an acid is added to water, it gives up protons (H^+ ions) that combine with water molecules and form hydronium ions, H_3O^+. For example, when hydrochloric acid is added to water, hydronium and chloride ions are formed.

$$HCl + H_2O \rightarrow H_3O^+_{(aq)} + Cl^-_{(aq)}$$

The (aq) written after the symbol for the ion means the ion is in a water solution. Acids are often defined as substances that increase the amount of hydronium ions in water.

Bases also form ions when added to water. Bases increase the number of hydroxide ions, OH^-, in water. For example, sodium hydroxide is a base. When it is added to water, sodium and hydroxide ions dissociate.

$$NaOH + H_2O \rightarrow Na^+_{(aq)} + OH^-_{(aq)}$$

The strength of an acid or a base is measured by how completely it separates into ions, or ionizes, in water. Strong acids or bases such as hydrochloric acid or sodium hydroxide ionize completely. For example, when hydrochloric acid is added to water, all of it separates into H^+ and Cl^- ions. No molecular HCl remains. A weak acid or base, such as acetic acid or aluminum hydroxide, does not ionize completely. Some ions form but some of the atoms remain bonded together in the compound.

A special scale has been developed to describe the relative strengths of acids and bases in solution. This scale, called the pH scale, reflects the relative number of H_3O^+ ions or OH^- ions in solution. Note in Figure 6–6 that the pH scale ranges from 0 to 14. Pure water, which is neutral, has a pH of 7.

An **indicator** can be used to tell if a solution is an acid or a base. Indicators behave as weak acids or bases. When added to a water solution, indicators do not ionize completely. The number of ions and the amount of compound vary depending on how acidic or how basic the solution is. Because the indicator compound and the indicator ions have different colors, the color of an acidic solution is different from the color of a basic solution. Many types of indicators change color at different pH ranges.

Activity: How do antacids compare?

MATERIALS

balance
baking soda
congo red indicator
buret
ring stand
buret clamp
500 mL flask
several different
    packages of antacid tablets

mortar and pestle
graduated cylinder
funnel
dilute HCl
dropper
stirring rod
goggles and apron

PROCEDURE

1. Fill a flask with 100 mL of water.

2. Dissolve 3 g of baking soda in it.

3. Mount the buret with a clamp on the ring stand as shown in Figure 6–7.

4. Using a funnel, carefully fill the buret with dilute HCl. **CAUTION:** *HCl causes burns; avoid skin contact. Rinse spills with plenty of water.* Record the initial volume of HCl in the buret.

5. Add six drops of congo red to the baking soda solution.

6. Place the flask under the buret. Allow the HCl to slowly drip into the solution while you gently swirl the flask. Con-tinue adding HCl until the solution turns light blue.

7. Record the remaining volume of HCl in the buret. Calculate the amount of acid neutralized by subtracting the remaining volume from the initial volume.

8. Crush one antacid tablet with a mortar and pestle.

9. Dissolve the ground tablet in 100 mL of water. Rinse the mortar and pestle with a little water. Add this rinse water to the flask also. Repeat steps 5–7.

10. Repeat steps 8–9, then 5–7 using a different antacid tablet each time. Fill the buret with additional HCl if needed.

DATA AND OBSERVATIONS

Antacid			Baking Soda
Initial Volume			
Remaining Volume			
Volume of HCl Neutralized			

FIGURE 6–7.

QUESTIONS AND CONCLUSIONS

1. Since your stomach contains dilute HCl, what is the purpose of antacids?

2. What might cause excess stomach acid?

3. Which antacid is most effective in neutralizing a milliliter of acid?

4. What kinds of compounds are antacid tablets composed of?

5. Compare the cost of a unit dosage of each sample. Is there a relationship between cost and effectiveness?

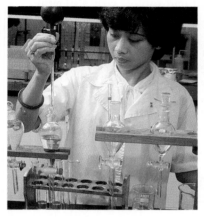

FIGURE 6–8. Prior to the 1820s, scientists thought carbon compounds were produced only by living organisms. Today millions of organic compounds can be produced synthetically.

Why are hydrocarbons often useful as fuels?

BACKGROUND The elementary forms of carbon, carbonic acid and its salts, carbides, cyanides, and the sulfides and oxides of carbon are all considered to be inorganic carbon compounds. In these forms, carbon does not exhibit the same tendency to catenate or "chain" as it does in most organic compounds. Also, carbon has a +2 oxidation state in most inorganic compounds.

6:7 Organic Compounds

Carbon forms a wide variety of compounds. Scientists classify most compounds that contain carbon as organic compounds. Compounds that do not contain carbon are called inorganic. The study of carbon and its compounds is referred to as organic chemistry.

All living things contain organic compounds. Prior to the 1820s, scientists believed that organic compounds were produced only by living organisms. In 1826, a German chemist named Friedrich Wohler synthetically produced urea in a laboratory. Urea is an organic compound that had previously been thought to come only from living organisms. Many other organic compounds are now produced synthetically.

Organic compounds have chemical and physical properties that differ from inorganic compounds. Carbon, a Group IVA element, has four outer energy level electrons. These electrons are able to form covalent bonds with carbon and other elements. Carbon forms many different compounds because of its ability to form chains.

Organic compounds are generally classified into groups that have a similar structure. One major group is the hydrocarbons. **Hydrocarbons** are compounds that contain only the elements carbon and hydrogen. Natural gas is mostly methane, CH_4, the simplest hydrocarbon. When methane is burned, energy is released. This property is common to many hydrocarbons, and they are often used as fuels. Propane and butane are other hydrocarbon fuels. Table 6–4 lists several classes of organic compounds.

See Teacher's Guide.

REVIEW AND REFLECT

1. Study Table 6–3. Why are acids and bases often said to be chemical opposites?
2. Would a strong or a weak acid be a better conductor of electricity? Why?
3. Why did scientists believe at one time that organic compounds were only formed by living organisms?
4. What class of organic compounds contains a hydrocarbon radical bonded to an —OH group?

TABLE 6–4.   SOME CLASSES OF ORGANIC COMPOUNDS

Class	General Description	Suffix	Example
Alkane	Hydrocarbon chain with single bonds between carbon atoms	-ane	Butane
Alkene	Hydrocarbon chain with one or more double bonds between carbon atoms	-ene	Propene
Alkyne	Hydrocarbon chain with one or more triple bonds between carbon atoms	-yne	Ethyne (acetylene)
Aromatic	Derivatives of benzene or compounds that behave similar to benzene-containing compounds		Benzene
Halogen derivative	Hydrocarbons in which one or more H atoms have been replaced by a halogen	-ane	Fluoromethane
Alcohol	Hydrocarbon radical* bonded to an —OH group**	-ol	2-propanol
Aldehyde	Hydrocarbon radical bonded to a $\overset{\text{O}}{\overset{\|}{—\text{C}—\text{H}}}$ group	-al	Methanal (formaldehyde)
Organic acid	Hydrocarbon radical bonded to a $—\text{C}\overset{\displaystyle \text{O}}{\underset{\text{OH}}{}}$ group	-oic acid	Ethanoic acid, acetic acid
Ether	Two hydrocarbon radicals bonded to an oxygen atom R—O—R′	-oxy	Methoxypropane
Ketone	Hydrocarbon radical bonded to a $\overset{\text{O}}{\overset{\|}{—\text{C}—\text{R}′}}$ group	-one	2-propanone (acetone)
Ester	Hydrocarbon radical bonded to a $\overset{\text{O}}{\overset{\|}{—\text{C}—\text{O}—\text{R}′}}$ group	-yl -oate	Methyl ethanoate (ethyl acetate)
Amine	Hydrocarbon radical bonded to an $—\text{N}\overset{\text{H}}{\underset{\text{H}}{}}$ group	-amine	Ethanamine
Amide	Hydrocarbon radical bonded to a $\overset{\text{O}}{\overset{\|}{—\text{C}}}—\text{N}\overset{\text{H}}{\underset{\text{H}}{}}$ group	-amide	Ethanamide (acetamide)

*Any hydrocarbon minus one hydrogen atom is a hydrocarbon radical, R, that can bond with carbon or groups.
**A group is one or more atoms bonded together that function as a unit and can bond with hydrocarbons.

FIGURE 6–9. A chemical reaction takes place as a flashbulb lights. A flashbulb has the same mass before and after it is used because matter is conserved in chemical reactions.

6:8 Chemical Equations

Compounds are formed in chemical reactions. Compounds also break down in chemical reactions. During a chemical reaction, a chemical change takes place. New substances are formed with properties different from the original substances. The original substances in a chemical reaction are called **reactants.** The new substances are called **products.** As shown in Table 6–5, reactants and products may be elements or compounds.

Matter is not created or destroyed in ordinary chemical reactions. The mass of the products is equal to the mass of the reactants. This relationship was first realized by the French chemist Antoine Lavoisier (1743–1794) in the late 1700s. Today this concept is known as the **Law of Conservation of Matter.** Figure 6–9 illustrates how matter is conserved during the chemical reaction that takes place when a flashbulb is used to take a picture.

An equation can be written to describe what takes place during a chemical reaction. An equation written to describe a chemical reaction is like a mathematical equation such as

$$6 + 4 = 10$$

Chemical equations are written in a similar format.

$$\text{reactant} + \text{reactant} \rightarrow \text{products}$$

The arrow is used instead of an equal sign in **chemical equations** and is read "yield" or "yields." A chemical

---

What are the reactants and products of a chemical reaction?

Explain the Law of Conservation of Matter.

SUGGESTION   Have students think of other analogous word equations, for example: students + teacher = school.

equation indicates that during a reaction, the reactants yield some new substance, the product. In order to provide a complete description of the reaction, the types and relative quantities of the substances also must be provided.

Consider the reaction of hydrogen and oxygen to form water. The first step in writing the equation is to indicate the reactants and products.

$$\text{reactants} \qquad \text{product}$$
$$H_2 + O_2 \rightarrow \quad H_2O$$

Notice that there are two hydrogen atoms and two oxygen atoms on the left side of the equation. There are two hydrogen atoms and one oxygen atom on the right side. Based on the Law of Conservation of Matter, an atom cannot be destroyed. The equation must be balanced so that the number of atoms in the reactants equals the number of atoms in the products.

A 2 placed in front of the H_2O molecule indicates that two molecules of H_2O are formed in this reaction.

$$H_2 + O_2 \rightarrow 2H_2O$$

Now there are two atoms of oxygen on each side of the equation. However, there are four atoms of hydrogen on the right now and still only two on the left. Placing a 2 in front of the hydrogen molecule on the left side results in a completely balanced equation.

$$2H_2 + O_2 \rightarrow 2H_2O$$

The total amount of matter in the reactants equals the total amount of matter in the products.

Why must a chemical equation be balanced?

TABLE 6–5.   TYPES OF CHEMICAL REACTIONS

Synthesis	**Decomposition**
element or compound + element or compound → compound	compound → two or more elements or compounds
$2H_2 + O_2 \rightarrow 2H_2O$	$CuCO_3 \rightarrow CuO + CO_2$
$NH_3 + HCl \rightarrow NH_4Cl$	$2Ag_2O \rightarrow 4Ag + O_2$

Displacement	
Single	**Double**
element A + compound XB → element B + compound XA	compound AB + compound CD → compound AD + compound CB
$Zn + H_2SO_4 \rightarrow H_2 + ZnSO_4$	$AgNO_3 + NaCl \rightarrow AgCl + NaNO_3$

Whole numbers placed in front of the symbols for reactants and products in chemical equations are called coefficients. Coefficients indicate the relative proportions of the reactants and products. Only coefficients can be changed when balancing a chemical equation. Never change the subscripts in a compound.

What are coefficients?

SUGGESTION Stress the point that students should never change subscripts in a compound. Be sure students understand that changing the subscripts would change the compounds represented.

EXAMPLE: Balancing Equations

Problem: Write a balanced equation for the reaction between iron and oxygen yielding iron(III) oxide (rust).

Solution: First, write the formulas for the reactants and the products.

$$Fe + O_2 \rightarrow Fe_2O_3$$

Next, balance the equation. There are two oxygen atoms on the left side of the equation and three on the right side. Placing a coefficient of 3 in front of the O_2 and a 2 in front of the Fe_2O_3 results in six atoms of oxygen on both sides of the equation.

$$Fe + 3O_2 \rightarrow 2Fe_2O_3$$

There are now four iron atoms on right side of the equation and only one on the left. Placing the coefficient 4 in front of the Fe results in four Fe atoms on both sides of the equation.

$$4Fe + 3O_2 \rightarrow 2Fe_2O_3$$

FIGURE 6–10. Photosynthesis is an important series of chemical reactions that are needed for plant growth. It is an endothermic reaction in which the sun's energy is used to combine water and carbon dioxide to form sugar.

6:9 Chemical Reactions

All chemical reactions involve changes in energy. The change in energy may be in the form of heat, light, or electricity. The energy of the products is always different from the energy of the reactants. If the energy of the products is less than the energy of the reactants, energy is released during the reaction.

reactants → products + energy

Reactions that give off, or release, energy are called **exothermic** (ek soh THUR mihk) reactions. Burning is an example of an exothermic reaction that produces energy in the forms of light and heat.

FIGURE 6–11.   The chemical reactions that take place when fireworks explode are exothermic.

If the energy of the products is greater than the energy of the reactants, energy must be absorbed during the reaction.

$$\text{reactants} + \text{energy} \rightarrow \text{products}$$

Reactions that absorb energy are called **endothermic** (en duh THUR mihk) reactions. An instant ice pack contains substances that react endothermically. When the substances react, they absorb heat from their surroundings. This heat is stored in the products as chemical energy. When energy is removed from the environment, it creates a cooling effect. Squeezing the ice pack breaks open an inner plastic container allowing the reactants to come in contact with one another.

BACKGROUND   *Endo-* means within; *exo-* means out.

Most synthetic fibers and plastics are made from molecules called polymers. A polymer is a very large organic molecule. By combining many smaller molecules that contain double or triple bonds in a polymerization reaction, synthetic polymers can be formed. A **polymerization** (pahl uh muh ruh ZAY shun) reaction is an example of a synthesis reaction. The double or triple bonds in a compound are broken in a polymerization reaction and the smaller molecules join to form large molecules. The polymer polyethylene is formed from ethene molecules as shown below.

What is a polymerization reaction?

TABLE 6–6.	SOME COMMON POLYMERS	
Polymer	**Uses**	**Formula**
Polybutadiene	Synthetic rubber used for golf ball covers, footwear, and floor tile	$(-CH_2-CH=CH-CH_2-)_n$*
Polypropylene	One of lightest plastics, used in sheets for packaging, many molded plastic parts including auto parts, utensils, housewares, bottles, and pipes	$(C_3H_6)_n$
Polyurethane	Used to produce soft foams: mattress padding, upholstery "foam rubber"; and rigid foams: airplane construction (to give strength to metal)	$(R_1NHCOOR_2)_n$
Polyvinyl chloride (PVC)	Widely used plastic in many different forms: films for rainwear, aprons, for floor tiles, phonograph records, foams for padding, cushions	$(-H_2CCHCl-)_n$

*The n in a formula means the basic unit is repeated many times.

Many of the fabrics used to make clothing, furniture, and carpets are polyesters. Several other common synthetic polymers are listed in Table 6–6.

In section 6:6, acids and bases were described as chemical opposites. When acids and bases react together, a neutral solution containing water and a salt is produced. This process is known as a **neutralization** reaction. A neutralization reaction is an example of a displacement reaction.

What is a neutralization reaction?

$$acid + base \rightarrow water + salt$$

There are many compounds that are classified as salts. In this broader sense, a salt is defined as a product of the neutralization of an acid and a base. Salts are generally ionic compounds of a metal and a nonmetal. Displacement reactions are often done in a water solution. When the reactants are combined, one of the products may form a precipitate. A precipitate is an insoluble substance that forms during the reaction.

Some compounds break down into simpler substances when energy, such as heat or electricity, is applied. For example, methane can be broken down with heat in the presence of a catalyst to form carbon and hydrogen.

$$CH_4 \rightarrow C + 2H_2$$

This type of decomposition reaction is called cracking.

See Teacher's Guide.

REVIEW AND REFLECT

1. Write balanced equations for each of the following.
   a. Iron and sulfur combine to form iron(II) sulfide.
   b. Calcium carbonate is heated, yielding calcium oxide and carbon dioxide.
   c. Lead(II) chloride and lithium sulfate react to form lithium chloride and lead(II) sulfate.
2. What is the difference between an endothermic and exothermic reaction?
3. What is a polymer?
4. Why would a laboratory assistant pour boric acid on a spilled sodium hydroxide solution?

See Teacher's Guide.

Career Profile

The Royal Prince Alfred Hospital is one of the largest hospitals in Sydney, Australia. At this hospital the department of nutrition, dietetics, and food service is headed by Jo Rogers. Jo began working as a dietitian at the hospital in 1945. She prepared for this position by acquiring a science degree in physiology and biochemistry. During a 12 month training program in dietetics, Jo counselled patients about their dietary needs. She discussed their food likes and dislikes, their eating habits, and how much money they could afford to spend on food. Based on this information and their need for certain nutrients, Jo developed dietary programs for them.

For several years Jo worked closely with doctors and made specific dietary recommendations for patients. For instance, she counselled patients with diabetes how to balance their food intake with their insulin production or injections.

Today, Jo Rogers manages a staff of 500 people at the hospital. She is busy organizing staff training programs, monitoring the budget, evaluating the food service system, and forming policies. She also lectures at the University of Sydney and has co-authored four books on nutrition. In addition, Jo talks with community groups, such as senior citizens and school children. She enjoys getting people interested in the value of the food they eat and showing them how to help themselves stay well.

6:10 Choices: Acid Rain

Perhaps you have heard about "acid rain." Pure rain is slightly acidic. It normally has a pH of about 5.6. Rain is acidic because as it falls, it combines with naturally occurring carbon dioxide in the atmosphere. Carbon dioxide is an acid anhydride. An acid anhydride is a substance that forms an acid when it combines with water. When water and carbon dioxide combine, carbonic acid is formed.

$$CO_2 + H_2O \rightarrow H_2CO_3$$

Many other acid anhydrides are being added to the atmosphere. Factories and electric power plants that burn fossil fuels for energy release sulfur oxides from smokestacks. Automobile and truck exhaust contains nitrogen oxides. Sulfur and nitrogen oxides are also acid anhydrides. When these compounds combine with rain, they form acids too.

$$SO_2 + H_2O \rightarrow H_2SO_3 \text{ (sulfurous acid)}$$
$$SO_3 + H_2O \rightarrow H_2SO_4 \text{ (sulfuric acid)}$$
$$2NO_2 + H_2O \rightarrow HNO_2 + HNO_3 \text{ (nitric and nitrous acids)}$$

Consequently, the rain in areas with these pollutants is called acid rain because it has a pH less than 5.6. For example, the pH of rain that falls in the Adirondack Mountains of New York averages about 4.2. Rain with a pH of 1.5 has been recorded in Wheeling, West Virginia. Acid rain is a major problem in parts of North America and Europe.

The source of most acid rain in North America is the industrialized part of the United States east of the Mississippi River. The Great Lakes region of the U.S. is less sensitive to acid rain than other areas, though. The geology of the Great Lakes region includes much limestone. The alkaline soil that forms from this rock acts as a buffer to acid rain. A buffer is a solution that can receive moderate amounts of either an acid or a base without much change in its pH. Alkaline soil counteracts the effects of acid rain, somewhat. However, tall smokestacks in the Great Lakes region release pollutants that are distributed many kilometers from their sources by wind. The soil of New England and eastern Canada is naturally acidic due to the geology of the regions. As a result, these regions are more sensitive to acid rain.

What is an acid anhydride?

BACKGROUND The reactions that yield nitric and nitrous acids are much more complex than indicated in these simple examples.

SUGGESTION Remind students that the pH scale is logarithmic. Each pH unit represents a tenfold increase in acidity.

FIGURE 6–12. Many parts of the world are now plagued by acid rain. The map shows the estimated pH of different world regions.

Acid rain dissolves some chemical elements needed for life that are normally cycled in an environment. For example, calcium, magnesium, potassium, sodium, and manganese are removed from leaves and soil by acid rain. When these elements are dissolved by acid rain, they are carried away by runoff and river outflow. Without these nutrients, plants die. Animals that depend on the plants for food die too, in time.

The effects of acid rain are serious. Acid rain has resulted in the death of fish in many lakes. In Ontario, Canada, over 140 lakes have been found to be totally without fish as a result of acid rain. In Norway and Sweden, similar destruction of wildlife has occurred. Acid rain also damages structures, such as buildings and bridges. Ancient buildings in Greece are decaying more rapidly than ever before due to acid rain. Many statues have been defaced by acid rain. Crops are damaged by acid rain, too. In Germany's Black Forest, half of the trees have been damaged by acid rain.

The problems of acid rain are severe and solving them is not easy. Lime has been added to some lakes to neutralize the acid rain. Liming is expensive, though, and its effectiveness is uncertain. Long range solutions to acid rain will require that the pollutants, acid anhydrides, be controlled at their sources. Currently, technology is available to remove some acid anhydrides in smokestacks and auto or truck exhaust systems. Also, low sulfur coal can be burned to reduce output of sulfur oxides. However, these solutions often are not used for economic or other reasons.

FIGURE 6–13.   Industry is challenged by consumers to make inexpensive, high-quality products. The cost of effective pollution-control equipment may make these demands difficult to meet.

What are some effects of acid rain?

See Teacher's Guide.

REVIEW AND REFLECT

1. What is acid rain?
2. Why is rainwater naturally acidic?
3. Why has lime been added to lakes affected by acid rain?
4. Tall smokestacks were built in the 1970s to improve local air quality. Why were they not a real solution to the acid rain problem?
5. Although technology exists to reduce acid anhydride pollutants, why has the problem of acid rain not been solved?

CHAPTER 6 REVIEW

SUMMARY

1. Atoms combine by either gaining or losing electrons or by sharing electrons. 6:1
2. Ionic bonds are formed when atoms gain or lose electrons. 6:2
3. Covalent bonds are formed when atoms share electrons. 6:3
4. Chemical formulas indicate the composition of compounds. Chemical equations describe chemical reactions. 6:4
5. Ions carry a positive or a negative charge. Groups of atoms may combine to form polyatomic ions. 6:5
6. Acids and bases are compounds whose strength depends on the amount of H_3O^+ and OH^- ions they produce. 6:6

7. The unique bonding capabilities of carbon results in millions of organic compounds. 6:7
8. Matter cannot be created or destroyed during ordinary chemical reactions. 6:8
9. All chemical reactions involve changes in energy. 6:9
10. Acids and bases can neutralize one another, producing a salt, in one type of displacement reaction. 6:9
11. Organic molecules are formed in synthesis reactions such as polymerization. 6:9
12. Complex substances break down into simpler substances during a decomposition reaction. 6:8, 6:9

VOCABULARY

chemical equation 15
chemical formula 10
covalent bonding 2
endothermic 9
exothermic 6

hydrocarbon 14
indicator 3
ion 1
ionic bonding 7
Law of Conservation of Matter 5

neutralization 13
oxidation number 11
polymerization 12
products 8
reactants 4

Match each definition with the correct word from the list.

1. An atom that has gained or lost an electron
2. Sharing of electrons between atoms
3. A substance used to determine whether a substance is an acid or a base
4. The substances that combine in a chemical reaction
5. Matter is not created or destroyed in ordinary chemical reactions
6. A chemical reaction that gives off heat
7. Bonding that results from transfer of electrons between atoms
8. The substances that are formed in a chemical reaction

9. A chemical reaction that absorbs energy
10. A shorthand way of indicating the relative proportions of elements in a compound
11. A description of the combining ability of an element
12. Synthesis reaction in which large organic molecules are formed by combining smaller molecules that contain double bonds
13. Displacement reaction in which salts and water are formed by combining acids and bases
14. An organic compound containing only hydrogen and carbon
15. A shorthand description of what takes place in a chemical reaction

QUESTIONS

MAIN IDEAS

Choose the correct answer to complete each sentence.

1. The process of losing electrons is called *(neutralization, synthesis, oxidation)*.

2. In an exothermic reaction, the reactants have *(more energy than, less energy than, the same energy as)* the products.

3. H_3O^+ ions are formed when a(n) *(acid, base, salt)* is added to water.

4. The pH of an acidic substance is *(higher than, lower than, the same as)* water.

5. The products of a neutralization reaction are a *(salt, polymer, reactant)* and water.

6. Most of the materials used by people are *(elements, compounds, ions)*.

7. The chemical formula for copper(II) chloride is *(CuCl, CuCl₂, 2CuCl, Cu₂Cl)*.

8. All organic compounds contain *(oxygen, nitrogen, carbon, silicon)*.

9. In a chemical reaction, the mass of the products is *(less than, more than, the same as)* the mass of the reactants.

10. *(Coefficients, subscripts, superscripts)* are placed before the formulas or symbols in a chemical equation in order to balance it.

See Teacher's Guide.

APPLICATIONS

Answer each question in one or more paragraphs. Show how to solve each problem.

1. How can there be millions of substances when only about 100 elements exist?

2. Why are there more organic compounds than inorganic compounds?

3. To prevent iron from rusting, it often is coated with zinc. How does this process prevent rust? What is the process called? (Hint: Review chapter 5.)

4. The food people eat undergoes chemical reactions within the body. These reactions produce energy. Are the reactions endothermic or exothermic? Explain.

5. Write balanced equations for the following reactions.
   a. Zinc oxide and carbon form zinc and carbon monoxide.
   b. Carbon dioxide and water form glucose ($C_6H_{12}O_6$) and oxygen.
   c. Carbon dioxide and water combine to form carbonic acid.
   d. Phosphorus(V) oxide (P_4O_{10}) and water combine to form phosphoric acid.

6. Explain why polymerization reactions have been important to advances in technology.

FURTHER STUDY

INVESTIGATIONS

1. Make several loaves of bread and vary the type and amount of yeast in each. Prepare a written report of your experimental results.

2. Find out the pH of the soil near your home. Check with a local nursery to determine what plants will grow best in your area. Develop a garden or landscape plan based on this information.

3. Write a report about how buffered aspirin is different than regular aspirin.

READINGS

+ Chen, N.Y. "Making Gasoline by Fermentation." *Chemtech.* August, 1983. pp. 488–492.

0 Leffler, William L. *Petroleum Refining for the Non-Technical Person.* PennWell Books: Tulsa, OK, 1979.

+ Sachtler, Wolfgang M. H. "What Makes a Catalyst Selective?" *Chemtech.* July, 1983. pp. 434–447.

0 Smith, H. "Chemical Reactions." *The New Book of Popular Science.* 1980. vol. 3, pp. 60–68.

MANY materials are mixtures. A beach is a mixture of sand, stones, and shell fragments. Oceans are mixtures of salts, plants, animals, and water. Clouds are a mixture of water vapor and air. What other mixtures do you find in this picture? How are mixtures different from compounds?

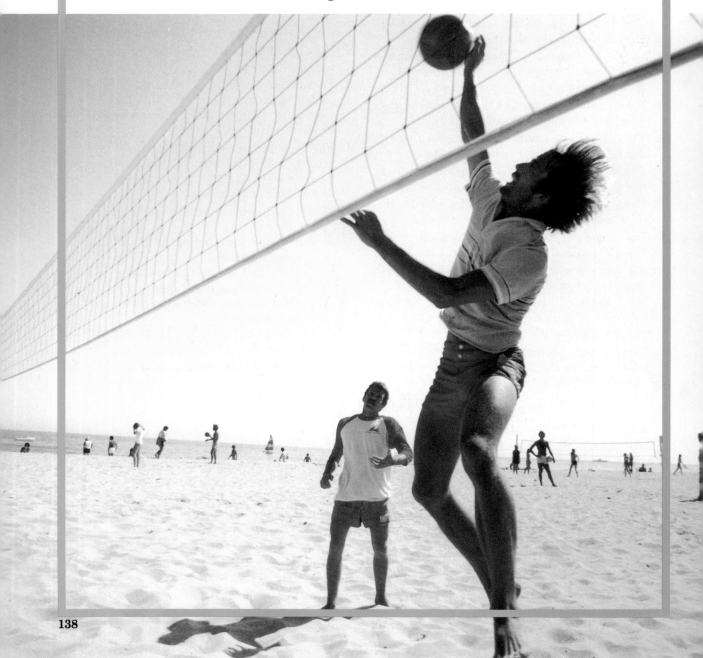

MIXTURES

INTRODUCING THE CHAPTER Take a small amount of sugar and add it to a beaker of water. Ask students how to separate the *mixture* of sugar and water. Boil the water away in an evaporating dish or a beaker leaving the sugar behind. In another evaporating dish or test tube, heat some sugar until it becomes carmelized. Note that the sugar has changed *chemically* by combining with oxygen. It cannot easily be changed back to sugar. Use the chapter opening photograph to point out that there are many mixtures.

7:1 Types of Mixtures

Mixtures are important in your life. Your blood is a mixture of solids, liquids, and gases. The air you breathe is a mixture. Many of the foods you eat are mixtures. For example, the milk and cereal you may have had for breakfast or the taco you may have had for lunch are mixtures.

Mixtures can be composed of any combination of solid, liquid, or gaseous substances. A **mixture** is formed when two or more substances are physically combined. Mixtures differ from compounds because the substances in a mixture are not chemically combined. The substances in a mixture retain their chemical properties and can be separated by physical means, such as filtering. Mixtures have a variable composition also. The elements in a compound are always in the same ratio.

Mixtures may be heterogeneous or homogeneous. The properties of a heterogeneous mixture are not the same throughout the mixture. For example, a taco is a heterogeneous mixture. The amounts of vegetables, meats, and cheese are not the same throughout a taco. Homogeneous mixtures are called solutions. **Solutions** have the same properties throughout. Solutions are formed when substances dissolve in other substances.

GOAL You will learn the characteristics of mixtures, how they are classified, and how they are separated.

How are mixtures different from compounds?

SUGGESTION Review the classification of matter introduced in chapter 3.

What are some properties of solutions?

139

7:2 Solutions

ACTIVITY   Provide some distilled water for students to taste.

Describe the solute and solvent in a solution.

Tap water is a solution that contains dissolved air and minerals. The dissolved minerals give water a slight taste and odor. Pure or distilled water is tasteless and odorless. The amount of minerals in tap water varies from place to place due to differences in the local environment. For this reason, water in another town may taste different to you.

In a solution, the substance in greater quantity is called the **solvent.** The substances of lesser quantity are called the **solutes.** The solutes are dissolved in the solvent. Dissolved solute particles are ions or molecules. These particles are so small they cannot be seen with an ordinary microscope. They also pass through filter paper. Solutes and solvents can be solids, liquids, or gases. Table 7–1 lists nine types of solutions.

TABLE 7–1.	TYPES OF SOLUTIONS	
Solute	**Solvent**	**Example**
Solid	Liquid	Instant coffee (coffee in water)
Liquid	Liquid	Vinegar (acetic acid in water)
Gas	Liquid	Carbonated drinks (CO_2 in water)
Solid	Gas	Mothballs (napthalene in air)
Liquid	Gas	Humidity (water in air)
Gas	Gas	Deep-sea diver's gas (helium in oxygen)
Solid	Solid	Pewter (lead in tin)
Liquid	Solid	Dentists' amalgam (mercury in silver)
Gas	Solid	Gas stove lighter (hydrogen in palladium)

How does the addition of a solute affect a solvent?

The addition of a solute to a liquid solvent causes the boiling point of the solvent to be raised and the freezing point to be lowered. These changes are referred to as boiling point elevation and freezing point depression. The amount of change in boiling and freezing points depends on the amount of solute dissolved in solution. The higher the concentration of solute, the greater the boiling point elevation and freezing point depression.

Boiling point elevation and freezing point depression are useful in many situations. Noodles and vegetables are of-

a

b
FIGURE 7–1. Many new buildings have safety outlets installed in bathrooms where electricity is used near water (a). The current flowing to these outlets is shut off automatically when the circuit overloads (b).

ten cooked in salt water. The added table salt causes the boiling point of water to be higher, which means the amount of cooking time can be less. In cold climates, calcium chloride is spread on icy roads and sidewalks. The salt reduces the freezing point of water and helps melt the ice.

The conductivity of a solution is affected by solution concentration. Some solutions readily conduct an electric current. Ionic solutes, like NaCl, and molecular solutes that ionize in solution, like HCl, generally form solutions that conduct electricity. These solutes are known as electrolytes. The greater the concentration of an electrolyte, the greater the amount of electric current that can be conducted. Some molecular solutes, such as sugar, do not form ions in solution. These solutes are called nonelectrolytes. Solutions of nonelectrolytes do not conduct a current. Pure or distilled water does not readily conduct an electric current. However, you must be cautious when using electrical appliances around tap water. Tap water is a solution of many dissolved solids, some of which are electrolytes.

What are electrolytes?

DEMONSTRATION Prepare saturated and supersaturated solutions of tea and sugar as described in section 7:3.

7:3 Solution Concentration

The proportions of solute and solvent in a solution are expressed in several ways. A **saturated** solution contains as much solute as can be dissolved in the solvent. If you add too much sugar to a glass of iced tea, some sugar will

What is a saturated solution?

FIGURE 7–2. The excess solute in a supersaturated solution cannot be seen until a seed crystal is added. The excess solute crystallizes around the seed crystal.

Describe dilute and concentrated solutions.

settle on the bottom of the glass. When no more sugar will dissolve in the iced tea, a saturated solution has been formed.

Generally, as temperature increases, more solid solute will dissolve in a liquid solvent. For example, more sugar will dissolve in hot water than in cold water. Suppose you made a saturated solution of sugar water at 90°C. If the saturated solution is cooled slowly to room temperature, the additional solute will stay in solution, forming a supersaturated solution. A **supersaturated** solution contains more solute than it would normally take to saturate it at a specific temperature. If a little more sugar is added to the supersaturated solution, the excess solute immediately will begin to crystallize out of solution, Figure 7–2. Perhaps you have made rock candy using this technique.

Often scientists simply describe a solution in relative terms. A concentrated solution contains a relatively large amount of solute. A dilute solution contains a relatively small amount of solute.

See Teacher's Guide.

REVIEW AND REFLECT

1. What is a mixture? Name the two types of mixtures and give an example of each.
2. Some frozen vegetables are cooked in a pan of water to which a spoonful of salt has been added. What is the solution, the solute, and the solvent?
3. What types of solutes will form conducting solutions?
4. How is orange juice concentrate different from regular orange juice?
5. Explain why it is not safe to swim during an electrical storm.

7:4 Solubility

Why is water called the universal solvent?

Most solutions are made up of a solid solute in a liquid solvent. The most common solvent is water. Water is often called the universal solvent because many substances will dissolve in it. A substance that dissolves in a solvent is **soluble** in the solvent. A substance that does not dissolve in a solvent is **insoluble** in the solvent. Sugar and table salt are soluble in water; motor oil is insoluble in water.

How readily a solute will dissolve in a solvent is known as solubility. Solubility is determined partly by the type of bonding in the solute and solvent. The attraction atoms have for electrons varies. When two different elements bond covalently, one has a greater attraction for the shared electrons than the other. This atom tends to have a slight negative charge. The other atom tends to have a slight positive charge. The slightly charged ends of the molecule are called poles. Molecules that have poles are **polar** molecules.

Water is a polar molecule. Oxygen has a greater attraction for the shared electrons than do the hydrogen atoms. The oxygen end of the molecule forms a negative pole. The hydrogen end of the molecule forms a positive pole. Other common polar solvents are methanol, CH_3OH, and ethanol, CH_3CH_2OH.

When two or more atoms of the same element bond or when the difference in attraction for shared electrons is small, **nonpolar** molecules are formed. Oxygen and chlorine molecules are nonpolar. Sometimes the atoms in a molecule are arranged in such a way that no poles can be formed, Figure 7–3. Cyclohexane, C_6H_{12}, and benzene, C_6H_6, are common solvents that have nonpolar molecular structures.

Solutes may also be polar or nonpolar. A polar solute will dissolve in a polar solvent, and a nonpolar solute will generally dissolve in a nonpolar solvent. However, a nonpolar solute will generally not dissolve in a polar solvent. For example, motor oil is a nonpolar substance and water is a polar substance. If motor oil and water are mixed and left to settle, they separate into distinct layers. A general rule for solubility is that "likes will dissolve likes."

What happens when a substance dissolves? Consider the simple example of table salt dissolved in water. A salt crystal, composed of Na^+ and Cl^- ions, dissolves as the ions are surrounded by the polar H_2O molecules as shown in Figure 7–4. The Na^+ ions are attracted by the partially negative oxygen poles of the water molecule. In a similar fashion, the Cl^- ions are attracted by the partially positive hydrogen poles of the water molecule. The ions on the surface of the crystal dissolve or dissociate from the crystal. This process continues until the crystal is dissolved completely or the solution is saturated.

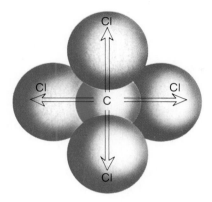

FIGURE 7–3. Chlorine atoms have a greater attraction for shared electrons than carbon atoms. However, the shape of the resulting molecule has no place for polar ends to form.

How is solubility affected by the polarity of the solute and solvent?

FIGURE 7–4. Polar water molecules surround sodium and chloride ions and pull them away from the salt crystal.

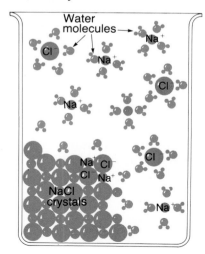

See Teacher's Guide.

Skill Inquiry

The atoms in a molecular substance bond covalently. Often the pair of shared electrons in a covalent bond is more strongly attracted to one of the atoms. For this reason, one end of the molecule has a partial negative charge, leaving the other with a partial positive charge. Such molecules are said to be polar.

The shape of a molecule is also a factor in whether it is polar or nonpolar. Consider, for example, the compound aluminum hydride, AlH_3, shown in the figure. The hydrogen atoms have a greater attraction for the shared electrons than the aluminum atom. However, the shape of this molecule does not allow for an unequal distribution of charge at any end. Because no poles are formed, the molecule is nonpolar. A water molecule has an angular shape. Oxygen has a slightly greater attraction for the shared electrons. The unequal distribution of charge and the molecule's shape result in the formation of a polar molecule. Look at the atomic shapes shown in the table. After studying each shape, try to determine whether each molecule is polar or nonpolar.

TABLE OF POLAR AND NONPOLAR MOLECULES

Molecular Formula	Atomic Structure	Polarity
HCl	H—Cl	Polar
H_2	H—H	Nonpolar
NH_3	N / | \ H H H	
CH_4	H | C / | \ H H H	
CO_2	O=C=O	
CH_3Cl	Cl | C / | \ H H H	

DEMONSTRATION   Hold a charged rod near a stream of water to show the polarity of water.

How does temperature affect the solubility of a solid in a liquid?

7:5 Factors Affecting Solubility

Several factors affect how much solute will dissolve and the rate at which it will dissolve in a solvent. Sugar is more soluble in hot tea than it is in iced tea. In section 7:3, you learned that in general, as temperature increases, the solubility of a solid in a liquid also increases. For example, the solubility graph in Figure 7–5 shows that more than twice as much potassium nitrate, KNO_3, can be dissolved in water at 40°C than in water at 20°C.

Why do people stir their coffee or tea after adding sugar or cream? One of the ways to increase the rate of solution

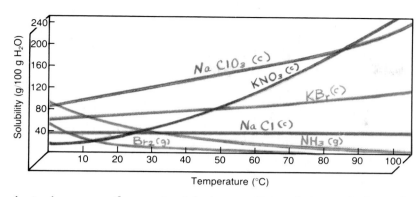

FIGURE 7–5. In general, with an increase in temperature, the solubility of solids (c, crystalline) increases and the solubility of gases (g) decreases.

is to increase the contact between the solute and the solvent. Stirring increases the contact making the solute dissolve more quickly.

Solute size also affects solubility rate. Smaller particles of a solute will dissolve faster than larger ones. The smaller the particles of solute are, the greater the contact between the solute and solvent. For example, bouillon, a brothlike soup, can be made by adding dried cubes or granules to boiling water. Bouillon granules take less time to dissolve than the larger cubes.

Gaseous solutes have some unique solubility factors. You may have noticed bubbles rising from a glass of carbonated soft drink. As the soft drink warms, less carbon dioxide remains in solution. The solubility of a gas in a liquid decreases as temperature increases. The same effect can be observed in water. As water is slowly heated, dissolved oxygen bubbles rise to the surface of the liquid and escape into the air. Many industries use water from rivers or lakes as a coolant and then return the water to the waterways. Although the water is not polluted, it is hot. The hot water is thermal pollution that raises the temperature of a waterway. Thermal pollution decreases the amount of dissolved oxygen in the water. A reduction in dissolved oxygen can significantly alter the quality and quantity of plant and animal life in the waterway.

Pressure also affects the solubility of a gas. More gas can be dissolved in a liquid as pressure is increased. The sound you hear when the top of a carbonated beverage is removed is due to escaping carbon dioxide. These beverages are bottled under pressure. When they are opened, the pressure is reduced and some of the dissolved gas comes out of solution.

How does particle size affect solubility?

ACTIVITY   Boil some sodawater (sparkling water). After it has cooled, have students compare its taste with that of a freshly opened bottle.

How does temperature affect the solubility of a gaseous solute?

What is thermal pollution?

How are pressure and solubility related?

REVIEW AND REFLECT

1. What factors affect solubility rate?
2. Two bottles of carbonated soft drink are opened and poured into two different glasses. One bottle had been in a refrigerator while the other was at room temperature. Which would fizz more? Why?
3. Water alone generally will not remove grease from your hands. Soap helps to remove grease. What types of molecules are in water and grease?

Career Profile

It is 7:00 A.M. when Dolores Morton opens the doors of the dry cleaning establishment she manages in Omaha, Nebraska. After completing an intensive three week training program, where she learned packaging, counter work, cleaning, pressing, and spot removal, she was given her own store to manage.

As manager, Dolores is primarily concerned with providing quality control over the work being done. She carefully oversees all stages of the dry cleaning process. Dolores especially enjoys the challenge of removing difficult spots on garments. Though the solvent in the cleaning machine can remove most dirt spots, stains such as blood, ink, or coffee require special treatment. Dolores follows a detailed chart that classifies most stains and their treatments into eight categories. A stain made by a ballpoint pen, for example, is usually treated first with a special dry solvent that evaporates very rapidly. This procedure is followed by treatment with an oily-type paint remover. Coffee, tea, or grass stains are treated first with a neutral detergent, then with a 28% acetic acid or tannin solution, and finally, if necessary, with a special formula remover.

Dolores manages the shop as if she owned it. She has learned to work well with customers. She appreciates the complete trust they now place in her ability to clean and press even the finest garments. When the day's work is completed, Dolores goes home with a feeling of accomplishment.

Activity: What affects solubility?

See Teacher's Guide.

MATERIALS

balance	stirring rod
sugar cube	spoon
granulated sugar	hot plate
powdered sugar	clamp
graduated cylinder	ring stand
3 150-mL beakers	apron
NH_4Cl	goggles

300 mL room-temperature water
thermometer in a rubber stopper
clock or watch with second hand

PROCEDURE

Part A

1. Place equal masses of a sugar cube, granulated sugar, and powdered sugar in separate beakers containing 75 mL of room-temperature water.

2. Time, up to five minutes, how long each mass of sugar takes to dissolve.

3. Repeat step 1 with clean beakers.

4. Repeat step 2 while stirring constantly.

Part B

1. Set up the apparatus shown below.

2. Put 20 mL of room-temperature water in a beaker.

3. Add spoonfuls of NH_4Cl to the water while stirring with a stirring rod until no more will dissolve. **CAUTION:** *Ammonium chloride, NH_4Cl, is poisonous.* Record how many spoonfuls you add.

FIGURE 7–6.

4. Heat the solution until the temperature reaches 40°C. While stirring with the rod, add more NH_4Cl until no more will dissolve. Record the total number of spoonfuls added up to now.

5. Repeat step 3 for 60°C and 80°C.

6. After the beaker has cooled, pour the solution down the drain and rinse the beaker and sink with plenty of water.

DATA AND OBSERVATIONS

Part A

Type of Sugar	Time to Dissolve	
	Without Stirring	**Stirring**
Cube		
Granulated		
Powdered		

Part B

NH_4Cl	Temperature
spoonfuls	20°C
spoonfuls	40°C
spoonfuls	60°C
spoonfuls	80°C

QUESTIONS AND CONCLUSIONS

1. Why did you need to find the mass of the sugar cube?

2. Why did you not need to mass the NH_4Cl? How could you estimate the mass of NH_4Cl dissolved in the supersaturated solution?

3. What is the effect of particle size on solubility? of stirring? of temperature?

4. What would a graph of your results look like?

a   b

FIGURE 7–7. A centrifuge can be used to separate the components of blood for testing (a). The Tyndall effect can be seen when fog scatters light (b).

What is a suspension?

BACKGROUND The difference among solutions, colloids, and suspensions is not distinct, but rather a continuum. Suspensions are usually classified as having particles larger than 1000 Å or 10^{-5} cm.

7:6 Other Mixtures

Homogeneous mixtures are classified as solutions, but many mixtures are heterogeneous. For example, chalk mixes with water but it does not dissolve. Instead, when shaken, particles of the powdered chalk are scattered through the water. This type of mixture is called a suspension. A **suspension** is a scattering of relatively large particles. The particles in a suspension are not molecules or ions. They are about one thousand times larger than the molecules or ions in a solution. Suspended particles can be seen with a microscope. Some are large enough to be seen by the unaided eye.

Many medicines and fruit juices contain suspended particles. You may have seen particles of oranges called pulp suspended in orange juice. Some brands of orange juice are filtered to remove the pulp. Suspended particles can be filtered easily from most suspensions. Suspended particles tend to settle to the bottom of a container when left to stand. Within several hours the dispersed particles in an undisturbed suspension generally settle out. For this reason, medicines and juices that are suspensions are labeled, "Shake well before using."

Another type of mixture that is not a solution is a colloid. **Colloids** are scatterings of particles of intermediate size. Emulsions, foams, and gels are colloids. A colloid is like a suspension except the particles are smaller. The particles in a colloid are larger than ions or molecules, but smaller than the particles in a suspension. The particles in colloids pass through filters and do not settle when left to stand. Colloidal particles usually can be separated by a centrifuge. A centrifuge is a device that spins very rapidly causing substances to separate according to their densities. Blood cells are separated from plasma by centrifuging.

Suspensions and colloids also exhibit the Tyndall effect. This property is seen when light passes through a suspension or colloid. The particles scatter the light causing the beam of light to become "visible." Sunbeams can be seen when bright sunlight shines through a window and is scattered by dust particles. The beam of a searchlight or auto headlight can be seen because it is scattered by the particles of dust and moisture in the air. The particles in a solution are too small to scatter light. Table 7–2 shows a comparison among the properties of solutions, colloids, and suspensions.

What are colloids?

What is the Tyndall effect?

Why do solutions not show the Tyndall effect?

BACKGROUND   The abbreviation nm is for the SI unit nanometer, which is 0.000 000 001 m.

TABLE 7–2.   COMPARISON OF SOLUTIONS, COLLOIDS, AND SUSPENSIONS

Solutions	Colloids	Suspensions
Do not settle out	Do not settle out	Settle out on standing
Pass unchanged through ordinary filter paper	Pass unchanged through ordinary filter paper	Separated by ordinary filter paper
Do not scatter light	Scatter light (Tyndall effect)	Scatter light (Tyndall effect)
Affect boiling point and melting point	Do not affect boiling point and melting point	Do not affect boiling point and melting point
Particles <1 nm	Particles <100 nm but >1 nm	Particles >100 nm
Examples—tea, salt water, carbonated drinks, coffee	Examples—milk, shaving cream, pudding, gels, mayonnaise, foams	Example—milk of magnesia

FIGURE 7–8. The nonpolar end of a soap molecule dissolves in grease. The polar end dissolves in water.

What is an emulsion?

If salad oil and water are mixed together in a jar, they quickly separate into two distinct layers. However, if a small amount of soap is added and the jar is shaken again, an emulsion is formed. An emulsion is a colloid of a liquid dispersed in another liquid. **Emulsifying agents,** such as soap, cause the formation of colloids. Soap molecules are large. One end will dissolve in salad oil and the other will dissolve in water. As shown in Figure 7–8, soaps are used to clean grease, an oily substance, because they can cause the grease to break up in water.

Why are emulsifying agents added to foods?

Emulsifying agents are often added to foods so they do not separate. Pectin is an emulsifying agent in jams and jellies. Eggs act as an emulsifying agent to combine the water and oil in mayonnaise.

What is homogenization?

A suspension can also be made more stable by reducing the size of the dispersed particles. This process is known as homogenization. When milk is homogenized, the suspended fat globules are broken down into smaller particles. Homogenizing milk helps to prevent the separation of the milk and cream.

7:7 Separating Mixtures

The water in lakes, rivers, and oceans is a mixture of substances. Many of the substances must be removed for residential or commercial use of the water. Water treatment plants have a variety of filters and settling tanks for removing various substances. Salts may be removed by evaporating or boiling.

Mixtures can be separated using methods that involve only physical changes. As stated in section 7:1, the substances that form a mixture are not chemically bonded to one another. The formation of mixtures involves no chemical changes, so the separation of mixtures involves no chemical changes. Mixtures can be separated in a number of ways. The type of method used depends on the physical properties of the substances to be separated.

One method used for separating mixtures is filtering. Filters are made in many different sizes for many different uses. A colander is a filter used to separate noodles from the water in which they were cooked. Filters are used in automobiles to remove particles of dirt from oil and gasoline.

Some substances can be separated from a mixture using a magnet. Magnetic separation methods are used in some solid waste recycling plants. Since iron and steel are magnetic, they are easily separated from paper, wood, aluminum, and other nonmagnetic materials. Then the iron and steel are recycled.

SUGGESTION   Point out that the substances in a mixture (or a solution) retain their own properties.

How can mixtures be separated?

FIGURE 7–9. Water treatment plants use filters to purify the local water supply. Here, water from sewage treatment trickles over a filter of approximately six meters of pebbles. Living organisms on the rocks eat the bacteria in the water as it filters through.

What is distillation?

Water can be purified by **distillation** (dihs tuh LAY shun). Water is distilled by evaporating it, usually by boiling. The boiled water is allowed to cool and condense into another container. Any dissolved or suspended impurities are left behind. Campers sometimes use this technique to obtain pure water for drinking. A container of water is covered with a sheet of plastic and placed in sunlight. The water evaporates and then condenses on the plastic covering. The distilled water that condenses on the plastic can be collected and used for drinking.

Petroleum, a mixture of many hydrocarbons, is refined by fractional distillation. The various hydrocarbons are separated into fractions, or portions, with similar boiling point ranges.

What is chromatography?

Another method of separating mixtures into fractions is **chromatography.** The fractions obtained using chromatography have different polarities. Chromatography is important in medicine and agriculture. One type of chromatography is column chromatography. A glass column is packed with a solid substance that has an attraction for polar materials. The mixture to be separated is added to the top of the column. Then a solvent is poured into the column. Depending on their polarities, the substances in the mixture are more or less attracted to the solvent and the solid substance in the column. As a result, the substances in the mixture are separated as they move down the column at different rates. The fractions, which are usually different colors, can be identified and analyzed.

See Teacher's Guide.

REVIEW AND REFLECT

1. Classify each of the following mixtures as a solution, a suspension, or a colloid.
   a. red blood cells (diameter: 7.5×10^{-6} cm) in plasma
   b. hot tea or coffee
   c. sediments in stream water
2. How could you separate the following mixtures?
   a. frozen vegetables cooked in salt water
   b. aluminum and steel soft drink cans
   c. plasma and blood cells
3. Why are chemical reactions not involved in the separation of a mixture?

Activity: How is chromatography used to separate mixtures?

MATERIALS

washable black or blue-black ink
food coloring, 4 colors
filter paper cut into 5 strips 20 cm long
5 toothpicks
stirring rod
400 mL beaker
aluminum foil
scissors
dropper
graduated cylinder
5 test tubes
metric ruler
apron

PROCEDURE

1. Put water in a beaker to a depth of about 2 cm.
2. Use a toothpick to place a small dot of black ink about 3 cm from the bottom of a strip of filter paper.
3. Place the filter paper in the water as shown in Figure 7–10. Do not allow the dot to go underwater.
4. Cover the beaker with aluminum foil and allow the filter paper to absorb the water.
5. Repeat steps 1 to 4 using various colors of food coloring.
6. When the water reaches the top of the filter paper strips, remove the strips and observe. Record your observations in a data table.
7. Use scissors to cut the best filter paper strip into the separate color bands formed.
8. Place each separate color band in a test tube. Add 2 mL of water and mix with a stirring rod to remove the dye from the filter paper.

FIGURE 7–10.

9. Mix the solutions formed from step 8 together in a clean beaker. Observe.

DATA AND OBSERVATIONS

Dye	Observations
Ink	

QUESTIONS AND CONCLUSIONS

1. How many substances did you observe in the ink?
2. How many substances did you observe in the food colors? If you compared different brands of the same color, were your results the same?
3. Describe what happened when you added a few drops of water to the separate color bands in step 8.
4. What happened when these solutions were mixed together in step 9?
5. How do you think this kind of chromatography may be useful to scientists?

153

7:8 Information: Water Softeners

The water supply in many areas is considered hard. Hard water contains dissolved salts of calcium, magnesium, and iron. Soft water has had these metal ions removed. Most water supplies contain between 5 and 50 parts per million (ppm) of these salts. Water containing more than 8 ppm is classified as hard.

Hard water causes several problems. When the magnesium, calcium, and iron ions come in contact with soap, they react forming an insoluble soap scum. Insoluble soap has no cleaning ability, therefore more soap is needed to clean with hard water. The soap scum may stick to clothing washed in hard water. Bathtub "rings" are a result of soap scum in hard water. Hard water also causes salt deposits, called scale, to build up inside water pipes, particularly hot water pipes, water heaters, and boilers. The scale may reduce water flow in plumbing. In addition, scale inhibits heat conduction. When scale is deposited in water heaters and boilers, much energy is wasted.

Why is hard water a problem?

A water softener may be used to soften hard water by removing metal ions. One of the most popular methods of water softening is the ion exchange method. Many ion exchangers use substances known as zeolites. Zeolites are in-

FIGURE 7–11. Soap does not clean as well in hard water. Soap residue remains in clothes leaving them gray and dingy-looking.

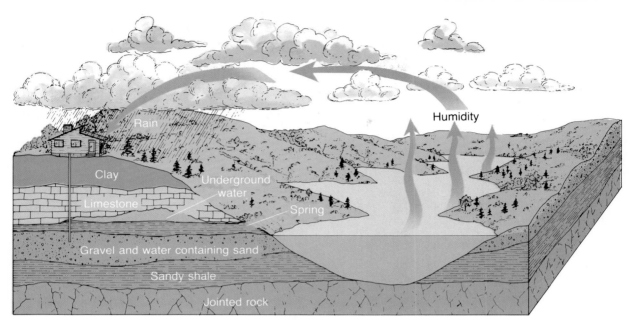

Rain

Humidity

Clay

Underground
water

Limestone

Spring

Gravel and water containing sand

Sandy shale

Jointed rock

soluble metal salts containing silicon and oxygen that occur naturally and also are produced synthetically. In a
water softener, hard water flows through a container of
zeolite. As the water flows through the zeolite, the calcium
or magnesium ions in the hard water are replaced by sodium ions from the zeolite. The following reaction takes
place in an ion exchange water softener.

$$2Na \, (Zeolite) + Ca^{2+} \rightarrow Ca(Zeolite)_2 + 2Na^{2+}$$

Sodium ions do not cause the same problems in the water supply as calcium or magnesium ions. The zeolite must
eventually be recharged with sodium ions. A water softener can be recharged by flushing it with a concentrated
solution of sodium chloride. Bags of salt are available for
this purpose at most hardware and grocery stores.

See Teacher's Guide.

FIGURE 7–12.   Nearly pure water falls to earth as rain or snow.
Impurities are picked up in the atmosphere and soil. As water seeps
through the earth before collecting in waterways, it collects particles of rocks and minerals. The
amount of dissolved rocks and
minerals determines the hardness
of the water supply.

**How does a water softener
work?**

REVIEW AND REFLECT

1. Differentiate between hard water and soft water.
2. What problems does hard water cause?
3. Why is one popular type of water softener known as an
   ion exchanger?
4. Find out the hardness of your local water supply.

CHAPTER 7 REVIEW

SUMMARY

1. Mixtures contain two or more substances that are not chemically combined. 7:1
2. Solutions are homogeneous mixtures. 7:1, 7:2
3. When a solute is dissolved in a solvent, the normal boiling point of the solvent is increased and the normal melting point is decreased. 7:2
4. Molecules may be polar or nonpolar. 7:4
5. Polar solvents dissolve polar solutes and nonpolar solvents dissolve nonpolar solutes. 7:4
6. The solubility of solids generally increases as temperature increases. 7:3, 7:5
7. The solubility of a gas decreases as temperature increases. 7:5
8. The rate at which a substance dissolves is affected by particle size, stirring, and temperature. 7:5
9. Suspensions and colloids are forms of heterogeneous mixtures. 7:6
10. Mixtures can be separated using physical methods such as distillation and chromatography. 7:7

VOCABULARY

chromatography 15
colloid 12
distillation 13
emulsifying agent 11
insoluble 7

mixture 4
nonpolar 8
polar 5
saturated 3
soluble 2

solute 1
solution 6
solvent 9
supersaturated 14
suspension 10

Choose a word from the list to complete each sentence correctly.

1. The _____ is the substance of lesser proportion in a solution.
2. A substance that will dissolve in a solvent is _____ in the solvent.
3. A solution that contains as much solute as can be dissolved in the solvent is a(n) _____ solution.
4. Any combination of solid, liquid, or gaseous substances that are not chemically combined is a(n) _____.
5. A molecule with slight charges on its ends is _____.
6. Any homogeneous mixture is a(n) _____.
7. A substance that will not dissolve in a solvent is _____ in the solvent.

8. A molecule with no charges on its ends is _____.
9. The _____ is the substance of greater proportion in a solution.
10. A(n) _____ is a scattering of relatively large particles.
11. A(n) _____ is a substance that will cause two liquids to form a colloid.
12. A(n) _____ is a scattering of intermediate-size particles.
13. _____ is a process of evaporation and condensation used to separate some mixtures.
14. A solution that contains more solute than it would normally take to saturate it at a specific temperature is _____.
15. _____ is a method of separating mixtures into portions with similar polarities.

QUESTIONS

MAIN IDEAS

Choose the correct answer to complete each sentence.

1. Carbonated soft drinks are a mixture of a *(solid in a gas, gas in a liquid, liquid in a gas).*

2. Mixtures that are homogeneous are called *(solutes, solvents, solutions, suspensions).*

3. When salt is added to water, the boiling point *(increases, decreases, does not change).*

4. Water is a *(polar, nonpolar)* molecule.

5. As the size of solid solutes increases, solubility *(increases, decreases, does not change).*

6. The solubility of a gas *(increases, decreases, does not change)* as pressure increases.

7. Nonpolar solutes generally are soluble in *(polar, nonpolar, saturated)* solvents.

8. Mayonnaise is an example of a *(solution, colloid, suspension).*

9. A method of separating a mixture into portions with different boiling point ranges is *(filtering, fractional distillation, chromatography).*

10. A *(solution, solvent, colloid)* will show the Tyndall effect when light is passed through it.

See Teacher's Guide.

APPLICATIONS

Answer each question in one or more paragraphs.

1. When making homemade ice cream, salt is added to the ice surrounding the ice cream maker. Why?

2. If a substance does not dissolve in benzene (C_6H_6), explain why it is likely to be soluble in water.

3. How is a supersaturated solution formed?

4. The wastewater that a factory is dumping into a lake has been tested and shown to be free of chemical pollutants. Explain why growth of algae in the lake is increasing, but many fish are dying.

5. Emulsifying agents and homogenization are methods used to prevent materials from separating. Explain how each process works.

6. Describe a method for separating the components of a mixture of water, salt, sand, and iron filings.

FURTHER STUDY

INVESTIGATIONS

1. Find out how soft drinks are bottled. Arrange to tour a local bottling company.

2. Read food labels and make a list of substances used as emulsifying agents.

3. Visit a Red Cross Center or a hospital where plasma is separated from blood cells. Prepare a report about the processes used.

4. Make posters for display that explain homogenization of milk.

5. Prepare a written report describing the processes used for water purification.

READINGS

+ Basta, Nicholas. "Biopolymers Challenge Petrochemicals." *High Technology.* February, 1984. pp. 66–70.

+ DeYoung, H. Garrett. "Plastic Composites Fight for Status." *High Technology.* October, 1983. pp. 639–68.

0 Holden, Alan, and Phylis Morrison. *Crystals and Crystal Growing.* MIT Press: Cambridge, MA, 1982.

0 Time-Life Books, Editors of. *Beverages.* Time-Life Books: Alexandria, VA, 1983.

NEW records in athletics are continually being set as healthier athletes using better equipment compete. Advances in chemical technology have led to more nutritious diets. Equipment like the pole and "all-weather" track in this picture are designed to give athletes the best possible conditions in which to compete. What other advances have been made in chemical technology? How do these advances affect you?

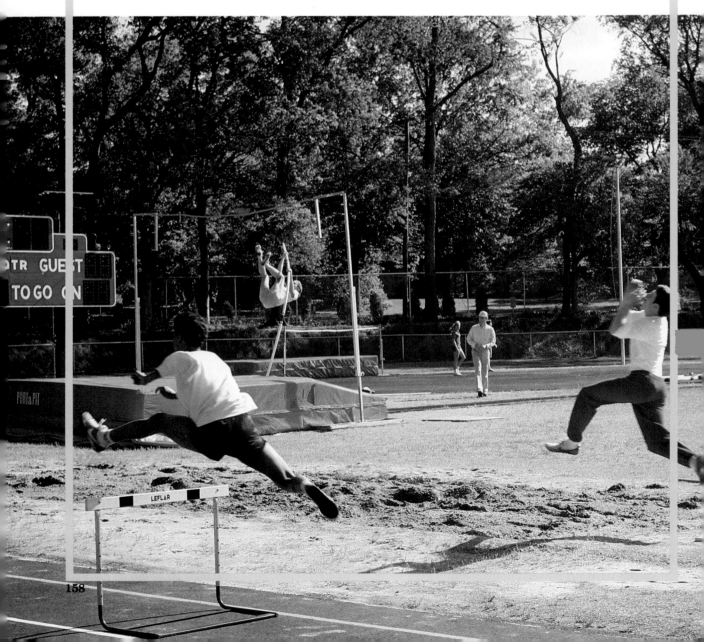

CHEMISTRY TODAY

INTRODUCING THE CHAPTER   Have students interview older people, such as parents, grandparents, teachers, and so on. Let the students develop a list of technological advancements that have occurred in this century. Have students do research to find out when various events occurred. Then make a time line with the information. See ACTIVITY idea on page 165 also.

8:1   Meeting Needs

A growing technical society has many needs and problems. Scientists use their knowledge of chemistry, from periodic trends to pH, to develop products to meet these needs. They research and test many solutions to problems. Scientists must deal with many people to develop products and solve problems. They must consider whether a product or solution is possible. How long will it last? How much will it cost? Is it safe? For example, fire detection devices have been used in industry for many years. These devices were not used in homes. They were too costly and hard to install. In recent years, technology has advanced in the area of fire detection equipment. Now, low-cost, easy-to-install smoke detectors are available for use in homes.

Perhaps you have never thought about the people and technology involved in providing the products you use. Consider how an ear of corn gets from a Florida farm to a supermarket in Maine. Farmers select the best varieties of corn seeds developed by plant scientists for their region. Fertilizers and pesticides developed by agricultural researchers are used to help ensure a good crop. Equipment designed by engineers and built by factory workers is used to plow the fields and harvest the corn. The corn is moved cross-country by transportation workers. The list of relationships seems endless. Yet, the Florida corn arrives at the store in Maine fresh, nutritious, and affordable. Many people work together to provide the products you use each day.

GOAL   You will learn about important advances in chemical technology and the impact of these advances.

How do scientists develop products and solve problems?

8:2 Petroleum

Many of the products you use daily are petroleum products. **Petroleum** is one of our most important natural resources. It is used to make fuels, plastics, industrial chemicals, and medications. What are some petroleum products that you use?

Usually, petroleum is found deep in the earth under layers of rock. It is pumped out of the ground as crude oil and refined for use. Occasionally, some petroleum is forced through cracks in rocks and collects in pools on the surface of the earth. These surface deposits are generally a very dense, semi-solid liquid form of petroleum known as pitch. Pitch is used as a patching material for road construction.

Petroleum has been used for several thousand years. The Persians used crude oil as early as 3500 B.C. for roadways and drainage systems. The Egyptians used pitch to preserve mummies. Crude oil was used by early American Indians for fuel and medicine. American settlers also found uses for crude oil. Kit Carson, famous on the frontier, sold it to pioneers as axle grease.

Widespread use of petroleum began in the United States about 100 years ago. The first oil well was drilled by Edwin L. Drake in Titusville, Pennsylvania, in 1859. At first, oil was used chiefly as a fuel for producing heat and light. By the beginning of the twentieth century, however, the uses and demand for petroleum had increased greatly. Annual production increased from about 2000 barrels in 1860 to 64 million barrels by 1900.

What is petroleum?

BACKGROUND Petroleum is also called crude oil.

Briefly describe the history of petroleum use.

FIGURE 8–1. Offshore wells have become important sources of oil. The large platforms are built atop steel legs that set on the ocean floor. These platforms can withstand 29 meter waves and winds up to 208 kilometers per hour.

FIGURE 8–2. House paint is one of the many products made from petroleum.

The availability of petroleum was important to the development of the industrial age. As technology advanced throughout the 1900s, the uses of petroleum increased steadily. For example, petroleum products were used as fuel for automobiles. As the automobile's popularity increased, the demand for petroleum products increased. Approximately 85 percent of the petroleum produced today is used to make fuels. Table 8–1 lists the major uses of petroleum products.

Petroleum is called a "fossil fuel" because it takes thousands of years to form from decayed organisms. For this reason, the supply of petroleum on earth is limited. Some experts predict that the demand for petroleum products may exceed the supply of petroleum by the early part of the next century. Imagine what your life would be like without petroleum products. Wise use of this valuable resource is important if we are to continue to enjoy the benefits of petroleum products.

Why is petroleum called a "fossil fuel"?

BACKGROUND A barrel of oil is about 159 liters.

TABLE 8–1. PROPORTIONS OF PETROLEUM FOR VARIOUS USES

Petro Product	%	Uses
Gasoline	45	Cars, lawnmowers, some industrial machinery
Diesel fuel	7	Trucks, buses, cars
Jet fuel	7	Jet planes
Heating fuel	26	Home heating oil, to produce steam to generate electricity
Raw material	13	Paints, solvents, cosmetics, plastics
Lubricating and other uses	2	Greases, lubricants

What is fractional distillation?

<u>8:3</u> Petroleum Refining

Petroleum is a mixture of many hydrocarbons that must be separated before they can be used. After crude oil is recovered from a well it is transferred to refineries. More than 10 million barrels are transported to refineries each day in the United States. Crude oil is transported by trucks, trains, ship tankers and barges, and pipelines.

The first pipeline was built near Titusville in 1865. It was about eight kilometers long. The Trans-Alaska Pipeline, which opened in 1977, crosses the state of Alaska carrying oil from Prudhoe Bay to Port Valdez in the Gulf of Alaska. It is 1270 kilometers long.

After crude oil is transported to a refinery, it is separated by fractional distillation. **Fractional distillation** separates a mixture into fractions that have different boiling points. Fractions are mixtures of substances with boiling points in the same narrow range. Fractional distillation of crude oil is done in a fractionating tower, Figure 8–3.

Once crude oil has been separated into fractions, the fractions are refined. The **refining** process removes impurities in the petroleum. One type of refinement involves the removal of impurities such as sulfur. Some fractions may have chemicals added to them to improve their qualities. Different amounts of heavier fractions often are blended together to produce lubricating oils of varying thicknesses.

You are probably most familiar with the lighter fractions, such as fuels, that are obtained from fractional dis-

FIGURE 8–3.   Crude oil is distilled in a fractionating tower (a). Some waterproofing materials (b) are made from heavy petroleum fractions.

a

b

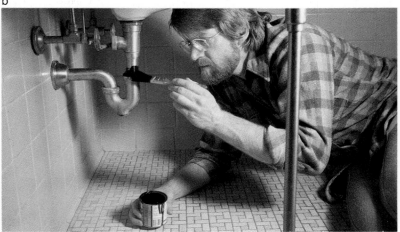

tillation of petroleum. However, many useful products are derived from the heavy fractions as well. Waxes and polishes are made from heavy fractions. Other materials produced from the heavy fractions include industrial oils, greases, petroleum jelly, and skin ointments. By far the most widely produced and used of the heavy fraction products is asphalt. **Asphalt** is a mixture of very large molecules with molecular masses ranging from 300 to 5000 atomic mass units. Asphalt is used mainly for road construction and roofing.

How is asphalt used?

See Teacher's Guide.

REVIEW AND REFLECT

1. What are some questions scientists may ask when considering how to solve a problem?
2. List three petroleum products.
3. Why is only a certain amount of petroleum available in the earth?

See Teacher's Guide.

Career Profile

When you sit on a padded car seat or sleep on a foam mattress, you may have Joyce Postlethwaite to thank for the comfortable ride or good night's sleep. Joyce is a relief chemical operator at a chemical plant in West Virginia. The plant makes the ingredients for polyurethane foam used as padding in many products.

Joyce monitors the process that separates natural gas into ingredients needed to make polyurethane. The raw materials are shipped to car manufacturers and other factories where the foam is made. Because of the extreme temperatures involved and the instability of the gases used, Joyce must know her job very well and be alert at all times. Any malfunction in the machinery must be reported and corrected immediately to avoid explosion or gas leak.

There are two types of chemical operators at the chemical plant. One type works indoors, monitoring chemical processes. The other type works outside, making sure that machinery is working properly. As a relief operator, Joyce has been trained in both jobs, so that she can fill in wherever she is needed. Joyce went through two training courses at her plant and had to pass two exams before she was considered qualified to be an operator.

FIGURE 8–4. Japanese artisans use plastic to make artificial food for displays.

8:4 Plastics

The development and use of **plastic** materials may represent the broadest use of technology during this century. Many plastics are derived from petroleum. These plastics are used in many products including hair combs, plumbing supplies, syringes, and toys.

Throughout their relatively short history, plastics have been developed to improve or replace natural materials. The first plastic produced in the United States was invented for this reason. Before 1868 billiard balls were made from ivory. Due to a shortage of ivory, a manufacturing company sponsored a contest to find a new material from which billiard balls could be made. John W. Hyatt, an American chemist, used cotton fibers to produce a new product he called celluloid. Although celluloid did not prove suitable for billiard balls, the discovery was the beginning of the plastics industry in the United States. The first photographic films were made of celluloid. It still is used today for making eyeglass frames.

Why are plastics used widely?

Plastics are used widely for two main reasons. First, they can be produced at less expense than many of the products they are replacing. In addition, plastics can be made with various properties that allow them to be used in many different applications.

An important property of plastics is that they can be molded into nearly any shape. In fact, the word plastic comes from the Greek word *plastikos,* which means to mold or form. Plastics can be made into thin, flexible sheets that can be used to wrap and store food. They can be formed into very strong but lightweight structural materials also. Plastics have been used to build an experimental engine that has been used in racing cars. The use of plastics to replace steel components in cars reduces the weight, and thus increases a car's fuel economy. Plastic panels also are being used rather than steel to make car bodies that are more resistant to dents and corrosion.

The first plastic was made from cotton fibers, called linters. Today most plastics are made from petroleum fractions. The substances in the petroleum fractions are polymerized. All plastics are composed of long chains of molecules called polymers. The polymerization of ethene to make polyethylene was discussed in section 6:9. More polyethylene is produced than any other plastic. It is used as a packaging material, for trash and dry-cleaning bags, in toys, and for detergent and milk containers.

The use of plastics has contributed to amazing advancements in medicine. Plastics are ideal for use in prosthetic devices. Prosthetic devices are artificial body parts such as limbs, joints, veins, and ligaments. Plastics have proven to be very successful for prosthetics because they can be made strong and flexible. In addition, because they have low chemical reactivity, the body's defense system does not identify plastic implants as foreign substances.

Although plastics have many advantages, they also have contributed to some problems. For example, recycling plastic products often is more costly than producing new ones. As a result, many plastic products are disposable. Consider how many disposable plastic products you use, such as ink pens, plastic bags, and beverage containers. They are designed to be used for a short time. After many plastic products have been used, you throw them away and get new ones. Disposable plastic products contribute to litter. Even when these products are put in sanitary landfills, they decompose slowly or not at all, because they are nonreactive. Potential solutions to these problems may be to use disposed plastic products to make new products or to use them as an energy source. As yet, these solutions have not proven to be worthwhile economically.

ACTIVITY   Invite students to interview older people about the use of plastics today. Have the students compile a list of consumer products currently made of plastic that were previously made of different materials.

How are most plastics made?

What are prosthetic devices and why are plastics used to make them?

FIGURE 8–5. The development of new plastic materials has been important to the manufacture of prosthetic devices. Lightweight, durable, and authentic-looking devices make it possible for wearers to participate in most daily activities.

BACKGROUND Polyesters were first introduced in England in 1941 and have become enormously popular for clothing during the last two decades.

What are the main resources for manufactured fibers?

FIGURE 8–6. Fake fur (a) is a manufactured textile. The comparatively low cost of fake fur makes this fashion more available without endangering animal species. Wool (b) is a natural fiber that is popular because it is warm, durable, and dyes well.

a

b

8:5 Textiles

If you have ever sorted laundry, you know that many different fabrics are used in clothing, towels, and bedding. Different fabrics are used for different purposes based on their properties, such as durability, warmth, texture, and wrinkle-resistance. Cotton, wool, polyester, and other fabrics are part of a broader class of materials called textiles. Textiles include woven and knitted fabrics, felts, laces, nets, and braids, as well as the fibers used to make these items.

Textiles are made from natural fibers and manufactured fibers. Some natural fibers are cotton, flax, silk, and wool. Cellulose and petroleum are the two main resources for manufactured fibers. Cellulose is a fibrous substance found in plants. Wood pulp is the primary source of cellulose used for fiber production. Rayon, acetate, and triacetate are made from cellulose. Rayon was first introduced as "artificial silk" in 1889 at an international exhibit in Paris.

At present, the majority of manufactured fibers come from petrochemicals obtained from fractional distillation of crude oil. In 1939, nylon became the first commercially produced petroleum-based fiber. One desirable property of nylon is its fiber strength. This property makes nylon a suitable fiber for clothing, hosiery, and carpets. The most widely used petroleum-based fibers are the polyesters. Polyester fibers can be made into very practical fabrics for clothing. The primary advantage of polyesters is that they are easy to care for. Polyester fibers can be blended with wool or cotton to produce fabrics that are wrinkle resistant. Permanent-press clothing is made from polyester or polyester-cotton fabrics.

The textile industry has changed greatly during the last 50 years. In 1940, about 10 percent of all fibers used in the United States were manufactured. Today, manufactured fibers account for nearly 75 percent of all fibers used in the United States. Manufactured fibers have replaced natural fibers for many applications. Some types of manufactured fibers are more durable, require less care, and are less expensive to produce than natural fibers. Compare the various types of fibers in Table 8–2.

Manufactured fibers have many applications in addition to fabrics. Nylon fibers are used to make strings for most tennis racquets. Nylon is less expensive and more durable than natural gut strings. Nylon sutures are used by surgeons to stitch wounds. The manufactured fiber vinyon is used to make items such as artificial trees and tea bags.

Fibers are used to reinforce some plastics to increase their strength. A well known **fiber-reinforced plastic,** or **FRP,** is fiberglass. Fiberglass consists of glass fibers held together with polyester resin. The properties of fiberglass make it useful in many different products. Many fishing rods are made of fiberglass because, like all FRPs, it is lightweight and strong. It can be molded into a variety of shapes. Boat hulls may be made of fiberglass. Fiberglass boats require less maintenance than wooden boats. They also leak less because their hulls do not have seams.

Due to the light weight and high strength properties of FRPs, they are used to make many items. These include golf clubs, skis, sailboat masts, tennis racquets, and belted radial tires. It is estimated that the weight of automobiles could be reduced as much as 30 percent with FRPs. Less energy is needed to move a less massive object, which results in lower gas consumption.

BACKGROUND Synthetic fibers now account for about two-thirds of all fibers used in clothing.

What is fiberglass?

BACKGROUND Another useful product that has been developed from fiber technology is the fiber-tip pen. The fiber-tip pen offers the smoothness of a fountain pen and the convenience of a ball point. It is made by binding synthetic fibers together with a plastic resin.

SUGGESTION You may choose to review Newton's laws of motion.

TABLE 8–2.	CHARACTERISTICS OF TEXTILES		
Fiber/Textile	**Source**	**Characteristics**	**Uses**
Cotton	Cotton plant	Soft, absorbent	Clothing, bedding
Linen	Flax	Strong, wrinkles easily	Clothing, tablecloths
Wool	Sheep, goats, camels	Warm, generally dry cleaned	Clothing, blankets, carpeting
Silk	Silkworms	Soft, very strong, lustrous, dyes well	Clothing, tires, upholstery, insulated clothing
Acrylic	Petrochemicals	Soft, resists mildew, fading, and wrinkling	Blankets, carpeting, clothing, upholstery
Nylon	Petrochemicals	Strong, easy to launder, dries quickly	Carpeting, hosiery, lingerie, parachutes, upholstery
Polyester	Petrochemicals	Resists wrinkling, easy to launder, dries quickly	Blankets, carpeting, clothing, fire hose, thread
Rayon	Cellulose	Absorbent, easy to launder, dyes easily	Carpeting, clothing, draperies, upholstery

Activity: How do fabrics compare?

MATERIALS

15 × 15 cm samples of white fabric (nylon, rayon, polyester, wool, cotton, silk, linen, and polyester/cotton blend)

ball-point pen

stereo microscope (optional)

2 600-mL beakers

paper towels

laundry detergent

300 mL fabric dye

tongs

clock or timer

apron

goggles

PROCEDURE

1. Obtain fabric samples from your teacher. Label each sample so you can identify each type of fabric.
2. Examine each sample under the microscope. Record your observations.
3. Put on the apron. Fill a 600 mL beaker about half full with warm soapy water. Wash and rinse each fabric sample. Pat out excess water with paper towels. Allow the samples to dry on clean paper towels.
4. Examine each sample under the microscope again. Record your observations.

FIGURE 8–7.

5. Cut the fabric samples in half. Make sure each half is labeled. Place about 300 mL of fabric dye in your clean 600 mL beaker. **CAUTION:** *Fabric dye is poisonous and will stain your skin and clothing.*
6. Place half of each sample in the dye. Soak the samples for 10 min. Remove the samples using tongs and rinse under cold tap water. Let samples dry on clean paper towels.
7. Observe the dyed fabric samples after they have dried. Record your observations.
8. Wash and rinse the dyed samples in warm water. Record any changes in color.

DATA AND OBSERVATIONS

Type of Fabric		
Before Washing		
After Washing		
Dyeing		
Dyeing & Washing		

QUESTIONS AND CONCLUSIONS

1. Which type of fiber changed after washing? Were these fibers natural or manufactured?
2. Which fabrics dyed the best? Were these fabrics natural or manufactured?
3. How did the test results for the polyester/cotton fabric compare to 100% natural and 100% manufactured fabrics?
4. How could your test results be helpful when selecting fabrics for clothing?

8:6   Ceramics

When you think of ceramics, you may think of pottery and jewelry. Ceramic materials also are used to make bricks, spark plugs, porcelain sinks, and sidewalks. People have used ceramic materials for building, cookware, and other purposes since prehistoric times.

Ceramics are materials made primarily from nonmetallic elements fired at high temperatures. Ceramic materials are classified into seven general types. Table 8–3 lists the types of ceramics and their uses.

TABLE 8–3. USES OF CERAMICS	
Type of Ceramic	**Uses**
Structural clay products	Roofing tiles, bricks, terra cotta, drain pipes
Whitewares	Dinnerware, wall and floor tile, electronic ceramics, conductive ceramics
Glasses	Window and plate glass, containers, fiberglass
Porcelain enamel products	Coating on metals to protect from heat and corrosion
Refractories	Furnace linings, insulators
Abrasives	Silicon carbide, emery
Cementing materials	Wall plaster, structural material for buildings and bridges

Recent advances in technology have led to a dramatic increase in the use of ceramic materials. Ceramics were important in the growth of the electronics industry in the 1950s. The development of integrated circuits, ICs, reduced the size and cost of electronic components and computers. However, if an IC becomes overheated, it does not function properly. Ceramic materials can be used to package ICs. The ceramic package conducts heat away from the IC into the air.

One type of ceramic material is **cement.** Various forms of cement have been used since ancient times. It is primarily composed of calcium silicate, prepared from chalk

BACKGROUND Another advantage of ceramics is the materials from which they are made. Most ceramic materials are made from silicon and aluminum which are two of the most abundant substances in the earth's crust. Raw materials for metals and plastics are more scarce.

What is a major advantage of ceramics?

FIGURE 8–8. One of the many advantages of ceramics is their versatility. The properties of ceramics make them an excellent choice for building materials (a) and for delicate artworks (b).

a

b

or limestone (calcium carbonate), and clay or shale (aluminum silicates). Cement is used to make mortar that holds bricks together. Plasters also are made from cement.

The largest use of cement today is in the production of concrete. Concrete is a mixture of cement, sand, gravel, and water. Concrete is quite strong when it is compressed but relatively weak when pulled. To increase its strength, concrete is often reinforced with steel rods or mesh. The steel rods are stressed, thus compressing the concrete. Because concrete is relatively unaffected by the environment and continues to harden with age, it is an ideal building material.

One of the most important advantages of ceramics is that they can withstand much higher temperatures than metals or plastics. Many metal alloys can withstand temperatures up to about 1000°C before melting. Ceramic materials have been developed that can withstand temperatures of about 3300°C. This property was used to solve one of the most difficult engineering problems associated with the United States space shuttle program. Friction encountered as the orbiter re-enters the earth's atmosphere can produce temperatures greater than 1500°C. To protect the space shuttle's metal hull from the high temperatures, more than 34 000 ceramic tiles were glued to the surface of the shuttle. The tiles are made of silica fiber and glass. The tiles are of low density, consisting of about 90 percent air, which allows them to absorb the great amount of heat. The air space increases the insulating ability of the tiles.

Scientists and engineers are trying to find ways to use ceramics in automobile engines. If engines could be made to operate at higher temperatures, they would burn fuel more efficiently and produce fewer pollutants. Ceramic engines also would be lighter than metal engines. Therefore, they would use less fuel. It has been estimated that the use of ceramic engines could save 500 million barrels of oil each year in the United States.

A major obstacle in the use of ceramics to replace metals is that ceramics are brittle. When metals are stressed, they tend to bend before they break. The major disadvantage of ceramics is that they crack when they are stressed. Research is currently underway to find solutions to this problem.

See Teacher's Guide.

REVIEW AND REFLECT

1. How can the nonreactive property of plastics be a problem?
2. What are two main sources from which manufactured fibers are derived?
3. What are properties of ceramics?
4. What is the difference between concrete and cement?
5. What are some advantages of FRPs?

See Teacher's Guide.

Skill Inquiry

You may not realize it, but chemistry has many useful applications to everyday life. For example, a simple task like doing laundry is based on chemical technology. In this chapter, you have learned about new fabrics developed in recent years and new products that are sources of stains. New laundry aids have been developed to meet our changing needs.

Cleaning and removing stains from fabrics can be easier if a few simple rules are followed. First, always read the care label of a garment. Some fabrics are not washable. They can be cleaned by professional dry cleaners who use solvents that are too hazardous for household use. Soaps, detergents, and bleaches are used for cleaning washable fabrics. Stains should be treated before garments are washed. Refer to the table to determine how you would treat the following items.

1. Tennis shoes with grass stains
2. Grease on blue jeans
3. Silk dress (dry clean only) with cosmetic stains
4. Paint on a T-shirt
5. Chocolate on a white tablecloth
6. Coffee on a cloth napkin
7. Ink on a shirt sleeve
8. Chewing gum on a wool sweater
9. Blood stain on a knee of pants
10. Tar on running shoes

TABLE OF STAIN REMOVAL TECHNIQUES	
Stain	**How to Remove**
Blood	Presoak in cold water. Wash.
Chewing gum	Harden with ice cube. Remove excess. Wash in hot water.
Chocolate	Presoak in warm water. Wash in warm water.
Coffee	Soak in cool water. Wash.
Cosmetic stains	Presoak in warm water.
Grass	Presoak in warm water. Wash.
Grease and tar	Presoak in warm water. Wash in hot water.
Ink	Rub with petroleum jelly. Wash in warm water.
Paint	Treat with paint remover. Wash.

FIGURE 8–9. Egyptians cast bronze in molds more than 3500 years ago.

What are some important uses of alloys?

8:7 Alloys

An **alloy** is formed when a metal is combined with one or more other elements. Sometimes the substances in an alloy combine chemically forming a compound. Most alloys are solid solutions or heterogeneous mixtures.

A metal's physical properties are altered when it is alloyed with other substances. Common solder, for example, is a heterogeneous mixture of about 50% tin and 50% lead. Solder has a melting point of approximately 220°C. The melting point of tin is 232°C and lead melts at 327°C.

The most widely used alloy is **steel.** Steel is used to form the support structure for large buildings as well as the wires in braces for teeth. The simplest forms of steel, called carbon steels, are alloys of iron and no more than 1.7% carbon. Other types of steel contain small amounts of silicon, manganese, phosphorus, and sulfur. These steels often are referred to as alloy steels to distinguish them from carbon steels. The carbon and other elements in steel make its properties different from pure iron. Steel is less brittle, more malleable, and stronger than iron.

One important type of alloy steel is stainless steel. Stainless steel is produced by alloying carbon steel with nickel and chromium. Stainless steel is resistant to corrosion. This property makes it a suitable material for tools, surgical instruments, and tableware.

There are many alloys besides those of iron. Alloys of mercury are known as amalgams. An amalgam of primarily silver and mercury is used by dentists to fill cavities in teeth. Table 8–4 lists some common alloys and their uses.

TABLE 8–4.   SOME COMMON ALLOYS

Alloy	Common Name	Properties/Uses
Tin, antimony, and copper	Babbitt metal	Low-friction bearings
Magnesium and aluminum	Magnalium	Light and strong, automobile and airplane parts
Zinc and copper	Brass	Decorative tableware, hardware
Copper and tin	Bronze	Marine fittings
Aluminum and copper	Aluminum bronze	Can be highly polished
Aluminum, copper, manganese, and magnesium	Duralumin	Very strong, airplane construction

Differences in metal alloys are important to the consumer. The cost of an alloy generally increases with the amount of time required to refine and process the alloy. Alloy cost also depends on the cost of the substances used to make the alloy. For example, the stainless steel used for knives is tempered, or heat treated, to increase its strength and hardness. More expensive knives are made from stainless steel that has been very carefully tempered. The cutting blade maintains its sharp edge because of the hardness and strength of the stainless steel.

8:8 Impact of Technology

Many valuable products have been developed from advances in technology. The developments in chemical technology are not without problems and controversy, however. Nearly every useful product has benefits as well as risks associated with it. The risks may be in the form of pollution, such as acid rain, or other problems including potential hazards to people's health. Often the risks are not apparent until after the product has been in use for some time.

During the energy crisis of the 1970s, many people wanted to increase the insulation in their homes. Their goal was to conserve energy and reduce fuel costs. Urea-formaldehyde foam seemed ideal for insulating homes that were already built. It could be mixed at the site in a liquid state and pumped through small holes drilled in the walls. Inside the walls, the foam hardened into a light-weight material with excellent insulating properties. More than one-half million homes in the United States were insulated with urea-formaldehyde foam in the 1970s. However, some people living in these homes began to experience health problems including eye irritations, headaches, respiratory ailments, and nausea. The problems were found to be caused by formaldehyde fumes from the insulation.

Often the risks associated with the use of a product lead scientists to develop new and better products. Estimates in the early 1970s suggested that treating children's sleepwear with flame retardants could reduce injuries and deaths of children in fires by 50 percent. For this reason, the United States government set flammability standards

FIGURE 8–10. Structural steel is strong and durable, which makes it an excellent material for the support of large buildings.

FIGURE 8–11. Advances in technology have led to attractive and efficient office buildings. However, some of the synthetic products used to build and furnish these offices emit harmful vapors that cause indoor air pollution.

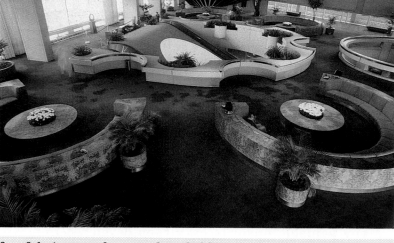

What are carcinogens?

for fabrics used to make children's sleepwear. Tris (2,3-dibromopropyl phosphate) was the most common chemical that manufacturers used as a flame retardant. Later, Tris was found to be a **carcinogen,** a substance that causes cancer. In 1977, the use of Tris in children's sleepwear was banned in the United States. The flammability standards for children's sleepwear were modified somewhat. In order to meet the new standards, manufacturers developed fabrics for children's sleepwear that are flame-resistant without chemical treatment.

Keep in mind that chemical technology has provided people with thousands of useful, even life-saving products. At the same time, realize that people must work together in order to weigh the risks and benefits of the products we use. Through cooperative efforts, the benefits can be maximized and the risks to the environment and health can be reduced to the lowest possible safe level.

See Teacher's Guide.

REVIEW AND REFLECT

1. Why is steel more desirable as a building material than pure iron?
2. Why are some products made from certain metal alloys more costly to the consumer than products made from other metal alloys?
3. How is it possible for a product to have risks and benefits to the consumer at the same time?

Activity: What affects the strength of plywood?

See Teacher's Guide.

MATERIALS

6 30 × 11 cm rectangles of
balsa wood sheeting
carpenter's glue
plastic foam cup
graduated cylinder
apron
water
2 boards, each about
5 cm thick and 30 cm long

PROCEDURE

1. Carefully apply glue to one piece of balsa wood. Lay a second piece on top, as shown in Figure 8–12a. Set aside to dry.
2. Place one piece of balsa wood between two wooden boards. Hold the boards together with your hand. Place a cup at the end of the wood strip as shown in Figure 8–12b.
3. Carefully pour water into the cup just until the end of the balsa wood strip touches the table. Measure the amount of water in the cup and record in a data table.
4. Place another piece of balsa wood on top of the first piece. Do not glue the pieces together. Place these two pieces between two blocks of wood as you did in step 2.
5. Repeat step 3 with the two pieces that have not been glued together.
6. Repeat step 3 using the two pieces of balsa wood that were glued together in step 1.
7. Glue another piece of balsa wood on top of the two pieces that are glued together. Set aside to dry.
8. Repeat steps 2 and 3 with three pieces that are not glued together.

FIGURE 8–12.

9. Repeat step 3 with the three pieces that were glued together in step 7.

DATA AND OBSERVATIONS

Sample	Amount of Water Supported (mL)
One strip	
2 unglued strips	
2 glued strips	
3 unglued strips	
3 glued strips	

QUESTIONS AND CONCLUSIONS

1. Were there any differences between the amounts of mass supported by the balsa wood strips? Explain your results.
2. How did gluing affect the amount of mass supported by the strips?
3. How much mass would you predict would be supported by more than three strips glued together? You may wish to test your prediction.

8:9 Information: Chemicals in Society

Chemicals are necessary for your health and comfort. The medicines you take, the foods you eat, and the shampoo you use are chemicals. The most widely produced and used chemical in the United States is sulfuric acid, H_2SO_4. More than 30 million kilograms are produced each year. Sulfuric acid is used in the manufacture of many other chemical products, such as fertilizers, dyes, rayon, and in petroleum refining. In fact, sulfuric acid is such an important chemical that its rate of production is an indicator of economic growth.

Some products today are advertised as "all natural." These products contain chemicals that occur in nature. Other products contain synthetic chemicals that are produced in industry. Some natural chemicals can be produced synthetically also. Ascorbic acid, vitamin C, occurs naturally in many fruits but is produced synthetically, too.

More than 2800 chemicals are added to foods. These additives are used to improve the taste and appearance of foods, keep them fresh, or make them more nutritious. When wheat is processed to make white flour, many of the natural vitamins are lost. Synthetic vitamins are added to white flour to make it more nutritious.

Natural products such as salt, sugar, and corn syrup are widely-used food additives. They are used to improve the flavor and appearance of some foods and also are used as preservatives. Salt has been used throughout history as a preservative to keep meat and fish from spoiling. Without preservatives, food can spoil and become contaminated with bacteria, which can cause illness or death if the food is eaten.

What is the most widely used chemical in the United States?

Why are additives used in foods?

SUGGESTION Botulism is discussed in section 22:7.

FIGURE 8–13. The great demand for sulfuric acid is met by large manufacturing plants like the one shown here.

Two main types of preservatives are antimicrobials and antioxidants. Antimicrobials prevent spoilage from molds, fungi, and bacteria. Sodium nitrate, sodium benzoate, propionates, and ascorbic acid (vitamin C) are commonly used antimicrobials. Antioxidants are added to foods to prevent changes in color, odor, or texture due to oxidation. Common antioxidants include ascorbic acid, BHA (butylated hydroxyanisole), BHT (butylated hydroxytoluene), and lecithin.

Foods often are colored with dyes to improve their appearance. Margarine is actually white, but yellow dyes are added to make it look more like butter. More than 60 percent of all food additives are used to enhance the flavor of foods. The most common flavor enhancer is monosodium glutamate, MSG.

While food additives help make food look and taste better, increase their shelf life, and add nutritional value, they are not without problems. In recent years, questions have been raised about the effects of food additives on health. Some scientists believe that certain additives contribute to allergies, cancer, or other health problems. In the United States, food additives are regulated by the Food and Drug Administration, FDA. The FDA can ban products they determine unsafe.

Even though ingredients that are unsafe for the general public may be banned, some other ingredients may be harmful to certain individuals. Some people restrict their intake of caffeine, which is found in coffee, tea, and many soft drinks. MSG contains 50 milligrams of sodium per teaspoon, so people on low sodium diets should limit their use of this substance. By reading food labels, people can avoid foods containing substances that are harmful to them.

See Teacher's Guide.

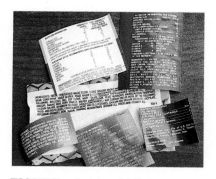

FIGURE 8–14. Additives are listed with other ingredients on food labels.

What is MSG?

BACKGROUND MSG sensitizes tastebuds. It does nothing to food.

What are some problems with food additives?

REVIEW AND REFLECT

1. Why do manufacturers use synthetic chemicals rather than the identical naturally-occurring chemical?
2. Name three natural products used as food additives.
3. What is the most produced chemical in the United States? How is it used?
4. List three reasons why chemicals are added to foods.

CHAPTER 8 REVIEW

SUMMARY

1. Many people work together to provide the products we use daily. 8:1
2. Petroleum is a source of fuels and many other products. 8:2
3. Petroleum is separated into fractions by a distillation process. 8:3
4. Plastics are widely used because they can be made inexpensively and have many desirable properties. 8:4
5. Manufactured fibers are generally more durable, require less care, and are less expensive than natural fibers. 8:5
6. Fibers are used to increase the strength of other materials. 8:5
7. Important advantages of ceramics are their ability to withstand high temperatures and the availability of the raw materials from which they are made. 8:6
8. Metals are combined to produce alloys with properties different from the individual metals. 8:7
9. Technological advancements have many benefits but also have caused costly problems and potential hazards. 8:8

VOCABULARY

alloy   1
asphalt   2
carcinogen   5
cement   3
ceramic   7
fiber-reinforced plastic   12
fractional distillation   10
petroleum   8
plastic   4
refining   9
steel   11
textiles   6

Choose a word from the list to answer each question.

1. What is a combination of metal and other elements?
2. What is the most widely produced and used heavy fraction of petroleum?
3. What ceramic material is used to make concrete?
4. What unreactive synthetic material can be easily molded?
5. What is a cancer-causing substance called?
6. What kind of materials are yarn and fabric?
7. What material is made primarily of aluminum silicates?
8. What mixture of hydrocarbons is the source of gasoline?
9. What is the removal of impurities from a material called?
10. How is petroleum separated into its components?
11. What is an alloy of iron and carbon?
12. What kind of material is fiberglass?

QUESTIONS

MAIN IDEAS

Choose the correct answer to complete each sentence.

1. Petroleum is a mixture of many different *(alloys, synthetics, hydrocarbons).*
2. Pitch is used primarily in *(the clothing industry, home construction, road construction, food additives).*
3. Approximately *(7, 13, 26, 45, 85)* percent of petroleum is used to produce fuels today.

178

See Teacher's Guide.

4. More *(celluloid, rayon, vinyl, polyethylene)* is produced than any other plastic.

5. The first petroleum-based fabric was *(nylon, rayon, acrylic, polyester)*.

6. The first plastic produced in the United States was *(celluloid, rayon, vinyl, polyethylene)*.

7. The synthetic textile that is most widely used today is *(polyurethane, polyester, polyethylene, acrylic)*.

8. A type of steel that is highly resistant to corrosion is *(tungsten, amalgam, stainless, carbon)*.

9. Fiberglass consists of glass fibers held together with *(graphite, aluminum, polyethylene, polyester resin)*.

10. Fractional distillation separates petroleum into mixtures of substances with *(melting points, freezing points, boiling points)* in a narrow range.

11. One property of plastics is described by the Greek word *plastikos*, which means *(to melt, to mold, a long chain, to replace)*.

12. *(Wool, Nylon, Cotton)* is not a natural fiber.

13. Ceramic materials do not include *(concrete, brick, cellulose, whiteware)*.

14. Tris is a product whose *(risks outweighed its benefits, benefits outweighed its risks, risks equaled its benefits)*.

APPLICATIONS

Answer each question in one or more paragraphs.

1. Identify some problems that scientists probably had to consider in producing toothpaste for people to use.

2. Petroleum is a nonrenewable resource. Explain the meaning of this statement.

3. Give three examples of products in which plastics have been substituted for another substance. Cite an advantage and disadvantage of substituting plastic in each case.

4. You have two red shirts, one made of cotton and one made of a polyester-cotton blend. After several washings of both shirts, you notice that the red cotton shirt is fading but the color of the polyester-cotton blend shirt seems as bright as when it was new. Why?

5. Imagine that you must decide where to locate a factory that will manufacture bricks. Discuss some of the important factors you would have to consider in making that decision. Which factor do you think would be most important? Explain.

6. Wood's metal is an alloy used to make the small metal blocks that hold the valves of some automatic sprinkler systems closed. What properties would this alloy need in order to be used reliably in sprinkler systems?

FURTHER STUDY

INVESTIGATIONS

1. Prepare a report about diesel fuel that explains the advantages and disadvantages of its use in automobiles.

2. Plastics are classified into two processing types—thermoplastic and thermosetting. Report the differences between them.

3. Prepare a report to demonstrate how chemical technology and genetic engineering may help prevent certain diseases.

READINGS

0 Cope, Dwight W., and Lee E. Schaude. *Plastics.* Goodheart-Willcox: South Holland, IL, 1982.

– How Things Are Made. *National Geographic Society*: Washington, DC, 1981.

+ LaDon, Joseph. "The Not-So-Clean Business of Making Chips." *Technology Review.* May/ June, 1984. pp. 22–36.

0 Langley, Andrew. *Modern Metals.* Wayland: East Essex, England, 1980.

THE NATURE OF ENERGY

UNIT 3

Unit Three focuses on the nature of the relationship between forces and motion. Anything that has energy can produce forces. For example, gasoline contains energy that is released when it is burned. Burning gasoline produces the forces needed to move a bus. Fuels are used in power plants to produce the forces needed to generate electricity for light. In this unit, you will learn how forces and motion relate to the nature of energy.

1. How do forces affect the motion of objects?
2. What are the classifications of energy?
3. How is energy measured?
4. How is electricity generated?
5. Why are sound and light described as waves?
6. What are the properties of waves?

THINK of how many times a day you move, are moved, or move other objects. What motion is occurring in the picture? Motion occurs many times in many different ways. When you walk, you change from one place to another. When you pick up an object, you change its position. Motion is defined as the process of changing place or position. What causes motion? How is motion measured?

MOTION

INTRODUCING THE CHAPTER   Help students apply their scientific learnings to the real world by relating the study of motion to sports. Without thinking about it, a person throwing a ball must take into account the laws of motion regarding the angle with which it is thrown, the force applied to the ball, and so on. *Discover* magazine has published a series of articles relating to the physics of sports.

9:1 Studying Motion

Moving objects have been investigated by people since ancient times. Motion was perhaps the first area of science to be thoroughly studied and understood. Of special interest to early observers was the motion of objects in the sky. Theories were proposed as early as the seventh century B.C. to explain the motion of stars. Early astronomers also identified five planets in our solar system—Mercury, Venus, Mars, Jupiter, and Saturn. The motion of these objects appeared different from the motion of stars. The planets seemed to move quickly compared to the background of the stars. Indeed, the word planet is from the Greek word *planete,* which means wanderer.

While some people studied the motion of stars and planets, others were interested in learning about the motion of objects on earth. The most notable people who studied motion were Aristotle (384–322 B.C.), Galileo (1564–1642), and Sir Isaac Newton (1642–1727).

Today the science of motion is understood quite well, largely due to the work of Newton. In 1686, Newton published a book called *Principia* describing his findings about moving objects. The basic principles set forth in this book are called Newton's laws of motion. All moving objects, from baseballs to airplanes, are governed by these laws.

GOAL   You will learn how motion can be described and about the forces that cause motion.

BACKGROUND   Mechanics is the study of motion. Kinematics is the study of the description of motion. Dynamics is the study of the cause of motion.

What motions were studied by early scientists?

Why is studying motion today important?

How is motion defined?

BACKGROUND   The word motion is derived from the Latin word *movere*, which means to move.

What is a frame of reference?

FIGURE 9–1.   From the frame of reference of the people sitting in the boat, the boy is moving toward the rear of the boat at 3 kilometers per hour. From the frame of reference of the girl, the boy is moving forward at a speed of 5 kilometers per hour.

9:2   Describing Motion

Motion is defined as a change in an object's position. To describe an object's motion, we need to know its position before and after it moves. That may not be as simple as it seems. The observed motion of an object depends not only on the position of the object, but also on the position of the observer. For example, imagine you are a passenger on a train. Another train going in the opposite direction passes you. From your position, it appears that the other train is moving. However, an observer in the other train would say that your train is moving. Motion is relative to the observer's frame of reference. **Frame of reference** is what an observer compares the position of an object to.

Perhaps you have been in a car waiting at a stoplight, and you observe a car next to you moving forward. From the frame of reference of your car, it is difficult to tell if the other car is moving forward slightly or if yours is moving backward! All that can be observed is that one car is moving relative to the other car. Unless you change your frame of reference by looking at the ground, you cannot be sure which car is moving relative to the earth. Minor traffic accidents have resulted from this confusion of relative motion.

Knowing the frame of reference is important in describing an object's motion. However, it is often also important to know the rate at which the object moves. **Speed** is a measure of the distance an object moves in a given amount of time. The speeds of some common objects are shown in Figure 9–2.

Most moving objects do not maintain a steady speed. They speed up and slow down over a period of time. Consider, for example, riding a bicycle to visit a friend. During your ride, you may stop at street corners. Your speed may increase when you go down a hill. Therefore, when making a trip, it is useful to find your average speed. You can find average speed by dividing the total distance traveled by the total time it takes to travel that distance.

$$\text{average speed} = \frac{\text{distance}}{\text{time}}$$

$$S = \frac{d}{t}$$

Jetliner (220 m/s)

Sound (331 m/s)

Radio waves (3 × 10⁸ m/s)

Person running (7 m/s)

Tennis serve (44 m/s)

Person walking (2 m/s)

Car on highway (24 m/s)

Baseball pitch (40 m/s)

FIGURE 9–2. Speeds of some common objects

In SI, speed is usually measured in meters per second, m/s, or kilometers per hour, km/h.

EXAMPLE: Calculating Speed

Problem: The distance from Los Angeles to Phoenix is 600 km. If it takes eight hours driving time to complete the trip, what is the average speed?

Solution: The average speed is the distance driven divided by the driving time.

$$S = \frac{d}{t}$$

$$S = \frac{600 \text{ km}}{8 \text{ h}}$$

$$S = 75 \text{ km/h}$$

SUGGESTION Make sure students do not confuse average speed with instantaneous speed. Instantaneous speed is the actual speed that an object is moving at any given instant of time.

9:3 Force and Motion

SUGGESTION   Review the concepts of scientific laws and theories presented in chapter 2.

What is Newton's First Law of Motion?

BACKGROUND   A net external force is the resultant of all separate external forces.

BACKGROUND   Newton's first law is also known as the Law of Inertia.

FIGURE 9–3.   According to Newton's first law, any object in motion will resist any change in motion. Proper use of seatbelts helps prevent passengers in a car from moving if the car is stopped suddenly. Investigations by auto manufacturers using unrestrained dummies indicate the dangers of not using seatbelts.

Newton's laws of motion were based on many observations of moving objects. Newton realized that an object's motion does not change unless a force acts on the object. When you throw a ball, you apply a force that makes the ball move. Newton also noted that once a force causes an object to move, the object will keep moving until a force causes it to stop. You may remember from chapter 3 that this concept is called inertia.

Newton's First Law of Motion states that an object at rest tends to stay at rest unless it is acted on by a force. Similarly, an object that is moving with constant speed tends to stay in motion unless it is acted on by external forces.

At first you might think that Newton's first law does not agree with what you have observed. The law seems to imply that when you throw a ball, it will continue moving forever. You know that it does not. Notice, however, that the law says objects tend to stay in motion unless they are acted on by another force. Think about the thrown ball. What forces act on it after it is thrown? Gravity exerts a downward force on the ball. As the ball travels through the air, friction acts on the ball as well. These forces act to stop a ball that has been thrown and allowed to move freely.

Before Newton's time, Galileo proposed the idea that if friction could be eliminated, a rolling ball could continue in motion indefinitely. Friction cannot be completely eliminated. However, objects do roll farther when friction is reduced. A bowling ball rolls farther on a hard wooden alley than it would on a carpeted floor.

An important application of Newton's first law is the use of automobile seatbelts. If a car stops suddenly, people inside the car tend to remain in motion. Most injuries in automobile accidents happen because people remain in motion and hit objects inside the car. Many people are injured seriously if they are not wearing seatbelts because they strike or go through the windshield. Wearing seatbelts helps prevent serious injury by not allowing people to keep moving if the car suddenly stops. Most cars made today are required to have seatbelts for this reason.

REVIEW AND REFLECT

1. What was the early astronomers' frame of reference when observing the motion of the planets?
2. In a 24 h endurance race, a car makes 640 laps of a race track that is 6 km per lap. How far did the car travel in 24 hours? What was its average speed?
3. Describe the forces that act on a golf ball as it is hit by the club, moves through the air, and finally rolls to a stop in the grass. How does this motion support Newton's first law?

Skill Inquiry

We often use the words speed and velocity interchangeably. Actually, velocity refers to both the speed of an object as well as the direction it moves. Speed, on the other hand, refers only to the rate of motion but not the direction. A quantity such as velocity that has both magnitude and direction is known as a vector quantity. A vector is usually represented by a symbol with an arrow. For example, $\vec{v}$ stands for velocity.

Vector quantities can be shown graphically using arrows. Velocity vectors are illustrated in Figure a. Note that the length of the arrow represents the magnitude of speed. The arrow is pointed in the direction of motion.

a

1. What vector quantities are represented in Figure a?
2. Draw vectors to show
   a. a car traveling north at a speed of 30 km/h
   b. an airplane flying southeast at a speed of 250 km/h

It is often useful to draw vectors when different motions are involved. For example, vectors can be used to show what happens when an airplane encounters a headwind. A headwind is a wind that blows in a direction opposite to the direction of travel.

b

The vectors in Figure b show an airplane flying with an airspeed of 325 km/h. Airspeed refers to the speed of the airplane relative to the air through which it moves. Figure b also shows the wind moving to the east at 50 km/h. Because of the headwind, the speed of the plane relative to the ground is less than the indicated airspeed. As a result, the airplane's velocity is 275 km/h in a westerly direction.

3. Draw vectors of a boat traveling with a velocity of 4 km/h to the southeast across a river flowing to the northeast with a speed of 3 km/h.

9:4   Acceleration

Objects do not always move with a constant speed or direction. As a car moves through traffic, it starts, stops, turns corners, speeds up, and slows down. Its speed changes and its direction changes also.

What is velocity?

Velocity refers to the speed as well as the direction of an object's movement. Some cars have "cruise control," which helps drivers maintain a constant speed as they move along an expressway. Even though the speed of the car does not change, its direction changes. Whenever an object changes speed or direction, its velocity changes.

Change in velocity is the difference between an object's final velocity and its initial (beginning) velocity.

change in velocity = final velocity − initial velocity

$$\Delta v = v_f - v_i$$

The symbol Δ is the Greek letter delta. It means change. Velocity is often measured in meters per second, m/s, and includes an indication of direction.

What is acceleration?

Acceleration (ak sel uh RAY shun) is a measure of the rate at which the velocity of an object changes. Whenever an object's velocity changes, it accelerates. Therefore, an object accelerates whenever its speed or direction changes.

Drag racer
(12 m/s^2)

Sprinter
(3 m/s^2)

Space shuttle
(30 m/s^2)

Family automobile
(1.8 m/s^2)

Cheetah
(1.5 m/s^2)

FIGURE 9–4. The acceleration given for the space shuttle system represents maximum acceleration experienced. All of the other values shown represent average accelerations.

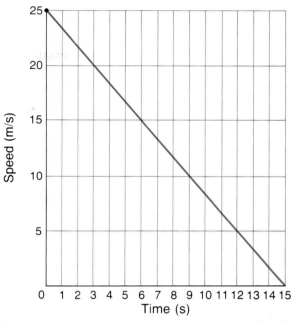

a

b

FIGURE 9–5. A car uniformly accelerating is represented by the straight line graph (a). Uniform deceleration of the car from 25 meters per second to 0 meters per second is 15 seconds (b).

Acceleration is the change in an object's velocity in a given amount of time.

$$\text{acceleration} = \frac{\text{change in velocity}}{\text{time}}$$

$$a = \frac{\Delta v}{t} = \frac{v_f - v_i}{t}$$

Acceleration is usually measured in meters per second squared, m/s^2.

Some cars can accelerate from rest to highway speed in about 10 seconds. Their acceleration can be represented in a graph, Figure 9–5a. Since the graph is a straight line, it represents constant acceleration. You can see from the graph that such a car accelerates 2.5 meters per second each second. The acceleration of the car is said to be 2.5 meters per second squared, 2.5 m/s^2.

SUGGESTION   If students are confused by the denominator, s^2, remind them that acceleration is a change in velocity (m/s) per unit of time (s).

What does a straight line graph of acceleration mean?

EXAMPLE: Calculating Acceleration

Problem: What is the acceleration of a car on a highway that accelerates from rest to 25 m/s in 10 s?

Solution: Acceleration is equal to the change in velocity of the car, which is the final velocity minus the initial velocity, divided by the time. Note that since the car started at rest, its initial velocity is 0.

$$\text{acceleration} = \frac{\text{change in velocity}}{\text{time}}$$

$$a = \frac{\Delta v}{t} = \frac{v_f - v_i}{t}$$

$$a = \frac{25 \text{ m/s} - 0 \text{ m/s}}{10 \text{ s}}$$

$$a = \frac{25 \text{ m/s}}{10 \text{ s}}$$

$$a = 2.5 \text{ m/s}^2$$

What if an object's final velocity is less than its initial velocity? The object has a negative acceleration. In other words, the object is slowing down. When an object's rate of change of velocity is negative, it is said to be decelerating. **Deceleration** (dee sel uh RAY shun) is negative acceleration. Think about the car example again. Suppose after reaching highway speed (25 m/s), the car encounters a stoplight. The driver applies the brakes and the car begins to slow down. The car is decelerating. Deceleration is calculated in the same way as acceleration.

What is deceleration?

EXAMPLE: Calculating Deceleration

Problem: What is the deceleration of a car traveling at 25 m/s if it takes 20 s to come to a complete stop?

Solution: Since deceleration is actually negative acceleration, find deceleration by calculating negative acceleration. The car comes to a complete stop, so its final velocity is 0 m/s. The negative acceleration is the negative of the change in the car's velocity from 25 m/s to 0 m/s divided by the time the car takes to stop.

$$\text{negative acceleration} = -\frac{\Delta v}{t} = -\frac{v_f - v_i}{t}$$

$$-a = -\frac{0 \text{ m/s} - 25 \text{ m/s}}{20 \text{s}}$$

$$-a = -\frac{-25 \text{ m/s}}{20 \text{ s}}$$

$$-a = -(-1.25 \text{ m/s}^2)$$

$$-a = 1.25 \text{ m/s}^2$$

9:5 Acceleration and Motion

According to Newton's first law, the motion of an object remains unchanged unless the object is acted on by a force. In other words, a book on a table has a velocity of zero. Unless acted on by a force, the velocity of the book will remain zero. The book cannot be accelerated without applying a force.

A force is required to accelerate (or decelerate) any object. Imagine that you are trying to push a stalled car. By applying a force, you may be able to accelerate the car. If someone helped you, you probably could accelerate the car more. If the force applied by two people was twice as large as the force applied by one person, the acceleration of the car would be twice as much. Three people could accelerate the car even more. The acceleration of an object is directly proportional to the amount of force exerted on the object.

Now imagine that instead of trying to push a car, you are trying to push a truck. To accelerate the truck at the same rate as the car would take a larger force. A larger force would be needed because the truck has more mass than the car. If the truck has twice the mass of the car, twice as much force would be needed to accelerate the truck at the same rate as the car. Therefore, the acceleration of an object is inversely proportional to its mass.

Newton's Second Law of Motion states that the acceleration of an object is directly proportional to the force exerted on it and inversely proportional to its mass. If you

What causes an object to be accelerated?

How is force related to acceleration?

How is mass related to acceleration?

FIGURE 9–6. The acceleration of the cart is directly proportional to the force exerted by the boy and inversely proportional to the mass of the newspapers.

Explain Newton's second law.

know the force needed to move an object of a certain mass, you can use Newton's second law to calculate the object's acceleration.

$$\text{acceleration} = \frac{\text{force}}{\text{mass}}$$

$$a = \frac{F}{m}$$

In honor of Sir Isaac Newton, the SI unit of force is called a newton, N. Newtons are actually kilogram-meters per second squared, kg · m/s².

EXAMPLE: Using Newton's Second Law to Calculate Acceleration

Problem: A net force of 2 N is exerted on a book as it is lifted off a desk. If the book has a mass of 1 kg, what is its acceleration?

Solution: The acceleration of the object is equal to the force used to move the object divided by the object's mass. A force of 2 N is 2 kg · m/s².

$$a = \frac{F}{m}$$

$$a = \frac{2 \text{ kg} \cdot \text{m/s}^2}{1 \text{ kg}}$$

$$a = 2 \text{ m/s}^2$$

See Teacher's Guide.

REVIEW AND REFLECT

1. A small plane accelerates from a velocity of 10 m/s to 70 m/s in 15 seconds. Calculate its acceleration.
2. An elevator is moving with a velocity of 5 m/s. As it approaches a floor, the brakes are applied and it comes to rest. If it takes five seconds to stop, what is its acceleration?
3. A net force of 4 N is applied to a 2-kg milk container. What is the acceleration?
4. Complete this statement. Acceleration is directly proportional to the _____ and inversely proportional to the _____ of an object.
5. What is the difference between speed and velocity?
6. What is the difference between acceleration and deceleration?

Activity: How can velocity and acceleration be calculated?

See Teacher's Guide.

MATERIALS

measuring tape or meter stick
masking tape or chalk
stopwatch or watch with second hand
metric bathroom scale
marker

PROCEDURE

1. Work with two partners.
2. Choose an area safe for running. Measure a distance of 50 meters and mark a starting line and a finish line. Also mark a line at 25 meters.
3. Determine your mass using a bathroom scale.
4. Have one partner time how long it takes you to run the 50-meter distance that you marked. Be certain that the person also notes the time when you cross the 25-meter line. After you cross the 25 meter line, try not to speed up or slow down until you cross the 50-meter line.
5. Have your other partner time how long it takes you to come to a stop after running the 50 meters. Then measure the distance from the finish line to where you came to a full stop. Record both measurements.
6. Calculate your average speed for the first 25 meters (S_1), the last 25 meters (S_2), the entire 50-meter distance (S_3), and your stopping distance (S_4). Record the speeds in the data table.
7. Calculate your average acceleration for the first 25 meters, the last 25 meters, the entire 50-meter distance, and the stopping distance. Assume that you were traveling at S_2 when you crossed the 25-meter and 50-meter lines. Record the values in the data table.

8. Repeat steps 4 and 5, making measurements for each of your partners. Be sure you include units.

DATA AND OBSERVATIONS

Distance	Time	Average Speed	Average Acceleration
First 25 meters	$S_1 =$		
Last 25 meters	$S_2 =$		
Full 50 meters	$S_3 =$		
Stopping	$S_4 =$		

QUESTIONS AND CONCLUSIONS

1. How did your average acceleration for the first 25 meters differ from your average acceleration in the last 25 meters? Explain the reason for the difference.
2. How did your average acceleration for the entire 50 meters differ from each 25-meter acceleration? Explain the reason for the difference.
3. How much force was needed for you to come to a complete stop at the end of the run?
4. How much quicker would you be able to stop if you had 20 kg less mass?
5. How did your acceleration compare with the acceleration of your classmates?

9:6 Equal and Opposite Forces

In Figure 9–7, the girl is applying a downward force to the rope. The rope, however, exerts an equal, but opposite or upward force on the girl. Forces always act in pairs on objects that interact. The girl exerts a force on the rope. The rope exerts an equal but opposite force on the girl. If the rope did not exert this upward force on the girl, she would fall to the floor. In order for her to climb the rope, both forces must exist.

What is Newton's third law?

The girl climbing the rope is one example of Newton's third law. Newton's Third Law of Motion states that for every force there is an equal force in the opposite direction. A book resting on a table exerts a downward force on the table. The table pushes up on the book with an equal amount of force. When a baseball is hit with a bat, the bat exerts a force on the ball. The ball also exerts a force on the bat, causing the bat to decelerate slightly.

REVIEW AND REFLECT

1. State Newton's Third Law of Motion.
2. Explain how Figure 9–7 illustrates Newton's Third Law of Motion.
3. Explain the acceleration of a rocket using Newton's laws of motion.

FIGURE 9–7.   The rope exerts an upward force on the girl in response to the downward force of the girl's weight (a). A bat accelerates as it moves toward the ball. As they meet, the bat decelerates slightly. The ball decelerates completely and begins to accelerate in the opposite direction (b).

Activity: How can forces cause motion?

MATERIALS

laboratory burner
clean, empty metal can with cap
hammer
large nail
water
ringstand and ring
fish line
graduated cylinder or 150 mL container
goggles and apron
scissors
oven mitt or hot pad

PROCEDURE

1. Lay the can on its side. Using the hammer and nail, carefully make a hole in the upper left corner of the can as shown in Figure 9–8. **CAUTION:** *The metal edges of the hole may be sharp.*

2. Turn the can over. Make a hole in the upper left corner on this side of the can. (The two holes should be on opposite sides of the can.)

3. Put 150 mL of water in the can and put the cap on.

4. Set up the ring and ringstand as shown. Cut a piece of fish line to attach the can to the ring.

FIGURE 9–8.

5. Gently heat the can until the water boils. **CAUTION:** *Be sure you have punched the two holes in the can before you begin heating. Steam will escape from the holes in the can and can cause severe burns. NEVER heat a liquid in a completely closed system.*

6. Remove the heat from the can and observe the motion of the can. Record your observations.

DATA AND OBSERVATIONS

Heat Source	Observations of Can
Present	
Absent	

QUESTIONS AND CONCLUSIONS

1. What happened to the can when you heated the water to boiling?

2. What happened to the can when you removed the heat source?

3. Explain how this activity demonstrates Newton's Third Law of Motion.

4. Make a sketch showing the pairs of forces acting on the can.

5. What would happen if you placed both holes on opposite sides but in the center of the can?

6. What do you think would be the effect of using a more massive can in this experiment? Explain.

7. You have made a device that is commonly called a Hero's engine. What useful work could be performed by your engine?

8. What is the energy source of the engine? How could it be made to operate more efficiently?

What did Aristotle believe about the speed of falling objects?

Describe Galileo's experiments with falling objects.

FIGURE 9–9. The distance traveled by a ball rolling down an inclined plane is directly proportional to the square of the time the ball was moving (a). Likewise, the distance traveled by a freely-falling object is directly proportional to the time squared although the object accelerates at a quicker rate (b).

a

b

9:7 Vertical Motion

The early Greeks believed that vertical motion was "natural" while horizontal motion was "forced." This idea is not as foolish as it may seem. Remember, many theories are developed to explain observations. It could be readily observed that a stone would move vertically (fall) by itself. However, it had to be thrown (a force had to be applied) for it to move horizontally.

Aristotle proposed that the speed at which an object falls is proportional to the mass of that object. In other words, the more mass an object has, the faster it should fall. Aristotle believed that if an object had twice the mass of another object, it should accelerate twice as fast. We know that this idea is not the case.

Galileo did many experiments to measure the rate at which objects fall. Because it was difficult to time objects as they fell, he devised a different method to test his hypotheses. Galileo rolled balls of different masses down a ramp and measured how far they traveled each second. As in Figure 9–9, the balls rolled an equal distance in each unit of time regardless of their mass. Notice, however, that the balls traveled farther during each successive second than they did during the previous second. In other words, the balls rolled farther in second number 3 than in second number 2. They rolled farther in second number 2 than in second number 1. Obviously, the velocities of the balls increase as they roll down the ramp. Therefore, as the balls roll down the ramp, they accelerate.

What if the ramp is made more steep? The balls then will accelerate more rapidly, but still at the same rate as each other. Imagine making the ramp as steep as possible. The balls would fall straight down. They would still, regardless of their mass, accelerate at the same rate.

From the Second Law of Motion, we know that for an object to be accelerated, a force must act on it. Therefore, a force must be exerted on all objects as they fall to earth.

Weight is a measure of the force of gravity between an object and the earth. When you weigh yourself on a bathroom scale, you are actually measuring the gravitational force between your body and the earth. Remember, in SI, forces are measured in newtons, so weight is measured in newtons.

$v = g \cdot t$

$r = g \cdot$

The gravitational force of the earth exerted on a falling object causes the object to accelerate. By careful measurement, it has been found that objects near the earth accelerate at a rate of 9.8 meters per second squared. In other words, the object's velocity increases 9.8 meters per second each second the object falls. The acceleration due to the earth's gravity is represented by the symbol g. Therefore, $g = 9.8$ m/s^2.

Using this information, the velocity of a falling object can be calculated. At any moment, the velocity of an object falling to earth is equal to the time it has been falling multiplied by its acceleration.

$$\text{velocity of falling object} = \frac{\text{acceleration}}{\text{due to gravity}} \times \text{time}$$

$$v = gt$$

EXAMPLE: Calculating Velocity of a Falling Object

Problem: What is the velocity of a skydiver after three seconds of free fall?

Solution: The velocity of the skydiver is equal to his/her acceleration due to gravity which is 9.8 m/s^2 multiplied by the time he/she has been falling.

$$v = gt$$
$$v = 9.8 \text{ m/s}^2 \times 3 \text{ s}$$
$$v = 29.4 \text{ m/s}$$

After seven seconds, using a similar calculation, the velocity of the skydiver should be 68.6 m/s ($v = 9.8$ m/s$^2 \times 7$ s $= 68.6$ m/s). Actually the skydiver probably will not reach a velocity of 68.6 m/s. Air resistance prevents an object from continually accelerating. Air resistance is the upward force of air on falling objects. Because of air resistance, falling objects reach what is called terminal velocity. **Terminal velocity** is the maximum velocity reached by a falling object. The terminal velocity of a falling object is reached when the upward force of air resistance is equal to the downward force of gravity. At that point the two forces, being equal but opposite in direction, balance each other. As we know from Newton's first law, an object will continue to move with constant velocity until a force acts on it. The terminal velocity for a skydiver is about 54 m/s. Once a skydiver reaches a velocity of about 54 m/s, he/she will not accelerate anymore.

$$V = \frac{9.8 m}{s^2} \times \frac{3s}{1}$$

How fast do objects accelerate when dropped?

BACKGROUND Students may have heard the legend of Galileo dropping objects from the Tower of Pisa. However, there is doubt about whether this event actually took place.

Describe terminal velocity.

FIGURE 9–10. A skydiver's terminal velocity is reached at 54 m/s when the force of the air resistance balances the force due to gravity. When the parachute is opened, the force due to air resistance increases and the skydiver decelerates.

Career Profile

At Wright State University, Nan Davis offers words of encouragement to people who are paralyzed. They have come to the Wright State National Center for Rehabilitation Engineering to participate in research. Nan was a research subject of Dr. Jerrold Petrofsky. He is studying computer stimulation of paralyzed muscles. Nan's spinal cord was injured in an automobile crash. After numerous experiments, Nan was the world's first paralysis victim to walk under her own strength while receiving stimulation from a computer.

Today, Nan is a research lab technician with Dr. Petrofsky. She works with people who are paralyzed in much the same way that Dr. Petrofsky first worked with her. Participants in the research build their muscle strength by lifting weights while receiving computer-controlled electrical stimulations. Nan assists participants with these exercises for approximately thirty minutes a day, three times a week. She straps them onto an exerciser, places electrodes on the muscle groups to be worked,

and then prints operating commands into the computer. While they exercise, Nan adjusts weights when necessary and records their heart action and blood pressure. Nan also is involved in a study to determine whether active physical therapy may help prevent loss of minerals from bones of people who are paralyzed.

Nan finds her work in the biomedical engineering lab personally rewarding. It gives her an opportunity to help advance research that some day may help her and other people who are paralyzed walk again.

9:8 Circular Motion

Many objects do not move in straight lines. A record on a phonograph is an example of uniform circular motion. What would happen if the person in Figure 9–11 let go of the rope? A force provided by the rope is required to keep the ball moving in a circular path. At any moment the force of the rope on the ball is perpendicular to the direction of the ball at that instant. In order for any object to move in a circular path with uniform speed, an inward perpendicular force is necessary. This inward force is

What is centripetal force?

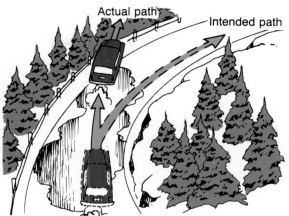

a   b

known as **centripetal** (sen TRIHP ut ul) **force.** If the person let go of the rope, the centripetal force on the ball would no longer exist. Without centripetal force there is no circular motion. The ball would fly off in a straight line.

As an object moves in a circular path, its speed may be constant, but its direction is constantly changing. Therefore, the object's velocity is changing. In other words, an object in circular motion is constantly accelerating. You know from Newton's second law that in order for an object to be accelerated, a force must act on that object. For an object in circular motion, that force is the centripetal force.

Another example of circular motion can be observed when an automobile goes around a curve. The friction between the tire and the road surface keeps the car on the road. According to Newton's first law, the car tends to continue in a straight line. The friction provides the centripetal force, however. The inward force due to friction enables the driver of the car to make the turn.

FIGURE 9–11. The rope provides the force on the moving ball to cause the ball to continually change direction (a). The icy road surface reduces friction on the tires, thereby increasing the centripetal force necessary to maintain the car in a circular path (b).

Why is an object in circular motion said to be accelerated?

BACKGROUND   Centripetal means center-seeking.

See Teacher's Guide.

REVIEW AND REFLECT

1. How much time does a skydiver take to reach terminal velocity?
2. Why is an object in circular motion said to be accelerated?
3. Why is it necessary to slow down when driving around a curve in the rain?

What is the shape of all projectile motion?

9:9   Information: Projectile Motion

What do baseballs and satellites have in common? They are both examples of a fourth type of motion known as projectile motion. There are many examples of projectile motion. Any thrown object like a baseball or a stone is an example of projectile motion. A bullet fired from a gun or an arrow shot from a bow are also examples of projectile motion. Satellites are examples of projectile motion, too. So are footballs that are kicked, and golf balls that are struck. Observe the projectile in Figure 9–12. Notice that it follows a curved path. The motion of all projectiles is always along a curved path. The curved path of a projectile is called its trajectory.

Why is the motion of a projectile curved? Consider the motion of a stone thrown horizontally from a high cliff. The horizontal motion of the stone is a result of the force of the throw. A downward motion is caused by the force of gravity. The effect of these two forces results in the curved trajectory.

FIGURE 9–12.   A thrown ball is an example of a projectile. Its curved path is called a trajectory.

a

b

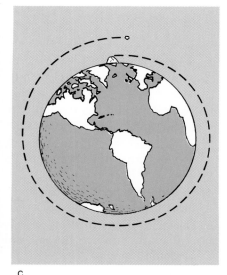

c

FIGURE 9–13.   An object thrown with little force will quickly fall to earth (a). The object thrown with more force will travel a greater distance (b). If the object can be thrown with enough force, its velocity will cause it to orbit the earth (c).

If the stone was thrown from a higher cliff, it would travel farther in a horizontal direction before it fell to the earth. Likewise, if the stone was given a greater horizontal velocity (thrown with more force), it would also travel farther before falling to the earth. If the horizontal velocity of the stone, or any projectile could be made great enough, it could fall "around" the earth. This is exactly what happens to a satellite as it orbits the earth.

The idea for an orbiting satellite is not new. Newton first considered the idea almost 300 years ago! Of course, in Newton's time it was not possible to project an object with sufficient horizontal velocity to orbit the earth. The first artificial satellite to circle the earth was launched in 1957. Today, there are many satellites orbiting the earth. They are used for communication, weather forecasting, locating valuable minerals and energy resources, and military purposes.

What keeps a satellite in orbit around the earth?

See Teacher's Guide.

REVIEW AND REFLECT

1. Give three examples of projectile motion.
2. What force causes projectiles to fall to earth?
3. Why are the trajectories of projectiles curved?

CHAPTER 9 REVIEW

SUMMARY

1. Newton's laws of motion describe basic principles that apply to all moving objects. 9:1
2. To understand the motion of an object, it is important to first define its position. 9:2
3. The observed motion of an object depends on the frame of reference of the observer. 9:2
4. In order for an object to move, some type of force must act on the object. 9:3
5. Because of its inertia, an object stays at rest or in uniform motion unless acted on by some force. 9:3
6. Velocity refers to both the speed and the direction of an object. 9:4
7. The acceleration of an object is directly proportional to the amount of force acting on the object and inversely proportional to the mass of the object. 9:5
8. An equal and opposite force exists for every force. 9:6
9. Objects that fall to the earth are accelerated by earth's gravity at the same rate, regardless of their mass. 9:7
10. Centripetal force is necessary for circular motion to occur. 9:8

VOCABULARY

acceleration 3	frame of reference 6	terminal velocity 4
centripetal force 5	speed 1	velocity 2
deceleration 7		

Match each definition with the correct word from the list.

1. A measure of how far an object moves during a unit of time
2. A measure of the speed and the direction of an object
3. The rate of change of velocity
4. The maximum velocity reached by a falling object
5. Inward force that keeps an object moving in a circular path
6. What an observer compares the position of an object to
7. Negative acceleration

QUESTIONS

See Teacher's Guide.
MAIN IDEAS

Correctly complete each sentence or answer each question.

1. All moving objects are governed by _____ laws of motion.
2. Two other scientists who studied motion in the 16th and 17th centuries were _____ and _____.
3. Motion is defined as a change in an object's _____.
4. What is the average speed of a baseball if it takes 0.5 seconds for a pitcher to throw the baseball to home plate 18.5 meters away?
5. In the SI system, speed is usually measured in _____ or _____.
6. Which of Newton's laws best describes the action of a hockey puck as it glides across the ice?
7. The symbol Δ means _____.

8. Acceleration is measured in SI units of _____.

9. Newton's Second Law of Motion can be stated mathematically as _____.

10. If the force on an object is doubled, what happens to that object's acceleration?

11. An inflated balloon is released. As the air escapes, the balloon is pushed forward. The motion of the balloon is an example of Newton's _____ law.

12. What does the speed at which an object falls depend on?

13. A falling object reaches a terminal velocity because of _____.

14. A boy applies a pushing force of 16 N to a wheelbarrow that has a mass of 40 kg. What is the acceleration of the wheelbarrow? Ignore the friction of the wheel.

15. A girl is running at a speed of 5 m/s. If she takes 1 second to increase her speed to 7 m/s, what is her acceleration?

16. A diver jumps off of a 3 m diving board and hits the water in 0.5 seconds. What was the diver's velocity upon entering the water?

17. An object's change in velocity is determined by subtracting _____ from _____.

18. Weight is a measure of _____.

APPLICATIONS

Answer each question in one or more paragraphs. Show how to solve each problem.

1. A car in which you are riding is traveling at 80 km/h. A car in the oncoming lane is traveling at 75 km/h. What is the relative speed of the approaching car as it passes you?

2. The distance by air from Detroit to Minneapolis is 855 km. How long is the flight if an airplane travels at an average speed of 570 km/h?

3. How far can you walk in 30 minutes at an average speed of 3.5 km/h?

4. In terms of Newton's second law, explain why a racing bicycle is constructed as lightweight as possible.

5. What force is required to push a wagon, which has a mass of 180 kg, with an acceleration of 0.7 m/s^2? Ignore friction.

6. What happens to the weight of an object as its distance from earth increases?

7. A construction worker accidentally drops a wrench from a bridge. If it takes 4.5 seconds to reach the water, what is the final velocity of the wrench?

8. Explain why racetrack curves are often banked (built up on one side).

FURTHER STUDY

INVESTIGATIONS

1. Analyze the position of the moon at the same time of night for several nights. Does its position change? If so, describe.

2. Calculate the speed and acceleration of a crawling or flying insect.

3. Use the library to research the life of Sir Isaac Newton. Write a paper or report orally to the class.

4. Investigate past and planned space flights and explorations.

READINGS

Brancazio, Peter J. "Sir Isaac and the Rising Fastball." *Discover.* July, 1984. pp.44–45.

Gardner, R., and D. Webster. *Moving Right Along.* Doubleday & Co.: Garden City, NY, 1978.

Narlikar, Jayant V. *The Lighter Side of Gravity.* W. H. Freeman and Co.: San Francisco, 1982.

Watson, Philip. *Super Motion.* Lothrop, Lee, & Shepard Books: New York, 1982.

HAVE you ever moved from one home to another? If you have, you know that it is hard work. Work has a special meaning to scientists. In order for any work to be done, a force must move an object through some distance. What are some examples of work being done in the picture? What machines are the people using to help them do the work?

FORCE AND WORK

INTRODUCING THE CHAPTER   Have students list on the chalkboard as many different forces as they can name. Let the class try to classify these forces into groups. Point out that scientists classify forces into just three groups: electromagnetic, gravitational, or nuclear.

10:1   Forces

People, cars, planes, the wind, and rivers all move because of forces. The forces exerted by muscles enable people to move. The force applied on the pedals of a bicycle is transmitted to the rear tire and then the ground, causing the bike to move. Every change in motion is caused by a force of some kind.

In order for any object that is at rest to move, a force must be applied to it. When a football is kicked, it moves because of the force of the kick. A force is also necessary to stop a moving object. When a player catches a football, a force also must be applied to stop the ball.

A force may cause a change in the motion of an object already in motion. When a batter hits a baseball, the ball's motion is changed. A moving car can be accelerated by pressing down on the gas pedal, thus increasing the force applied by the engine.

Sometimes there is no observable motion when forces are applied. Consider a tug-of-war in which the two teams are equally matched. If both teams pull with an identical force, but in opposite directions, no motion results. The forces applied cancel each other. The net force is zero. Whenever the net forces on an object are zero, the forces are said to be balanced and no change in motion results. Table 10–1 summarizes the effects of force on an object.

GOAL   You will learn about the relationships among forces, work, and energy.

What is needed in order for an object to move?

When do forces not result in motion that can be observed?

TABLE 10–1. EFFECTS OF FORCE ON AN OBJECT			
Condition of Object	At rest	In motion	At rest
Description of Force	One force applied	One force applied in opposite direction of motion	Two or more balanced forces in opposite directions
Result	Object in motion	Object at rest	Object at rest
Example	Kicking a football	Brakes on a bike	Tug-of-war

What are fundamental forces?

While there are many different examples of forces, scientists classify all forces into three groups. All forces can be classified as either electromagnetic, gravitational, or nuclear. These three forces are **fundamental forces.**

What are some examples of electromagnetic forces?

You are probably familiar with electromagnetic forces. They include forces between charged particles. Magnetic forces are produced by moving electric charges. All forces are able to act over a distance. A magnet is able to exert a force on another object without actually coming in contact with the object. Electric forces exist between stationary charged particles. As you know, like electric charges repel. Opposite charges are attracted to each other. Frictional forces are also electric forces.

How is gravitational force measured?

A force of attraction exists between any two objects because of their masses. This force is called a **gravitational force.** Gravitational forces are quite weak compared to the other types of forces. Weight is a measure of gravitational force. Weight is measured in newtons. A **newton** is the force required to accelerate a one-kilogram mass at the rate of one meter per second squared.

$$1 \text{ N} = 1 \text{ kg} \cdot \text{m/s}^2$$

While the earth pulls on every object, every object also pulls on the earth. The gravitational force between two objects is proportional to the masses of the objects. Your weight on earth is a measure of the gravitational force between you and the earth. You weigh more than a book, which means that the gravitational force between the earth and you is greater than between the earth and a book. On the moon you would weigh less than you do on earth. Your weight on the moon is a measure of the gravitational force between you and the moon. The moon has less mass than the earth, so the gravitational force between the moon and you is less than between the earth and you. In outer space you would be considered "weightless." This is because gravitational force decreases as the distance between two objects increases.

Nuclear forces are the strongest of all forces although they act only over a very short distance. Nuclear forces hold the nucleus of an atom together. If there were no strong nuclear forces, the nucleus of the atom, which is made of positively-charged protons, would fly apart.

The repulsive force between charged particles in the nucleus is an example of electromagnetic force. This force is overcome, however, by the stronger nuclear force. There is another form of electromagnetic force that acts on the particles in the nucleus. It is called the weak force and is responsible for the decay of some unstable nuclei.

As stated above, all forces act through a distance. In order to explain this action-at-a-distance, the concept of fields has been developed. A field is a region of space in which a certain quantity has a definite value at every point. In a gravitational field the acceleration due to gravity, g, has a value at every point defining the field.

While much is yet to be known about fundamental forces, most scientists currently believe that all three fundamental forces are related to one another. This idea is known as the Supersymmetry Theory and is presently the subject of much research.

What type of forces are the strongest?

What is a field?

FIGURE 10–1. The European research center, CERN, houses the world's largest particle accelerator. Research at CERN has been important in studying nuclear forces.

Activity: What is your reaction time?

See Teacher's Guide.

MATERIALS

metric ruler
graph paper

PROCEDURE

1. Have a partner drop a ruler through your fingers as shown in Figure 10–2.
2. Measure how far the ruler falls in centimeters before you catch it. Repeat 9 times and record the data. Use this data to determine your visual reaction time.
3. Repeat steps 1 and 2 with your eyes closed. Your partner should say "now" when the ruler is dropped. Determine your auditory reaction time.
4. Repeat steps 1 and 2 again with your eyes closed. Your partner should now tap your shoulder when the ruler is dropped. Determine your tactile reaction time. (Tactile means sense of touch.)
5. Find the average distance the ruler drops for your visual, auditory, and tactile tests.
6. Table 10–2 lists the time it takes for a freely-falling body to drop a given distance. Locate your average values in the table and find your reaction times.
7. Graph your reaction times against the average distances the ruler dropped.
8. Determine your average reaction time by averaging the three values.

FIGURE 10–2.

DATA AND OBSERVATIONS

Trial	Distance

QUESTIONS AND CONCLUSIONS

1. Were all of your readings for the average distance the ruler fell before you caught it about the same?
2. Were your reaction times the same or different for each of the three tests? Explain these results.
3. Look at Table 10–2. Why do you think it is possible to predetermine how long it will take the ruler to fall a certain distance?

TABLE 10–2. REACTION TIME			
Distance	Time	Distance	Time
5 cm	0.101 s	16 cm	0.180 s
6 cm	0.110 s	17 cm	0.186 s
7 cm	0.119 s	18 cm	0.191 s
8 cm	0.127 s	19 cm	0.196 s
9 cm	0.135 s	20 cm	0.202 s
10 cm	0.142 s	25 cm	0.225 s
11 cm	0.149 s	30 cm	0.247 s
12 cm	0.156 s	35 cm	0.267 s
13 cm	0.162 s	40 cm	0.285 s
14 cm	0.169 s	45 cm	0.303 s
15 cm	0.174 s	50 cm	0.319 s

10:2 Pressure

When you apply pressure to something, you increase the force on it. **Pressure** is force per unit area.

pressure = force/area

$$P = F/A$$

In SI, pressure is measured in pascals, Pa. One **pascal** is a pressure of one newton per square meter.

$$1 \text{ Pa} = 1 \text{ N/m}^2$$

A pascal is a rather small amount of pressure. A stick of butter weighs about one newton. Imagine spreading one stick of butter over an area of one square meter. The resulting pressure of the butter would be one pascal. Because the pascal is such a small unit, kilopascals, kPa, often are used. A kilopascal equals 1000 pascals.

To understand how the area over which a force is spread affects pressure, consider the following example. The pressure exerted by a person on the ground can be found by dividing the person's weight (the force with which the person pushes down) by the area covered by the person's feet. If the person stands on one foot, the pressure on the area covered by that foot will increase. The person's downward force, or weight, remains the same, but the area upon which this force is exerted is reduced.

EXAMPLE: Calculating Pressure

Problem: A person weighs 650 N and each of the person's feet covers an area of 0.025 m². What pressure does the person exert on the ground while standing on one foot?

Solution: The pressure exerted is equal to the force exerted by the person, 650 N, divided by the area covered by one foot, 0.025 m².

$$P = F/A$$
$$P = 650 \text{ N}/0.025 \text{ m}^2$$
$$P = 26\ 000 \text{ Pa or } 26 \text{ kPa}$$

Problem: What pressure does the person exert on the ground while standing on both feet?

Solution: Since the person is now on two feet, the person exerts the same force on the area covered by two feet.

FIGURE 10–3. Differences in air pressure above and below the wings of a plane are key factors in keeping the plane airborne.

What is a pascal?

BACKGROUND The unit of pressure, the pascal, was named in honor of the Frenchman Blaise Pascal (1623–1662). Pascal's Law states that the pressure exerted at any point in a confined liquid is transmitted in all directions.

$$P = F/A$$
$$P = 650 \text{ N}/(2 \times 0.025 \text{ m}^2)$$
$$P = 13\,000 \text{ Pa or } 13 \text{ kPa}$$

Solids, liquids, and gases exert pressure. Air exerts pressure on the earth. The average pressure of the air at sea level is known as **standard atmospheric pressure.** Standard atmospheric pressure is 101 kPa. Changes in atmospheric pressure are monitored and used to explain and predict weather.

See Teacher's Guide.

What is standard atmospheric pressure?

BACKGROUND   Standard atmospheric pressure often is expressed in terms of barometric pressure in units of centimeters (or inches) of mercury. 101 kPa = 76 cm Hg (or 29.92 in Hg)

REVIEW AND REFLECT

1. What are the three fundamental forces?
2. How are pressure and force different?
3. A 500 N force is exerted on an area of 2 m². Find the pressure in both Pa and kPa.
4. Why is it a good idea to lie down if you find you are on thin ice in the winter?

FIGURE 10–4. Work is done when a force is applied through a distance.

a

b

$\boxed{10:3}$ Work and Energy

People talk about having a lot of work to do or going to work. They may describe some difficult activity as hard work. In a scientific sense, these activities may not be actual examples of work. In science, **work** is the result of a force applied through a distance.

Notice in Figure 10–4a, the girl exerts a force of 40 newtons over a distance of one meter in order to lift the bag of groceries and put it on the table. Work is done by the girl on the bag of groceries. In Figure 10–4b, the girl is holding the bag of groceries. She is not lifting it through a distance. The girl must exert a force of 40 newtons to balance the force of gravity on the bag of groceries. However, even though the girl's arm may grow tired from holding the grocery bag, no work is done since the force does not act through a distance.

The amount of work done can be found by multiplying the force on the object by the distance through which the force acts.

$$\text{work} = \text{force} \times \text{distance}$$
$$w = Fd$$

Because force is measured in newtons and distance in meters, the units for work are newton-meters. This unit of work has been given the name **joule,** J. One joule equals one newton-meter. This unit was named in honor of the English physicist James Prescott Joule (1818–1889) for his accomplishments in the study of work and energy.

How is work measured?

EXAMPLE: Calculating Work

Problem: Calculate the amount of work done in Figure 10–4. In Figure 10–4a, a force of 40 N is used to lift a bag of groceries onto a table 1 m high. In Figure 10–4b, a force of 40 N is used to hold the bag.

Solution: In Figure 10–4a, the work done is equal to the force applied to move the grocery bag, 40 N, multiplied by the distance the bag was lifted, 1 m.

$$w = Fd$$
$$w = 40 \text{ N} \times 1 \text{ m}$$
$$w = 40 \text{ N} \cdot \text{m or } 40 \text{ J}$$

In Figure 10–4b, no work is done to hold the bag at the 1 m height because the work done equals the force used to hold the bag, 40 N, multiplied by the distance the bag was lifted, 0 m.

$$w = 40 \text{ N} \times 0 \text{ m}$$
$$w = 0 \text{ N} \cdot \text{m or } 0 \text{ J}$$

Work, as well as energy, is measured in joules. **Energy** is defined as the ability to do work. If a 100-newton toolbox is lifted one meter, then 100 joules of work was done on the toolbox. The energy required to lift the toolbox was 100 joules. The amount of work done on an object is a measure of the amount of energy needed to do that work.

Why is energy measured in the same units as work?

Whenever work is done, energy is transferred. In the previous example, 100 joules was required to lift the toolbox. The person lifting the toolbox used 100 joules and the toolbox gained 100 joules. Note that the amount of energy used to move an object equals the amount of energy gained by the object.

BACKGROUND   Some energy will always be lost to friction.

In an isolated system, the total amount of energy remains constant. This important concept is known as the Law of Conservation of Energy. Energy exists in many different forms and can be transferred from one object to another. Energy can change from one form to another, but it cannot be destroyed or created.

See Teacher's Guide.

REVIEW AND REFLECT

1. How would a scientist define work?
2. How much work is done by a woman who weighs 500 N in climbing a ladder to a height of 2 m?
3. A person does 375 J of work to move a piano 2.5 m. How much force did the person use?

See Teacher's Guide.

Career Profile

When Fred Ice tells people that he works with robots, he is often asked, "Will they ever be able to wash the dishes?" The answer is yes, but Fred's work is not with robots that do household or personal tasks. Fred is a service representative for a company that specializes in industrial robots. Fred traces his interest in electronics and machines back to the sixth grade, when his brother received an electrical kit as a gift. Fred later got a college degree in Electrical Engineering Technology. He received much of his training in robotics while on the job.

Fred works with a group of machines called a welding work cell. The robot is only one part of the cell. The cell also consists of a positioner, a welding power supply, a cooling system, and a control unit that includes a control pendant with a digital display. The positioner moves the piece to be welded to exactly the right place and holds it there. The robot does the actual welding. The work cell allows the human welder to work faster and more accurately on a continuous basis with improved quality. Also, the human welder can supervise the work at a distance from the heat, sparks, and noise generated in the welding process. The work cell may, in fact, be unattended at times.

In addition to installing and maintaining the welding work cell, Fred also collects data about how the cell functions. Because the field of robotics is new, the machinery is being modified constantly to work better and to meet the specific needs of customers. The information Fred gathers assists engineers who plan the robots of the future and helps support today's products.

10:4   Kinetic and Potential Energy

Energy is found in many forms. Some of the forms include chemical, electric, nuclear, and solar. All of these forms can be classified as either kinetic or potential.

Kinetic (kuh NET ihk) **energy** is energy of motion. To understand kinetic energy, consider a bowling ball. As the ball moves down the alley, it has energy since it is able to knock down the pins. When the ball hits the pins, some of the ball's energy is transferred to the pins. Thus, the ball does work on the pins.

The kinetic energy of an object can be found by multiplying one half its mass by the square of its velocity.

$$\text{kinetic energy} = \frac{1}{2} \text{ mass} \times \text{velocity}^2$$

$$KE = \frac{1}{2} mv^2$$

EXAMPLE: Calculating Kinetic Energy

Problem: A bowling ball has a mass of 7 kg and a velocity of 6 m/s. What is the kinetic energy of the ball?

Solution: The kinetic energy of the ball is half the mass of the ball multiplied by the ball's velocity squared.

$$KE = \frac{1}{2} mv^2$$

$$KE = \frac{1}{2}(7 \text{ kg}) \times (6 \text{ m/s})^2$$

$$KE = 126 \text{ kg} \times \text{m}^2/\text{s}^2 \text{ or } 126 \text{ J}$$

Under ideal conditions, the bowling ball in the example above could do 126 joules of work on the pins. Ideal conditions mean that all of the kinetic energy of the bowling ball can be transferred to the pins. Under real conditions, however, the amount of work done by the ball on the pins will be less than 126 joules. You know that friction between the alley and the ball causes the ball to slow down. The friction produces heat. As the ball rolls down the alley, both the alley and the ball become hotter. Some of the energy of the moving ball is changed to heat. The ball slows down as this energy transfer takes place. When the ball strikes the pins, more energy is changed to heat. The amount of energy gained by the ball and pins is less than the 126 joules of work done on the ball.

BACKGROUND   Some of the energy also is transferred into mechanical energy in the form of sound.

What is kinetic energy?

BACKGROUND   Kinetic comes from the Greek word *kinetikos*, which means motion.

SUGGESTION   Students may wonder why kg·m^2/s^2 is changed to joules in this example. You may wish to show the following dimension analysis or let students compute it.

$$\begin{aligned} \text{joule} &= F \times d \\ &= mA \times d \\ &= \text{kg·m}/\text{s}^2 \times \text{m} \\ &= \text{kg·m}^2/\text{s}^2 \end{aligned}$$

FIGURE 10–5.   The explosion of rocket fuel is a chemical reaction. During this chemical reaction, energy in the form of heat, light, and sound is released.

FIGURE 10–6. The skier's potential energy changes to kinetic energy as she skis down the mountain.

How is potential energy defined?

An object also may have the ability to perform work due to its position. Energy of position is called **potential energy.** Fuels such as coal, oil, or natural gas have potential energy in the form of chemical energy. When the fuels are burned, the energy is released in the form of heat and/or light energy.

What are some examples of potential energy?

A skier at the top of a hill has potential energy. The amount of work the skier can perform is equal to her weight times the height of the hill. Remember, the skier's weight is equal to her mass times the acceleration due to gravity. The skier's potential energy is found as follows.

$$\text{potential energy} = \text{mass} \times \frac{\text{acceleration}}{\text{due to gravity}} \times \text{height}$$
$$PE = mgh$$

SUGGESTION   Again, you may want to have students verify the units of potential energy, kg·m²/s². Mass must be in kilograms for the units to work out right.

EXAMPLE: Calculating Potential Energy

Problem: If a skier's mass is 60 kg and she is standing on top of a 20-m hill, what is her potential energy?

Solution: The skier's potential energy equals her mass, 60 kg, times her acceleration due to gravity, 9.8 m/s², times the height of the hill, 20 m.

PE = mgh
PE = 60 kg × 9.8 m/s² × 20 m
PE = 11 760 J

The energy transformation in this example should be noted. When the skier is at the top of the hill, all of her energy is potential energy. As she skis down the hill, her potential energy changes to kinetic energy. As she reaches the bottom of the hill, all of her energy is kinetic.

See Teacher's Guide.

REVIEW AND REFLECT

1. What is the difference between kinetic and potential energy?
2. What is the potential energy of a 2-kg book on a shelf 1.25 m above the floor?
3. What is the kinetic energy of a 900-kg car traveling down a highway at 72 km/h?

10:5   Machines

People often use machines to do work. In order for work to be done, a force must be applied to an object through a distance. Machines are used to either change the direction or the magnitude of an applied force.

A lever is a machine that changes both the direction and the amount of a force. In Figure 10–7, the woman pushes down on the lever of the jack to lift the 12 000-newton car. Each tire of the car is supporting about one fourth of the car's weight, or about 3000 newtons. If the pivot point, called the fulcrum, is placed in the middle of the lever, a downward force of 3000 newtons is required to lift the 3000-newton corner of the car. However, if the fulcrum is moved closer to the car, as shown in Figure 10–7, the amount of force required to lift the car is reduced. In this case, a force of only 300 newtons is needed.

Why are machines used?

What is the fulcrum of a lever?

FIGURE 10–7. Simple machines, like the lever used to lift the car, can be used to change the magnitude or direction of an applied force.

Lever

Changes direction
or amount of force

Pulley

Changes amount
and/or direction
of force

Wheel
and axle

Changes
amount of force

Inclined plane

Changes
amount of force

Screw

Changes
amount of force

Wedge

Changes
amount of force

FIGURE 10–8. Simple machines
change the direction or amount of
force needed to do work.

How much work can a
machine do?

The six types of simple machines are shown in Figure
10–8. Most machines you use are actually compound machines. A compound machine is made by combining two or
more simple machines. A pair of scissors is a compound
machine. The two blades are levers and the cutting edges
are wedges.

It may seem that we are somehow able to get more out
of a machine than we put into it. However, the amount of
work done by a machine cannot be more than the amount
of work done on a machine. Actually, because of friction
and other inefficiencies, the amount of work a machine is
able to do is always less than the work done on the machine.

Consider the jack and car example in terms of work input and output. The woman pushed down on the lever
with a force of 300 newtons for a distance of one half meter. The amount of work done by the woman is 150 joules.

$$w = Fd$$
$$w = 300 \text{ N} \times 0.5 \text{ m} = 150 \text{ J}$$

Notice, however, that the 3000-newton corner of the car was lifted only five centimeters. Therefore, the work done on the car is 150 joules.

$$w = Fd$$
$$w = 3000 \text{ N} \times 0.05 \text{ m} = 150 \text{ J}$$

This example describes an ideal situation. In real life, the woman would have to do more than 150 joules of work because some of her work is lost to friction.

Mechanical advantage is a measure of how much a machine changes a force. The mechanical advantage, MA, of a machine can be found by dividing the force exerted by the machine by the amount of force that must be applied to the machine.

What is the mechanical advantage of a machine?

$$\text{mechanical advantage} = \frac{\text{force exerted by machine}}{\text{force applied to machine}}$$
$$\text{MA} = \frac{\text{output force}}{\text{input force}}$$

EXAMPLE: Calculating Mechanical Advantage

Problem: What is the mechanical advantage of the jack the woman used to lift the car in Figure 10–7?

Solution: The mechanical advantage of the lever equals the output force, which is the weight of the load, divided by the input force the woman applied to the jack.

$$\text{MA} = \frac{\text{output force}}{\text{input force}}$$
$$\text{MA} = \frac{3000 \text{ N}}{300 \text{ N}}$$
$$\text{MA} = 10$$

SUGGESTION   Point out that sometimes it is desirable to have a machine with a mechanical advantage less than 1. In this case, an input force exerted over a short distance would result in a longer (and consequently faster) motion. The overdrive gear in some automobiles is one example.

10:6   Efficiency

The work output of all machines is less than the work that must be supplied to them. The **efficiency** of a machine is a measure of the amount of the output work compared to the amount of work that must be put into the machine.

What is efficiency?

While all machines have an efficiency less than 100 percent, some machines are more efficient than others. The percent efficiency of a machine is found by dividing the machine's work output by its work input and multiplying by 100.

$$\% \text{ efficiency } = \frac{\text{work output}}{\text{work input}} \times 100$$

EXAMPLE: Calculating Efficiency

Problem: Using a pulley, a force of 10 N (including friction) is required to raise a flag 10 m. If the flag weighs 8 N, what is the efficiency of the pulley?

Solution: $\% \text{ efficiency } = \dfrac{\text{work output}}{\text{work input}} \times 100$

The efficiency of the pulley equals the work output divided by the work input multiplied by 100. The work input is equal to the force applied times the distance the flag is raised.

w = Fd
w = 10 N × 10 m = 100 J

The work output is equal to the weight of the flag times the distance the flag is raised.

w = Fd
w = 8 N × 10 m = 80 J

With these values, the efficiency of the pulley can be calculated.

$$\% \text{ efficiency } = \frac{80 \text{ J}}{100 \text{ J}} \times 100$$

$$\% \text{ efficiency } = 80\%$$

FIGURE 10–9. Woodburning stoves are replacing traditional fireplaces in many homes because the stoves have higher fuel efficiency than fireplaces.

The efficiencies of most compound machines, such as engines in cars, are much lower than the efficiencies of simple machines, such as a flagpole pulley. For many machines, the work input comes from the heat released by burning fuels. These machines are usually rated in terms of fuel efficiency. A machine's fuel efficiency rating tells what percentage of the fuel's potential energy is actually converted to useful work by the machine. The fuel efficiency of a gasoline auto engine is about 25 percent. Diesel engines are somewhat more fuel efficient. Their fuel efficiency is 38 percent. The fuel efficiency of a steam locomotive is only 10 percent. For a jet engine, it is 36 percent.

See Teacher's Guide.

Skill Inquiry

If the mechanical advantage of a machine is known, the input force needed to produce a desired output force can be determined easily.

$$\text{input force} = \frac{\text{output force}}{\text{MA}}$$

For example, if the mechanical advantage of a machine is two, and an output force of eight newtons is desired, a four-newton input is needed.

$$\text{input force} = \frac{8 \text{ N}}{2} = 4 \text{ N}$$

1. What input force is needed to produce an output of 12 N if the mechanical advantage is 3?

A lever is a simple machine that consists of two arms supported by a fulcrum. As shown in the figure, the position of the fulcrum can be used to determine the mechanical advantage. The ratio of the effort arm

to the resistance arm gives the mechanical advantage of the lever. For example, if the effort arm of a lever is five meters and the resistance arm is two meters, the mechanical advantage is 2.5.

$$\frac{5 \text{ m}}{2 \text{ m}} = 2.5$$

2. If the effort arm is 9 m and the mechanical advantage of the lever is 4.5, what is the length of the resistance arm?
3. The force required to lift the lid from a crate is 300 N. A girl decides to use a crowbar to open the crate. She determines the length of the effort arm of the crowbar to be 0.75 m and the resistance arm to be 0.025 m. How much force must the girl exert to pry open the crate?

10:7 Power

Often, it is important to know how fast a machine can do work. To demonstrate the usefulness of the steam engine, James Watt (1736–1819), a Scottish engineer, compared the amount of work the steam engine could perform with the amount of work horses could perform in one day. From these experiments, he developed the concept of horsepower. **Power** is the amount of work done during a given period of time.

How was the concept of horsepower developed?

How is power defined?

$$\text{power} = \frac{\text{work}}{\text{time}}$$

$$P = \frac{w}{t}$$

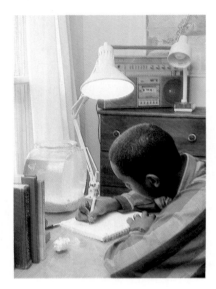

FIGURE 10–10. Conserving energy includes using the correct wattage in light fixtures and using only the lights you need.

In SI, power is measured in watts, W. One **watt** of power is defined as work being done at the rate of one joule per second. One horsepower equals 746 watts. One watt is a relatively small amount of power, thus it is often useful to measure power in kilowatts, kW. One kilowatt is equal to 1000 watts.

EXAMPLE: Calculating Power

Problem: A girl weighs 450 newtons. How much power does she use climbing a flight of stairs 3 m high in 5 s?

Solution: The power the girl uses to climb the stairs is equal to the work she does divided by the time it takes. The work she does equals her weight times the distance she climbed.

$$P = \frac{w}{t}$$
$$w = Fd$$
$$w = 450 \text{ N} \times 3 \text{ m}$$
$$w = 1350 \text{ J}$$

Now the power used can be found.

$$P = \frac{1350 \text{ J}}{5 \text{ s}}$$
$$P = 270 \text{ J/s} = 270 \text{ W}$$

Many electric appliances have a power rating given in watts. Wattage refers to the rate with which an appliance uses energy. An electric light bulb rated at 60 watts converts electric energy to light and heat at a rate of 60 joules per second. An electric heater rated at 1500 watts converts electric energy to heat at a rate of 1500 joules per second.

REVIEW AND REFLECT

1. Why is the amount of work a machine is able to do always less than the work done on the machine?
2. A series of pulleys provides an output force of 750 N when an input force of 250 N is applied. What is the mechanical advantage of the system?
3. A boy exerts a constant force of 225 N on a refrigerator to move it 2.5 m across a room. It takes the boy 4.5 s to move the refrigerator. How much power does he use?

Activity: What factors affect friction?

See Teacher's Guide.

MATERIALS

2 blocks of wood (about 3.5 cm ×
  8.5 cm × 15 cm)
sandpaper (medium to coarse)
2 cup hooks
2 soda straws
stapler
spring scale

FIGURE 10–11.

PROCEDURE

1. Prepare each block of wood by stapling a piece of sandpaper to one surface of each block. Insert a cup hook in one end of each block so it can be pulled.

2. Using the spring scale, pull the block at a steady speed across a table as shown in Figure 10–11. The sandpaper side should be down. Record the force necessary to pull the block. Repeat two more times and find the average force.

3. Turn one block over so that the sandpaper is up. Again, pull the block across the table, record the forces, and determine the average force.

4. Now turn the block on its side. Again, pull the block at a steady speed and record the required force. Try to pull the block at about the same speed each time. Repeat two more times and determine the average force.

5. Stack two blocks on top of each other. Pull the blocks across the table at a steady speed. Record the force needed. Repeat two more times and find the average force.

6. Place two soda straws under one block. Pull the block across the table at a steady speed. Repeat two more times and find the average force.

DATA AND OBSERVATIONS

Condition	Force			
	1	2	3	Average

QUESTIONS AND CONCLUSIONS

1. What force is being measured by the spring scale?

2. What is the effect of the surface area in contact with the table on the force needed to move the block?

3. How did the effect of friction vary when more weight was added to the block?

4. What happened, in terms of friction, when the block with the sandpaper was pulled on the table?

5. When was the frictional force the least?

6. What variables seem to affect friction the most?

10:8 Information: Momentum

Another characteristic of moving objects is momentum. An object's momentum is related to both its mass and velocity. A car and a truck both traveling at the same velocity do not have the same amount of momentum. The truck's momentum will be greater since it is more massive. An object's momentum is found by multiplying its mass times its velocity.

$$\text{momentum} = \text{mass} \times \text{velocity}$$
$$p = mv$$

How is momentum calculated?

EXAMPLE: Calculating Momentum

Problem: What is the momentum of a 3000-kg truck moving at 20 m/s?

Solution: The momentum of the truck is equal to its mass times its velocity.

$$p = mv$$
$$p = 3000 \text{ kg} \times 20 \text{ m/s}$$
$$p = 60\,000 \text{ kg} \cdot \text{m/s}$$

A light object moving rapidly may have more momentum than a slowly-moving massive object. For example, a 2000-kilogram car moving at 25 meters per second has more momentum than a 5000-kilogram truck moving at five meters per second.

FIGURE 10–12. Signs indicating hills are helpful to truck drivers who must decrease the velocity of their trucks in order to prepare for emergency stopping. Decreasing velocity will decrease the truck's momentum (a). The velocity and the mass of a moving vehicle determine its momentum (b).

a

b

FIGURE 10–13. The player in green has greater momentum so he is able to push the red player backwards.

The momentum of any closed system is always conserved. For this reason, momentum is very helpful in understanding what happens when objects collide. The combined momentum of two objects, x and y, before a collision equals their total momentum after they collide.

$$\frac{\text{total momentum}}{\text{before collision}} = \frac{\text{total momentum}}{\text{after collision}}$$

$$m_x v_x + m_y v_y = m_{(x + y)} \times v_{(x + y)}$$

The two football players in Figure 10–13 are running toward each other with the same velocity, 5.5 meters per second. Because the player in green has more mass than the player in red, he has more momentum. The total momentum of the system before the players collide is the sum of their individual momenta. When the players collide, they will move together as a single unit. Therefore, the momentum after they collide will equal the sum of their masses times their new joint velocity. The net momentum will be toward the right and the player in red will be moved backwards.

Explain how momentum is helpful in understanding what happens when objects collide.

See Teacher's Guide.

REVIEW AND REFLECT

1. How is momentum defined?
2. Which car has more momentum, a 1000-kg sports car traveling at 85 km/h or a 1800-kg sedan traveling at 45 km/h? Show your work to prove your answer.
3. If a 7-kg and 5-kg bowling ball were thrown down an alley at the same speed, which ball would be likely to knock down more pins? Explain.

CHAPTER 10 REVIEW

SUMMARY

1. Change in motion occurs only if the forces on an object are unbalanced. 10:1
2. Electromagnetic, gravitational, and nuclear are the three fundamental forces in nature. 10:1
3. Pressure is calculated by determining the force per unit of area. 10:2
4. In science, the term work refers to a force exerted through a distance. 10:3
5. The energy of an isolated system is constant. 10:3
6. Energy can be kinetic or potential. 10:4
7. Applied forces can be altered by simple and compound machines. 10:5
8. Mechanical advantage is a comparison of the work done by the machine to the work done on the machine. 10:5
9. The output work of a machine is always less than the amount of work done on the machine. 10:6
10. Power is a measure of the rate at which work is done. 10:7

VOCABULARY

efficiency 8
energy 11
fundamental forces 2
gravitational force 15
joule 3

kinetic energy 5
mechanical advantage 13
newton 1
pascal 7
potential energy 6

power 9
pressure 4
standard atmospheric pressure 12
watt 14
work 10

Match each definition with the correct word from the list.

1. Force required to accelerate one kilogram one meter per second per second
2. Three kinds of forces into which all other forces can be classified
3. A unit for measuring energy or work
4. Force per unit area
5. Energy of motion
6. Energy of position
7. A force of one newton per square meter
8. The ratio of output work to input work of a machine
9. The rate at which work is done
10. Accomplished when a force causes an object to move a distance
11. The ability to do work
12. The average pressure of air at sea level
13. A measure of how much the magnitude of a force is changed by a machine
14. One joule of work per second
15. A force of attraction between objects

QUESTIONS

MAIN IDEAS

Choose the correct answer to complete each sentence.

1. (*Running, Breathing, Holding a pencil*) does not require work.
2. Friction always produces (*motion, light, heat, pressure*).
3. (*Lifting a feather, Kicking a football, Holding a brick, Pulling a wagon*) requires no work.

4. Expressed in kPa, 105 Pa equals *(0.105 kPa, 1.05 kPa, 10.5 kPa)*.

5. The Law of Conservation of Energy states that energy *(cannot be created or stored, in the universe is increasing, put into a machine is always less than the work the machine does, cannot be created or destroyed)*.

6. All forms of energy can be classified as either *(kinetic or potential, kinetic or nuclear, nuclear or potential, nuclear or electromagnetic)*.

7. As an object falls, potential energy is changed to *(nuclear, electromagnetic, kinetic, gravitational)* energy.

8. *(A green salad, Coal, Water behind a dam, A turning windmill)* is an example of kinetic energy.

9. Machines change the *(amount and direction, magnitude and amount, direction and energy, magnitude and output)* of a force.

10. Power is measured in *(pascals, watts, newtons, joules)*.

11. The amount of work a machine does is always *(more than, less than, the same as, either more or less than)* the amount of work done on the machine.

12. All machines have an efficiency *(less than 100%, more than 50%, equal to 100%, more than 100%)*.

See Teacher's Guide.
APPLICATIONS

Answer each question in one or more paragraphs. Show how to solve each problem.

1. Explain why forces do not always produce an observable motion.

2. A person weighs 600 N. Each of the person's feet covers an area of 0.020 m^2.
   a. What force does the person exert on the ground while standing on one foot?
   b. What is the pressure on the ground?

3. A force of 0.5 N is exerted on a doorbell. The doorbell button has an area of 0.0001 m^2. What is the pressure on the doorbell?

4. A constant force of 5 N is needed to push a book 1.2 m across a desk. How much work is done? If the book weighs 10 N, how much work is done if it is lifted 1.2 m?

5. A 75-kg man is walking with a velocity of 2 m/s. What is his kinetic energy?

6. A force of 35 N is required to push a bicycle up a ramp. If the bicycle weighs 98 N, what is the mechanical advantage of pushing it up the ramp?

7. If the ramp in problem 6 is 3 m long and 0.75 m high, what is the efficiency of pushing the bicycle up the ramp?

8. How much power does a 675-N person use if he/she runs up a flight of stairs 2 m high in 2.5 s?

FURTHER STUDY

INVESTIGATIONS

1. Prepare a chart showing kinds of lubricants, their sources, and uses.

2. Find out about the differences in tires and their uses. Make advertising brochures for three different tires. Highlight their uses, costs, and advantages.

3. Prepare a report on inventors' efforts to make a perpetual motion machine. Include an explanation of why they have never been successful.

READINGS

– Brown, Henry T. *Five Hundred and Seven Mechanical Movements.* Nicholas T. Smith: Bronxville, NY, 1981.

0 Clarke, Donald. *How It Works: The Illustrated Science and Invention Encyclopedia.* A & W Publishers: New York, 1983.

+ D'Ignazio, Fred. *Working Robots.* Elsevier/Nelson Books: New York, 1982.

+ Ord-Hume, Arthur W. J. G. *Perpetual Motion.* St. Martins Press: New York, 1977.

HEAT is associated with many daily activities. At school it may be used to cook your lunch and warm the building. The effect of heat on materials is important in welding. In what other ways is heat used? Everyone is familiar with heat and its uses but many people do not understand it very well. Exactly what is heat? What is the difference between heat and temperature? How are heat and energy related?

HEAT

INTRODUCING THE CHAPTER   Do a demonstration to introduce a discussion of what students already know about heat. Tie a string around the middle of a meter stick. Tie a paper bag upside down on each end of the meter stick. Suspend the meter stick by the middle string from a support. Balance the meter stick, then bring a bright light bulb under one of the bags. Ask students to explain their observations. (The bag will rise because the air in it expands when heated.)

11:1 Heat and Temperature

When someone asks you how hot it is, you probably answer by telling them the temperature. The concepts of temperature and heat often are confused. Temperature and heat are related, but they are not the same. To understand the difference between temperature and heat recall that all matter is composed of particles. The particles, which may be atoms, ions, or molecules, are in constant motion. Remember, energy of motion is kinetic energy. Because particles are in motion, they have kinetic energy. However, not all of the particles are moving at the same speed. So, some particles have more kinetic energy than others. The **temperature** of an object is a measure of the average kinetic energy of the particles of that object. Therefore, the particles of objects with higher temperatures have more kinetic energy than the particles of objects with lower temperatures. For example, the average kinetic energy of the particles in air at 30°C is greater than at 20°C.

The total amount of internal kinetic energy an object has is referred to as its **thermal energy**. We are able to detect thermal energy as heat by touch. For example, when you pick up a lunch tray, it may feel warm. The thermal energy of the hot food is transferred to the tray and from the tray to your hand. The thermal energy that is transferred is called heat. **Heat** is the amount of thermal energy that an object is able to transfer to another object.** Heat is measured in joules.

GOAL   You will learn about heat, and how it is transferred, used, and conserved.

SUGGESTION   Review the concept of kinetic energy developed in chapter 10.

How is temperature defined?

What is thermal energy?

How is heat defined?

227

FIGURE 11–1. This turbine is part of a system that changes potential energy in fuel to electric energy.

What is thermodynamics?

SUGGESTION   Review the Law of Conservation of Energy.

SUGGESTION   Make sure students understand the difference between heat and temperature.

Why do solids, liquids, and gases have different properties?

Thermal energy, like all forms of energy, has the ability to do work. The amount of work done is measured as heat. The turbine shown in Figure 11–1 is used to turn very large generators in order to produce electricity. The potential energy in a fuel, such as coal, is changed to thermal energy as it burns. The thermal energy increases the kinetic energy of the molecules in water; therefore, the temperature of the water is increased. The thermal energy needed to boil the water is transferred from the burning coal to the water. The steam produced is used to drive the turbine that turns the generator, producing electricity. Keep in mind the Law of Conservation of Energy when considering these energy transformations. No more electrical energy can be produced than the amount of potential energy stored in the coal. In fact, far less electric energy will be produced because some energy will be lost to friction and other inefficiencies. Remember, the efficiency of any machine is less than 100%.

The Law of Conservation of Energy is also known as the First Law of Thermodynamics. Thermodynamics is the study of the interaction of thermal energy and matter. The First Law of Thermodynamics states that the total amount of energy in any isolated system remains constant.

11:2   Change of State

An object's temperature increases when heat increases the kinetic energy of the object's particles. Consider what happens when an object changes state. The particles of matter are held together by bonds formed by forces of attraction between particles.

In a solid, the particles of matter are bonded in a rigid pattern. The bonds between particles are weaker in a liquid than in a solid. As a result, the physical properties of solids and liquids are different. Liquids can be poured because the forces of attraction between particles are weak, and the particles move easily over one another. The bonds between particles in gases are even weaker than the bonds in liquids. Gases can expand and fill their containers because the force of attraction between particles is too weak to overcome their kinetic energy. Therefore, they move independently of each other.

In order for a substance to change state from solid to liquid, energy is needed to overcome the force of attraction between particles. Perhaps you have noticed that an iced drink does not begin to become warm until all of the ice has melted. Ice absorbs energy as it melts. The energy absorbed by the melting ice is changed into work used to overcome the forces of attraction between molecules. None of the absorbed energy increases the kinetic energy of the molecules, so the temperature does not increase.

Like ice, all solids absorb energy as they melt. The heat (amount of thermal energy) that is required to change a substance from the solid to the liquid state is called the **heat of fusion**. The heat needed to change a substance from solid to liquid is equal to the substance's heat of fusion times its mass. The heat of fusion for ice is 334 joules per gram. In other words, 334 joules are required to melt one gram of ice. Remember, this 334 joules does not cause an increase in temperature.

Ice is useful for cooling because it absorbs energy when it melts. If two kilograms of ice are put into a picnic cooler, the ice will absorb 668 kilojoules of thermal energy from the food as it melts.

$$\frac{\text{thermal energy}}{\text{absorbed (heat)}} = \text{heat of fusion} \times \text{mass}$$
$$\text{H} = 334 \text{ J/g} \times 2000 \text{ g}$$
$$\text{H} = 668\ 000 \text{ J or } 668 \text{ kJ}$$

Energy also is necessary for a substance to change from a liquid to a gas. This energy is the **heat of vaporization**. The heat of vaporization for water is 2260 joules per gram. The heat needed to change a liquid to a gas is equal to the liquid's heat of vaporization multiplied by its mass. For example, 1695 kilojoules of thermal energy are needed to change 750 grams of boiling water to steam.

$$\frac{\text{thermal energy}}{\text{absorbed (heat)}} = \text{heat of vaporization} \times \text{mass}$$
$$\text{H} = 2260 \text{ J/g} \times 750 \text{ g}$$
$$\text{H} = 1\ 695\ 000 \text{ J or } 1695 \text{ kJ}$$

As water is heated, its temperature increases steadily as its molecules gain kinetic energy. When the water begins

What is heat of fusion?

How is heat of fusion calculated?

Define heat of vaporization.

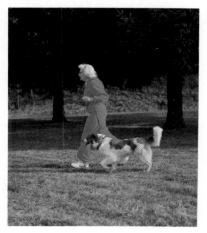

FIGURE 11–2. When your body becomes overheated, you perspire. For each gram of perspiration that evaporates, 2260 joules of thermal energy are removed from your body. As a result, you feel cooler.

to boil, however, its temperature no longer increases. The energy absorbed when a substance changes from a liquid to a gas does not cause an increase in temperature.

Energy is absorbed when matter changes from the liquid to the gaseous state. When your body becomes overheated, you perspire. For each gram of perspiration that evaporates, 2260 joules of thermal energy are removed from your body. As a result, you feel cooler.

See Teacher's Guide.

Skill Inquiry

The chart shown is called a zone chart. Zone charts may be made by carefully analyzing solar energy, soil temperatures, and/or frost dates.

1. In what zone do you live?
2. What states are at least partly in zone 9?
3. How many zones are there in Georgia?

Scientists obtain information about what plants thrive in various conditions by studying the effects of soil and climate on different plants. The table indicates the northern limit in which a plant is likely to grow.

Many people besides scientists use zone charts. Nursery workers can use zone charts to help them order stock that will grow well in their area. They also can use the information to answer planting questions their customers may have. You can use a zone chart to determine when and what to plant where you live.

4. Where in North America would you not successfully grow white pine?
5. Would a person who plants star jasmine probably live in Denver or Miami?
6. Use the zone chart and table to list the types of vegetation that are likely to thrive in your area.

Zone 1	below −46°C
Zone 2	−46° to −40°
Zone 3	−40° to −34°
Zone 4	−34° to −29°
Zone 5	−29° to −23°
Zone 6	−23° to −17°
Zone 7	−17° to −12°
Zone 8	−12° to −6°
Zone 9	−6° to −1°
Zone 10	−1° to 4°

TABLE OF PLANT HARDINESS	
Plant	**Hardiness Zone**
White pine	3
Forsythia	5
Azalea	some as far as 5
Rhododendrons	4
Pyracantha	7
Chinese holly	lower 6
Passionflower	9 and 10
Star jasmine	lower 8

Activity: How is energy absorbed when matter changes state?

See Teacher's Guide.

MATERIALS

clock or watch
600 mL beaker
ice cubes
graduated cylinder
thermometer
water
hot plate
graph paper
goggles and apron

PROCEDURE

1. Fill a 600 mL beaker with 100 mL of water.
2. Place four or five ice cubes in the beaker.
3. After several minutes, measure the temperature of the ice-water mixture.
4. Place the beaker of ice water on the hot plate and heat slowly.
5. Continue to heat slowly. Record the temperature of the ice-water mixture every minute and record in the data table.
6. Continue heating and recording the temperature until the ice melts. Note when the ice melts.
7. Heat the water until it begins to boil. Note when the water begins to boil.

FIGURE 11–3.

8. Continue measuring and recording the temperature until the water has boiled for five minutes.
9. Graph your data.

DATA AND OBSERVATIONS

Time	Temperature

QUESTIONS AND CONCLUSIONS

1. Describe the shape of your graph.
2. What do the horizontal portions of your graph represent?
3. How would your graph be different if additional ice cubes were used in the first step?
4. Assuming the ice does not melt, is a glass of iced tea cooler after sitting 10 minutes or five minutes?
5. What was the maximum temperature reached when you heated the water?
6. Why did the temperature of the water not continue to increase?
7. What would be the outcome of the experiment if a hotter source of heat were used?
8. When you remove the boiling water from the heat source, it will begin to cool. What do you think the cooling curve will look like?

11:3 Expansion and Contraction

What makes the liquid in a thermometer move up when temperature increases and down when temperature decreases? Most substances, like the liquids used in thermometers, expand when they are heated and contract when they are cooled. In a thermometer the liquid, usually mercury or alcohol, expands as it gets hotter. Thus, it moves up in the glass tube. As it gets colder, the liquid contracts and moves down.

When a substance is heated, its particles gain kinetic energy and move more rapidly. The faster the particles move, the farther apart they tend to bounce after they collide. The harder you throw a tennis ball, the faster its velocity is when it hits the ground. The faster the ball hits the ground, the higher it bounces. Imagine the particles in the liquid of a thermometer are like tiny tennis balls bouncing off one another and the sides of the thermometer. As a result of this movement, the substance expands. As the heat is increased, the particles move faster and the liquid expands more. When the heat is reduced, the particles slow down and the liquid contracts.

Not all materials expand and contract the same amount. Solids do not expand as much as gases or liquids when heated. A bimetallic strip is made by welding thin strips of brass and steel together. When the bimetallic strip is heated, it bends toward the steel because the brass expands more than the steel. Bimetallic strips are used in heat sensitive switches, such as thermostats, Figure 11–4.

What happens when most substances are heated?

FIGURE 11–4. The bimetallic strip in a thermostat uncoils as the temperature in the room goes down. The tube containing mercury is then tilted causing the mercury to roll down and the switch closes. Once the temperature reaches the desired level, the bimetallic strip coils up. The mercury moves back in the tube and the switch is left open.

Dial of thermostat
Desired temperature
Actual temperature
Mercury
Switch
Wires to heating system
Uncoiled bimetallic strip
Coiled bimetallic strip

The contraction and expansion of matter must be considered during the construction of highways. Strips of tar are placed between each section of a concrete highway. The tar strips allow for expansion of the concrete. If the concrete was poured in one long, continuous section, it would buckle and crack during hot weather as it expanded.

The effects of thermal expansion and contraction must be considered by architects and engineers in most construction and machine design. The Coefficient of Linear Expansion of a material is the factor by which the material's length expands for each degree Celsius its temperature increases. For example, when the temperature of a 24 centimeter length of brass pipe increases 25 C°, its length will increase 0.011 centimeters.

$$\frac{18.9 \times 10^{-6} \ (24 \ \text{cm} \times 25 \ \text{C}°)}{\text{C}°} = 0.011 \ \text{cm}$$

What is the coefficient of linear expansion?

DEMONSTRATION Obtain a bimetallic strip from a scientific supplier. Show how it bends when heated.

TABLE 11–1. SOME COEFFICIENTS OF LINEAR EXPANSION	
Substance	**Coefficient (increase per C°)**
Aluminum	25.5×10^{-6}
Brass	18.9×10^{-6}
Diamond	1.2×10^{-6}
Graphite	7.9×10^{-6}
Brick	9.5×10^{-6}
Concrete	10 to 14×10^{-6}
Glass (plate)	8.9×10^{-6}
Steel	13.2×10^{-6}
Silver	18.8×10^{-6}
Tin	26.9×10^{-6}

See Teacher's Guide.

REVIEW AND REFLECT

1. What is the First Law of Thermodynamics?
2. What is the difference between heat and temperature?
3. How much thermal energy is absorbed as 75 g of ice melt?
4. If you wanted to put in a large concrete patio, what could you do to prevent the concrete from buckling during hot weather?

FIGURE 11–5. Water is an excellent material to use as a solar energy collector. It has a high specific heat capacity, which means it can absorb a large amount of energy during the day without a large increase in temperature. At night, the energy is released and the surrounding area is warmed.

BACKGROUND C_p is measured in J/kg·K in SI. Δt is equal to $t_2 - t_1$.

How are specific heat capacities used?

$\underline{11:4}$ Heat Capacity

The amount of thermal energy a material must absorb to raise the temperature of one gram of it one Celsius degree is called its **specific heat capacity,** C_p. Specific heat capacity is measured in joules per gram Celsius degree, J/g·C°. Table 11–2 lists the specific heat capacities of some common materials.

The specific heat capacity of water is 4.18 J/g·C°. For steel, it is 0.45 J/g·C°. Water is able to absorb almost 10 times more heat than an equal amount of steel can absorb. Compared to most other materials, water has a high heat capacity. For this reason, it is used in many heating systems and as a coolant for engines.

The heat needed to increase an object's temperature can be found by multiplying the object's specific heat capacity times its mass times the number of degrees the object's temperature changes. The change in the object's temperature is indicated by Δt. Remember, the symbol Δ, pronounced delta, means "change."

$$\text{heat} = \frac{\text{specific heat}}{\text{capacity}} \times \text{mass} \times \frac{\text{change in}}{\text{temperature}}$$

$$H = C_p \times m \times \Delta t$$

Specific heat capacities can be used to find out how much thermal energy is required to increase the temperature of various materials. For example, 4.18 joules are needed to increase the temperature of one gram of water one Celsius degree.

$$H = 4.18 \text{ J} \times 1 \text{ g} \times 1 \text{ C°}$$

TABLE 11–2. SOME SPECIFIC HEAT CAPACITIES			
Material	C_p (J/g · C°)	**Material**	C_p (J/g · C°)
Aluminum	0.89	Glass	0.83
Copper	0.39	Leather	1.51
Glycol $(CH_2OH)_2$	2.39	Paraffin	2.91
Brass	0.39	Porcelain	1.09
Steel	0.45	Sugar	1.15
Rubber (synthetic)	1.87	Charcoal	0.67

Specific heat capacity also can be used to find how much heat is lost by an object as it cools.

EXAMPLE: Calculating Heat Needed to Lower Temperature

Problem: How much heat is given off by 2.0 g of steel as it cools from 95°C to 25°C?

Solution: The heat lost is equal to the specific heat capacity of steel, 0.45 (from Table 11–2), times the mass of the steel, 2.0 g times the change in temperature, 95°C − 25°C = 70 C°.

$$H = C_p \times m \times \Delta t$$
$$H = 0.45 \text{ J/g·C°} \times 2.0 \text{ g} \times 70 \text{ C°}$$
$$H = 63 \text{ J}$$

You may be more familiar with another unit of measuring heat, the calorie. One **calorie** is the heat needed to raise the temperature of one gram of pure water one degree Celsius. One calorie is equal to 4.18 joules. A calorie is a rather small unit of heat. For this reason, the unit kilocalorie often is used. A kilocalorie is equal to 1000 calories. A kilocalorie is the heat required to raise the temperature of one kilogram of water one degree Celsius. Commonly, a kilocalorie is written Calorie, with a capital C. Nutritionists often use Calories to measure the amount of energy stored in foods. Table 11–3 lists the amount of energy stored in some common foods.

BACKGROUND   Technically, a calorie is the amount of energy required to raise one gram of water from 15°C to 16°C.

What is a Calorie?

TABLE 11–3.	**CALORIE CONTENT OF SOME COMMON FOODS**		
Food	**Calories/Serving**	**Food**	**Calories/Serving**
Skim milk	90	Chocolate chip cookie	75
Whole milk	150	Tossed salad	150
Cola soft drink	145	Ice cream	150
Diet soft drink	1	Peanuts	110
Orange juice	120	Bagel	150
Hamburger	380	Baked potato	250
Sausage pizza	245	Celery and carrot sticks	20
Beef taco	215	Green beans	25
Hard-boiled egg	75	Broccoli	25
Apple	70	Cheese	150
French fries	235	Bread	79

FIGURE 11–6. Our body temperature increases when we have a fever. This mother can detect changes in her baby's temperature by conduction.

BACKGROUND   While it is not advisable to have students convert units from SI to metric to English, some students may have heard of the English measure of heat, the BTU or British Thermal Unit. One BTU is the amount of heat energy needed to raise one pound of water one degree Fahrenheit.

Compare conduction and convection.

11:5 Thermal Energy Transfer

When two objects of different temperatures come in contact with one another, thermal energy is transferred. Thermal energy is always transferred from the warmer object to the cooler one, never in the other direction. This phenomenon is known as the Second Law of Thermodynamics. Thermal energy never flows from a cooler object to a warmer one. For example, if a cold drink is set on a picnic table on a hot summer day, thermal energy is transferred from the warm air to the cold drink. The air warms the drink, the drink does not cool the air around it.

Thermal energy can be transferred in three ways: conduction, convection, and radiation. To understand conduction, think of walking on a sandy beach in the sun. If you walk barefoot on the hot sand, your feet get hot. The transfer of some of the sand's thermal energy to your feet is an example of conduction. The sand is at a higher temperature than your feet. Therefore, the particles that make up the sand have greater kinetic energy than the particles in your feet. When your feet come in contact with the sand, some of this kinetic energy is transferred to the particles in your feet, increasing their kinetic energy. The average kinetic energy of the particles in your feet goes up. Thermal energy is transferred by **conduction** from particle to particle. Transfer of thermal energy by conduction can occur in solids, liquids, and gases.

It is often said, "heat rises." Technically, this statement is not correct. Thermal energy has no natural tendency to rise or fall. A more accurate statement is "Hot fluids tend to rise." A fluid is a substance that conforms to the the shape of its container, so both liquids and gases can be considered fluids. Thermal energy transfer by convection takes place in fluids. **Convection** occurs as thermal energy causes currents to be formed that transfer energy in fluids.

Imagine that a small space heater is placed in a room as shown in Figure 11–7. The air immediately around the heater is warmed. The particles of the heated air have more kinetic energy than the particles of the cooler air elsewhere in the room. Therefore, the particles in the heated air move with greater velocity and, on the average,

FIGURE 11–7. Space heaters warm the surrounding air. The warm air rises setting up convection currents in the room.

move farther apart from one another. For this reason, the heated air is less dense than the cooler air. The more dense, cooler air is pulled down by the force of gravity. Warm, less dense air rises to take its place. As the cooler air falls, it too is heated by the space heater, and the process continually repeats itself. This process, called convection, sets up currents. Many homes are heated by convection currents.

Conduction occurs only through solid and fluid matter, and convection occurs only through fluid matter. By these processes, thermal energy is transferred from the particles in one mass of matter to the particles in another mass of matter. The third method of thermal energy transfer, radiation, can take place in a vacuum where no particles of matter exist. **Radiation** is a process by which energy is transmitted by waves.

Describe radiation.

The radiant heat from the sun can be felt when you stand near a sunny window. Thermal energy is transferred through the window and into the room by radiation. In cold climates, heating bills can be reduced by opening curtains and shades on windows facing the sun during the daylight hours. However, it is important to close the curtains or shades at night or on cloudy days.

Activity: What makes the best radiator?

MATERIALS

two empty soup cans—one painted
  black inside and out
hot water
cold water
thermometer
graph paper
graduated cylinder
clock or watch

PROCEDURE

1. Pour 30 mL of hot water into each can.
2. Record the temperature of the water in each can. The temperature of the water in each can should be about the same.
3. Predict in which can the water will cool more rapidly. Record your prediction.
4. Measure the temperature of the water in each can every minute for 15 minutes and record in the data table.
5. Make a graph of your data.

FIGURE 11–8.

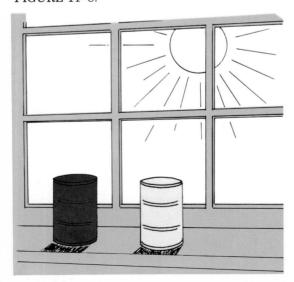

6. Pour cold water in each can and place in a sunny window or under a bright light. Repeat steps 2–5.

DATA AND OBSERVATIONS

Time	Temperatures (°C)	
	Painted Can	Unpainted Can

QUESTIONS AND CONCLUSIONS

1. Which can of water had the lowest temperature after 15 minutes?
2. Which can of water lost the most heat after 15 minutes?
3. Use your data to determine the total amount of heat lost by each can of water after each minute. Remember one milliliter of water has a mass of one gram.
4. What happened when cold water was placed in each can and they were both heated the same amount?
5. The linings of most thermos bottles are silver. Why do you think this is so?
6. Why do you think radiators in automobiles are black?

11:6 Insulation

The only process of thermal energy transfer in solids is conduction. Thermal energy is conducted by all solid matter. However, some materials, such as most metals, are better conductors of thermal energy than others. Copper is an excellent conductor. Some pots and pans have copper bottoms that distribute thermal energy quickly to cook foods evenly. The ability of a material to conduct thermal energy is known as its thermal conductance, C. **Thermal conductance** is the amount of energy that passes through a material in one hour.

Materials that are poor conductors are called **insulators** (IHN suh layt urz). Insulators are used in walls and ceilings to prevent heat loss to the outdoors by conduction. The furnace in a well-insulated home does not have to produce as much heat to keep the home warm as the furnace in a poorly-insulated home does. A materials' insulating ability is called its thermal resistance, R. The thermal resistance or **R-value** of an insulator is the reciprocal of the thermal conductivity.

FIGURE 11–9. Many volunteer groups are helping others in their community insulate their homes to reduce heating costs.

What is the thermal resistance of a material?

$$\text{thermal resistance} = \frac{1}{\text{thermal conductivity}}$$
$$R = \frac{1}{C}$$

TABLE 11–4. R-VALUES FOR SOME COMMON BUILDING MATERIALS

Material	R-Value	Material	R-Value
Interior Walls:		Exterior Walls:	
Plasterboard (drywall)	0.35/cm	Exterior sheathing board	1.82/layer
Plywood	0.49/cm	Building paper	0.06/sheet
Plaster	0.24/cm	Stucco	0.08/cm
Insulation:		Brick	0.08/cm
Fiberglass (batts)	1.23/cm	Sandstone or limestone	0.03/cm
Vermiculite (loose)	1.09/cm	Wood siding	0.60/cm
Mineral fiber	1.36/cm	Asbestos shingle siding	0.21/layer
Air space	1.82–3.56/cm	Aluminum siding	0.01/layer
Polystyrene foam sheets	1.52/cm	Steel siding	0.03/layer
		Roofing:	
		Roofing paper	0.15/sheet
		Asphalt shingles	0.44/layer

FIGURE 11–10. The type and amount of materials used in construction determine the R-values of walls and ceilings.

Asphalt shingles
1 layer

Roofing sheets
1 layer

Plywood
1.9 cm

Fiberglass
15 cm

Drywall
2 cm

Exterior sheathing
1 layer

Polystyrene foam sheets
1.75 cm

Aluminum siding
1 layer

Fiberglass
10 cm

The total insulation or R-value for a building can be found by adding the individual R-values for each layer in the building's construction. For maximum insulating efficiency in cold climates, R-values of 19 for walls and 30 for ceilings and attics are recommended for most homes.

What are recommended R-values for houses?

EXAMPLE: Calculating Total R-value

Problem: Would the R-value of the walls shown in Figure 11–10 provide recommended insulating efficiency in a cold climate?

Solution: The total R-value of each layer is found by multiplying the thickness of the layer times the R-value of the material (from Table 11–4).

drywall: $R_1 = 2$ cm $\times$ 0.35/cm $= 0.70$
fiberglass: $R_2 = 10$ cm $\times$ 1.23/cm $= 12.30$
sheathing: $R_3 = 1$ layer $\times$ 1.82/layer $= 1.82$
foam sheets: $R_4 = 1.75$ cm $\times$ 1.52/cm $= 2.66$
siding: $R_5 = 1$ layer $\times$ 0.0l/layer $= 0.0l$

The total R-value of the walls is the sum of the R-value of each layer.

Total $R_{wall} = R_1 + R_2 + R_3 + R_4 + R_5$
Total $R_{wall} = 0.70 + 12.30 + 1.82 + 2.66 + .01$
Total $R_{wall} = 17.49$

Since an R-value of 19 for walls is recommended in cold climates, the walls of the house shown in Figure 11–10 would not provide recommended insulating efficiency.

See Teacher's Guide.

REVIEW AND REFLECT

1. What are the three ways in which heat is transferred?
2. A car's cooling system contains 6.0 kg of glycol as a coolant. How much heat will the glycol absorb if its temperature increases 30 C° when the engine heats up?
3. Calculate the R-value of the ceiling in the house shown in Figure 11–10.
4. On a cloudy day after a heavy snow, a person noticed that all of the snow on the roofs of a few houses had melted. Explain the person's remark, "Those houses must not be well-insulated."

See Teacher's Guide.

Career Profile

In Minnesota, the wind chill factor drops temperatures to −10°C. So, people think seriously about having an energy efficient home. Many people call Mary Jarnot who is an energy utilization coordinator for a power company in St. Paul, Minnesota. Mary does home energy audits.

She checks both the inside and outside of a home for cracks and loose-fitting windows. Basements and attics are inspected, too. Mary crawls into attics to check the amount of insulation and to look for moisture damage that develops from inadequate ventilation.

At the end of an inspection, Mary discusses her findings with the homeowner. She makes recommendations such as weatherstripping windows and doors, filling cracks, insulating walls and attics, and installing glass doors on fireplaces. Mary may give instructions in the proper installation

of these features or may recommend a qualified contractor. She also is prepared to talk about alternative sources of energy such as solar and wind power when these seem appropriate. Finally, Mary leaves a list of low cost/no cost energy saving tips with her customers.

Mary also keeps records of audits, inspects the installation of energy-saving devices in homes, trains and supervises other auditors, and administrates programs. She is developing her public speaking skills as a volunteer with the company's speakers bureau, too.

11:7 Choices: Energy Sources

Energy has been a popular topic of discussion since the early 1970s. You have probably heard phrases like "energy crisis" and "energy conservation." What does the term energy make you think of? Figure 11–11 shows how energy is used in the United States.

Before 1885, almost all of the energy people used was produced by burning wood. Most of the energy people use today comes from burning coal, oil, and natural gas. The potential energy that is stored in these fuels is released as heat and light when they are burned.

Not all fuels produce the same amounts of energy. A kilogram of coal produces more energy than a kilogram of wood. One kilogram of pine produces 18 500 kilojoules of thermal energy when burned. A kilogram of bituminous coal produces over 32 000 kilojoules. The amount of energy produced when a fuel burns is known as its heat of combustion. A fuel's heat of combustion is usually expressed in kilojoules per kilogram, kJ/kg, or kilojoules per cubic meter, kJ/m^3. The heats of combustion for some fuels are listed in Table 11–5.

FIGURE 11–11. Energy use by each of the four energy markets.

TABLE 11–5. HEAT OF COMBUSTION FOR SOME FUELS	
Substance	Heat of Combustion in kJ/kg
bread	10 000
trash	10 000
wood	14 000
charcoal	28 000
coal	29 000
butter	33 000
crude oil	43 000
gasoline	44 000
natural gas	55 000
uranium ore	1 200 000
fissionable fuel	600 000 000

SUGGESTION   Point out that oil, coal, and natural gas are composed of organic molecules. You may wish to review organic compounds (chapter 6).

Demand for energy is increasing but supplies of coal, oil, and natural gas are limited. The combination of increasing demand and decreasing supply results in higher fuel prices. Heats of combustion are significant in determining the cost of using an energy source. However, many factors need to be considered in determining the cost of using an energy source. For example, wood may cost less per kilogram than coal but more wood than coal is needed to produce an equal amount of energy. Coal may be less costly to mine but more costly to transport than uranium ore. In nearly all cases, some kind of trade off must be made when determining what energy sources a community will use. The costs and benefits of each source must be carefully analyzed by members of a community.

FIGURE 11–12. Trash burning power plants are an effective way of using a local, abundant source of fuel.

Some communities and industries have trash-burning power plants that produce electricity. Think of how much you throw away in a day. Most of these wastes are burned or buried. Billions of kilograms of urban, agricultural, and industrial wastes are disposed of each year. Even though some wastes have relatively low heats of combustion, they are available and need to be disposed of anyway. Many of these wastes could be burned to provide energy.

The use of wastes as fuels could reduce our use of traditional fuels like coal, oil, and natural gas. However, the wastes must be collected and transported to power plants. Because some of the wastes cannot be burned safely, they must be separated from those that can be used safely as fuels. Currently these factors often make use of wastes as fuels more costly than traditional fuels. As demand for traditional fuels continues to increase and supplies continue to decrease, the use of wastes as fuels is likely to become more economical.

What variables affect the price of energy?

SUGGESTION   Let students think of cost factors involved in using trash as fuel, such as transporting the trash to power plants and polluting the air when it is burned.

See Teacher's Guide.

REVIEW AND REFLECT

1. Oak has a higher heat of combustion than pine. What is a drawback of using oak as fuel for a woodburning stove instead of pine?
2. What are some advantages and disadvantages of trash as a fuel?
3. What fuel in use today can produce the most energy per kilogram?
4. What factors should be considered in deciding to use a particular fuel as a source of energy?

CHAPTER 11 REVIEW

SUMMARY

1. Heat, temperature, and thermal energy are related, but they are not the same.   11:1
2. The thermal energy absorbed by a substance in changing state does not cause an increase in temperature.   11:2
3. Most objects expand when they are heated and contract when they are cooled.   11:3
4. Water is used as a coolant because it has a high heat capacity compared to most other materials.   11:4
5. Thermal energy is transferred when two objects of different temperatures come in contact.   11:5
6. Thermal energy always flows from areas of higher temperature to areas of lower temperature.   11:5
7. Thermal energy is transferred by conduction, convection, and radiation.   11:5
8. Not all materials conduct thermal energy at the same rate.   11:6

VOCABULARY

calorie   6
conduction   2
convection   3
heat
heat of fusion   12

heat of vaporization   13
insulator   5
radiation   4
R-value   9

specific heat capacity   8
temperature   1
thermal conductance   10
thermal energy   7

Choose a word from the list to answer each question.

1. What is the measure of the average kinetic energy of the particles in an object?
2. What is the transfer of thermal energy when objects are in direct contact?
3. What is the transfer of thermal energy caused by currents?
4. What is the transfer of thermal energy by waves?
5. What is a poor heat conductor?
6. What is the amount of thermal energy needed to raise the temperature of one gram of water one degree Celsius called?
7. What is the total internal kinetic energy of an object?
8. What is a measure of the amount of heat a material can absorb?
9. What is a measure of an object's thermal resistance?
10. What is a material's ability to conduct heat?
11. What is the total thermal energy that an object can transfer to other objects?
12. What amount of thermal energy is needed to change a solid to a liquid?
13. What amount of thermal energy is needed to change a liquid to a gas?

QUESTIONS

See Teacher's Guide.
MAIN IDEAS

Complete each sentence with the correct word or phrase.

1. Thermal energy is measured in _____.
2. The three methods by which heat is transferred are _____.
3. The method of heat transfer that does not require matter is _____.

4. Thermal energy flows from areas of _____ to _____ temperature.

5. The total R-value of a building is the _____ of the individual R-values for each layer in the building's construction.

6. Heat of fusion is measured in _____.

7. The best conductors are usually _____.

8. A kilocalorie is equal to _____ calories.

9. Specific heat capacity is measured in _____.

10. Water has a specific heat capacity _____ than most other materials.

See Teacher's Guide.

APPLICATIONS

Answer each question in one or more paragraphs. Show how to solve each problem.

1. Explain the difference between heat and temperature.

2. Explain why heat registers are often placed near the floor in a room.

3. Why is it usually warmer on the second floor of a building than on the first?

4. Two sheets of cookies were baked in the same oven at the same time. One cookie sheet was aluminum and the other steel. After baking, the cookies were left on the cookie sheets to cool. The cookies on one of the sheets burned on the bottom. Which cookies burned? Why?

5. How much energy is given off when 150 kg of water in a bathtub cools from 40°C to 25°C?

6. Why is the water in lakes often still cool in late May even though the temperature of the air may be quite warm?

7. Use Table 11–4 to determine the R-value for a roof without insulation. It is made of plywood 2 cm thick and has asphalt shingles over two layers of roofing paper.

8. During a 10 km race a runner produces 1 liter of perspiration. How much energy is removed from the runner's body as the perspiration evaporates?

9. From an energy point or view, which is more efficient, a ranch style or a two-story house? Why? (Assume both houses have the same amount of floor space.)

10. What methods of heat transfer are involved when food is cooked on a charcoal grill? Explain.

FURTHER STUDY

INVESTIGATIONS

1. Inflate two balloons of equal size. Place one in a refrigerator and the other at room temperature. After several hours, compare the balloons. Write a report of your results and conclusions.

2. Ask your doctor what your daily Calorie requirement should be. Determine your average daily Calorie intake. Compare it to your daily Calorie requirement.

3. Use Table 11–4 to determine the R-values of the sidewalls and ceilings in your home. Find out what changes could be made to insulate your home to recommended R-values.

READINGS

+ Albright, Roger, et al. *The Complete Book of Insulating.* Stephen Greene Press: Brattleboro, VT, 1980.

0 Berger, Melvin. *Energy.* Franklin Watts: New York, 1983.

+ McGuigan, Dermot, and Amanda McGuigan. *Heat Pumps.* Garden Way Publishing: Charlotte, VT, 1981.

0 Millard, Reed. *Solar Energy for Tomorrow's World.* Julian Messner: New York, 1980.

− Smay, V. Elaine. "Thinking Window Can Switch Off the Sun." *Popular Science.* March, 1984, pp. 102–104.

PEOPLE use electricity for many purposes. Think of the different ways you use electricity when doing a simple task like laundry. Electric lights, washers, dryers, and irons may be used. You probably seldom spend time without using electricity or being affected by it. Even clothes may have "static electricity" when you remove them from a dryer. How is electricity generated? How can it be used safely?

ELECTRICITY

INTRODUCING THE CHAPTER   Compile a list of uses for electricity. Refer students to the chapter opening photograph to initiate this discussion. Demonstrate static electricity by rubbing an inflated rubber balloon with a piece of wool. (Note: It is difficult to obtain a static charge under conditions of high humidity.) Have students discuss various circumstances that produce static electricity.

12:1   Static Electricity

You probably have walked across a carpeted room and received a shock when you touched a doorknob. You experienced one effect of electricity. To understand electricity, recalling the atomic structure of matter is helpful. Remember that the nuclei of atoms contain protons and, in all elements except hydrogen, neutrons. Around an atom's nucleus is a cloud of electrons. Protons and neutrons stay in the nucleus of an atom. The electrons, however, are relatively free to move from atom to atom. This movement of electrons gives rise to electricity.

As you know, a proton has a positive charge, and a neutron has no net charge. An electron has a negative charge. Normally, any object, including you, has an equal number of protons and electrons so the object has no net charge. When you walk across a nylon carpet while wearing rubber-soled shoes, some electrons are rubbed off the carpet onto you. You gain electrons, but you do not gain any protons. So, you have a net negative charge. Any object that has an unequal number of protons and electrons is said to be charged with **static electricity.** The shock that you hear and feel when you touch a doorknob after walking across a carpet is caused by the excess electrons moving from your hand to the doorknob.

GOAL   You will learn what electricity is, and how it is measured and used.

How does atomic structure account for electricity?

Define static electricity.

SUGGESTION   Point out that the word *static* means stationary or not moving.

247

Electrons are removed more easily from some substances than others. For example, electrons are more easily removed from a nylon carpet than from a shoe with a rubber sole. Objects that give up electrons also gain a static charge. In the example, the carpet you walked across gains a net positive charge because it is left with more protons than electrons. However, the positive charge in the carpet is only temporary. Gradually, electrons will flow from the earth through the walls and floor and balance the excess positive charges in the carpet.

Sometimes the effects of static electricity are a nuisance. Have you ever noticed how clothes sometimes stick together when you take them out of a dryer? As the fabrics rub against each other in the dryer, they become charged. Laundry products that prevent static cling help keep charges balanced by coating the fabric with chemicals that allow electrons to move back to their original positions.

Static electricity also can be helpful. Plastic wraps stick to bowls because of static electricity. As the plastic wrap comes off the roll it acquires some static charge. As it is rubbed and stretched on the bowl, it acquires more charge. Excess electrons tend to leak off objects in the presence of moisture. For this reason, plastic food wraps tend to stick better to dry bowls than wet ones.

As a charge on an object becomes greater, electrons move from the object to air molecules that touch the object's surface. If the static charge on an object is too great, a rapid discharge from the object may occur.

Lightning is an example of a sudden static discharge. Air and water droplets move rapidly within a storm cloud. As a result, regions of very great positive and negative static charges build up. Most lightning occurs within a cloud or between clouds. However, discharges between clouds and the earth's surface cause the most damage. Cloud-to-ground lightning occurs when a negatively-charged cloud induces a positive charge at the earth's surface. When a cloud becomes sufficiently charged, electrons are explosively transferred to the earth's surface.

The amount of electric charge that an object has is measured in **coulombs** (KOO lahms), C. The unit was named in honor of a French scientist, Charles Coulomb (1736–1806). Coulomb was one of the first scientists to investi-

Why are most static charges temporary?

SUGGESTION   Caution students that even small static charges, such as those resulting from static cling, may be hazardous. Tiny sparks can ignite flammable gases and vapors from flammable liquids, such as gasoline.

How can static electricity be useful?

What is lightning?

What units are used to measure electric charge?

gate forces caused by static electricity. One coulomb, 1 C, is defined as the electric charge of 6.25×10^{18} electrons or protons. An object that gains 6.25×10^{18} electrons has a static charge of one coulomb. The object that gave up the electrons also has a charge of one coulomb because it has an excess of 6.25×10^{18} protons.

FIGURE 12-1. Laws of static electricity

Objects with like static charges repel each other.

Objects with opposite static charges attract each other.

Negatively charged balloon repels electrons away from the surface of the wall. The wall's surface then has a net positive charge so balloon "sticks" to the wall.

Charged objects can induce a charge in uncharged objects by attracting or repelling electrons.

Lightning rod

Cable to ground

Electric charges tend to concentrate at points. As a result, charges tend to leak away from pointed objects.

12:2 Current Electricity

Substances such as rubber or glass can hold an electric charge for some time. The charge does not flow away because electrons in most nonmetallic substances like rubber and glass do not readily move from atom to atom. Most nonmetals are insulators.

Electrons can flow easily in most metals. Recall that most metal atoms have one, two, or three electrons in their outer energy levels. These electrons are not held as strongly as electrons in atoms with more electrons in their outer energy levels. So, the electrons in metals are able to move easily from one atom to another. Most metals are conductors. The flow of electrons through a conductor is usually referred to as **current electricity.**

Batteries and generators are sources of electrons to produce electric currents. An ordinary flashlight battery consists of a carbon rod surrounded by a zinc casing. The carbon and zinc are separated by a thick electrolyte paste. When a battery produces electricity, a chemical reaction between the electrolyte and the zinc transfers electrons to the casing of the battery. The bottom of a flashlight battery, where the casing is exposed, is the negative terminal. At the same time, the chemical reaction removes electrons from the carbon rod, which is connected to the top of the battery. The top of the battery is the positive terminal. When a wire is connected to both terminals, the chemical reaction begins.

Electrons flow through the wire because the excess electrons at the negative terminal have higher potential energy than the electrons at the positive terminal. So electric current flows from the negative to the positive terminal. The difference in potential energy between an electron at the negative terminal and one at the positive terminal is called the **potential difference.** Potential difference between the terminals is measured in **volts,** V, in recognition of Alessandro Volta (1748–1827). He was the first scientist to construct a battery. Potential difference often is referred to simply as voltage. An ordinary flashlight battery has a potential difference of about 1.5 volts. The voltage of a car battery is about 12 volts. Most elec-

What kinds of materials are insulators and conductors? Why?

SUGGESTION   Be sure students recognize that only electrons (negative charges) are conducted.

Define current electricity.

FIGURE 12-2.   In atoms of an insulator, outer level electrons are tightly held (a). In atoms of a conductor, outer level electrons are loosely held. Therefore, they are free to move from atom to atom (b).

Insulator

a

Conductor

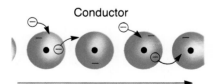

b   Direction of current flow

a Current can flow through each pathway provided by bulbs.

b Current must flow through both bulbs before returning to battery.

c Burned out bulb breaks one pathway but not the other.

d Current cannot pass through the burned-out bulb, so circuit is broken.

FIGURE 12–3. A parallel circuit (a); a series circuit (b); a parallel circuit with a burned-out bulb (c); a series circuit with a burned-out bulb (d)

trical outlets in a home have a potential difference of about 110 volts between the two metal strips inside the holes.

The path through which electricity flows is called a circuit. When one coulomb of electrons flows through a circuit with a potential difference of one volt, they do one joule of work. To get useful work from electric current, some electrical device such as a light bulb or motor must be placed in the circuit.

In Figure 12–3a, electric current that flows through either of the light bulbs does not pass through the other. Figure 12–3a shows a parallel circuit. In a **parallel circuit,** current that passes through each electric device does not have to pass through any others. Figure 12–3b shows a series circuit. In a **series circuit,** current must pass through all the electric devices. In Figure 12–3b, the electric current must pass through all of the light bulbs in the circuit.

When a light bulb burns out, the filament breaks. This means that current can no longer flow through this bulb. In a parallel circuit, if one bulb burns out, as in Figure 12–3c, the other bulb will remain lit because the circuit is still complete. If two bulbs are connected in a series circuit, however, and one burns out, as in Figure 12–3d, the other bulb will not remain lit because the circuit has been broken.

What is a circuit?

SUGGESTION Discuss the meaning of the word *circuit* with students. Note the everyday usage of the word, to mean a closed, circular path.

How do parallel and series circuits differ?

See Teacher's Guide.

REVIEW AND REFLECT

1. Why are most objects not electrically charged?
2. How can an object become positively charged?
3. What are the differences between current electricity and static electricity?
4. Why are wires usually covered with rubber or plastic?
5. Describe what happens at the positive and negative terminals of a battery.
6. Are the lights in your classroom wired in series or parallel? Why?

See Teacher's Guide.

Career Profile

It is 2:00 Saturday morning when Jacqueline Couillard returns to her motel room near Seabrook, New Hampshire. Tired after working a 40 hour week, she still must drive 176 kilometers to her home in Maine to be with her two children for the weekend. Jacqueline would have it no other way though. She loves her work as a journeyman electrician.

After finishing high school, Jacqueline held several jobs as a receptionist. In a job with an electrical contractor, she was given the added responsibility of estimating the cost of electrical work. She enjoyed the work. Soon she applied and was accepted into the International Brotherhood of Electrical Workers. For four years, Jacqueline went to night school to learn her trade. By day she worked a 40 hour week to obtain on-the-job training. After finishing school and accumulating the required 8000 hours of work experience, Jacqueline became certified by the state of Maine.

Jacqueline was very satisfied when the first lighting system she installed really worked. Having a job in which she constantly can see the results of her labor is rewarding. Jacqueline has done most of her work at paper mills and power companies—though shopping malls and hospitals are frequent locations as well. She owns all of her electrical tools. For safety she wears a hard hat and safety glasses.

Jacqueline occasionally returns to the classroom to update her skills. She finds her work challenging and interesting. Each day brings new assignments and new learning opportunities.

12:3 Measuring Electricity

An electric current flowing through a wire can be compared to water flowing in a stream. The current of a stream is a measure of the amount of water flowing past a certain point in a given amount of time. A very small stream's current may be 20 L/s. Twenty liters of water pass the point each second.

Electric current is a measure of the number of electric charges, or coulombs, that pass a given point in a wire each second. The electric current in a wire might be one coulomb per second, 1 C/s. One coulomb, which is 6.25×10^{18} electrons, passes a given point in the wire each second. If a wire has one coulomb of electrons flowing through it per second, we say that it is carrying a current of one ampere (AM pihr), or one "amp". The **ampere, A,** is the unit used to measure electric current. It was named in recognition of André M. Ampère (1775–1836), a French scientist who studied the relationship between electricity and magnetism. Current is usually represented by the letter I in equations and graphs.

A German scientist, Georg Ohm (1787–1854), discovered a relationship among electric current, voltage, and resistance in a circuit. Ohm found that as the potential differ-

How is electric current measured?

What is the symbol for electric current?

SUGGESTION You may want to point out that electrons do not actually "flow" through a wire like water does in a stream, although the analogy is useful to explain many electrical phenomena. Electrons are actually "bumped" from one atom to another. This situation is more analogous to adding a drop of water to a soaked sponge. A drop will leak from the bottom, but it will not be the same drop that was added to the top.

Bulb is brighter.

Voltmeter

Voltage is higher.

Ammeter

More current flows.

FIGURE 12–4. As predicted by Ohm's Law, doubling the voltage in a circuit causes current to double.

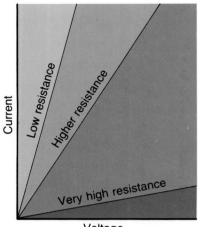

Current

Low resistance

Higher resistance

Very high resistance

Voltage

FIGURE 12–5. The graph shows how the current flowing through a circuit increases as voltage increases. The lower the resistance in the circuit, the faster the current increases.

Describe the relationship between electric current, voltage, and resistance.

BACKGROUND   The unit dimensions of resistance are volts per ampere. Resistance usually is represented by the Greek letter omega, Ω.

ence (voltage) of a circuit is increased, the amount of current flowing through that circuit also is increased. For example, you can double the voltage in a circuit by connecting it to two batteries instead of one, as shown in Figure 12–4. When the voltage is doubled, the current flowing through the circuit also is doubled. Electric current is directly proportional to voltage.

The amount of resistance, R, of the circuit determines how much current can be "pushed" through per volt of potential differrence. **Resistance** is a measure of how much a conductor resists or holds back the flow of electrons. Good conductors have low resistance while poor conductors and insulators have high resistance. Resistance is measured in units called **ohms,** Ω. In Figure 12–5 note that as voltage increases, the current increases more steeply in the circuit having lower resistance. This shows that the current flowing through a circuit is inversely proportional to the resistance in the circuit.

This relationship between electric current, voltage, and resistance is described by Ohm's Law. Ohm's Law states that the amount of electric current flowing in a circuit increases as voltage increases and decreases as resistance increases.

$$current = \frac{voltage}{resistance}$$

$$I = \frac{V}{R}$$

EXAMPLE: Calculating Electric Current

Problem: A circuit has a resistance of 100 ohms and a potential difference of 110 volts. What is the resulting current in the circuit in amperes?

Solution: The current in amperes equals the voltage, which is the potential difference of 110 volts, divided by the resistance of 100 ohms.

$$I = \frac{V}{R}$$

$$I = \frac{110 \text{ V}}{100 \ \Omega}$$

$$I = 1.1 \text{ A}$$

REVIEW AND REFLECT

1. Describe Ohm's Law.
2. A current of 0.2 amperes passes through a lamp with a resistance of 75 ohms. What is the voltage?
3. What are two ways to reduce the amount of current flowing through a circuit? If this were a circuit in your home, which way would be the best? Explain.

Skill Inquiry

Many people are injured each year because of electrical accidents. One out of every eight fires in homes is caused by improper use of electricity or faulty electrical equipment. The major reason for these accidents is a lack of knowledge regarding how electricity works and its safe use. The effects of electric current are dangerous. Severe electric shock can lead to involuntary contraction of chest muscles and abnormal heartbeat. This can cause a person to stop breathing, have a heart attack, and possibly die. The heat generated by high electric current can damage other organs as well.

Because almost everyone uses electricity, knowing how to use it safely is important. For example, electricity should not be used near water. Waterproof cords should be used outdoors. If you see a worn or frayed cord on an electric appliance, the cord should be replaced or repaired. Always disconnect electrical appliances before cleaning or repairing. Pull cords out of wall sockets by grasping the plug, not the wire itself. Avoid using extension cords whenever possible. Never bend or kink cords.

1. If you have an electric lawn mower, when should you avoid mowing?

2. If you see a child yank on an electric cord to remove it from a wall socket, what should you do?

Even when electricity is used safely, accidents may happen. Knowing what to do when problems occur is important, too. Never use water to put out an electrical fire. Use a CO_2 or dry chemical fire extinguisher. Disconnect the electric power when safely possible. Call the fire department or police. If you see downed or broken power lines, call the electric company or police. Do not try to move or touch the wires. If someone receives an electric shock, turn off the power if safely possible. If you cannot turn off the power safely, call the police. Try to remove the person from the source of the shock. Do not touch them directly, but use a wooden stick, rope, or other insulator. Give first aid until medical help arrives.

3. If you see sparks and smoke coming from your toaster at breakfast one morning, what should you do?
4. If, during a storm, you see a power line break and fall on a car outdoors, what should you do?
5. If you get a slight shock when you plug in your vacuum cleaner, what should you do?

Activity: How are circuits different?

See Teacher's Guide.

MATERIALS

insulated hookup wire
6-V lantern battery
2 flashlight bulbs with sockets
ammeter

PROCEDURE

1. Use the wire to connect the bulbs, battery and ammeter as described in the steps below. After each step, record the ammeter reading (current) and your observations of the bulbs. **CAUTION:** *Do not connect the ammeter in any way other than shown here.*
   a. Connect one bulb with the battery and ammeter, shown in Figure 12–6a.
   b. Place another bulb in the circuit as shown in Figure 12–6b.
   c. Carefully unscrew one of the bulbs from its socket. **CAUTION:** *Bulbs may be hot.*
   d. Rearrange the two bulbs as shown in Figure 12–6c.
   e. Carefully unscrew one of the bulbs from its socket.
   f. Screw the loose bulb back into its socket and carefully unscrew the other bulb.
2. Disassemble your circuit.

DATA AND OBSERVATIONS

Step	Current	Observations
1a		
1b		
1c		
1d		
1e		
1f		

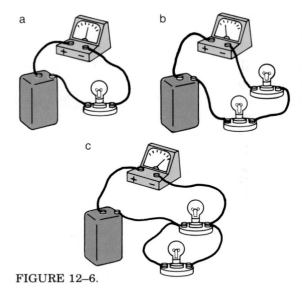

FIGURE 12–6.

QUESTIONS AND CONCLUSIONS

1. Describe the flow of electrons in the circuit in step 1b.
2. Explain your observations in step 1c.
3. What kind of circuit have you constructed in step 1b?
4. Describe the flow of electrons in the circuit in step 1d.
5. What kind of circuit have you constructed in step 1d?
6. In which circuit were the bulbs brightest? dimmest?
7. Explain your observations in step 1e.
8. Compare the current readings in all steps. Explain why the current varies in the way it does.
9. Use Ohm's Law, your current readings, and the rated voltage of your battery to calculate the resistance of the circuits in steps 1a, 1b, and 1d. Explain why the resistances of these circuits differ in the way they do.

12:4 Using Electricity

Electric current flowing through any conductor produces heat. As the current flowing in a conductor increases, so does the heat produced. Electrical wiring in homes and other buildings must be designed to carry all the current needed without overheating. If too much current is allowed to flow through a circuit, the circuit is said to be overloaded. Overloaded wiring may overheat and cause a fire.

A short circuit is one way an overload may occur. When a frayed appliance cord allows two wires to touch, the current can then bypass the appliance as shown in Figure 12–7a. The circuit now has very little resistance because the low-resistance wiring provides the only resistance. As resistance decreases, the amount of current flowing through a circuit increases.

A similar situation occurs when too many electrical devices are connected to a parallel circuit, as shown in Figure 12–7b. As each device is added to the circuit, more pathways for current to flow are available. An overload occurs when the amount of current used by all the devices exceeds the safe limits of the circuit. To prevent overheating and fires caused by circuit overloads, buildings have fuses or circuit breakers. The operation of each of these devices is shown in Figure 12–8. "Blown" fuses and "thrown" circuit breakers prevent the flow of too much current by breaking a circuit.

How can a short circuit occur?

BACKGROUND Since $I = \dfrac{V}{R}$, current increases as resistance decreases.

How can wiring be protected from overloads?

FIGURE 12–7. A short circuit creates a current pathway of very low resistance (a). As each appliance is turned on, a new current pathway is created (b). Both situations can cause too much current to flow in a circuit, resulting in an overload.

a

b

Fuse box

Fuse box

a

b

FIGURE 12–8. The fuse element is made of a metal that melts quickly during an overload, breaking the circuit (a). When the circuit breaker "trips" during an overload, two metal contacts are pulled apart by springs to break the circuit (b).

What type of electrical devices usually use the most energy?

Define electric power.

ACTIVITY Obtain a copy of local electrical safety codes for homebuilders. Have students examine some of these codes and discuss why they are needed. You may want to discuss ideas for bringing older buildings up to modern electrical standards.

Recall that when electrons move through a circuit, they give up energy by doing work. Electric devices use energy at different rates. A color television may use more energy per second than a small lamp. A toaster uses more energy per second than a TV. In general, electric devices that change the energy of flowing electrons into thermal energy—devices such as hair dryers or toasters—use energy at the most rapid rates.

Electric devices are rated in watts according to the amount of energy per second they need to operate. Recall that power is the rate at which work is done or energy is used. The watt is the unit for measuring power. **Electric power** is a measure of the rate at which the energy of flowing electrons is used. A current of one ampere flowing through a circuit with a potential difference of one volt produces one watt of power. Power is equal to the amount of current flowing through a circuit times the voltage.

EXAMPLE: Calculating Power

Problem: At 110 volts, 0.25 amperes of current flow through a small black-and-white TV. How much power is used by the TV?

Solution: The power in watts is equal to the current of 0.25 A multiplied by the voltage of 110 V.

$$P = IV$$
$$P = 0.25 \text{ A} \times 110 \text{ V}$$
$$P = 27.5 \text{ W}$$

An electric company charges its customers for the amount of energy they use. The total amount of energy used depends on two factors. The first is power—how fast the electrical devices consume energy. The second is time—how long the devices are used. Therefore, the energy a device uses is equal to its power multiplied by the time it is on.

$$\text{energy} = \text{power} \times \text{time}$$
$$\text{energy} = Pt$$

For example, a 100-watt light bulb left on for one hour uses 100 watt-hours of energy. A watt-hour is a relatively small amount of energy. For this reason, electric energy is usually measured in kilowatt-hours, kWh. A kilowatt-hour is equal to 1000 watt-hours. Electric companies measure the amount of electric energy customers use with a kilowatt-hour meter. Electric bills are figured on a price per kilowatt-hour.

Example: Calculating Electric Energy Used

Problem: How much energy is used by a 750-watt room air conditioner in 8 hours?

Solution: The energy used is equal to the power, which is 750 watts, multiplied by the time, which is 8 hours.

$$\begin{aligned} \text{energy} &= Pt \\ &= 750 \text{ W} \times 8 \text{ h} \\ &= 6000 \text{ Wh} \\ &= 6 \text{ kWh} \end{aligned}$$

See Teacher's Guide.

REVIEW AND REFLECT

1. Describe two ways in which circuits may become overloaded.
2. What factors affect the amount of energy used by an electric appliance?
3. How much energy is used by a 500 W toaster if it is on for 6 minutes a day for 250 days?
4. If the cost of electricity is $0.07 per kWh, what would it cost to use a 4 W night light 8 h a night for a year?
5. Why do housing codes require that large appliances, such as electric dryers and ranges, each be on separate circuits?

FIGURE 12–9. Energy usage by an electric device depends on its power rating and the length of time it is used. The radio may use energy at the rate of 10 watts but may be left on for a long time. The power rating of the toaster may be 500 watts, but a toaster is used only a few minutes a day.

How do electric companies measure electric energy used?

ACTIVITY   Find out from your local power company the cost per kWh. If you have difficulty obtaining this information, use 10¢ per kWh. Have students calculate hypothetical electric bills.

12:5 Magnetism and Electricity

In 1820, Hans Christian Oersted noticed that the needle of a compass was deflected when placed near a wire carrying an electric current. Oersted's observation demonstrated the existence of a magnetic field around the wire. Any moving electric charge produces a magnetic field. This magnetic field can be increased by forming the wire into a coil as shown in Figure 12–12. Placing an iron core, such as a nail, through the wire coil causes the magnetic field to become more intense. A wire coiled many times around an iron core forms an electromagnet. Electromagnets differ from permanent magnets, such as bar magnets or compass needles. When the electric current is turned off, electromagnets are no longer magnetic. Some important uses of electromagnets are shown in Figure 12–10. The magnetic field around a wire carrying an electric current is used to make an electric motor turn. An electric motor is one kind of device that uses a magnetic field to change electrical energy to mechanical energy.

How are electricity and magnetism related?

FIGURE 12–10. Examples of devices that use electromagnets in their operation include: scrapyard crane (a), television (b), stereo speaker (c), automatic washer (d), phonograph cartridge (e), automobile alternator and control relays (f).

a

b

c

d

e

f

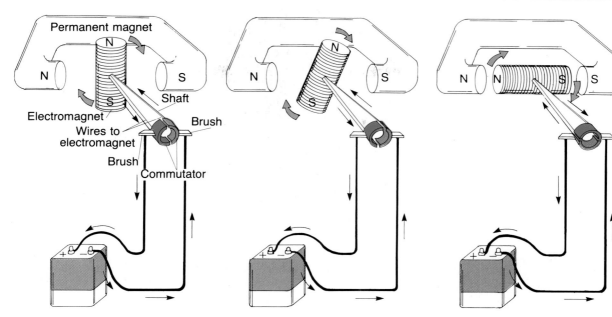

Permanent magnet

N

S

Shaft

Electromagnet

S

Brush

Wires to
electromagnet

Brush

Commutator

To understand how a motor works, look at Figure 12–11. An electromagnet is attached to the motor shaft between the poles of a permanent magnet. When current passes through the coil, the ends of the electromagnet become opposite magnetic poles, depending on the direction of the current flow. The electromagnet will turn to align with opposite poles of the permanent magnet. If nothing else happened, the motor would simply stop turning. What if the direction of the current flow could be reversed just as the electromagnet becomes aligned? The poles of the electromagnet would then reverse. It would continue turning to align itself in the opposite direction. At that point, the current would reverse once more and the electromagnet would continue turning. As long as the current switching occurred, the motor would continue to turn and be able to do useful work. In electric motors, current switching is done by a device called a commutator, shown in Figure 12–11. A set of brushes deliver current to the commutator. As the motor turns, the contacts between the commutator sections and the brushes continually reverse. This causes the current direction in the electromagnet to continually reverse. As a result, the motor continues to turn.

FIGURE 12–11. A simple electric motor is shown. As the poles of the electromagnet line up with the poles of the permanent magnet, each commutator ring contacts a different brush. This reverses the current flow to the electromagnet, causing the poles to switch.

How does an electric motor work?

BACKGROUND All magnetism is believed to be produced by electric current. The magnetic field of a bar magnet is thought to be caused by the motion of electrons as they spin on their axes. In certain (magnetic) materials, electrons tend to spin in the same direction within small regions known as domains. This produces the magnetic effect found in iron and certain alloys.

Activity: What affects the strength of an electromagnet?

See Teacher's Guide.

MATERIALS

2 or 3 long nails
enameled wire
insulated hookup wire

3 1½-V batteries
paper clips
sandpaper

PROCEDURE

1. Wind 50 turns of wire around one nail. Use the sandpaper to remove the enamel insulation from the ends of the wire.
2. Connect the ends of the wire to one battery as shown. **CAUTION:** *The wires leading from the coil to the battery may become hot.*
3. Record how many paper clips can be lifted with the electromagnet. Disconnect the electromagnet from the battery. Note what happens.
4. Predict how many paper clips your electromagnet will pick up if one and then two additional batteries are used.
5. Add a second battery in series with the first as shown. Record the number of paper clips that can be picked up with two batteries.
6. Now add a third battery in series with the first two. Record the number of paper clips that can be picked up with three batteries.
7. Using two batteries, make an electromagnet by wrapping 50 turns of wire around two nails. Record the number of paper clips that can be picked up.
8. Repeat step 7 using two batteries and three nails.
9. Using two batteries, make three more electromagnets by wrapping 75, 100, and 150 turns of wire around one nail. Record the number of paper clips each electromagnet will lift.

Free lead 50 cm

FIGURE 12–12.

DATA AND OBSERVATIONS

Nails						
Wire Turns						
Batteries						
Paper Clips Lifted						

QUESTIONS AND CONCLUSIONS

1. What units did you use to measure the strength of your electromagnet?
2. What happens to the strength of an electromagnet as
   a. the voltage increases?
   b. the mass of the core increases?
   c. the number of turns in the coil increases?
3. Powerful electric motors usually are large. Based on the results of this experiment, why do you think this is so?
4. The strength of an electromagnet depends on current, not voltage. How can you explain your answer to question 2a?

12:6 Generating Electricity

You know that an electric current moving through a wire produces a magnetic field. Likewise, when a wire moves through a magnetic field, an electric current flows in the wire. A generator produces electricity by turning coils of wire in a magnetic field.

In hydroelectric power plants, water is released from behind a dam. The water flows through the blades of a turbine, causing them to turn. The movement of the blades causes coils of wire in a large generator to turn in a magnetic field, producing electricity. Most electric power plants burn fuel, such as coal, to produce steam. Steam is used to turn the blades of turbines that are connected to generators.

The electric current produced by power plants changes direction as the coil of wire rotates through the magnetic field. Current that reverses direction is called **alternating current**, AC. The current produced by a battery flows steadily from one terminal to another. This current is called **direct current**, DC. Alternating current has completed one cycle when it has reversed twice and resumed its original direction. In the United States, power plants generate electric current at 60 cycles per second. One cycle per second is one hertz, Hz. Electric current alternates at a rate of 60 hertz.

Electricity is carried to homes and businesses over power lines. Electric current is transmitted most efficiently at high voltages. The voltage is increased by "step up" transformers for transmission. A **transformer** is a device that changes the voltage of alternating current. Then the voltage is reduced by "step down" transformers before it is used. See Figure 12–13.

See Teacher's Guide.

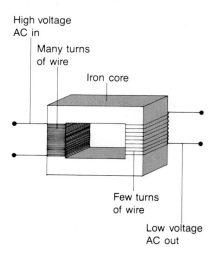

High voltage
AC in

Many turns
of wire

Iron core

Few turns
of wire

Low voltage
AC out

FIGURE 12–13. A step down transformer is shown. Transformers consist of coils of wire wrapped around the same iron core. How the voltage is changed depends on the number of turns of wire on each coil.

How does a generator produce electricity?

BACKGROUND   The hertz is named in honor of German physicist Heinrich R. Hertz (1857–1894), who is best known for his work with electromagnetic waves.

Why are transformers used?

REVIEW AND REFLECT

1. How is an electromagnet different from a bar magnet?
2. Name a common device that contains an electromagnet. Explain how it works.
3. What is the basic purpose of a commutator?
4. How are direct and alternating currents different?
5. How are electric motors and generators similar?

What is happening to demand for electric energy?

12:7 Choices: Electricity Use

Demand for electricity increases with each generation of people. It has been predicted that people will use three to six times more electric energy by the year 2000 than we use today. In order to meet the increasing demand for electricity, electric companies have built additional power plants. The capacities of existing power plants have also been increased to meet demands.

The increased production of electricity has caused environmental problems. For example, coal is a main source of energy for production of electricity. Burning coal pollutes the air with particulates and dangerous gases. Coal contains sulfur. When coal is burned, sulfur oxides combine with moisture in the atmosphere. Sulfuric acid is formed. It returns to the earth as acid rain. (See pages 134–135.) As more and more coal is burned to produce electricity, these environmental problems increase.

Nuclear power plants produce electricity, too. Use of nuclear fuels produces highly radioactive wastes. The wastes are very dangerous and remain radioactive for thousands

FIGURE 12–14. Hot water inside a cooling tower is cooled by large fans (a). The water is cooled further as it passes over cascades on the outside of the tower (b).

a

b

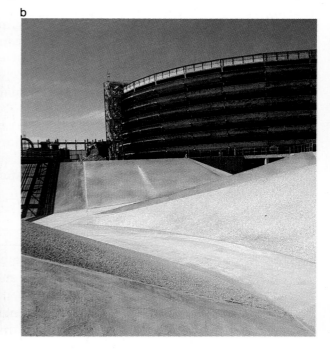

of years. Exposure to the wastes can cause sickness and death. As more and more electricity is produced from nuclear fuels, more and more dangerous wastes are produced.

Both coal and nuclear power plants require a great deal of water for cooling turbines, after the steam passes through them. For this reason, power plants usually are located near waterways. Water is taken from the waterway, used for cooling, and then returned. Thermal pollution occurs when water returned to a waterway is at a higher temperature than when it was removed. Thermal pollution can produce changes in the ecology of the waterway. Some aquatic organisms cannot survive in the warmer water.

Why is thermal pollution from power plants a problem?

To prevent thermal pollution, some power plants have cooling towers. Before returning water to a waterway, it is pumped to the cooling tower where it falls over a series of cascades. An updraft of air cools the water as it falls over the cascades, transferring the heat in the water to the air. The cooled water then can be returned safely to a waterway.

Because of the environmental problems caused by generating electricity from coal and nuclear power plants and because our supply of these fuels is somewhat limited, alternative methods of electricity generation are gaining importance. Hydroelectric power plants produce about one fourth of the world's electricity outside the United States. Some cities have trash-burning power plants. Many people feel more time and money should be spent to develop new technology for electricity generation, such as solar and wind.

Why are scientists searching for alternate methods of generating electricity?

See Teacher's Guide.

REVIEW AND REFLECT

1. Why is demand for electric energy increasing and how will the demand be met?
2. What are some environmental problems associated with increased production of electric energy?
3. What fuel is used to produce the most electricity?
4. Interview a parent and a grandparent or someone their approximate ages regarding the use of electricity. Report how their use of electric energy differs from yours.

CHAPTER 12 REVIEW

SUMMARY

1. Many objects can become charged with static electricity. 12:1
2. The effects of static charges can be both useful as well as a nuisance. 12:1
3. Current electricity differs from static electricity. 12:2
4. Substances are either insulators or conductors of electric current. 12:2
5. The relationship among current, resistance, and voltage in a circuit is described by Ohm's Law. 12:3
6. The total amount of energy used by electric devices depends on power and time. 12:4
7. The rate at which electric energy is used is measured in watts. 12:4
8. Electric companies base customer's bills on the number of kilowatt-hours used. 12:4
9. Any moving electric charge produces a magnetic field. 12:5
10. The magnetic field around a current-carrying wire can be used to make an electric motor. 12:5
11. The electromagnetic effect can also be used to generate an electric current. 12:6
12. The two types of electric current are direct and alternating. 12:6

VOCABULARY

alternating current 1	electric power 13	series circuit 12
ampere 3	ohms 7	static electricity 5
coulombs 4	parallel circuit 10	transformer 14
current electricity 6	potential difference 2	volts 8
direct current 11	resistance 9	

Choose a word or phrase from the list to complete each sentence correctly.

1. _____ reverses its direction at a rate of 60 Hz.
2. The difference in potential energy that causes electrons to flow from negative to positive is called _____.
3. A(n) _____ is a measure of the number of electrons flowing past a point in a given amount of time.
4. The amount of electric charge that an object has is measured in _____.
5. _____ results from an object having an unequal number of electrons and protons.
6. The movement of electrons through a conductor is called _____.

7. Resistance is measured in _____.
8. Potential difference is measured in _____.
9. _____ is a measure of the degree to which a conductor holds back the movement of electrons.
10. In a(n) _____, electric current that passes through each electric device does not have to pass through any others.
11. _____ flows in only one direction.
12. In a(n) _____, electric current must pass through all of the electric devices in order to complete the circuit.
13. A measure of the rate at which the energy of flowing electrons is used is _____.
14. A(n) _____ is a device used to change the voltage of alternating current.

QUESTIONS

MAIN IDEAS

Choose the correct answer to complete each sentence.

1. Electricity is caused by the movement of (*protons, electrons, neutrons, static*).

2. An object with an unequal number of (*protons and electrons, protons and neutrons, neutrons and electrons*) has a static charge.

3. Most metals are (*conductors, transformers, resistors, insulators*).

4. The best insulators are (*metals, nonmetals, metalloids, conductors*).

5. The path through which electricity flows is a (*coulomb, circuit, hertz, current*).

6. If one light bulb in a circuit burns out, but the other bulb remains lit, the circuit must be a (*series, parallel, short, overloaded*) circuit.

7. Electric current is measured in (*amperes, volts, ohms, coulombs*).

8. A circuit that has a current of 2 A and a voltage of 120 V has a resistance of (*120Ω, 240Ω, 60Ω, 2Ω*).

9. Electric power is measured in (*A, W, Ω, V*).

10. A 1500 W electric dryer draws (*125, 12.5, 1.25, 0.125*) A current at 120 V.

APPLICATIONS

See Teacher's Guide.

Answer each question in one or more paragraphs. Show how to solve each problem.

1. Why are static electric effects less noticeable during humid weather?

2. A lamp has a resistance of 240 ohms. At 120 volts, how many watts of power does the light bulb use?

3. A family's monthly electric bill is $38.48. If their electric company charges $0.08 per kWh, how much electric energy did the family use?

4. A factory uses 500 40-watt light bulbs for 16 hours per day. If they pay $0.09 per kWh what is the cost to light the factory per day? If the company operates 250 days each year, how much money would the factory save per year if 30-watt bulbs were used instead of 40-watt bulbs?

5. Why is it unwise to replace a 15-ampere fuse with a 20-ampere fuse?

6. What would be the effect on the current if the voltage in a circuit is doubled?

7. If the voltage and the resistance in a circuit are both increased five times, what would be the effect on the current in the circuit?

FURTHER STUDY

INVESTIGATIONS

1. Through library research, find out how a xerographic copier works. Prepare a poster showing the operation of this type of copier.

2. Prepare a report on some of the main electrical rules that builders must follow during construction of a new house. Explain the reasons for each of these rules.

3. Prepare a poster showing the ways that electromagnets are used in sound recording and reproduction.

READINGS

+ Bolton, W. *Basic Electricity and Magnetism.* Butterworths: Boston, 1980.

0 Branley, F. M. *The Electromagnetic Spectrum.* Thomas Y. Crowell: New York, 1979.

0 Leon, George deLucenay. *The Electricity Story.* Arco Publishing: New York, 1983.

0 Lindsley, E. F. "Programmable DC Motor." *Popular Science.* March, 1984. pp. 38–42.

+ Math, Irwin. *Wires and Watts.* Charles Scribner's Sons: New York, 1981.

Do you play a musical instrument? You probably know that different instruments produce different sounds. All sounds are alike in some ways, though. Sounds are produced by vibrations. The sounds of a flute, your voice, and traffic all are produced by vibrations. What makes sounds different? How are sounds transmitted?

WAVES AND SOUND

INTRODUCING THE CHAPTER Construct a "sound visualizer" to initiate a discussion of waves and sound. Cut both ends out of a soup can. Glue a 1 cm^2 piece of a flat mirror to a piece of latex (a rubber glove or balloon). Stretch the rubber over one end of the can and secure with a rubber band. The mirror should be slightly off-center since this is a nodal point. Darken the room and shine a bright light (projector bulb) at the mirror so that the reflection is projected on a screen. Sing a scale or shout into the open end of the can. Observe the patterns formed on the screen from the vibrations.

13:1 Waves

If you throw a pebble into a lake, waves move outward in all directions. The action of wind also produces waves in lakes and the oceans. Recall from chapter 11 that thermal energy can be transferred by waves. All waves transfer energy.

In Figure 13–1, as the wind blows, the waves move toward the shore. The water and the bobbers floating on it do not. The bobbers move only up and down as each wave passes because waves transfer energy, not matter. Energy is the ability to produce motion or change. Because the bobbers move up and down, we know that energy is being transferred. Some of the energy that is transferred to the water from the wind is transferred to the bobbers by the waves.

Study the features of the waves shown in Figure 13–1. Notice that the crests and troughs are perpendicular to the direction of the wave travel itself. Waves of this type are called **transverse waves.** The height of a transverse wave depends on how much energy the wave is carrying. Waves with more energy have higher crests and deeper troughs. For transverse waves, the height of a crest or the depth of a trough is called the **amplitude.** For example, tiny ripples carry little energy and have small amplitudes. Tidal waves carry great amounts of energy and have very large amplitudes.

GOAL You will learn some principles of waves and how they relate to the production and transmission of sound.

What do waves transfer?

DEMONSTRATION Explain this concept using a small aquarium of water and a bobber.

What are transverse waves?

269

FIGURE 13–1. As the waves travel toward shore, the bobber and bait move up and down only. This motion shows that while the wave's energy passes through the water, the water is not carried along with it.

SUGGESTION   Remind students that hertz, Hz, is in units of cycles per second.

How is the velocity of a wave calculated?

The distance between two successive crests or two successive troughs is a measure of the length of one wave. This distance, called the wavelength, is represented by the Greek letter lambda, λ. The wavelength of waves in the ocean may be as much as 30 meters. Waves caused by a tiny fish splashing in an aquarium may have wavelengths of only a few centimeters.

Another feature of wave motion is frequency. Frequency, f, refers to the number of times an event repeats itself in a unit of time. Each repetition is called a cycle. Frequency is measured in cycles per second or hertz, Hz. Recall from chapter 12 that alternating current commonly has a frequency of 60 hertz. You may tune your radio to a station broadcasting radio waves having a frequency of 850 kilohertz.

The frequency of a wave can be found by counting the number of crests (or troughs) that pass a given point in one second. If one wave crest passes a given point each second, the frequency of the wave is one cycle per second, or one hertz. If two wave crests pass a point in one second, the frequency is two hertz. If 12 crests pass in three seconds, the frequency is four hertz. Notice that the frequency of a wave is found by dividing the number of wave crests that pass a point by the time, in seconds, required for the waves to pass.

How fast a wave is moving can be found by measuring the frequency and the wavelength. The velocity of a wave is equal to its wavelength multiplied by its frequency:

$$\text{velocity} = \text{wavelength} \times \text{frequency}$$
$$v = \lambda \times f$$

If a wave has a frequency of one hertz, then one wave passes a given point in one second. If the wavelength of each wave is one meter, its velocity must be one meter per second.

EXAMPLE: Calculating Wave Velocity

Problem: A boat is tied to a stake in a lake. The frequency of the waves passing beneath the boat is 3.0 Hz. The wavelength of the waves is 1.5 m. What is the velocity of the waves?

Solution: The frequency of the waves is 3.0 Hz, which means that three waves pass the boat each second. The length of each wave is 1.5 m, so waves must be passing the boat at a rate of 4.5 meters each second

$$v = \lambda \times f$$
$$= 1.5 \text{ m} \times 3.0 \text{ Hz}$$
$$= 4.5 \text{ m/s}$$

13:2 Reflection and Interference

If you play billiards, you know the importance of predicting the angle at which the ball will bounce away from the rail. Regardless of the angle at which the ball strikes the rail, it is reflected away at an equal angle but in the opposite direction, as shown in Figure 13–2.

When waves strike a barrier, they may be reflected in the same way as the billiard ball is reflected from the rail. The Law of Reflection states that the angle at which a wave strikes a barrier is equal to the angle at which the wave is reflected away from the barrier. When waves strike an object, some of their energy may do work rather than be reflected. Water waves may do work wearing away beaches and shorelines. The wave energy that is not absorbed doing work is reflected.

Two or more waves traveling along different paths can pass through one another without being changed. At the point where two waves meet, however, they interact. This interaction is called **interference.**

Waves traveling in the same path but in opposite directions also interfere. If waves are sent continuously along a

FIGURE 13–2. When a billiard ball without sidespin strikes a table rail, its angle of reflection is equal to the angle of incidence (the angle at which it strikes). Note that these angles are measured against the normal, a line perpendicular to the surface.

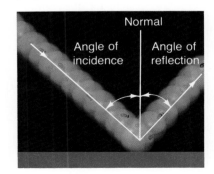

FIGURE 13–3. Two waves traveling in opposite directions can pass through each other. If two crests or two troughs meet, their energies add to produce momentarily a single wave of greater amplitude. This is called constructive interference (a). If a crest meets a trough, their energies subtract and the waves cancel each other. This is called destructive interference (b).

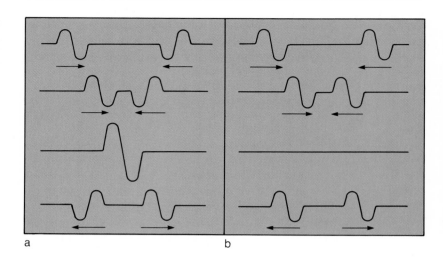

a   b

string that is attached at one end, the waves strike the fastened end and reflect back along the string. The reflected waves and the incoming waves interfere both constructively and destructively as they pass through one another. If the string is attached at both ends, the waves will continue to reflect back and forth. At certain frequencies, the string will show interference patterns in which waves seem to vibrate up and down but do not appear to travel back and forth along the string. These patterns are called **standing waves.** See Figure 13–4. A guitar string is attached at both ends. Plucking the string causes it to vibrate at frequencies that produce standing waves. When disturbed, any object will tend to absorb energy by vibrating at frequencies that produce standing waves. These frequencies are called the natural frequencies of the object. For a string, the natural frequencies depend on its length, mass, and tension. See Figure 13–11 on page 280.

Standing waves, however, are not always musical or helpful. Sometimes destructive amounts of energy build up. In high winds, power and telephone wires often break as the wind's energy causes the wires to vibrate in standing wave patterns. In 1940, winds caused standing waves to destroy a new suspension bridge in the state of Washington. In one large city, the balcony of a large arena was closed during rock concerts. Safety officers were concerned that standing waves built up by the foot-stamping audience would cause the balcony to collapse.

What frequencies produce standing waves?

FIGURE 13–4. Some of the standing wave patterns of a vibrating string are shown. The simplest one (top) is called the fundamental. The other strings (below) are vibrating at resonant frequencies of 2, 3, and 4 times the fundamental frequency. The nodes labeled N are points that do not move as the string vibrates.

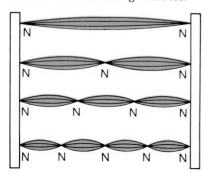

Activity: How do waves behave?

MATERIALS

coil spring, 10 cm diameter (Slinky™)
meter stick
goggles

PROCEDURE

1. Work with a partner. Stretch the spring a distance of 10 meters across a smooth floor. **CAUTION:** *Do not let go of the spring while it is stretched.*

2. Produce a single wave pulse by shaking your end from side to side one time. Note what happens when the pulse reaches the stationary end of the spring. Repeat several times and record your observations.

3. Make the spring tighter by gathering several coils into your hand. Repeat step 2 and note any differences.

4. Repeat step 2 but increase the amplitude by shaking the spring farther from side to side.

5. Repeat step 2, but vary the wavelength of the pulses by shaking the spring slower and faster.

6. Produce continuous waves by shaking the spring with a constant rhythm. Vary the frequency and observe the wavelengths.

7. Have your partner hold the end of the spring very tightly. Shake your end and vary the frequency until the spring vibrates in one large wave. Increase the frequency until the spring vibrates in two sections. Try to get the spring to vibrate in three or more sections.

DATA AND OBSERVATIONS

Step	Observations
2	
3	
4	
5	
6	
7	

QUESTIONS AND CONCLUSIONS

1. Based on your observations, how do waves behave when they reach a barrier?

2. Review your observations in steps 3, 4 and 5. What had the most effect on the speed of wave travel? What had little or no effect?

3. In step 6, how did the frequency and wavelength relate to each other?

4. What kinds of waves were produced in step 7? What do we call the frequencies that produced these wave patterns?

5. Recall how shaking the spring felt when you found the frequencies that produced single, double, and triple waves in step 7. Did it seem easier to produce those frequencies than other frequencies? How can you explain this observation?

FIGURE 13–5.

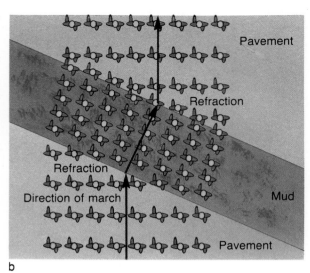

a
b

FIGURE 13–6. If the drill team marches straight across the mud, they are only slowed down for a moment (a). If they march into the mud at an angle, however, the direction of march is "refracted" (b). The same effect occurs when waves pass into a material that slows them down.

Explain refraction.

What is diffraction?

BACKGROUND   Some sound usually is reflected off other objects to the person behind the tree.

13:3   Refraction and Diffraction

Waves travel with different velocities in different substances. When waves pass from one substance to another at an angle, they change direction because of the change in velocity. **Refraction** is the bending of waves as they pass from one substance into another. The amount of refraction depends on the properties of the two substances.

To understand how refraction occurs, consider Figure 13–6. Each row of the drill team can be thought of as a wave crest or trough. As the drill team marches from pavement into mud, the team members are slowed down. Suppose the drill team encounters the boundary between the pavement and the mud at an angle. The first members in a row to reach the mud will be slowed down. The others in that row are still marching at the same speed. Therefore, the row is bent, or refracted. Note that as the drill team marches back onto the pavement, it is refracted again but in the opposite direction.

Waves also bend as they pass the edges of objects in their path. This type of bending is called **diffraction.** You can talk to someone who is standing behind a tree because sound waves bend as they pass the sides of the tree. Waves are diffracted when they pass through openings, too. Sound waves passing through a door diffract. For this reason, people in another room may hear you call them even though they cannot see you.

See Teacher's Guide.

REVIEW AND REFLECT

1. What is transported by waves?
2. Draw a diagram of a transverse wave and label its features.
3. If a wave has a frequency of 120 Hz and a wavelength of 1 cm, what is its velocity?
4. What causes refraction?
5. Why do you think engineers must consider resonant frequencies and standing waves when they design the springs of an automobile?

13:4 Sound Waves

Striking a drum transfers energy to the drumhead, causing it to vibrate. The vibrating drumhead transfers energy to air molecules. As the drumhead moves in an upward direction, it compresses the air directly above it by pushing the molecules closer together. As the drumhead moves downward, the air molecules become more loosely packed. We say they become rarefied. As the molecules of air collide with other air molecules, they transfer energy to them. In this way, the compressions and rarefactions of molecules move away from the drumhead in all directions. Sounds are compressional waves. A **compressional wave** is a series of compressions and rarefactions traveling through matter.

Compressional waves, like transverse waves, have frequencies, wavelengths, and amplitudes. The amplitude of

Explain compressional waves.

FIGURE 13–7. A vibrating object produces sound as compressional waves (a). Sound waves have features similar to transverse waves (b). The sound wave pictured at the top has a higher frequency, shorter wavelength, and greater amplitude than the one at the bottom. We would say the top sound is higher pitched and louder than the bottom sound.

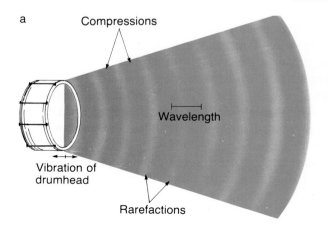

a

Compressions

Wavelength

Vibration of drumhead

Rarefactions

b Louder, high-pitched sound

Softer, low-pitched sound

Wavelength

What determines the amplitude of sound?

DEMONSTRATION Stretch a Slinky®, then pinch together several coils and release. A compressional wave pulse will be formed and move along the stretched spring.

BACKGROUND Audible comes from the Latin word *audire,* which means to hear.

Explain the term ultrasound.

a sound depends on the energy of the compressional wave created by the vibrating object. The energy (amplitude) of a sound wave depends on how much the matter carrying the wave is compressed or rarefied by each vibration. Sound waves of greater amplitude seem louder than sounds of less amplitude. The frequency of a sound wave is the same as the frequency of the vibration that produces the sound. The wavelength is the distance between successive compressions or rarefactions.

Most people are able to hear sounds that have frequencies between about 20 and 20 000 hertz. These sounds are within the **audible range** for people. Sounds with frequencies between 20 and 20 000 hertz have wavelengths between about 17 meters and 1.7 centimeters. The higher the frequency of a sound, the shorter its wavelength is.

The audible range for dogs includes sounds of much higher frequency. Some dogs can hear sounds with frequencies of 50 000 hertz. A dog whistle, audible to dogs but not to humans, produces a sound with a frequency greater than 20 000 hertz. Sounds with frequencies greater than 20 000 hertz are referred to as ultrasounds. The Latin word, *ultra,* means beyond. Bats can hear sounds with frequencies as high as 100 000 hertz. Bats can avoid obstacles by emitting high frequency sounds and listening to the reflection, or echo, of the sounds.

13:5 How Sounds Are Produced

All sounds are produced by vibrations. Objects may vibrate when energy is put into them. Many musical sounds are produced by vibrating strings. The vibrations of a string alone do not produce very loud sounds. For this reason, most stringed instruments have a sounding board or must be electronically amplified. The sounding board of a violin is its body. The energy of the vibrating strings is transferred to the sounding board through a small piece of wood called the bridge. See Figure 13–8. The vibration of the string causes the sounding board to vibrate at the same frequency producing louder and richer sound.

FIGURE 13–8. In a violin, the strings are made to vibrate by plucking or rubbing them with the bow. The vibrations are passed to the top plate by the bridge and to the back by the soundpost.

Tuning pegs

Bridge

Sound post

Bass bar

Top plate

The mass, length, and tension of a string affect the frequency at which it vibrates. Thicker strings have more mass and produce sounds at lower frequencies. As the tension of the string increases, the frequency at which it vibrates also increases. Stringed instruments are tuned by turning screws to adjust the tension of the strings. Some instruments, such as harps and pianos, have strings that vary not only in tension and thickness, but also in length. When the string of a violin is plucked, a standing wave is produced. The string can be shortened by placing a finger on the string and pushing it down onto the fingerboard, effectively shortening the length of the standing wave. As a result, the frequency of the sound wave is increased. Recall from section 13:1 that sounds with shorter wavelengths have higher frequencies.

Sounds can be produced when columns of air vibrate. Blowing air across the top of a bottle produces a column of vibrating air in the bottle. Many musical instruments produce sound by causing a column of air to vibrate. Generally, wind instruments are classified into two categories: woodwinds and brass instruments. In most woodwind instruments, the vibrating air column is produced by blowing air across one or two reeds. Musicians produce sound in brass wind instruments by blowing air through their lips causing a vibrating air column in the instrument.

Your vocal cords work in much the same way. When you sing, you control how high or low your voice is by increasing or decreasing the tension of your vocal cords. When they are relaxed, low sounds are produced. Sounds of higher frequency are produced by increasing the tension of your vocal cords.

FIGURE 13–9. A pipe organ produces musical sounds by causing columns of air to vibrate. The length of the pipe determines the standing wave produced, and thus the pitch of the tone.

How is the sound of the human voice produced?

See Teacher's Guide.

REVIEW AND REFLECT

1. What is the audible range that most people can hear?
2. What two conditions are necessary for sound to be produced?
3. What is ultrasound?
4. Why are the bodies of most electric guitars solid instead of hollow like other guitars?

Career Profile

As a very young boy in Japan, Akira Kagawa liked to listen to his mother and brother play the piano. He was fascinated with the work of the person who tuned their piano. After moving to Los Angeles, California, Akira took a class in piano technology at the University of California. Soon he began an apprenticeship with his instructor to learn still more about the piano.

Today, Akira tunes about four pianos a day for a piano dealer in Los Angeles. He finds that the work takes much concentration and patience.

Akira carries a toolcase with tuning tools. He uses a method of piano tuning known as equal temperament. He begins by using a metal tuning fork A, which vibrates at 440 hertz. Then, he matches the pitch of the piano string A above middle C to the tuning fork, using a tuning hammer to turn the tuning pin to adjust the string tension. If the vibration of the string A is not exactly 440 hertz, he can hear the beats pro-

duced when the string and the fork are sounded together. He adjusts the string until no beats can be heard. Next, he tunes the A an octave below until there are no beats. Then he builds up the scale one note at a time.

Akira believes that being a musician is not necessary in his work. However, his musical ability provides him with satisfaction toward his work. He is a flutist in the Japanese Harmonic Orchestra of Los Angeles. According to Akira, a person needs to tune at least 5000 pianos before becoming good at it. Akira would like to start his own piano tuning business someday.

13:6 Pitch and the Doppler Effect

Have you ever sung a musical scale—Do Re Mi Fa So La Ti Do? No matter how loud or soft you sing, as you sing up a scale you go from a lower to a higher sound by increasing the tension of your vocal cords. The highness or lowness of sounds is called **pitch.** Low frequencies produce sounds of low pitch. The higher the frequency of a sound wave, the higher the pitch.

You have probably noticed that as a car approaches you, the sound you hear is higher in pitch than the sound you hear as the car moves away. The greater the speed of the car, the more noticeable is this difference in pitch. The change in pitch is known as the **Doppler effect.** It is named after an Austrian scientist, Christian Doppler (1803–1853) who first explained it.

What is pitch?

What is the Doppler effect?

a

b

The Doppler effect occurs with all kinds of wave motion. Look at Figure 13–10. As the swimmer moves through the water, the wavelength of the waves ahead is shorter than the wavelength of the waves behind. In general, the waves ahead of a moving object tend to become bunched together and, therefore, have shorter wavelengths. Likewise, the waves behind a moving object tend to have longer wavelengths. The same thing happens to the sound waves produced by a moving automobile.

As a car approaches, you hear the sounds with shorter wavelengths. Because the wavelength is shorter, the frequency of the sound is greater. Consequently the pitch is higher. As the car moves away, you hear the longer wavelengths. The frequency is lower so you hear a lower pitched sound.

FIGURE 13–10.   Waves move out evenly in all directions from a stationary object (a). If the object is moving in a line, the waves in front are pushed together while those behind are spread further apart (b). This is the Doppler effect.

SUGGESTION   Remind students that v = λf. Therefore, if λ is increased, f must increase. If f is increased, λ must decrease.

13:7   Quality and Volume

Why does a piano sound different from a trumpet or a violin? If you hear a note of the same frequency or pitch played on all three instruments, you can tell easily which note came from which instrument. People's voices also do not sound the same. It is not difficult to recognize friends' voices on the telephone even before they tell you who they are. The characteristic of a sound that allows a listener to distinguish it from another sound of the same pitch is its quality.

What is the quality of a sound?

FIGURE 13–11. When the string of a guitar (or other stringed instrument) vibrates in several segments, overtones are produced. In general, the nearer to the end that the string is bowed or plucked, the more overtones are produced. Slight differences in the shape of the instrument change the quality of the sound produced. For this reason, fine instruments are carefully constructed and expensive.

Why do musical sounds have different qualities?

BACKGROUND The tone quality of a sound often is called timbre. Overtones often are referred to as harmonics.

Musical sounds have different qualities because of overtones. Recall from section 13:2 that the simplest standing wave in a string is produced by the string vibrating in a single segment with nodes only at the ends of the string. The frequency of this standing wave is called the **fundamental frequency.** Recall also that a string can be made to vibrate in 2, 3, 4 or more segments. These additional standing waves are called overtones. **Overtones** are whole number multiples of the fundamental frequency.

When the string of a guitar is plucked, it vibrates not only at the fundamental frequency but also at many overtone frequencies. The fundamental frequency has the greatest amplitude. The overtones produced combine with the fundamental frequency to give a guitar its unique sound.

The column of air in wind instruments also vibrates with a fundamental frequency as well as a number of overtones or harmonics. The shape of an instrument determines which overtones are emphasized.

What causes the qualities of people's voices?

Likewise, the shapes of the throat, mouth, and nasal passages vary among people. These variations cause different combinations of overtones to be emphasized in the voice. The emphasized overtones help give each person's voice a recognizable quality. Congestion in your nasal passages changes the shape within which your voice resonates. Therefore, the overtones are not the same as usual.

If a cymbal is struck gently, it vibrates back and forth with a small amplitude and a soft sound is produced. If the cymbal is struck with more force, it still vibrates at the same frequency but its amplitude is greater. That is, the cymbal moves back and forth through a greater distance and transfers more energy to the air molecules around it. As a result, the sound is louder.

The **volume,** or loudness, of a sound is our perception of the intensity of the sound. Intensity is a measure of how much energy a sound wave transmits. The amount of energy transmitted by a sound wave depends on the amplitude of the wave.

The relative intensity of sounds is measured in units called **decibels,** dB. The softest sound that the average human can detect is given the rating of zero decibels. Zero decibels is called the threshold of human hearing. Note that zero decibels does not mean there is no sound or that the wave has zero amplitude. It refers to a sound wave having an intensity that is barely audible to most humans. The relative intensities of some common sounds are listed in Table 13–1. Sounds louder than 120 dB cause pain by exerting too much pressure on the eardrum.

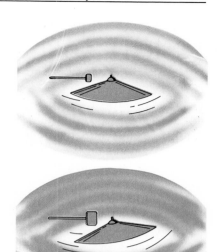

FIGURE 13–12. An object vibrating with more energy produces sound waves having more intense compressions. We experience this as a louder sound.

What is sound intensity and how is it measured?

BACKGROUND The intensity of sound is directly proportional to the density of the medium, the square of the frequency, and the square of the amplitude.

TABLE 13–1. RELATIVE INTENSITIES OF SOME COMMON SOUNDS	
Sound	**Relative Intensity (dB)**
Hearing threshold	0
Rustling leaves	10
Whisper	20
Normal conversation	65
Heavy traffic	80
Subway train	90
Thunder	110
Rock concert (indoor)	110–120
Pain threshold	120
Jet plane	140–160

See Teacher's Guide.

REVIEW AND REFLECT

1. What causes the Doppler effect?
2. Why do peoples' voices sound different?
3. What units are used to measure the intensity of sound?
4. Explain the difference between pitch and volume.

See Teacher's Guide.

Skill Inquiry

The bars in the figure show the ranges of fundamental frequencies for some common instruments and the choral voices. The range of each instrument and voice is keyed to the notes on the staff.

1. Which instrument produces the highest fundamental frequency?

2. What instrument can duplicate the pitches of the alto and soprano choral voices?

3. What is the frequency range of a five-part chorus?

This information is useful to musicians who arrange music for bands, orchestras, or choruses. From the figure, you can see that a musical part with notes below 100 hertz could not be played by a trumpet. A part including the note is not in the alto range.

4. Look at the following musical passage. Determine which instruments and which voice have the range to produce the part.

Pitch ranges of the human singing voice

Pitch ranges of common musical instruments

$\underline{13:8}$ Noise

How is noise defined?

Not all sounds are pleasant. Generally, unpleasant sounds are defined as noise. In addition to hearing loss, exposure to noise, especially loud noises, can result in both physical and nervous disorders.

Designers have found ways to limit the amount of noise to which workers are exposed in factories and other workplaces. Sound absorbing materials are used on machinery as well as on floors, walls, and ceilings.

Unwanted and unnecessary noise in the environment is noise pollution. Many communities have laws that attempt to limit unnecessary noise. Noise barriers often are built between busy freeways and residential areas as shown in Figure 13–13. Airports have tried to control noise pollution. Whenever possible, jet planes take off and make landing approaches over water or away from residential areas. However, research has shown that office workers' productivity decreases when they work in a totally quiet environment. For this reason, background music is played softly in many offices. In addition, air conditioners and heating fans are not made totally silent.

A field of study related to sound is **acoustics.** The word acoustics comes from the Greek word, *akoustikos*, which means "of hearing." Acoustics is the science that deals with the production, control, transmission, reception, and effects of sound.

The acoustical properties of auditoriums are controlled by the placement of sound absorbers, such as curtains, upholstery, and carpeting, and by the shape of the room. Acoustical engineers design auditoriums and concert halls to control the amount of reflected sound. If an auditorium is poorly designed, a listener hears echoes reflected from many different surfaces. This causes the sound to become "muddy" and less distinct. The repeated reflection of sound is known as reverberation. Auditoriums in which reverberations last between one and two seconds provide sound that appeals to most audiences.

FIGURE 13–13. Barriers next to highways can help prevent noise pollution in residential areas.

What is noise pollution?

Define acoustics.

BACKGROUND   Most auditoriums are designed acoustically with a "full house" of people in mind.

<u>13:9</u> Speed of Sound

Up to this point, we have been discussing the movement of sound waves in air. Sound can travel through other substances, too. Keep in mind that sound is transmitted as regions of molecules are compressed and rarefied. Sound waves must have some substance through which to travel. Sound cannot be transmitted in a vacuum.

Why can sound not be transmitted in a vacuum?

TABLE 13–2. SPEED OF SOUND AT 20°C	
Substance	**Speed**
Air	344 m/s
Mercury	1407 m/s
Water	1500 m/s
Wood (along the fibers)	3300 to 4700 m/s
Brick	3652 m/s
Glass	5000 to 6000 m/s
Iron	5130 m/s

How does a substance's state affect the speed of sound?

BACKGROUND   Sonar is an acronym for *sound navigation ranging.*

How does sonar work?

The speed of sound is not the same in all substances. Generally, sound travels faster in liquids than in gases and faster in solids than in liquids. Table 13–2 lists the speed of sound in some common substances.

Regardless of the frequency of a sound, its speed in dry air is 330 meters per second at 0°C. The speed of sound increases as temperature of the air increases. Warmer air is less dense than cooler air and sound travels faster in less dense air. At 20°C, the speed of sound in air is about 344 meters per second.

A speed of 344 meters per second seems quite fast, but it is almost a million times slower than the velocity of light waves. Perhaps you have seen a batter hit a baseball and then heard the sound of the bat striking the ball. This time delay is caused by the difference in the speeds of light and sound. Assume you are sitting in the bleachers 170 meters away from the batter. The light from the batter reaches your eyes almost instantly. The sound waves take about half a second to travel this distance.

Sound is frequently used to measure distances within the ocean. A sonar device on a ship can send a pulse of sound toward the ocean bottom and then detect the reflected echo. The depth of the ocean at that point is determined by measuring the time taken for the sound pulse to complete a round trip. In ocean water, sound travels about 1450 meters per second. So, if a pulse takes two seconds to make a round trip, the ocean depth is about 1450 meters. By taking depth readings in the oceans, the contours of the ocean floor have been mapped. Sonar is used by treasure and salvage hunters to find sunken shipwrecks and on fishing boats to find schools of fish.

See Teacher's Guide.

REVIEW AND REFLECT

1. What are two effects of loud noise on people?
2. What is acoustics?
3. How can the reverberation of sound be controlled in a room?
4. Middle C on a piano has a frequency of 262 Hz. What is its wavelength in air at 20°C?
5. A sound underwater has a wavelength of 2 meters. What is its frequency?

Activity: How can you measure the speed of sound?

See Teacher's Guide.

MATERIALS

plastic tube, 40 cm length and 2.5 cm diameter
2 tuning forks of known frequencies
2000-mL beaker
rubber hammer
water
metric ruler
thermometer

PROCEDURE

1. Fill the beaker with water.
2. Insert the tube so one end is just beneath the water surface, Figure 13–14.
3. Strike a tuning fork with a rubber hammer. Hold the tuning fork just above the end of the tube as shown.
4. Lower the tube into the water. Move the tube up and down until you find the position where the sound is loudest. (You may need to strike the tuning fork again until you find the position. Keep the tuning fork close to the top of the tube.)
5. Measure and record the length of the tube above the water surface.

FIGURE 13–14.

6. Repeat steps 4 and 5 two more times. Find the average of all three trials.
7. Repeat steps 1 through 6 using a tuning fork of a different frequency.
8. Using the average value for each tuning fork, calculate the wavelength of the sound produced by each tuning fork. The wavelength is equal to four times the length of the tube above the water surface.
9. Calculate the speed of sound using the frequency of each tuning fork and the wavelength you determined.
10. Measure and record the air temperature of the room.

DATA AND OBSERVATIONS

Air temperature:

Trial	Length of Tube (cm)	
	Tuning Fork 1	Tuning Fork 2
1		
2		
3		

QUESTIONS AND CONCLUSIONS

1. How do your calculations of the speed of sound for each tuning fork compare? How can you account for any differences?
2. The speed of sound is 330 m/s at 0°C. It increases 0.6 m/s for each Celsius degree above zero. Using your temperature measurement, calculate the actual speed of sound in the room.
3. How would your results be affected if the tuning fork was held several centimeters above the top of the tube?

13:10 Information: Hearing

The human ear is divided into three parts: the outer, middle, and inner ear, as shown in Figure 13–15. The shape of the outer ear collects and directs sounds into the middle and inner ear. Before electronics, a hearing aid was simply a funnel-shaped tube. The small end was placed in the ear. The large end collected more sound waves than the outer ear could and directed them into the ear.

The eardrum is a thin, tight membrane, located at the end of the ear canal. When sound waves travel into the ear, they transfer some of their energy to the eardrum, causing it to vibrate. This energy is transferred by three small bones in the middle ear that are linked together. The bones that form this linkage are the hammer, the anvil, and the stirrup. The hammer is connected to the eardrum. When the eardrum vibrates, the hammer vibrates too. The hammer causes the anvil to vibrate which causes the stirrup to vibrate. The stirrup is connected to a part of the inner ear called the oval window. Vibration of the oval window causes motion in a fluid inside the cochlea. The cochlea is coiled like the shell of a snail. Cochlea comes from the Greek word, *kochlias,* which means land snail. The inner surface of the cochlea has many cells that have fibers extending into the fluid. These cells are called hair cells and are stimulated by motion of the fluid. The nerves from the hair cells combine to form the auditory nerve that connects the ear to the brain.

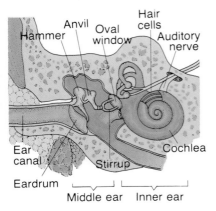

FIGURE 13–15. Diagram of the human ear

How can loud noise affect hearing?

Severe hearing loss can be caused by exposure to loud sound. Loud, sharp sounds from guns and fireworks can burst the eardrum when heard at close range. However, most loudness-related hearing loss develops very slowly. As a result, the loss may not be noticed for a long time.

Any loud sound can produce hearing loss. Some typical sources are lawnmowers, motorcycles, jet aircraft, power saws, factory machines, household appliances, and amplified music. Even some typewriters and computer printers can produce levels of sound that may be harmful. Scientists have found that continual exposure to loud sounds may cause people to develop ulcers, high blood pressure, memory loss, and nerve disorders.

The main cause of loudness-related hearing loss is quite simple. Recall that the loudness of a sound wave depends on amount of compression and rarefaction. The intense compression waves transmitted to the fluid inside the cochlea destroy the hair cells. Once destroyed, these cells are never replaced. The hair cells most likely to be destroyed are those that transmit frequencies of between 4000 hertz and 20 000 hertz to the auditory nerve. Very loud sound in this frequency range is often produced by power saws, jet aircraft, and highly amplified guitars and synthesizers.

Why, then, do people not notice loudness-related hearing loss sooner? Most of the frequencies of the average adult human voice are between 250 hertz and 2000 hertz. Hearing loss occurs at much higher frequencies in early stages. As a result it is seldom noticed. Often, the first clue to loudness-related hearing loss is misunderstood speech. Many consonants are distinguished by differing amounts of high frequency "hiss" in their sounds. Examples are the sounds of f, s, and th. The person begins confusing words like "fun" and "sun" or "thaw" and "saw."

Have you ever left a noisy area or a concert with your ears ringing or feeling "full"? If so, you may have been exposed to sound loud enough to cause hearing loss—and may have already suffered hair cell damage. Hearing damage depends on both the loudness of the sound and the length of exposure to it. A United States government agency has determined that exposure to more than 75 decibels for eight hours a day over an average person's working life is harmful. Workers in areas where sound intensities are above 90 dB are required to wear ear protectors.

See Teacher's Guide.

FIGURE 13–16. Wearing ear protectors in noisy surroundings can help workers prevent hearing loss.

What can be done to help prevent loudness-related hearing loss?

REVIEW AND REFLECT

1. What are the three main parts of the human ear?
2. What purpose is served by the shape of the outer ear?
3. Describe how sound waves are changed into nerve impulses.
4. What is the main cause of loudness-related hearing loss? Explain why this loss may not be noticed for a long time.

CHAPTER 13 REVIEW

SUMMARY

1. Energy, not matter, is transferred by waves.   13:1
2. The velocity of a wave can be determined from its wavelength and frequency.   13:1
3. The angle at which a wave is reflected is equal to its incidence angle.   13:2
4. Interference occurs when waves interact.   13:2
5. Waves bend when they pass the edges of objects and when they pass from one substance to another at an angle.   13:3
6. Sounds are compressional waves that transmit mechanical energy.   13:4
7. All sounds are produced by vibrations.   13:5
8. Because of the Doppler effect, to a stationary observer the apparent pitch of a sound produced by a moving object varies.   13:6
9. Tone quality makes sounds with the same fundamental pitch sound different.   13:7
10. Sound intensity is a measure of how much energy a sound wave transmits.   13:7
11. Noise can be harmful to one's physical and mental health.   13:8
12. Engineers are developing ways to control noise pollution.   13:8
13. Sound waves must have a substance through which to travel.   13:9
14. The speed of sound is not the same in all substances.   13:9

VOCABULARY

acoustics   14
amplitude   15
audible range   2
compressional wave   11
decibel   1

diffraction   3
Doppler effect   13
fundamental frequency   12
interference   8
overtones   10

pitch   9
refraction   7
standing wave   4
transverse wave   5
volume   6

Match each definition with the correct word from the list.

1. Unit used to measure sound intensity
2. Frequencies between 20 and 20 000 Hz
3. Bending of waves as they pass the edges of obstacles
4. Interference pattern in which waves do not appear to be moving
5. Wave in which crests and troughs are perpendicular to the direction of wave travel
6. Perception of sound intensity
7. Bending of waves as they pass from one substance into another
8. Interaction of two or more waves
9. Highness or lowness of a sound
10. Standing waves produced at whole number multiples of fundamental frequency
11. Wave that consists of a series of compressions and rarefactions traveling through matter
12. Lowest frequency standing wave produced by a vibrating object
13. Change in pitch of a sound produced by a moving source
14. Science of production, control, transmission, reception, and effects of sounds
15. Height of a crest or depth of a trough of a transverse wave

QUESTIONS

MAIN IDEAS

Complete each sentence or answer each question with the correct word or phrase.

1. The distance between successive crests and troughs of a wave is called the _____.
2. The symbol for wavelength is _____.
3. What is the frequency of a wave of which a crest passes a given point every 2 s?
4. What is the velocity of a wave with a frequency of 3 Hz and a wavelength of 0.5 m?
5. The interference of two waves with opposite amplitudes is _____.
6. Refraction is caused by a change in a wave's _____.
7. Two causes of diffraction are _____.
8. The area of a sound wave where there are few molecules is called a(n) _____.
9. An average person has an audible range of _____.
10. Sounds with frequencies higher than the audible range are called _____.
11. Sound intensity is measured in _____.
12. What happens to the wavelengths of sounds in front of a moving source?

APPLICATIONS

Answer each question in one or more paragraphs. Show how to solve each problem.

1. The action of waves in a lake causes a boat weighing 1000 newtons to move up and down 10 centimeters. How much work is being done on the boat each time it rises? If the frequency of the waves is 0.5 hertz, what is the rate at which the waves do work lifting the boat?
2. Suppose your car begins to shake while driving over a dirt road. Should you speed up or slow down? Why?
3. Why are waves not refracted when they are perpendicular to a boundary between two different substances?
4. Why is it not possible for sound to travel through outer space?
5. How far away is lightning if you hear the sound of the thunder 4.5 seconds after you see the flash of lightning?
6. A saxophone and a trumpet play the same pitch. Why do they sound different?
7. Why do children usually have higher-pitched voices than adults?

FURTHER STUDY

INVESTIGATIONS

1. Analyze the acoustics of your school auditorium. You may wish to interview the band or choir director.
2. Do library research on the sound absorbing characteristics of various building materials. Find out how these materials are used.
3. Find out how well sounds are reproduced on a good stereo system compared to an inexpensive transistor radio.
4. Study the history of the development of musical instruments. Write a report.

READINGS

- Kettelkamp, Larry. *The Magic of Sound.* Rev. ed. William Morrow and Company: New York, 1982.

0 Knight, David C. *Silent Sound.* William Morrow and Company: New York, 1980.

+ Read, Oliver, and Walter L. Welch. *From Tin Foil to Stereo.* 2nd ed. Howard W. Sams & Company: Indianapolis, 1976.

+ Zipfel, George G. "Selecting Sounds from the Sea." *Bell Laboratories Record.* April, 1983. pp. 11–13.

HAVE you ever been in a school play? The students in the play know about the importance of light. The lighting crew changes the amounts and colors of the light depending on the scene. Adjustments must be made so that the audience can see clearly what is happening on the stage. Light also is used to set the mood. What is light? How are color and light related? What is a spectrum?

LIGHT

INTRODUCING THE CHAPTER   Use the chapter opening
photograph to discuss how lighting affects not only how well an object
can be seen, but also how it is perceived. Encourage students to
explore how lighting and color can be used to convey a particular
mood. You may also wish to share some optical illusions with
students. Analyze how illusions occur when perceptions are distorted.

14:1   Electromagnetic Waves

Since ancient times, people have wondered what light is.
Some have thought light is a wave motion similar to water
waves. Others, such as Newton, have thought light is a
stream of tiny particles since it appears to move in a
straight line.

Thomas Young, an English scientist, knew that if light
were a wave motion, it should show interference. In 1801,
Young did experiments that confirmed this idea. As a result of Young's experiments, scientists generally accepted
the idea that light is a kind of wave energy. However,
near the end of the nineteenth century, scientists discovered some properties of light that could be explained only
if light acted like a stream of particles.

Today we realize that some properties of light can be
explained by a wave model. Other properties are best explained by a particle model. This idea is known as the
wave-particle duality of light. When referring to the
particle model of light, the particles are called photons.
Photons are visualized as being tiny bundles of light energy. In this chapter, we will consider light as a wave.

Light is a type of electromagnetic wave. Electromagnetic waves are produced whenever charged particles,
such as electrons, vibrate back and forth. Each vibrating
charged particle produces a changing electric field that, in
turn, generates a changing magnetic field (chapter 12).
Therefore, an electromagnetic wave is a wave that consists
of electric and magnetic fields continuously generating
each other as the wave travels.

GOAL   You will learn some of
the properties of the production
and control of light.

What is meant by the wave-
particle duality of light?

What are photons?

At what speed do electromagnetic waves travel?

BACKGROUND   The portion of the electromagnetic spectrum that we call light covers an extremely narrow band. The wavelength of visible light is from about 4×10^{-7} to 7×10^{-7} meters.

Describe electromagnetic waves.

SUGGESTION   A helpful mnemonic device for remembering the colors of the visible spectrum is the name ROY G. BIV. R stands for red, O for orange, Y for yellow, G for green, B for blue, I for indigo, and V for violet.

Recall that sound waves need atoms or molecules to transmit their energy. Electromagnetic waves do not need matter to carry them, and so they can travel through empty space. Energy from the sun is transmitted to earth by electromagnetic waves. Experiments have shown that electromagnetic waves travel through space (a vacuum) at about 3×10^8 meters per second.

14:2   The Electromagnetic Spectrum

Electromagnetic waves are transverse waves that have a broad range of frequencies and wavelengths. This range of waves, known as the electromagnetic **spectrum,** is shown in Figure 14–1. The higher the frequency (shorter the wavelength) of a wave in the electromagnetic spectrum, the more energy it has.

People's eyes are sensitive to only a very small part of the spectrum. This part is known as visible light. Within this range, light waves with short wavelengths appear violet. As the wavelengths become longer, the colors of the light change from violet to red, which has the longest wavelengths. See Figure 14–1.

Infrared radiation has wavelengths somewhat longer than those of visible red light. Because infrared radiation is easily absorbed by matter, it is used to warm objects. "Heat" lamps that give off infrared radiation are used to keep food warm in restaurants.

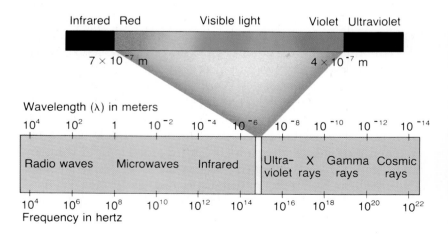

FIGURE 14–1.   Visible light occupies only the narrow band near the center of the electromagnetic spectrum.

Radio waves and microwaves are like light waves except they have longer wavelengths and frequencies. You may have used a microwave oven. Microwaves excite some of the molecules in food, increasing their kinetic energy and thus their temperature. Microwaves also are used for communication with satellites and for radar.

In radio broadcasting, the compressional waves of a voice or music are changed to a varying electric current by a microphone. This varying current is amplified and combined with an electromagnetic carrier wave of a certain frequency. Commercial AM radio is broadcast with high frequency carrier waves between about 500 and 1600 kilohertz. The letters AM stand for amplitude modulation. Modulate means to vary or change. In AM radio, the amplitude of the carrier wave is varied as shown in Figure 14–2b. FM stands for frequency modulation. In FM radio, the frequency, not the amplitude, of the carrier wave is varied. See Figure 14–2c. FM radio is broadcast using carrier frequencies between about 88 and 108 megahertz. (A megahertz is equal to one million hertz.)

In television broadcasting, both an audio and a video signal are combined with a carrier frequency. A television separates the audio and the video signals. As in a radio, the audio signal is changed to a varying electric current that causes vibrations in a speaker. The speaker produces compressional waves that we hear as sound. The picture on a television screen is formed by electrons hitting the inside surface of the screen. This surface is coated with dots of substances that light up briefly when struck by electrons. The number of electrons striking these dots is controlled by the video signal.

Ultraviolet radiation has wavelengths slightly shorter than violet light. Ultraviolet radiation is not visible, but can penetrate and damage living cells. Ultraviolet radiation can cause sunburn but also is used to kill bacteria.

X rays and gamma rays are electromagnetic radiation with shorter wavelengths and higher energy than ultraviolet radiation. In 1895, a German scientist, William Roentgen, discovered rays that exposed sealed photographic film. Roentgen called this radiation "X" rays because he was not sure what they were. He also discovered that more dense substances are more likely to absorb X

a   Amplified audio signal

b Amplitude-modulated carrier wave

c Frequency-modulated carrier wave

FIGURE 14–2. In broadcasting, an amplified audio signal (a) is used to modulate carrier waves to produce an amplitude-modulated signal (b), or frequency-modulated signal (c).

How are pictures formed on a TV screen?

BACKGROUND The first radio, or wireless as it was known then, was invented by the Italian engineer Guglielmo Marconi (1874–1937) in 1895.

What are X rays and gamma rays?

a

b

c

FIGURE 14–3. Special cameras using computers can analyze the infrared radiation given off by diseased tissue, such as a tumor, which is warmer than surrounding healthy tissue (a). X rays are absorbed more easily by dense materials, such as bone, which makes diagnoses of fractures and dislocations possible (b). Hair stylists and hospitals use ultraviolet radiation to sterilize instruments (c).

BACKGROUND   Radiologists sometimes refer to X-ray photographs as roentgenograms.

rays. This property makes X rays useful for medical purposes. However, X rays change the cells through which they pass, so the radiation must be carefully controlled.

Gamma rays have shorter wavelengths than X rays. Recall from chapter 4 that gamma rays are given off as radioactive substances decay. Gamma rays generally have much greater penetrating power than X rays. People who work in nuclear power plants, where radioactive fuels are used, are closely monitored for exposure to gamma rays.

See Teacher's Guide.

REVIEW AND REFLECT

1. What is the wave-particle duality of light?
2. Which has more energy, low or high frequency electromagnetic radiation?
3. Why must precautions be taken with X rays and gamma rays?

14:3 Producing Light

Recall that electromagnetic radiation is produced by vibrating charges. Visible light is produced by electrons moving between energy levels in individual atoms. For this to happen, an outside energy source must excite the electrons, raising them to higher energy levels. When the electrons drop back to lower energy levels, light is given off. The wavelength of the light produced depends on the energy given up by each electron as it drops back. A

How is visible light produced?

"short" drop produces lower energy (longer) wavelengths at the red end of the visible spectrum. A "long" drop produces higher energy (shorter) wavelengths at the violet end of the spectrum.

The most important source of light energy is the sun. Energy released by nuclear reactions gives the sun an interior temperature of about 1.3×10^7 K. As this energy radiates to the outer layers of the sun, it excites the atoms of these layers. The electrons of these atoms are elevated to higher energy levels. As the electrons return, this energy is radiated away as light.

Thermal energy also can excite atoms to produce light. This process is called **incandescence.** The heat of burning fuel can produce light by incandescence. However, producing light from fire is not very efficient. During burning, most of the energy radiated is infrared. In incandescent light bulbs, the energy of electric current is changed to heat in the filament of the bulb. This increase in heat energy excites atoms in the filament. Even though an incandescent bulb produces mostly infrared waves, it is much more efficient and convenient than fire.

Another method of light production is gas discharge. High voltage electrons passing through a gas in a glass tube excite the atoms of the gas. Neon signs, as well as mercury vapor and sodium vapor street lamps, are examples of gas discharge tubes.

Fluorescent lamps work in nearly the same way. A fluorescent tube contains mercury vapor that emits ultraviolet radiation when excited by an electric current. The inside of the tube is coated with a fluorescent substance. **Fluorescence** is the emission of light as the result of the

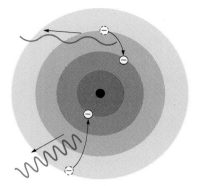

FIGURE 14–4. Long electron drops give off higher-energy light in the blue-violet region of the spectrum. Shorter drops produce redder light having lower energy and longer wavelengths.

What is incandescence?

BACKGROUND Incandescent is derived from the Latin word *candere,* which means to glow.

How do fluorescent lamps produce light?

a

b

FIGURE 14–5. An object can become incandescent when atoms are excited by heat (a). In fluorescence, atoms are excited by higher-energy electromagnetic radiation. The absorbed energy is given off as visible light as electrons drop from higher to lower energy levels (b).

BACKGROUND A common phosphor used in fluorescent tubes is calcium tungstate.

What is luminescence?

Define illuminance.

absorption of radiation. The ultraviolet radiation strikes the fluorescent coating of the tube causing it to glow.

Chemical energy released during a chemical reaction can produce light. If the process takes place in a living organism, it is called bioluminescence. Luminescence is the production of light without heat. Fireflies, some jellyfish, and many deepwater fish are examples of organisms that are bioluminescent.

The amount of light that strikes a surface per unit of area is known as **illuminance.** The illuminance falling on a given surface depends on both the intensity of the light source and its distance from the surface. Architects must keep this in mind when planning the lighting, colors, and textures in a room or building.

14:4 Reflection

When light strikes the pages of this book, it is reflected in many directions. Some of the light is reflected in the direction of your eyes. Thus, you are able to see this page even though the page does not produce light. Light waves are reflected according to the Law of Reflection (section 13:2). Highly polished and very smooth surfaces, such as mirrors, reflect light in predictable ways.

Flat mirrors are called plane mirrors. Your reflection in a plane mirror appears to be behind the mirror. Note in

FIGURE 14–6. A ray of light from the object may follow the path shown. When it strikes the mirror, the ray reflects at an equal angle toward the camera (a). As a result, the camera "sees" the ray as if it were coming from an object behind the mirror (b).

a

b

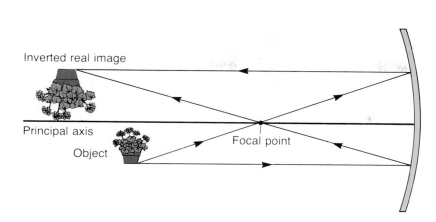

Inverted real image

Principal axis

Object

Focal point

Magnified virtual image

Object

b

FIGURE 14–7. If an object is placed farther than the focal point from a concave mirror, the light rays can be focused to form a real image in front of the mirror (a). If the object is closer than the focal point to the mirror, the image will be larger, virtual, and behind the mirror (b).

Figure 14–6 that if you follow the reflected rays back (along the dotted line), the image appears behind the mirror. This type of image formed by a mirror is known as a virtual image.

Some mirrors are curved. Maybe you have seen yourself in a mirror that made you appear tall and thin or short and squat. Mirrors that curve inward are concave. Mirrors that curve outward are convex.

A concave mirror can focus an image of an object on a screen. This type of image is called a real image. A concave mirror can form a real image only when the object is placed farther from the mirror than its focal point. In order to form a real image, the mirror must be able to reflect all the light rays coming from each point on the object to a single point on the screen. Light rays from the object that strike the mirror parallel to the principal axis are reflected in such a way that they pass through the focal point. Light rays that pass from the object through the focal point and strike the mirror are reflected parallel to the principal axis. As shown in Figure 14–7a, the image will be upside down in front of the mirror.

Concave mirrors have many practical uses. Makeup mirrors that magnify are concave. A concave mirror will magnify an object that is placed closer to the mirror than the focal point as shown in Figure 14–7b. A concave mirror used in this way forms a virtual image.

What are virtual and real images?

BACKGROUND A virtual image appears behind a mirror and, therefore, cannot be focused or projected onto a screen.

How are concave mirrors used?

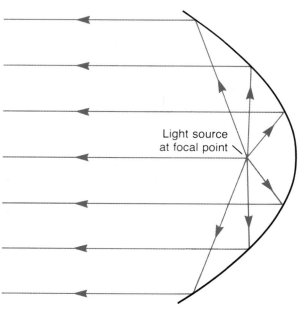

Light source
at focal point

a

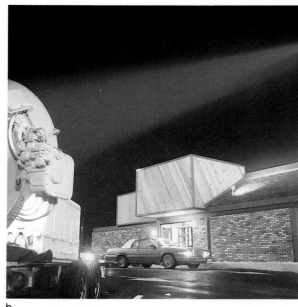

b

FIGURE 14–8.   If a light source, such as an incandescent filament, is placed at the focal point of a parabolic mirror, the mirror can reflect the rays into a parallel beam (a). As a result, the light can be concentrated in one direction (b).

How are convex mirrors used?

SUGGESTION   You may wish to review or introduce the idea of a parabolic curve, depending on the mathematics background of your students.

SUGGESTION   Make sure students realize that not all concave mirrors are parabolic.

The concave mirror used in Figure 14–8 is shaped like a parabola. Parabolic mirrors are used as reflectors for flashlights, spotlights, and headlights, too. When a parabolic mirror is used as a reflector, the lamp is placed at the focal point. Since the lamp is at the focal point, all of the light that strikes the mirror is reflected back parallel to the principal axis. Because the light does not spread out, a powerful beam of light can be produced.

Convex mirrors often are used in stores so employees can watch a large area of the store. Some side mirrors on cars are convex mirrors. These mirrors are sometimes called wide-angle mirrors. Perhaps you have noticed that the virtual image formed by a convex mirror is smaller than the object. Because the image is smaller, a greater area can be seen with a convex mirror.

See Teacher's Guide.

REVIEW AND REFLECT

1. What source of energy produces sunlight?
2. Why are incandescent light bulbs inefficient?
3. How do fluorescent tubes produce light?
4. What is the difference between a real image and a virtual image?

Activity: How is light reflected?

MATERIALS

cardboard
straight pins
plane mirror

protractor
metric ruler
notebook paper

PROCEDURE

1. Use a ruler to draw a horizontal line across a sheet of paper.
2. In the center of the line, make a dot and label it point A. Make another dot anywhere in the lower right quarter of the paper. Label it point B. Draw a line from point A to point B.
3. Place the paper on top of the cardboard. Insert a straight pin through the paper and into the cardboard at point B.
4. Place the mirror on the paper exactly along the horizontal line. Sight along the edge of the ruler and line up the image of the pin and point A. See Figure 14–9. Draw a line along the ruler.
5. Remove the pin and the mirror. Draw a line perpendicular (normal) to the line across the paper at point A.

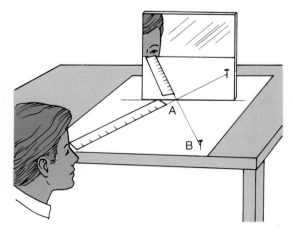

FIGURE 14–9.

6. Use the protractor to measure the angle of incidence and the angle of reflection. Record your data.
7. Repeat steps 1–6 three more times using different angles of incidence. Use a new sheet of paper for each trial.

DATA AND OBSERVATIONS

Trial	Angle of Incidence	Angle of Reflection
1		
2		
3		
4		

QUESTIONS AND CONCLUSIONS

1. How did the angles of incidence and reflection compare?
2. How far behind the mirror does an object's image appear?
3. Some periscopes are made using mirrors. At what angle do you think the mirrors are situated?
4. Make a sketch of how you would construct a periscope. Draw a diagram showing the path of a light ray.
5. The angles of incidence and reflection are measured between the ray of light and the normal line to the mirror. There is another (complementary) angle between the ray and the mirror. What is the relationship between these angles?
6. Construct a diagram to show how long a vertical plane mirror needs to be in order for you to see your entire height.

See Teacher's Guide.

Career Profile

Debbie Dean's enthusiasm for photography began with a brief adult education class on how to use a 35 mm camera. With practice, her photographic skills developed as she learned how to use other photographic equipment. In time, Debbie began submitting and selling her photographs to magazine, textbook, and greeting card companies. Debbie took the picture of the pharmacist on page 118. Presently as a freelance photographer, Debbie is joining forces with a writer friend in producing children's books.

In addition to her camera, Debbie uses a macro lens for close focusing or nature shots and a telephoto lens for people shots. She also uses various filters to correct or alter lighting effects. Debbie uses a tripod to steady the camera.

One of the most crucial considerations in photography is the amount of light necessary to take the best pictures. A 35 mm camera has two adjustments that control light. The shutter speed determines how long the light is allowed to enter the lens, and the f-stop, or aperture reading, indicates how wide the lens is to be open. In most cameras today, a built-in light meter indicates how both of these features should be adjusted for the best results. To freeze action, a fast shutter speed is necessary. A slow shutter speed is usually used in dim light.

14:5 Refraction

Recall that when a wave passes from one substance into another, its velocity may change. If the wave enters the second substance at an angle, it is bent, or refracted. Like all waves, light waves are refracted in this same way.

Why do the legs of a person standing in water appear shorter than usual?

Maybe you have noticed that the legs of a person standing in water appear shorter than usual. Light waves reflected from the person's legs are refracted as they pass from water to air. This refraction is due to the fact that the velocity of light is less in water than in air.

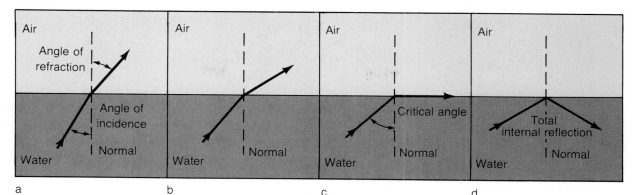

FIGURE 14-10. As light passes from water into air, it speeds up and therefore refracts away from the normal (a). As the angle of incidence increases, so does the angle of refraction (b). At an angle of incidence of about 48.5°, the angle of refraction becomes 90° and the light is refracted along the surface (c). At an angle greater than 48.5° the light reflects totally and no longer leaves the water (d).

The degree to which a substance slows down light is given by the index of refraction of the substance. For example, the index of refraction of a vacuum is 1.00. The speed of light in air is so near the speed of light in a vacuum that the index of refraction of air also is considered 1.00. The index of refraction of water is 1.33. This value means that light travels through water 1.00/1.33 as fast as it travels through air.

As light passes from a substance with a higher index of refraction to a substance with a lower index of refraction, the light wave is refracted away from the normal as shown in Figure 14-10. The normal is a line perpendicular to a surface. The angle of refraction is larger than the angle of incidence. The incident angle that causes the light wave to be refracted along the boundary between the substances is called the **critical angle**. Any light wave that strikes the boundary of a substance at an angle greater than the critical angle will be reflected. This effect is called **total internal reflection**. The brilliant sparkle of diamonds is the result of total internal reflection.

Perhaps on a sunny day you have thought you saw a puddle of water on the pavement ahead of you. When you approached the "puddle," it was not there. The puddle was a mirage (muh ROZH). A layer of warm air often exists just above the pavement. Hot air has a lower index of refraction than cooler air. Light from the sky is refracted as it passes from the cool air to the hot air. As a result, you see an inverted image of the sky. It appears to you that a water surface is reflecting the sky.

Explain total internal reflection.

How are mirages formed?

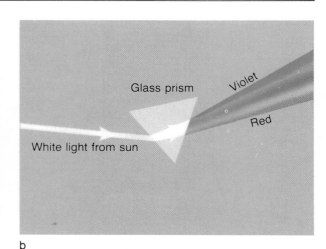

a

b

FIGURE 14–11. When you see a rainbow, you are seeing sunlight refracted and spread into its component colors by millions of raindrops (a). The same effect happens when white light is refracted by a prism (b). A spectrum is formed because shorter wavelength light (violet) is refracted more than longer wavelengths (red).

What is white light?

How does a color TV produce different colors?

ACTIVITY   Students can produce a "rainbow" by standing with their backs to the sun and spraying a fine mist of water into the air with a garden hose.

14:6 Colors

Light that appears white to us, such as sunlight, is actually a mixture of colors. As shown in Figure 14–11, white light can be separated into a spectrum, or the colors of a rainbow. When white light passes at an angle into another substance, such as glass or water, the light waves are refracted. Light with shorter wavelengths is refracted more than light with longer wavelengths. So, violet light is bent more than blue light, which is bent more than green light and so on. Red light is refracted the least.

Any color can be produced by combining different colors of light. A color television screen consists of dots or stripes of three fluorescent substances. These substances fluoresce either red, blue, or green when their atoms are excited by an electron beam. With only these colors, the set can produce almost any color needed in a picture. For example, when the substances for green and red are lit, our eyes and brain perceive the result as yellow. When all the substances are lit, we perceive the mixture as white. This process is known as **color addition.**

Objects that do not produce their own light appear to have color because of how they reflect light. Consider why grass is green. Sunlight, a mixture of all colors, strikes blades of grass. The grass absorbs most of the colors of the spectrum except green, so the grass appears green. An object that appears black absorbs nearly all colors. Very little light is reflected.

See Teacher's Guide.

REVIEW AND REFLECT

1. What causes refraction of light?
2. Why do cut diamonds sparkle and show color?
3. Explain why the pages of this book appear white and the ink appears black.
4. Under red light, blue and green objects appear almost black. How can you explain this?

See Teacher's Guide.

Skill Inquiry

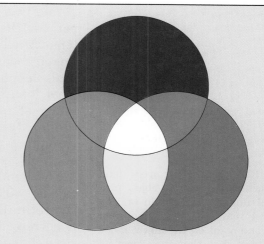

When red and green light are mixed together, we perceive the combination as yellow light. This process is color addition. The colors of light are added together before we see them.

Red and green paint do not produce yellow when they are mixed together, though. Paints contain pigments. Pigments are solid particles that produce colors by absorbing or reflecting certain wavelengths of light. When pigments are combined, the process is color subtraction. You see the color of the combined pigments as the result of the remaining light reflected after absorption has occurred.

Red, green, and blue are called additive primary colors. Mixing various amounts of these colors will produce any color in the spectrum. Cyan, magenta, and yellow are subtractive primary colors. Each represents the two additive primaries left after one has been subtracted from white. See the figure.

1. What color is produced when red and blue light are mixed?
2. What pigments could be used to make green paint? Explain.

The subtractive primaries are the colors of ink, along with black, used to print the pictures in this book. Color pictures can be reproduced in print by photographing them three times, once each with red, green, and blue filters. Consider that the negative made with the red filter absorbs red light, allowing only the green and blue light of the original picture to pass through. This red separation negative is used to make a metal plate that is treated with cyan ink for printing. The plate will hold ink only in the areas where light has passed through.

The combination of the inks on the plates made from all three negatives produces colors like those in the original picture. Black is added to improve the quality of the reproduction.

3. What color of ink is used to treat the plate made from the blue separation negative? the green separation negative? Explain.

14:7 Lenses

What is a lens?

A lens is a curved piece of glass or plastic through which light can pass. Light is refracted as it passes through a lens. The way a lens is curved controls the degree to which light rays change direction while passing through the lens. Lenses may be concave or convex. **Concave** lenses are thickest at the edges. **Convex** lenses are thickest in the middle.

A convex lens causes parallel rays of light to come together at a focal point. The distance from a lens to its focal point is the focal length of that lens. The focal length of a lens varies depending on how much the lens is curved. The image formed by a convex lens may be either virtual or real, depending on where the object is in relation to the focal length. You can use a convex lens to project a real image of an object if the object is located at a distance from the lens greater than the focal length. Also, you can look through a convex lens to view a magnified virtual image of an object located between the focal point and the lens.

The lens of the eye is a convex lens whose focal length can be varied. The images of objects seen are focused on the retina by the lens of the eye. The upside-down image is corrected when the brain interprets it, so objects seem right-side-up.

What is the difference between concave and convex lenses?

BACKGROUND   A magnifying glass is a convex lens. A compound microscope is made of two (or more) convex lenses. The objective lens is nearest the object being viewed. The ocular lens is nearest the observer's eye. The lenses are arranged so that the image produced by the objective lens is greatly magnified by the ocular.

FIGURE 14–12. A convex lens can focus light from an object into a real image on a screen (a). To form a real image, all the rays from one point on the object must be refracted so that they meet at one point on the image (b).

a

b

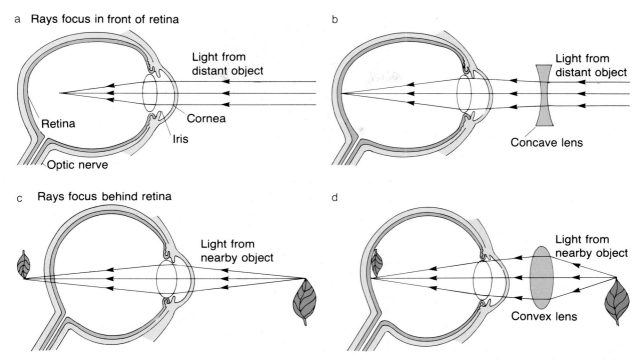

a Rays focus in front of retina

Light from distant object

Retina

Cornea

Iris

Optic nerve

b

Light from distant object

Concave lens

c Rays focus behind retina

Light from nearby object

d

Light from nearby object

Convex lens

If you hold one finger near your eye, you cannot focus your eyes on your finger and on an object across the room at the same time. In order to focus an image of a closer object on the retina, muscles in the eye contract making the lens more convex. As a person ages, the lens of the eye becomes less elastic. For this reason, as many people age, they may become farsighted and have difficulty seeing close objects clearly. The image formed by the eyes of farsighted people is focused behind the retina. The convex lenses of "reading glasses" help focus the image of nearby objects on the retina. Nearsighted people are not able to see faraway objects sharply. The eyes of nearsighted people focus an image of a faraway object in front of the retina. To correct nearsightedness, concave lenses are used.

A camera lens focuses the image of an object on film. In some cameras, the focus of the lens cannot be adjusted. Objects that are too near the camera will not be in focus. The lens in other cameras can be moved farther from the film to focus images of nearby objects.

FIGURE 14–13. The nearsighted eye is usually too long (a). A concave lens helps bring rays from distant objects into focus on the retina (b). The farsighted eye is usually too short (c). A convex lens helps focus rays from nearby objects on the retina (d).

BACKGROUND Farsightedness is known as hyperopia and nearsightedness as myopia.

How are nearsightedness and farsightedness corrected with lenses?

14:8 Diffraction and Polarization

Waves are diffracted as they pass around obstacles or through openings in their path. When light passes through narrow slits, it is diffracted. A diffraction grating is a series of very close slits on a coated piece of glass or plastic. Light waves interfere after being diffracted through closely-spaced slits. Different wavelengths of light interfere at different positions. As a result, light passed through a diffraction grating is spread into its component wavelengths. White light gives a complete spectrum.

Diffraction gratings are used in instruments known as spectrometers. Spectrometers are useful to study the light from the stars. By analyzing the spectra formed by the light of stars, astronomers can deduce the stars' compositions. This is possible because each element, when heated, gives off its own mixture of wavelengths.

A light ray is composed of waves that vibrate in many directions. These waves are represented in Figure 14–14. Some materials filter light so that only waves vibrating in one direction can pass. The resulting light wave is said to be **polarized**.

The most familiar use of polarizing filters is for some kinds of sunglasses. The effect of polarizing filters can be seen easily if you look through a pair of polarizing filters and then rotate one pair as shown (Figure 14–14). When the filters are situated at right angles to one another, very little light passes through them. The first filter tends to cut out all waves except those vibrating in the horizontal direction. The second lens eliminates waves except those vibrating in the vertical direction. Most sun glare from horizontal surfaces is polarized in the horizontal direction. For this reason, some sunglasses are polarized vertically to decrease the glare of the reflected sun.

See Teacher's Guide.

REVIEW AND REFLECT

1. What is the focal point of a lens?
2. What type of lens is in the human eye?
3. Why can a concave lens not form a real image?
4. How can a diffraction grating be used to find out what elements are in an unknown substance?

BACKGROUND   The first diffraction grating was used by Bavarian scientist Joseph von Fraunhofer (1767–1826) in 1819 to study sunlight.

How are spectrometers used?

What is polarized light?

FIGURE 14–14. Light waves vibrating in only the horizontal direction can pass through the first polarizing filter. The second filter will allow only vertically vibrating waves to pass through. As a result, no light can pass through.

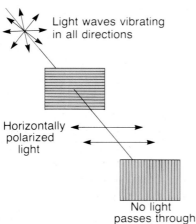

Light waves vibrating in all directions

Horizontally polarized light

No light passes through

Activity: How can you make a camera obscura?

See Teacher's Guide.

MATERIALS

two cardboard tubes, one shorter with
  slightly larger diameter than the other
scissors
wax paper (15 cm square)
aluminum foil (15 cm square)
masking tape
straight pin
black construction paper (20 × 30 cm)
metric ruler or meter stick

PROCEDURE

1. Center the wax paper square over the end of the longer tube. Press the paper down around the sides of the tube and wrap tightly with tape to hold it in place. The paper over the hole in the tube should be smooth.

2. Place the end of the longer tube just inside the short tube. Join the two tubes with masking tape. The wax paper forms a screen between the two tubes.

3. Center the aluminum foil square over the open end of the short tube. Tape it in place. The foil over the hole should be smooth. Make sure the tubes are light tight by looking in the open end. Patch any light leaks with masking tape.

Aluminum foil   Tape
                          Open end
Pinhole
Wax paper screen

FIGURE 14–15.

4. Use a straight pin to make a small hole in the center of the foil.

5. Aim the camera obscura out a window. **CAUTION:** *Do not aim the camera at the sun.* Look through the tube at the wax paper screen. (Wait a few seconds until your open eye adjusts to the dim light.) Record your observations. (If the image is too dim, try enlarging the pinhole slightly.)

6. Move the camera obscura slowly to the right. Record your observations.

7. Look through the camera obscura at someone moving. Record your observations about the directions of movement.

DATA AND OBSERVATIONS

Image Viewed	Observations

QUESTIONS AND CONCLUSIONS

1. Describe the images produced by the camera obscura. Why are the images inverted? Why are distant objects small?

2. When you moved the camera obscura slowly to the right, in which direction did the image move?

3. Draw a ray diagram of how an image is produced by a camera obscura.

4. What does this activity demonstrate about how light travels?

Adapted from Joan Steinberg. "A Simple Camera Obscura." *Elementary School Science Association of Northern California Newsletter:* Spring, 1983.

<u>14:9</u> **Information: Lasers**

Ordinary white light emitted by the sun or a light bulb is a mixture of different wavelengths traveling in all directions. A laser, on the other hand, produces coherent light traveling in only one direction as shown in Figure 14–16. Many lasers produce light of only one wavelength (color). The term "LASER" stands for Light Amplification by Stimulated Emission of Radiation. The first lasers were produced in 1960.

Laser light can be produced using a variety of substances, such as carbon dioxide and vaporized metals. One type of laser consists of a ruby crystal in the shape of a rod. Red laser light is produced by chromium atoms contained within the crystal. Mirrors are placed at both ends of the rod. The mirror at one end is slightly transparent. An outside high intensity light source excites the electrons of the chromium atoms to a higher energy level. The excited electrons then fall back to their original level and emit red light. This red light in turn stimulates other excited atoms to release light waves. Meanwhile, more chromium atoms are excited by the outside light source. The waves of red light bounce back and forth between the mirrors, stimulating more chromium atoms to release light. In this way, the intensity of the red light is amplified. A beam of laser light finally emerges from the slightly-transparent end. The beam is a narrow concentrated beam of coherent light having only one red wavelength moving in one direction.

What is a laser?

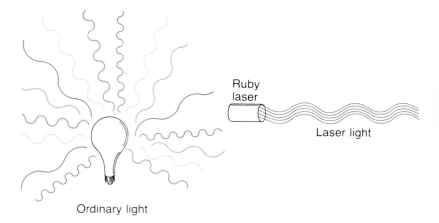

FIGURE 14–16. Ordinary light is a mixture of many wavelengths. Laser light usually has only one wavelength and is coherent. Coherence means that the crests and troughs of the light waves all move in the same direction at the same time.

a

b

Because of its properties, laser light can have many uses. For example, a very intense beam of laser light is used to cut and weld pieces of metal. In fact, powerful lasers are being developed that can completely vaporize metal objects even from a long distance. Many supermarkets today use lasers to read a product code and record the price at checkout counters. Videodisc players use lasers to scan thin discs on which entertainment programs, data, or information are recorded.

Lasers aboard satellites can measure concentrations of water vapor and certain pollutants in the air. Also, the beam of laser light is so precise that it can be used to detect small movements within the earth's surface that precede earthquakes and volcanic eruptions. For communication, engineers are developing laser systems to carry thousands of times more information than radio waves.

Medical applications are probably the most important uses of the laser. Sharply-focused beams can cut tissue and reduce bleeding. Large tumors also have been vaporized with a surgical laser. Lasers are commonly used in eye surgery. The transparent outer parts of the eye allow the beam to pass through to weld detached retinas and repair broken blood vessels.

See Teacher's Guide.

FIGURE 14–17. Because the beam does not spread out, laser light allows surveyors to make precise measurements (a). Tiny beams of laser light can be used to carry out delicate surgery, sometimes without hospitalization (b).

What properties of laser light make it useful in medical applications?

REVIEW AND REFLECT

1. What does LASER mean?
2. What are some uses of lasers?
3. How is laser light different from ordinary light?

CHAPTER 14 REVIEW

SUMMARY

1. Light behaves as both waves and particles. 14:1
2. Electromagnetic waves are produced by vibrating charges. 14:1
3. Electromagnetic waves travel at about 3×10^8 meters per second in a vacuum. 14:1
4. The higher the frequency (shorter the wavelength) of an electromagnetic wave, the more energy it has. 14:2
5. People's eyes can see only the visible light part of the electromagnetic spectrum. 14:2
6. Besides visible light waves, the electromagnetic spectrum includes radio waves, microwaves, infrared radiation, ultraviolet light, X rays, and gamma rays. 14:2
7. Visible light is produced when an energy source excites atoms causing electrons to vibrate between energy levels. 14:3

8. Objects that do not emit light are visible because of the light reflected from the surface of the object. 14:4
9. Mirrors can reflect light forming with virtual images and real images. 14:4
10. Light is refracted if it slows down or speeds up as it passes at an angle from one substance into another. 14:5
11. The degree to which a substance slows down light is given by the index of refraction of the substance. 14:5
12. White light is a combination of all colors of visible light. 14:6
13. The curvature of a lens determines how it will change the direction of light rays. 14:7
14. Waves of polarized light vibrate in one plane. 14:8

VOCABULARY

color addition 4
concave 6
convex 5
critical angle 8

fluorescence 10
illuminance 11
incandescence 9
photon 1

polarized 2
spectrum 7
total internal reflection 3

Choose the correct word from the list to answer each question.

1. What is a tiny bundle of electromagnetic energy called?
2. What kind of light has waves vibrating in only one direction?
3. What occurs when light strikes a boundary between two substances at an angle greater than the critical angle?
4. What occurs when different colors of light are combined?
5. What kind of lens is thicker in the middle?

6. What kind of lens is thin in the middle and thick at the edges?
7. What is a broad range of electromagnetic radiation called?
8. At what point is light refracted along the boundary between two substances?
9. What do we call the production of light from atoms excited by heat?
10. What is the emission of light as a result of the absorption of radiation called?
11. What is the amount of light striking a given surface called?

QUESTIONS

MAIN IDEAS

Choose the correct answer to each question.

1. Which of the following is not a use of microwaves? *(communications, cooking, radar, light)*

2. Which of the following has the shortest wavelength? *(microwaves, red light, infrared rays, radio waves)*

3. What type of radiation in sunlight normally causes sunburn? *(infrared, ultraviolet, microwave, gamma rays)*

4. Which type of radiation is least likely to damage human tissue? *(X rays, gamma rays, ultraviolet light, radio waves)*

5. What type of mirror should be used to make a reflector for a flashlight? *(plane, concave parabolic, convex parabolic)*

6. What causes mirages? *(reflection, diffraction, refraction, polarization)*

7. In bioluminescence, what kind of energy is changed to light? *(chemical, thermal, atomic, electromagnetic)*

8. What type of lens is used to make a magnifying glass? *(convex, concave, plane, polar)*

9. Which two processes combine to produce a rainbow? *(fluorescence and refraction, refraction and total internal reflection, diffraction and refraction)*

10. What kind of coating would glow under ultraviolet light? *(incandescent, fluorescent, illuminescent, polarized)*

11. Which of the following best describes the behavior of light? *(wave, particle, wave-particle)*

See Teacher's Guide.

APPLICATIONS

Answer each question in one or more paragraphs. Show how to solve each problem.

1. A wave in the electromagnetic spectrum has a frequency of 6×10^9 hertz. What is the wavelength of this wave? What type of radiation is it?

2. What is the difference between AM and FM radio?

3. A bear is standing on a shore and wants to catch a fish it sees. Where should the bear aim?

4. How does a prism cause white light to be separated into a spectrum?

5. How can infrared photographs be used to improve energy conservation in buildings?

6. Why does the water in a swimming pool look shallower than it actually is?

7. It is said that a rainbow signifies the end of a storm and that the rain has stopped. Why?

FURTHER STUDY

INVESTIGATIONS

1. Research and write a report on the use of microwaves in communication.

2. Study the history of the development of telescopes and microscopes.

3. Find out how a camera takes photographs. Construct a pinhole camera and try to take some pictures with it.

READINGS

0 Ardley, Neil. *Sun and Light.* Franklin Watts: New York, 1983.

– "The Light Fantastic." *Science 84.* May, 1984. pp. 50–57.

+ Safford, Edward L. *The Fiberoptics & Laser Handbook.* Tab Books: Blue Ridge Summit, PA, 1984.

THE SYSTEMS OF OUR WORLD

UNIT 4

Unit Four focuses on systems of organization in the study of the universe. For example, the Earth is part of the solar system. On Earth, layers of rock are studied. Ocean water circulates in currents. Patterns of air movements occur in the Earth's atmosphere. In this unit, you will learn about these and other systems of our world.

1. How old are stars?
2. Who discovered the planets?
3. How can weather be predicted?
4. How does climate affect organisms on Earth?
5. How are rocks classified?
6. What do scientists know about the Earth's interior?
7. What causes ocean circulation?
8. What information do fossils contain about the Earth's past?

THE students shown are learning about the stars, sun, moon, and planets in a special classroom. It is a planetarium. Have you ever been to a planetarium? In a planetarium, people can learn about astronomy, the study of the universe. How does studying the universe help people understand the Earth? How big is the universe compared to the Earth?

THE UNIVERSE

INTRODUCING THE CHAPTER   Many of the concepts of the physics and chemistry units are applied in this chapter. It would be helpful to review atomic structure, the electromagnetic spectrum, forces of nature, density, and temperature. Scientific notation might also be reviewed. Since World War II, astronomers have revolutionized their thinking about the universe. The universe has been observed via many wavelengths besides the visible spectrum, which has revealed new information and promoted new theories.

15:1 Origin of the Universe

Most scientists think that about 18 billion years ago the universe was tightly packed together smaller than a proton. Then, according to scientists' theory, it exploded. Matter and energy were flung in all directions.

Suppose you travel back in time to a fraction of a second after the **"Big Bang."** The major events of the Big Bang are shown in Figure 15–1. It is unbelievably hot. No atoms exist. Only subatomic particles, such as leptons and hadrons are present. The universe has expanded to about the size of a marble now. It is super-dense, and you feel the strong pull of its gravity if you look in from the outside. At the time of the Big Bang, all the forces in the universe existed as one unified force. Gravity was the first force to separate. (See A in Figure 15–1.)

The universe expands to the size of a baseball when atomic particles such as quarks, neutrinos, and electrons start to form. The other main forces of the universe—the electromagnetic force and the strong nuclear force—separate (B).

The universe is becoming much larger. At about one millionth of a second after the Big Bang, it is about the size of our present-day solar system. Protons and neutrons form. The temperature is still over one trillion K, but that is a lot cooler than before (C).

GOAL   You will learn about a model that describes the origin of the universe and about objects in the universe.

How were all the forces of the universe arranged, according to theory, at the time of the Big Bang?

SUGGESTION   Discuss why it would not be possible to have been an observer of the early stages of the universe, even if one could travel back in time.

FIGURE 15–1. Major events of
the Big Bang

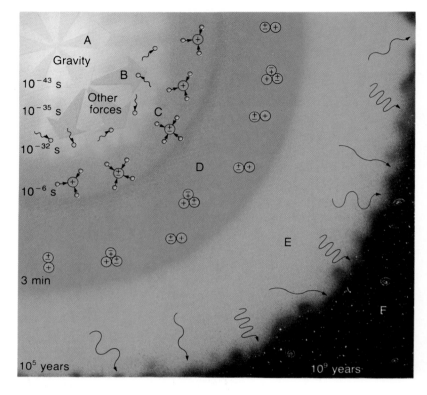

At about three minutes after the Big Bang, protons and
neutrons form light atomic nuclei. At a temperature of
about one billion K, deuterium, tritium, helium-3, and he-
lium-4 begin to form. The universe continues to expand
and cool (D).

At about 300 000 years after the Big Bang, the temperature was about 3000 K. The first neutral atoms of hydrogen and helium came into being (E). Galaxies began to
form about one billion years later. By then the temperature of the universe was only 15 K (F).

Evidence indicates that the universe is still expanding
today. Recall the Doppler effect discussed in chapter 13.
As with sound, light emitted by an object is affected by the
object's motion. Wavelengths of light from the object appear to change as the object moves towards us or away
from us. Astronomers observe shifts in spectral lines of
distant galaxies to the longer (red) wavelengths. This "red
shift" indicates the galaxies are moving away from the
Earth.

According to the Big Bang
theory, when did galaxies
begin to form?

SUGGESTION   Review the
Doppler effect of sound and relate
this to light.

What evidence indicates that
the universe is expanding
now?

A polka-dot balloon is a good model of the expanding universe. As the balloon is blown up, the dots get farther and farther apart. As the Big Bang continues, the galaxies in the universe get farther and farther apart. As we look out on the universe, we are looking back into time. The farther we look, the farther back in time we see.

The most convincing evidence that the Big Bang took place is the microwave radiation coming from all directions in the universe. If the Big Bang theory is correct, scientists have calculated that the whole universe should be emitting microwave radiation. In 1965, scientists discovered the microwave radiation exactly as the Big Bang theory predicted. The radiation is thought to be the radiation first emitted 300 000 years after the Big Bang.

See Teacher's Guide.

FIGURE 15–2. Stars may be studied by analyzing the spectrums of the light they emit. A shift of colors toward the red indicates the object is moving away.

REVIEW AND REFLECT

1. What evidence supports the Big Bang theory?
2. If the Big Bang theory is correct, where was the matter that makes up your body about 18 billion years ago?
3. If the universe eventually stops expanding, what might happen after that?

15:2   How the Universe Is Organized

Galaxies are arranged in clusters, which in turn are found in still larger clusters. For example, the Milky Way Galaxy is one of about 20 galaxies in a small cluster. This cluster is known as the Local Group. The Local Group is one of hundreds of galaxy clusters within the Virgo Supercluster.

Astronomers group most galaxies into the three categories shown in Figure 15–3. The majority of large galaxies are spirals. A **spiral galaxy** is disk-shaped with a center bulge of old stars and spiral arms of gas and young stars. The spiral arms rotate rapidly about the center of the galaxy. Gas in the spiral arms condenses forming stars. About one third of all spiral galaxies are barred spirals. They have "bars" of gas and young stars, such as found in spiral arms, cutting across their centers.

Describe the location of the Milky Way in the universe.

BACKGROUND   Old stars are those which formed long ago, early in the history of a galaxy. Young stars are stars that formed relatively recently.

How are gas and stars distributed in spiral galaxies?

Our Milky Way Galaxy is a typical spiral galaxy. The Milky Way is so large that it takes light about 100 000 years to travel across its disk. Our solar system is about halfway between the center of the Milky Way Galaxy and the outer edge.

The second group of galaxies is called the irregulars. An **irregular galaxy** has a patchy, noncircular appearance. Almost all irregular galaxies are smaller than the spirals.

A third category of galaxies is called the ellipticals. An **elliptical galaxy** has a smooth round or oval outline, with old stars and little gas. Some of the largest as well as the smallest galaxies are elliptical. Elliptical galaxies do not rotate as fast as spirals. Their slow rotation probably prevents them from flattening like the spirals.

The Milky Way and some other galaxies are outlined by round clusters of stars. These globular clusters are stars that formed early in a galaxy's history. In 1917, an astronomer discovered that the sun and Earth are not at the Milky Way's center. His conclusion was based on data that showed the system of globular clusters centered in another part of the galaxy.

Where is our solar system located?

Describe elliptical and irregular galaxies.

BACKGROUND The hazy band of distant stars called "the Milky Way" that we see from Earth is widest and brightest in the direction of the center of the Milky Way Galaxy.

FIGURE 15–3. NGC 2997 in the constellation Antlia is a spiral galaxy (a). The Large Magellanic Cloud is an irregular galaxy (b). M32 (NGC221) is an elliptical galaxy (c).

a

b

c

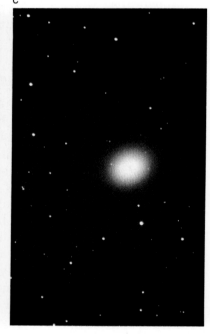

Recently astronomers have found that the centers of many galaxies emit great amounts of radiation. The radiation may be coming from the remains of a tremendously active object. As galaxies formed in the early universe, most appear to have passed through a stage called a quasar. A **quasar** is a massive object that may shine as bright as 1000 average galaxies. However, a quasar varies in brightness in just a few days. As astronomers look great distances through the universe, they see many quasars. Scientists hypothesize that quasars became active as huge dense galaxy centers attracted nearby stars and gas. The stars and gas were absorbed. A tremendous release of energy resulted. Our Milky Way, perhaps, was once an active quasar. Even today the Milky Way's center releases enough energy that we suspect a very dense region there, which draws in some gas and stars. Today there is much less gas to be pulled into the region, so the core of the galaxy may be becoming fairly inactive.

What are quasars?

FIGURE 15–4. Organization of the universe

See Teacher's Guide.

Skill Inquiry

Distances in space are so large that astronomers use special units to measure them. One unit that astronomers use to measure distances to stars is the light-year.

When you turn on a lamp, a short time passes before the light reaches your eyes. When the source of light is relatively near, the delay is so short you do not notice it. However, when the source of light is very far away, for example as distant as a star, the light does not reach your eyes for years.

One light-year is the distance light travels in one year, which is 9.46×10^{12} km. If a star is one light-year away, then it is 9.46×10^{12} km away, and it takes one year for its light to reach us.

1. If Sirius is about 8×10^{13} km away, how long does it take for its light to reach you?

A larger unit, called a parsec, is equal to 3.26 light-years. Astronomers observe stars at six month intervals and determine the stellar parallax as shown in the figure. The

angles for stellar parallax are measured in seconds of arc rather than degrees. One second of arc equals 1/3600 of a degree. One parsec is the distance at which a star would have a stellar parallax of one second of arc. Scientists use the following equation to calculate distance from parallax angles.

$$\frac{\text{distance}}{\text{(parsecs)}} = \frac{1}{\substack{\text{stellar parallax} \\ \text{(seconds of arc)}}}$$

2. The parallax angle of Kapteyn's star is 0.251 seconds of arc. How long does it take for light from the star to reach you?

BACKGROUND/SUGGESTION
If a cup (about 200 cm³) were placed a light-year from the sun or any other such star, it would collect about 20 hydrogen atoms. Compare this with a cup of air, which contains about 10^{22} atoms of mostly nitrogen and oxygen.
Describe nebulae.

15:3 Interstellar Matter

Gas and dust between stars in galaxies is called interstellar matter. *Inter* means between and *stellar* has to do with stars. Interstellar gas is mostly hydrogen and helium. Interstellar dust is water, ice, silicon compounds, and graphite. Some ellipticals have almost no interstellar matter. Some spirals, like the Milky Way, have as much mass in interstellar gas in their spiral arms as they have in all their stars. Concentrations of interstellar matter are called **nebulae.** Nebulae appear dense. However, the volume of space they occupy is large. The distances between particles is so great that a nebula is actually a better vacuum than can be produced on Earth.

Also, there are dark clouds of dust and gas. A dark cloud contains nonionized hydrogen and other atoms and dust. Deep inside dark clouds, away from all starlight, many molecules can exist. More than 50 different molecules, including alcohols and water, have been detected by the radio waves they emit through the dark clouds. Very large dark clouds are called giant molecular clouds. Giant molecular clouds are the places where gas pulls together to form new stars. Astronomers have observed dark globules, too, outlined against starry backgrounds in many parts of the sky.

Nebulae near very luminous stars glow. These nebulae are called bright nebulae. The hydrogen gas in a bright nebula absorbs ultraviolet radiation emitted by the nearby stars. The radiation heats the hydrogen to a very high temperature and causes the nebula to fluoresce like a neon sign. Bright nebulae that are mostly dust reflect the light of nearby stars.

Some nebulae are not near brighter stars. Dark nebulae appear as silhouettes against a bright background of distant stars. Figure 15–5 shows examples of bright and dark nebulae.

BACKGROUND   Bright nebulae are also known as reflection nebulae.

What happens in giant molecular clouds?

What causes some nebulae to glow?

FIGURE 15–5.   Reflection nebulas in the Pleidaes cluster contain dust grains, which reflect and scatter light from nearby stars (a). The Horsehead Nebula is a dark nebula in which clouds of gas and dust are opaque preventing starlight from passing through (b).

a

b

See Teacher's Guide.

REVIEW AND REFLECT

1. How are galaxies organized within the universe?
2. Sketch and describe a(n)
   a. spiral galaxy
   b. irregular galaxy
   c. elliptical galaxy
3. Describe the nature of
   a. bright nebulae
   b. dark nebulae
   c. giant molecular clouds
4. If you could ride a spaceship at the speed of 96 km/h (just over normal highway speed), how long would it take to cross the Milky Way Galaxy? The Milky Way is about 1×10^{18} km in diameter.

15:4 The Sun

Why does the sun appear to be the largest and brightest star?

The closest star to the Earth and the easiest to study is the sun. The sun is smaller than many of the bright stars in the sky. It appears larger and brighter because it is much closer to the Earth—1.5×10^7 kilometers away. The next closest star to the Earth is about 4.1×10^{13} kilometers away.

Although the sun appears solid, it is composed entirely of gases. The sun rotates, but not in the same way that a solid globe rotates. The gas at the sun's equator rotates more quickly than the gas near its poles. The sun is divided into layers as shown in Figure 15–6. Characteristics of each layer are also listed.

BACKGROUND There is a gradual blending of one solar layer into the next.

What are sunspots?

The part of the sun you see is the photosphere. Within the photosphere are dark spots called sunspots. Sunspots appear dark because they are cooler than the surrounding photosphere. Sunspots vary in size. Some are larger than the Earth's diameter. The number of sunspots increases and decreases over a cycle of about 11 years. Other sun changes follow this cycle as well. A year when the greatest number of spots occur in a sunspot cycle is known as the solar maximum. The most recent solar maximum was 1980. Sunspots seem to be related to the magnetic fields on the sun. Some scientists think that our weather is affected by changes on the sun. Droughts and rainfall patterns often seem to follow the sunspot cycle, for example.

Bursts of energy called **flares** are associated with sunspots. During a flare, bursts of X rays and gamma rays as well as visible light are released. Charged atomic particles may be blasted from the sun into space. Some of the particles may be trapped by the Earth's magnetic field. Radio communications and electric power are disrupted as a result. As the sun rotates, sunspots move around the sun. Flare particles can be predicted to fly toward Earth when a sunspot is near the center of the sun's disk. Predictions of flares are valuable in communications work and in space travel.

The charged atomic particles released when solar flares occur also cause vivid auroras. Auroras are shimmering colored lights seen in the night sky near the Earth's north and south poles. The Earth's poles are places where charged sun particles can "rain" down onto the air. When

What are flares? How do they affect the Earth?

BACKGROUND   A special NASA satellite, the Solar Mission Satellite, studied X rays and gamma rays during the last solar maximum, 1980. A satellite is necessary for such study because this radiation cannot be detected within the Earth's atmosphere.

What causes auroras?

BACKGROUND   Another place besides flares, where particles are emitted in large amounts, is near the sun's poles in cooler parts of the corona called "coronal holes."

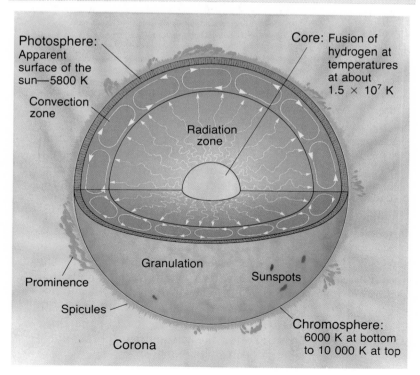

Photosphere: Apparent surface of the sun—5800 K

Convection zone

Core: Fusion of hydrogen at temperatures at about 1.5×10^7 K

Radiation zone

Granulation

Sunspots

Prominence

Spicules

Corona

Chromosphere: 6000 K at bottom to 10 000 K at top

FIGURE   15–6. Features and structures of the sun

the particles collide with air molecules, the electrons in the atoms of gases move to higher energy levels. As the electrons return to their lower energy levels, the atoms emit visible light seen as an aurora.

See Teacher's Guide.

Career Profile

For Shelly Garland, becoming a planetarium assistant was a dream come true. Ever since the third grade when she witnessed her first planetarium show, Shelly has been fascinated by the sky. In high school, she served as president of the astronomy club. At Richland College in Dallas, Texas, she studied astronomy and did volunteer work producing slides of the night sky. After earning her degree, Shelly did four years of volunteer work at the Nobel Planetarium at the Museum of Science and History Planetarium in Fort Worth. Now she has a full-time position as a planetarium assistant for this museum.

During the week, Shelly narrates two 45-minute slide shows a day for students. An especially exciting show developed for young children is called "Neighbors in Space." For this age group, she produced a slide show that simulates a trip to the moon. Shelly uses slides to show such special effects as the sunrise over Mercury. She uses a star projector to show the sky as it will appear at night over Fort Worth.

Shelly also develops slide shows for the public that center on current topics. For example, "How to Watch a Flying Saucer" is a popular show that demonstrates how Venus can be mistaken for a UFO. On the job, Shelly enjoys helping people gain a better understanding of astronomy.

Occasionally, Shelly makes special appearances on television to talk about astronomy. Sometimes she accompanies astronomers on searches for meteorites that have fallen in Texas. In order to produce a slide show about the space shuttle program, Shelly traveled to Florida to photograph the launching of the shuttle.

Shelly enjoys her work because each day brings something exciting and different. She loves meeting and working with people, and she appreciates the opportunities she has to be creative. Shelly recommends that young people who are interested in planetarium work first become volunteers. In this way, they can learn most of the skills necessary for the job and can be available when a position opens up.

15:5 Other Stars

What we know about the sun helps us understand other stars. As more is learned about distant stars, astronomers find that other stars have features like the sun. For example, other stars have photospheres with starspots (like sunspots), coronas, and chromospheres.

Astronomers also find differences between the sun and other stars. The sun appears to be a single star. About two thirds of all stars are binary star systems. A binary is a double star. When a companion star is present, the shape and history of a star are affected. The photospheres of some stars are hotter than the sun while others are much cooler. There are stars with over 30 times the sun's mass. There are stars with as little as 0.1 of the sun's mass. A few stars have diameters as large as the orbit of Mars. A few stars have diameters as small as the Earth. Some stars are brighter than the sun and some are not as bright. How bright stars appear to us on Earth depends not only on how bright they are, but also on how far away they are. Remember that many stars actually are brighter than the sun, but the sun appears brighter because it is so close. Absolute brightness is a comparison of how bright stars would be if they were all the same distance away.

The color of a star is determined by its temperature. The hotter a star is, the whiter or bluer it appears. The cooler a star is, the redder it appears. When the light of a star is spread out into its spectrum, it shows certain features that depend mostly on surface temperature. Stars are classified on the basis of their spectra. The spectral classes from hottest to coolest are O, B, A, F, G, K, M.

An **H-R diagram** is a graph that shows the relationship between the spectral class of a star and its luminosity. **Luminosity** is the rate at which a star radiates energy, often compared with the sun. Stars that are the same temperature radiate equal amounts of energy per unit area. So, it might seem that stars in the same spectral class should have the same luminosities. However, from the H-R diagram in Figure 15–7, you can see that they do not. The differences in luminosity are due to star size. A more massive star radiates more total energy than a less massive star at the same temperature.

Compare the sun with other stars.

BACKGROUND The actual appearance of star colors is that of pastel chalk. Thus a star called "red" is actually light orange, such as the red giant star Betelgeuse in Orion.

What determines star color?

SUGGESTION Students can remember the sequence of spectral classes by the first letters of: "Oh, Be A Fine Girl. Kiss Me."

What is an H-R diagram?

BACKGROUND Note that the sun, a yellow G-class star, is an intermediate class in the sequence.

FIGURE 15–7. On the H-R diagram, stars are classified according to their spectral type, temperature, and color in relation to their true brightness. The majority of stars lie along a diagonal band called the main sequence.

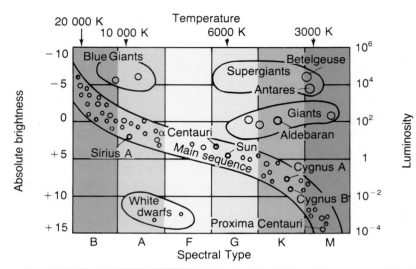

BACKGROUND   The H-R diagram, a type of graph, was named for the Danish astronomer E. Hertzsprung and the American astronomer Henry Norris Russell, who independently began plotting stars in this way.

What effect does star mass have on other star characteristics?

A star's mass controls its brightness and its color. The larger a star's mass, the brighter and bluer it shines for most of its life. A star that has a small mass is dim and red. In Figure 15–7, note that the dots representing the stars fall into groups. The slightly S-shaped curve is known as the main sequence. Note that the sun is a main sequence star.

Scientists have used H-R diagrams to determine how far away stars are. Most stars are too far away to measure their distances directly. So scientists calculate distances indirectly, noting each star's spectral class. The luminosity of a star can be determined from an H-R diagram. Then the absolute magnitude this luminosity represents is compared with the apparent magnitude to find the star's distance.

See Teacher's Guide.

REVIEW AND REFLECT

1. What are sunspots? Why are they important?
2. How is the sun similar to other stars? different?
3. How are each of the following related?
   a. star temperature and star color
   b. star mass and star temperature
   c. temperature and star spectrum
4. What affects the brightness of a star in the night sky?
5. Why do scientists have difficulty concluding if changes in weather are related to the sunspot cycle?

Activity: How is absolute brightness found?

See Teacher's Guide.

MATERIALS

dark area
2 bulbs—15 watts, 75 watts
photometer
meter stick
socket (for bulb) with wire and plug

FIGURE 15–8.

PROCEDURE

1. Draw a sketch of the photometer scale.
2. Move to the dark area.
3. Place the 15-watt bulb at a distance of 50 cm from the photometer. Determine the apparent brightness of the bulb by reading the needle on the photometer. Record this value in your data table. Mark the position of the photometer needle on your sketch and label the mark as "15 watts, 50 cm."
4. Use the inverse square law,
$$\frac{I_1}{(d_1)^2} = \frac{I_2}{(d_2)^2}$$
to predict the brightness of the 15-watt bulb at a distance of 100 cm. I_1 is the apparent brightness you determined with the photometer. d_1 is 50 cm. d_2 is 100 cm. I_2 is the absolute brightness predicted.
5. Check your prediction by measuring the brightness of the 15-watt bulb at 100 cm with the photometer. Record this value.
6. Place the 75-watt bulb at a distance of 200 cm from the photometer. **CAUTION:** *To avoid electric shock, be sure to unplug the wire before changing bulbs.* Find and record the apparent brightness of the bulb with the photometer.
7. Use the inverse square law to predict the absolute brightness of the 75-watt bulb at a distance of 100 cm.
8. Check your prediction. Record.

DATA AND OBSERVATIONS

Bulb		15-watt	75-watt
Brightness	Apparent		
	Absolute Predicted		
	Absolute Measured		

QUESTIONS AND CONCLUSIONS

1. How is absolute brightness found? What information must one have to determine a star's absolute brightness?
2. Why is absolute brightness rather than apparent brightness used in the H-R diagram?
3. Why is the apparent brightness of the sun greater than that of every other star?
4. What are the possible reasons for a star's dimness in the sky?
5. How are your distance measurements in this activity different from astronomers' measurements of star distances?

15:6 Star Evolution

The sun and other main sequence stars are stable. To be stable, a star's outward and inward forces must be balanced. Gravity from within a star causes it to contract. The gravity is balanced by radiation from a steady production of energy within the star that causes it to expand. In stable stars, hydrogen nuclei fuse in a series of nuclear reactions producing helium and energy. A little mass is converted to a lot of energy. As the hydrogen in stars is used up, changes occur. This set of changes, from when stars form until they die, is called star evolution.

When a large cloud of gas and dust begins to break up, some areas of the cloud may condense under gravitational force into shrinking dark globules. The contraction causes an increase in temperature. When the temperature reaches more than 1.0×10^6 K, nuclear fusion of hydrogen into helium begins, and a star is "born."

The young star continues to shrink until the pressure from the radiation caused by the nuclear fusion balances the force of gravity. Then the star is a stable star. It starts its longest stage of life, as a **main sequence** star.

BACKGROUND Break-up probably is caused by slow turbulent motions within a cloud.

What is star evolution?

FIGURE 15–9. Stars are born from dark globules within a nebula. The longest stage after formation is the main sequence. After the red giant stage, small stars shed their outer layers and become white dwarfs. Stars with larger masses usually become neutron stars after supernovae. A star with 30 to 50 times the sun's mass becomes a black hole.

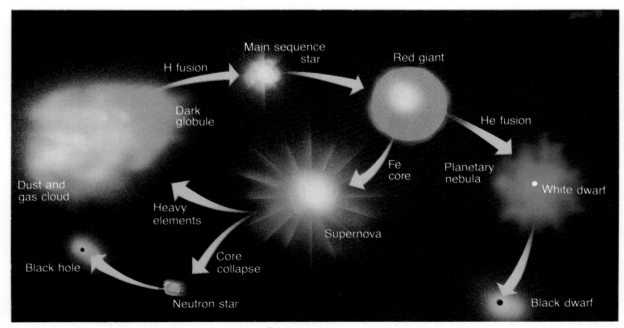

A star's mass appears to control not only its brightness and its surface temperature but its evolution as well. A massive star converts hydrogen to helium quickly. Its total life is shorter, since it is a "spendthrift" star, using up its energy in a relatively short time. A less massive star converts hydrogen to helium more slowly. Its life may be several thousand times longer than the life of a more massive star.

Eventually the hydrogen at a star's center is used up. The star begins a new stage in its evolution. Gravity causes the helium core formed by fusion to shrink to a smaller volume. As a result, the core temperature rises to about 1.0×10^8 K. At this temperature, helium is converted to carbon by nuclear fusion. Meanwhile, the added radiation from a hotter center upsets the balance of forces in the stable star. The star expands, becoming a **red giant.**

Nuclear reactions in red giant stars sometimes continue, forming elements heavier than carbon. Eventually the elements that fuel the nuclear reactions in red giants are used up. The stars collapse from the inward force of their own gravity, becoming **white dwarfs.** Without a source of energy the stars gradually get cooler and dimmer, "dying" as black dwarfs.

Some stars may go through other stages. A star's mass may be reduced by explosions that send out clouds of matter from the star. The explosions may occur over and over again. They cause the star, called a **nova,** to brighten suddenly. Most novae are thought to occur due to interaction between a pair of binary stars.

In very massive stars, temperatures are high enough to convert the carbon core into iron by fusion. After the formation of iron in the red giant stage, fusion can no longer occur. The star collapses violently followed by a tremendous explosion. During the explosion, the heavier elements, such as uranium, are produced. Such a stellar explosion is called a **supernova.** The Crab Nebula, Figure 15–11a, is the matter ejected from a supernova. The supernova that made the Crab Nebula was viewed in daylight for 23 days by Chinese astronomers in 1054 A.D.

After a supernova explosion, a "star remnant" is left. The remnant may become a neutron star. A **neutron star** is a very dense object consisting entirely of neutrons. A

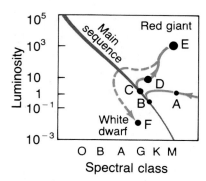

FIGURE 15–10. After initial contraction (A), the sun began hydrogen fusion about five billion years ago (B). Eventually it will leave its current position (C) and will begin to expand about five billion years from now (D). In six billion years it will begin helium fusion (E) before it eventually becomes a white dwarf (F).

Describe the red giant and white dwarf stages of a star's life.

What is a supernova?

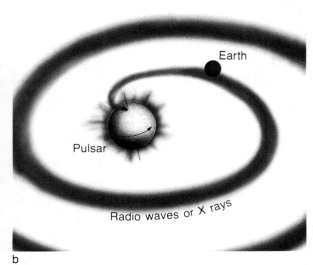

a   b

FIGURE 15–11. The Crab Nebula is a remnant of a supernova that occurred more than 900 years ago (a). A spinning neutron star, or pulsar, emits bursts of energy as it rapidly rotates (b).

spoonful of neutron star matter would weigh millions of metric tons on earth.

For a few hundred years after the supernova, its neutron star spins very rapidly. One neutron star observed spins as fast as 642 times per second. As a neutron star spins, a shower of radiation is sent out like the blink of light from a lighthouse. Our direction of space gets sprayed with radiation with every turn. Because they emit pulses of radiation, some neutron stars are also called pulsars.

What is a black hole?

More massive star remnants left after supernovae are predicted to become stellar black holes. A **black hole** is even more dense than a neutron star. Its gravity is so great that radiation is bent back on itself and cannot leave the star. A black hole would appear dark, blocking the light of background stars. Although no one has directly observed a black hole, evidence indicates that they exist.

See Teacher's Guide.

REVIEW AND REFLECT

1. a. What conditions make a stable star?
   b. How do stable stars produce energy?
2. How is a star born?
3. Briefly describe the stages of star evolution for the sun.
4. How is a star's mass related to its length of life?
5. How were the Earth's elements formed?

Activity: What determines the powers of a telescope?

MATERIALS

3 convex lenses of different short focal
   lengths (5–10 cm): the eyepieces
2 convex lenses with longer focal lengths,
   different diameters: the objectives
ring stand
buret clamp
2 lens holders
a screen (metal or cardboard frame) with a
   hole about 4 cm in diameter covered with
   thin white paper
meter stick
metric ruler

FIGURE 15–12.

PROCEDURE

1. Place the meter stick horizontally on the
   ring stand with the buret clamp. Place
   one lens holder near an end of the meter
   stick.

2. Place a lens in the lens holder. Adjust
   the screen to form a clear image of a distant object such as a tree or part of a
   building. See Figure 15–12.

3. Repeat step 2 to measure and record the
   focal length of each of the five lenses.

4. Place the objective lens with the small
   diameter in the lens holder. Hold the
   screen at the focal length of this lens.
   Put an eyepiece lens in the second lens
   holder. Mount this holder on the opposite
   side of the screen. **CAUTION:** *Do not
   look at the sun or a bright light.* Slide the
   holder along the stick until you see the
   image of a distinct object on the screen.
   Measure and record the distance from
   the eyepiece to the screen. Describe the
   image. Remove the screen and note what
   you see.

5. Repeat step 4 with the two other eyepieces.

6. Replace the small objective with the
   larger objective. Use each eyepiece again
   to see an image. Compare these images
   with those seen with the small objective.
   Record your comparisons.

DATA AND OBSERVATIONS

Eyepiece	Focal Length	Objective	Focal Length
1		1	
2			
3		2	

QUESTIONS AND CONCLUSIONS

1. How did varying the eyepiece used with
   each objective affect the image?

2. What is the relationship between eyepiece focal length and magnification?

3. How did using an objective with a larger
   diameter affect the image?

4. Why can't you see faint sky objects better with a small telescope by replacing
   the eyepiece with another of shorter focal length?

5. An ad for a telescope says that it is a 120
   power telescope. What do you think this
   means? Why is it misleading?

15:7 Information: The Celestial Sphere

As you know stars and other objects are located at various distances from the Earth. However, when you observe the night sky, the stars and planets appear to be located on the inside of a large sphere. One half of the sphere is visible above the horizon. The other half, which cannot be seen, is below the horizon. This sphere of sky is known as the celestial sphere. The celestial sphere is a useful model because it helps astronomers locate objects in the sky. The Earth is represented as a small point in the center of the sphere. See Figure 15–13.

On the celestial sphere, an object is located by using a system of circles similar to Earth's latitude and longitude. On the Earth, the east or west location of an object is measured in degrees of longitude. The location north or south is given in degrees of latitude. The circles of longitude and latitude are referred to as a coordinate system.

To locate a star on the celestial sphere, you must determine its position relative to the celestial equator. The celestial equator is the imaginary circle where the plane of the Earth's equator intersects the celestial sphere. The term declination is used to describe the location north or south of the celestial equator. Declination is like latitude measured on the Earth. Declination is measured in degrees, °, and minutes, ′. Points having a declination of 90° are called the celestial poles.

Measuring positions east or west on the celestial sphere is somewhat different from measuring longitude on the Earth. Recall that the Prime Meridian, passing through Greenwich, England, represents 0°. Measurements in degrees can be made either east or west in relation to the Prime Meridian. On the celestial sphere, the starting place is determined by the sun's position on the first day of spring. This position is called the vernal equinox. The term right ascension is used to describe the distance measured in an eastward direction only. Circles of right ascension pass through the north and south celestial poles. The main circles are spaced 15° apart and are called hour circles. Right ascension is measured in hours and minutes of arc.

What is the celestial sphere?

FIGURE 15–13. The celestial sphere is a projection of Earth's equator and poles on an imaginary sphere (a). A star's position is determined by its right ascension and declination (b).

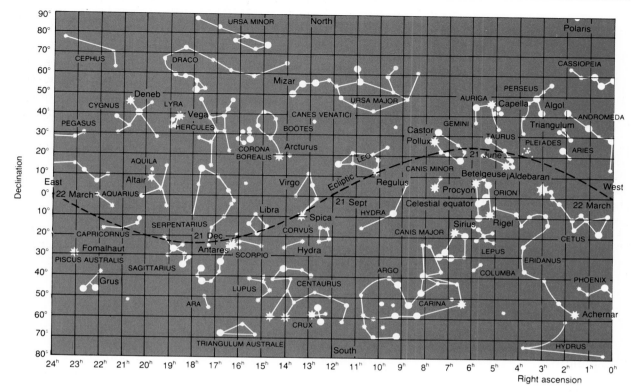

FIGURE 15–14. A celestial map shows the positions of stars and constellations.

Figure 15–14 is a flat projection of the celestial sphere called a star chart. A star's position changes very little on the celestial sphere in a human lifetime. Therefore, right ascension and declination are like a star's permanent address. Betelgeuse, for example, is a red giant in the Orion constellation. On the star chart, Betelgeuse is located at about 5 h 50 min right ascension and about + 7° 24′ declination.

See Teacher's Guide.

REVIEW AND REFLECT

1. Why is the celestial sphere described as a model?
2. Why is a star's declination and right ascension considered to be the star's permanent address?
3. How are right ascension and longitude different?
4. How does the horizon change with respect to the celestial sphere as the Earth rotates?

SUMMARY

1. The theory of the origin of the universe best supported by scientific evidence is the Big Bang.   15:1

2. The universe is organized into clusters and superclusters of galaxies.   15:2

3. The three major types of galaxies are spirals, irregulars, and ellipticals.   15:2

4. Much gas and dust exist among the stars.   15:3

5. New stars form from the dust and gas in giant molecular clouds.   15:3

6. Scientists can learn about stars by studying the sun because it is a typical star.   15:4

7. The color, surface temperature, brightness, and diameter of a star for most of its life are determined largely by its mass.   15:5

8. A stable star has a main sequence position on the H-R diagram and produces energy by nuclear fusion of hydrogen to helium.   15:6

9. End stages of star evolution include white dwarfs, black dwarfs, neutron stars, and black holes.   15:6

10. Lighter elements were formed in the Big Bang and heavier elements were formed within stars.   15:6

VOCABULARY

Big Bang   7
black hole   13
elliptical galaxy   5
flare   1
H-R diagram   8
irregular galaxy   16

luminosity   2
main sequence   10
nebulae   4
neutron star   14
nova   3

quasar   6
red giant   9
spiral galaxy   15
supernova   11
white dwarf   12

Match each definition with the correct word from the list.

1. A burst of energy from the sun associated with sunspots

2. The rate at which a star radiates energy

3. A star that brightens suddenly due to explosions sending out clouds of matter

4. Concentrations of interstellar matter

5. Has a smooth, round, or oval outline

6. A massive object that may shine as bright as 1000 galaxies, but varies in brightness in a few days

7. A theory of the origin of the universe

8. A graph that shows the relationship between the absolute brightness and spectral class of stars

9. An unstable stage in a star's life when nuclear reactions within it form elements heavier than carbon

10. The longest stage in a star's life

11. A tremendous explosion preceded by a violent collapse of a star in which fusion can no longer occur due to the formation of iron

12. An unstable stage in a less massive star's life, forms when it collapses from the inward force of its own gravity

13. An object so dense that its radiation cannot leave because its gravity is great

14. A very dense object made only of neutrons

15. Is disk-shaped with a center bulge and rapidly rotating arms

16. Has a patchy, noncircular appearance

QUESTIONS

MAIN IDEAS

Choose the correct answer to complete each sentence.

1. According to the Big Bang theory, the age of the universe is closest to *(10^3, 10^6, 10^{10})* years.

2. Helium is thought to have formed *(shortly after the Big Bang, in stable stars, shortly after the Big Bang and in stable stars)*.

3. The Milky Way is a(n) *(spiral, elliptical, irregular)* galaxy.

4. Elements are now forming in *(the Big Bang, stars, black holes)*.

5. Quasars *(probably were common in the young universe, have no radiation escaping them, are one type of object formed at the end of star evolution)*.

6. The Horsehead Nebula is an example of a *(black hole, dark nebula, corona)*.

7. An important star feature that controls many other features is *(mass, color, distance from the sun)*.

8. Someday, the sun probably will be a *(black hole, neutron star, white dwarf)*.

9. Flare particles and auroras are associated with *(the production of energy at the Earth's center, the Crab Nebula's neutron star, solar activity)*.

10. A star on the H-R diagram with high luminosity and a spectral class of M would be a *(white dwarf, black hole, red giant)*.

See Teacher's Guide.

APPLICATIONS

Answer each question in one or more paragraphs.

1. What is the relationship between temperature and density of the universe in relation to the events following the Big Bang?

2. What would happen to a beam of light as it passed very close to a black hole?

3. Why do solar flares sometimes disrupt radio and television communications on Earth?

4. What happens to a star's spectrum as the star approaches the Earth?

5. Calculations involving the numbers and distances of stars in the Milky Way show that the night sky would be as bright as day. Why is the night sky as dark as it is?

FURTHER STUDY

INVESTIGATIONS

1. Write a poem or prepare another creative interpretation of the Big Bang.

2. Draw, paint, or make a three-dimensional model of one of the objects or materials of the universe.

3. Obtain a map of the constellations of the current night sky. Find at least five constellations. Draw the constellations and record the colors you observe for the brightest stars of each constellation.

4. Visit an observatory to learn about astronomers' work.

READINGS

+ Asimov, Isaac. *The Universe.* 3d ed. Walker and Company: New York, 1980.

+ Bartusiak, Marcia. "Missing: 97% of the Universe." *Science Digest.* December, 1983. pp. 51–57, 120–122.

+ Ferris, Timothy. *The Red Limit.* 2d ed. Quill: New York, 1983.

0 Jacobs, Francine. *Cosmic Countdown.* M. Evans: New York, 1983.

0 Jenkins, Edward B. "The Stuff Between the Stars." *Science Year, 1981.* 1980. pp. 156–169.

HAVE you ever looked through a telescope at the night sky? The students in the picture find the night sky interesting. Perhaps you, like them, have wondered what the distant objects in space are like. What objects can you see with a telescope? What objects are there that you cannot see? What have scientists learned about the solar system?

THE SOLAR SYSTEM

INTRODUCING THE CHAPTER   Most students know some things about the solar system from past study. Find out what they know and their misconceptions by discussing objects, motions, and the study of space before they begin reading the chapter. A common misconception is the size of the solar system. Many students may think that the planets are much closer together than they really are. You may want to have students construct a scale model of the solar system using objects such as a pea, a walnut, and an orange for planets, set up in the gym.

16:1   The Origin of the Solar System

The solar system is thought to have formed about five billion years ago from a rotating gas and dust cloud. Along with hydrogen and helium, the cloud contained some heavier elements, probably produced by a supernova. According to the **nebular theory** of the origin of the solar system, the cloud rotated faster and faster. It flattened into a disk and shrank. Contraction continued until the density became great enough for fusion to occur at the center. The sun was born. At different distances from the young sun, small currents caused matter in the disk to separate. Due to gravity, the matter collapsed into spheres. The spheres of matter became larger, like small snowballs rolled in the snow, as they revolved around the sun. Radioactive elements in the spheres heated matter so that the spheres melted. When the spheres cooled, they became the planets.

Matter in the early cloud that was not pulled into the planets became the other objects, such as moons, in the solar system. At later times, collisions changed many of the original objects.

GOAL   You will learn the nature of the objects in the solar system and some ways people have learned about them.

DEMONSTRATION   Watch a film, such as the NASA "Universe" film, which shows the solar system forming from a nebula.

How are the sun and planets thought to have formed?

Today, the solar system as we know it contains nine planets that revolve about the sun. The **revolution** of an object is its motion in its orbit around another object. Many objects revolve in orbits that are close to the plane of the **ecliptic.** The ecliptic is the plane of the Earth's orbit. The planets also rotate. **Rotation** is the spinning motion of an object on its axis. See Figure 16–1. Other objects in the solar system also revolve and rotate.

What is the plane of the ecliptic?

SUGGESTION Visit a planetarium, ask for demonstrations of the following: (1) Earth rotation, (2) motion of the sun along the ecliptic resulting from Earth revolution, (3) introduction of naked-eye planets, noting their positions relative to the ecliptic, (4) speeded motion of the planets, noting that paths closely follow the ecliptic.

16:2 Early Ideas of the Solar System

About 500 B.C., Greek thinkers proposed that the planets, sun, and moon moved on spheres that rotated about the Earth. More careful observations of the planets show that they appear to back up along their normal paths. This motion is called retrograde motion. It was first explained by Claudius Ptolemy, a second century Greek. According to the Ptolemaic theory, as shown in Figure 16–2, the Earth was thought to be stationary. In 1543, during the European Renaissance, Nicholas Copernicus (1473–1543) of Poland published a different

Compare the theories of Ptolemy and Copernicus.

BACKGROUND Ptolemy's theory was geocentric, meaning Earth-centered. Copernicus's theory was heliocentric, or sun-centered. Aristarchus of Samos (c. 310–230 B.C.) was the first known person to suggest a heliocentric theory for the solar system.

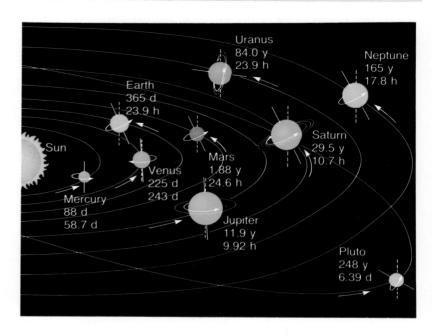

FIGURE 16–1. Planets revolve around the sun in elliptical orbits and rotate about their axes. Except for Mercury, the axis of each planet is tilted with respect to the plane of its orbit.

theory. According to the Copernican theory, the Earth was considered a planet revolving about the sun in a circular orbit. When Copernicus presented his theory, there was no scientific proof that it was any more correct than the Ptolemaic theory. The plan just seemed simpler and therefore better.

Another Renaissance thinker, a German named Johannes Kepler (1571–1630), found problems with the Copernican theory. Kepler found that the orbits of planets were not circles. The data plotted for the position of Mars showed that the orbit of Mars and every other planet is an ellipse. An ellipse is a closed curve in which the sum of the distance to a point on the curve from two fixed points is constant. In other words, an ellipse is a slightly flattened circle. The sun is at an inside point called a focus. This idea became known as Kepler's First Law of Planetary Motion.

Late in the 1600s, Sir Isaac Newton of England published his ideas. He set the stage for understanding motions within the solar system as well as the universe. Newton's First Law of Motion explained the natural tendency of a moving object to continue in a straight line at constant speed. Newton's Law of Gravitation states that every object in the universe attracts every other object. The law explained why the planets do not move into space in a straight line, but orbit the sun according to Kepler's Laws.

In 1916, Albert Einstein of Germany published his general theory of relativity. In this theory, Einstein said it is not necessary to think of gravitation as the force pulling objects closer. Instead, he said that time and space are distorted around every object in space. Time and space are most distorted around the objects with the most mass.

See Teacher's Guide.

REVIEW AND REFLECT

1. What is the difference between revolution and rotation?
2. Briefly describe the nebular theory.
3. How does the history of changing ideas about the solar system show international involvement?
4. Would an outer planet such as Saturn show a shorter or longer retrograde motion path than Mars?

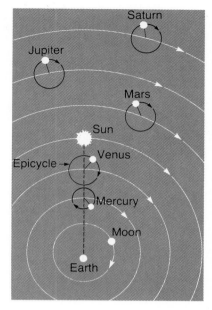

FIGURE 16–2. According to the Ptolemaic model of the solar system, the Earth did not move. Each planet and the sun revolved around the Earth. Retrograde motion was explained by a movement called an epicycle.

What did Newton contribute to our understanding of the solar system?

BACKGROUND Kepler developed two other laws of planetary motion. Second Law: A line between a planet and the sun sweeps out equal areas within the ellipse in equal intervals. Third Law: The squares of the periods of revolution of the planets are directly proportional to the cubes of the semi-major axes of their orbits.

16:3 Earth and Its Moon

As we look from Earth into space, it is not obvious the Earth is rotating and revolving. A large sphere seems to carry the sun, stars, and other planets around us. It is easy to understand why people once thought that the Earth did not move.

Observations show that the Earth rotates and revolves. The period of rotation is about 23 hours and 56 minutes. This turning of Earth on its axis results in day and night. The Earth's revolution period is about 365¼ days, or about one year. The Earth revolves about the sun in a nearly circular orbit about 300 million kilometers in diameter. However, what moves about the sun is not the center of the Earth. It is the center of mass of the earth-moon system called the barycenter. Locate this point in Figure 16–3a. The center of the Earth and the moon's center both revolve about the barycenter. The revolution period of the moon around the barycenter is about 27⅓ days. The moon rotates in the same period that it takes to revolve. For this reason, the same side of the moon always faces the Earth.

The relative positions of the sun, Earth, and moon are always changing. As a result, the half of the moon lit by the sun is not always completely visible from Earth. We observe the phases of the moon shown in Figure 16–3b. A **phase cycle** is a complete set of changes—from new moon to new moon. The phase cycle takes about 29½ days or

What is the basis of the day and year?

What is the barycenter?

FIGURE 16–3. Both the moon and the Earth revolve around a common center called the barycenter (a). The phase cycle of the moon is shown (b).

a

b

a

b

FIGURE 16–4.   A time-lapse photograph of a solar eclipse shows the Earth passing through the moon's shadow (a). The moon passes through the Earth's shadow during a lunar eclipse (b).

about one month. In fact, the word month comes from "moon."

A **solar eclipse** occurs when the new moon lies in the plane of the ecliptic and casts a shadow on the earth. A solar eclipse is shown in Figure 16–4a. A lunar eclipse is shown in Figure 16–4b. A **lunar eclipse** occurs when the full moon lies in the plane of the ecliptic. Even though it is in the Earth's shadow, the full moon appears copper-colored because the longer wavelengths of sunlight are refracted by the Earth's atmosphere into the shadow. The short wavelengths are absorbed by the Earth's atmosphere.

Between 1969 and 1972, six Apollo spacecraft carried astronauts to the moon. Two astronauts from each successful mission collected and studied rocks and soil. They explored both the light-colored lunar highlands and the dark, smoother lowlands called maria (MAH ree uh). Some of the rocks brought back to Earth by the astronauts were found to be more than 4 billion years old. The rocks contain no organic materials or water. The great age of the lunar rocks shows that the moon formed about the same time as the Earth. It is not yet known, however, if the moon and the Earth were formed together or separately.

The oldest rocks, as well as most of the craters, make up the lunar highlands. The craters are thought to have resulted when meteoroids crashed into the surface more than three billion years ago. Meteoroids crashed onto the Earth, too. However, most that might have hit the Earth were burned up in the atmosphere before reaching the surface. Erosion has destroyed the Earth's ancient craters formed by meteoroids that did reach the surface.

Describe the positions of the Earth, sun, and moon during a solar and lunar eclipse.

ACTIVITY   Have students drop marbles into slightly wet plaster-of-Paris or into bentonite to simulate the formation of craters. Marbles may be rolled down grooved rulers to simulate meteorites striking from various angles.

How are lunar craters thought to have formed?

FIGURE 16–5. The darker lunar lowlands or maria were the result of extensive lava flows when the moon's surface erupted between 2.5 and 3 billion years ago.

Describe Earth's core and mantle.

The Apollo missions found that the lowland maria, Figure 16–5, are areas once filled with as many craters as the highlands. Each lowland was formed as an asteroid struck the moon. Lava welled up from the moon's interior, filling old craters.

The moon we observe today appears much like the moon observed by ancient astronomers. A few large craters may have formed in the past three billion years, but meteoroids are much less abundant in the solar system than they were then. Tinier particles still bombard the surface and may smooth it slightly. The lack of water and an atmosphere on the moon prevent erosion of the craters. Because of the moon's small mass, its gravitational force is much less than that of the Earth. Therefore, if water vapor and other gases were present, they would have escaped into space. Gravity and solar wind change the moon's features very slowly. The solar wind is a continuous flow of hydrogen nuclei and electrons emitted by the sun into space.

Earth is an inner planet. It consists of a core, mantle, and crust. The core contains mostly iron and nickel. It extends more than halfway to the surface. The core accounts for about one third of the Earth's mass. Through scientific study, it has been determined that the inner regions of the core are solid, while the outer regions are liquid. Slow movements within the core are thought to produce Earth's magnetic field.

During Earth's early years, when heavier molten elements sank toward the center, less dense materials moved to the outer edges. The outer layer became the mantle. The thin outer crust is a solid light layer that actually floats on the mantle. Although the mantle is mostly solid, scientists believe that extreme heat and pressure cause parts of the mantle to move very slowly. These movements are thought to be the cause of changes that we observe in the crust today.

See Teacher's Guide.

REVIEW AND REFLECT

1. Describe the movement of the Earth-moon system.
2. Why has there been so little change in the moon's features since they were formed?
3. Describe what you would see during a total solar eclipse.

Activity: How do models of the solar system compare?

See Teacher's Guide.

MATERIALS

flashlight   Ping-Pong ball

PROCEDURE

Part A   Copernican Model

1. Work in a group with two other students. Play the roles of the sun, moon, and Earth. When you are the Earth, record your observations of retrograde motion and phases of the planets.

2. **Sun**: Shine the flashlight on the Ping-Pong ball. **Planet**: Hold the Ping-Pong ball above your head to represent a planet. Standing between the Earth and the sun, walk quickly counterclockwise around the sun. **Earth**: Walk counterclockwise around the sun more slowly than the planet.

3. **Sun**: Shine the flashlight on the Ping-Pong ball. **Planet**: Standing beyond the Earth, walk slowly around the sun. **Earth**: Walk counterclockwise around the sun more quickly than the planet.

4. Repeat steps 2 and 3 two more times so that each person represents the Earth.

Part B   Ptolemaic Model

1. **Sun**: Shine the flashlight on the Earth as you revolve counterclockwise at a constant rate around it. **Earth**: Stand still. **Planet**: Hold the Ping-Pong ball above your head. Standing between the Earth and sun, walk in a small circle (the epicycle) counterclockwise around an imaginary point that revolves counterclockwise around the Earth. Imagine that a straight line always connects the sun, the imaginary point, and the Earth, Figure 16–6.

2. **Sun**: Shine the flashlight on the Earth as you revolve counterclockwise at a constant rate around it. **Earth**: Stand still.

Planet: Hold the Ping-Pong ball above your head. Standing beyond the sun, walk in a small circle counterclockwise around an imaginary point that revolves around the Earth. This time there is no line connecting the point, the sun, and the Earth. The imaginary point moves counterclockwise more slowly than the sun.

3. Repeat steps 2 and 3 two more times so that each person represents the Earth.

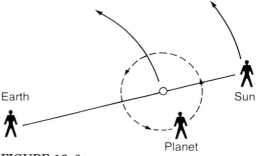

FIGURE 16–6.

DATA AND OBSERVATIONS

Views From Earth	Model:	
	Retrograde Motion	**Phases Seen**
Inner Planet		
Outer Planet		

QUESTIONS AND CONCLUSIONS

1. When did you see retrograde motion?

2. When did you observe all the phases in a phase cycle?

3. A small telescope shows that Mercury and Venus go through complete phase cycles. What theory does this observation support?

16:4 Mercury and Venus

Mercury and Venus revolve in orbits inside Earth's orbit. Because Mercury is nearest the sun, it is difficult to observe. It can usually be seen close to the horizon shortly before sunrise and after sunset. During the day it is obscured by sunlight.

Because of Mercury's distance from the sun, temperatures more than 300°C are possible. The high temperatures cause gas molecules to have high velocities. Mercury's surface gravity is too weak to prevent the molecules from escaping into space. So, Mercury has no atmosphere, although some helium molecules ejected from the sun are found near the surface.

Notice in Figure 16–7 that Mercury looks very similar to the moon. Scientists think the craters on both the moon and Mercury were formed near the end of the time the solar system was a nebula. Unlike the moon, however, the surface of Mercury has "wrinkles." The wrinkles indicate Mercury contracted as it cooled. In addition, Mercury's large core is probably mostly iron, which produces an observed weak magnetic field.

The closest planet to Earth, Venus, is almost the same size as Earth. At times Venus, except for the moon, is the brightest object seen in the night sky. Venus has an atmosphere that is mostly carbon dioxide. Blankets of clouds containing droplets of sulfuric acid always hide the surface. Radio waves from Venus show that lightning constantly flashes within the clouds, never touching the planet.

Although we cannot see through the clouds, orbiting spacecraft have mapped the surface of Venus with radar. As Figure 16–8 shows, the surface is mostly wide plains, a few deep valleys, and two areas that seem to contain volcanoes. Evidence indicates some of the volcanoes may be active. Venus has no oceans. Liquid water is not possible because of the high temperatures. The sun's energy is converted to heat and is held near the surface.

The Earth's atmosphere might be similar to Venus's except that the Earth is much cooler. Therefore, oceans of liquid water are possible on Earth. Most of the carbon dioxide on Earth is dissolved in the oceans. Scientists

Where in the sky should one look for Mercury?

BACKGROUND Scientists hypothesize that Venus's internal structure is similar to Earth's.

What feature makes Mercury look like the moon?

BACKGROUND Both Mercury and Venus change from "morning planet" to "evening planet." Many cultures have (incorrectly) called them "morning and evening stars."

Describe Venus's atmosphere and surface.

FIGURE 16–7. The cratered surface of Mercury is similar to the surface of the moon. The ridges and scarps (or cliffs) between the craters probably formed when the planet contracted after it was first formed.

think Venus once was cooler and had water oceans. They believe that the sun and the volcanoes on Venus heated the atmosphere.

Venus is a useful model for helping scientists understand how Earth could change. Human activities, such as industry and transportation, add large amounts of carbon dioxide to the Earth's atmosphere. Drastic changes in the air temperature on Earth may result as the amount of carbon dioxide in the atmosphere increases.

FIGURE 16–8. Radar images of the surface of Venus show much volcanic activity.

16:5 Mars

Often called the "red planet," Mars is the first planet outside Earth's orbit. The redness of its surface is due to the soil and rocks that contain compounds of iron and oxygen, much like rust.

What makes Mars red?

In 1976, Viking spacecraft (Table 16–1) landed on Mars. Robots performed organic chemistry experiments in search of life on Mars. Some scientists conclude that the data show no life. Others say that the data do not allow a person to make a conclusion one way or another.

The surface of Mars has more different features than the moon or Mercury. The surface has two very different halves. The northern hemisphere is mostly smooth lava plains. Some craters cut across these plains. Once Mars had active volcanoes, but the eruptions ended thousands of years ago. There is a group of large inactive volcanoes near the equator. One, Olympus Mons, is the largest volcano in the solar system. It is almost three times as high as Mt. Everest, the highest mountain above sea level on Earth. The southern hemisphere of Mars is covered with old battered craters. These craters formed at the same time as those on Mercury and the highlands of the moon.

Many narrow lines called rills are seen on Olympus Mons and other volcanoes. They are probably lava channels or lava tubes that have caved in. Large cracks and canyons also are located on Mars. One canyon extends about 4500 km in an east-west direction. The large cracks are thought to be a result of movement of large sections of the crust. The alignment of volcanoes on Mars also is evidence of large-scale crustal movements.

What was the mission of the Viking spacecraft?

How are the northern and southern hemispheres of Venus different?

FIGURE 16–9. As the sun rises over Noctis Labyrinthus, bright clouds of water and ice can be observed in and around the tributary canyons of this high plateau region of Mars.

BACKGROUND   The rills are not the so-called "canali," lines sometimes observed by people on Earth observing Mars with a telescope. The latter seem to be illusions, as they were not confirmed by Viking and other spacecraft data.

Some of the rills on Mars appear similar to dry river beds on Earth. Careful studies show that they must have held liquid during periods of sudden flooding. Although running water is not present on the surface of Mars, water may have flowed until about one billion years ago.

Describe the Martian polar caps.

Like Earth, Mars has polar caps. The south polar cap is largest. The caps have a thin layer of carbon dioxide ice on the surface. Underneath is a layer of frozen water. The caps shrink in Martian summers and get larger in the winters. (The seasons are reversed in the two hemispheres.) The ice caps rest on layers of sediments, possibly produced during past ice ages. Mars' thin atmosphere is composed of mostly carbon dioxide with some water vapor.

See Teacher's Guide.

Skill Inquiry

Notice in the figure, the shape of the shadow of the Earth on the partially eclipsed moon. The shape of the Earth's shadow seen during lunar eclipses tells much about the Earth's shape. Some early Greeks deduced the shape of the Earth by observing lunar eclipses.

You see only part of the Earth's shadow on the moon during a lunar eclipse. The Greeks understood that the extended shadow on the moon produces a round shape. They realized that if you could see a cross-section of the shadow of the entire Earth, the shadow would be round. At different times during eclipses, the full cross-section of the Earth's shadow can be seen.

Some Greeks thought the Earth is disk-shaped. Some thought it is a cylinder. Others thought the Earth is a sphere. Any of these shapes could produce a round shadow if the Earth and sun were oriented in certain ways. However, based on other observations of the Earth and sky, the Greeks assumed that the orientation of the Earth to

the sun at the time of lunar eclipses varies. Many observations of lunar eclipses showed that the Earth always produced a round shadow.

1. If the Earth were a disk, might it ever produce any other shape of shadow except round?

2. If the Earth were a cylinder, might it ever produce any other shape of shadow except round?

3. If the Earth were a sphere, might it ever produce any other shape of shadow except round?

4. Which of the early Greeks were correct about the shape of the Earth?

16:6 Jupiter and Saturn

Jupiter and Saturn are the largest planets. Each has an atmosphere and rotates rapidly. Their shapes are distorted by the rotation, Figure 16–10. The rapid rotation also results in the colored bands of clouds on both planets. Within Jupiter's Red Spot, gases swirl in a huge stormlike wind system. Lightning is believed to cause a chemical reaction, which changes the color and composition of the gases. The bright bands on both Jupiter and Saturn are higher and cooler than the dark bands. The atmospheres of both planets get more dense with depth. At a few hundred kilometers below visible clouds, scientists believe oceans of liquid hydrogen exist. In the center of each planet, there are probably very small cores of liquid metallic hydrogen. Both planets have magnetic fields that are much stronger than Earth's. The magnetic fields are most likely a result of large electric currents produced by motions within the metallic hydrogen.

Both Jupiter and Saturn are much like miniature solar systems. Each has at least 18 natural satellites. The Voyager 1 and 2 spacecraft (Table 16–1) flew by some of the moons and revealed many differences. Jupiter's closest moon, Io, has active volcanoes and is covered with sulfur. Jupiter's Europa, which looks like a cracked egg, is thought to have a deep water ocean beneath icy cracks. Ganymede, another moon of Jupiter, looks a lot like Earth's moon. Ganymede is the largest natural satellite in the solar system. Saturn's largest moon is Titan. Titan is the only natural satellite in the solar system with an atmosphere. Some scientists think that conditions on Titan may make some form of life possible.

Saturn is famous for its rings but Jupiter has rings too. Saturn's rings were observed when the planet was first viewed with a small telescope in 1609 by Galileo. Jupiter's rings first were seen in images transmitted by the Voyager spacecraft in 1978. Three-ring systems can be distinguished on Saturn with a large Earth-based telescope. Voyager images, however, showed that each system consists of thousands of smaller rings, much like the grooves on a record. The rings consist of millions of fragments—boulder to dust size.

How are Jupiter and Saturn alike?

BACKGROUND Jupiter might have become a star, and the solar system might have become a double-star system, except Jupiter has always rotated too rapidly. After Jupiter gathered the mass it now has in the early nebula, it spun off matter at the same rate that it pulled it in. Jupiter has 0.0001 the mass of the sun, and it rotates in 9 hours, 50 minutes.

FIGURE 16–10. The colored bands on Jupiter are produced by rapidly-spinning gases (a). An image of Saturn taken by Voyager 1 from a distance of 34 million kilometers is shown (b).

a

b

Activity: How are Jupiter's moons arranged?

See Teacher's Guide.

MATERIALS

compass	scissors
metric ruler	tape
adding machine paper roll	string
	calculator (optional)
large sheet of paper	pencil

PROCEDURE

1. Convert the values below to a smaller scale assuming 5000 km = 1 cm. Record in a data table.

Object	Diameter (km)	Distance from Jupiter's Edge (km)
Metis	40	57 000
Adrastea	25	58 000
Amalthea	170	109 000
Thebe	80	151 000
Io	3630	351 000
Europa	3140	600 000
Ganymede	5260	999 000
Callisto	4800	1 814 000
Leda	15	11 039 000
Himalia	185	11 399 000
Lysithea	35	11 639 000
Elara	75	11 669 000
Ananke	30	20 629 000
Carme	40	22 279 000
Pasiphae	50	23 259 000
Sinope	35	23 299 000

2. Draw a line across one end of a paper roll. Assume this is the edge of Jupiter.

3. Measure from the edge of Jupiter along the center of the paper roll to the scale distances of the natural satellites. Make a dot at each measured distance and label each dot.

4. Draw circles to scale around the dots that mark the natural satellites that are larger than dots in this model. Use the scale diameters in the table.

5. Tie a 50 cm length of string to your pencil. Using the string and pencil as a compass, draw a circle with a 30 cm diameter on the large sheet of paper. Cut out the circle to represent Jupiter. Tape it so it aligns with the edge of Jupiter marked on the paper roll.

6. Stretch out the paper roll in a hallway or around the walls of a classroom.

DATA AND OBSERVATIONS

Object	Scale Diameter (cm)	Scale Distance (cm)

QUESTIONS AND CONCLUSIONS

1. If Jupiter has a diameter of 30 cm in this model, what is the approximate actual diameter of Jupiter?

2. How does the amount of space between objects compare with the diameters of the objects themselves?

3. What difficulty, if any, would you have in showing both correct distance and diameters on a piece of notebook paper?

4. Which natural satellite must have the longest period of revolution about Jupiter? Why?

5. In what ways is the Jupiter system (Jupiter with its natural satellites) like the solar system?

6. In spite of correct scale, what is still misleading about this model?

16:7 Uranus, Neptune, and Pluto

At present, little is known about the three outer planets of the solar system. More is expected to be learned about Uranus and Neptune when Voyager 2, which left Saturn in 1981, encounters these two planets.

All of the other planets were known to ancient astronomers. Uranus was discovered in 1781 by William Herschel who was an amateur astronomer at that time. As he looked through his homemade telescope, he saw Uranus changing position against stars. Neptune was discovered in 1846 after two scientists predicted where it should be. The scientists observed movements of Jupiter, Saturn, and Uranus that seemed to be the result of the gravitational effect of another object. The object was Neptune.

Pluto was discovered in 1930. Calculations had been made that suggested a planet beyond Neptune, so an extensive sky search for "Planet X" was begun. After many years, Pluto was discovered.

Uranus and Neptune are large gaseous planets containing hydrogen and helium. However, unlike Jupiter and Saturn, a large concentration of methane gas is also present. Because of the extreme low temperatures, Uranus and Neptune consist of more ice and less gas than the other large planets. Astronomers observing Uranus move against a background star found that a number of times the star became dim and then brightened. This observation indicated that Uranus's ring system is made of a number of separate rings.

Because Pluto is so far from the sun, its temperature is estimated to be cold enough to solidify any gas present. Pluto is a rocky, bitterly cold planet. Pluto has one natural satellite, Charon.

See Teacher's Guide.

REVIEW AND REFLECT

1. What two factors may account for the lack of an atmosphere on Mercury?
2. How are Mars, Mercury, and the moon alike?
3. How do the inner planets differ from the outer planets?
4. Why are Neptune and Uranus thought to contain more ice than gases like Jupiter and Saturn?

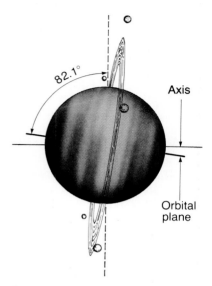

FIGURE 16–11. The rotational axis of Uranus is tilted so that it almost lies in the plane of orbit. The rings along with five moons revolve about the equatorial plane.

When were the three outer planets discovered?

BACKGROUND The two astronomers given credit for Neptune's discovery are Leverrier of France and John Couch Adams of England. It is a remarkable accident that Pluto was discovered in a location predicted, as it was later determined that there were faulty assumptions in the calculations on which the prediction was based. The discoverer of Pluto was Clyde Tombaugh of the United States.

See Teacher's Guide.

Career Profile

When the sky is clear above Kitt Peak in Arizona, Rik Hill may stay up all night taking photographs of stars with a large telescope. Rik is the resident observer of the Warner and Swasey Observatory, which has its headquarters in Cleveland, Ohio. The telescope Rik uses in Arizona used to be in Ohio. It was moved west because the air is clearer, enabling better photos to be made.

Rik takes and develops pictures in Arizona as directed by the astronomers in Cleveland. He judges when the weather conditions are right for photographs. In addition to taking photographs, Rik is responsible for inspecting the condition of the telescope, darkrooms, and other observatory facilities. He contacts maintenance people when necessary.

Rik has always liked astronomy, although he never imagined he would one day be paid to stay up at night and look at stars. After graduation from high school, he spent four years in the Navy. As a radar technician, he learned about electricity and electronics. After his Navy discharge, he worked in photography and later in optics. He pursued his interest in astronomy by taking courses at community colleges. Rik Hill's combined experience and education helped prepare him for his job as a resident observer.

16:8 Other Objects of the Solar System

SUGGESTION   Discuss how long it would take to walk across a 40-km minor planet. A good walker could cover the distance in a day if on Earth. Of course, there would be very different gravity conditions on minor planets.

Why do asteroids vary in brightness?

Minor planets are objects that orbit the sun like planets but are smaller. Sometimes they are called asteroids. Most of the known minor planets are less than 40 kilometers in diameter. Astronomers think that there are about 100 000 minor planets large enough to be seen from the Earth with telescopes. Minor planets have irregular shapes and rotate. As a result, their brightness changes depending on which side is facing the Earth at any given time. Most minor planets revolve about the sun between Mars and Jupiter. Some come close to the Earth, but one is thought to collide with the Earth only every million years. Some scientists hypothesize that the effects of asteroid impacts have changed the Earth's climate drastically in the past.

Objects smaller than minor planets that revolve about the sun are **meteoroids**. The smallest meteoroids, dust-sized objects called micrometeoroids, are the most common. Millions of meteoroids enter the Earth's atmosphere at high speeds everyday. Friction with the air creates so much heat that the air and vaporized gases from the meteoroids glow. Often the glowing gases are called shooting stars. However, the glowing, hot rock fragment is called a **meteor.** About 10 times a year the Earth passes through a swarm of meteoroids that are revolving about the sun. A collision with such swarms causes a meteor shower.

Sometimes meteors do not burn up entirely in the atmosphere. Fragments that reach the surface of objects, such as Earth, are called **meteorites.** The majority of meteorites are small. Most craters on the moon, Mars, and other objects of the solar system were formed by large meteorites billions of years ago.

Meteoroids and other small objects of the solar system give important clues about the history of the solar system. The origin of meteoroids can be determined by analyzing meteorites. Many probably are left from the early nebula. Some are fragments from collisions. It appears that some meteoroids were once part of small planets. Larger fragments from collisions of small planets probably produced minor planets and even some of the present moons of planets. A third source of meteoroids is the break-up of comets.

A **comet** is a mass of frozen materials such as water, methane, and ammonia, along with bits of rock and dust. With either the unaided eye or a telescope, one sees the coma, a cloud of gases, and a tail of ions and dust particles. Within the coma is a nucleus, a collection of tightly packed rocks about 10 kilometers in diameter. The nucleus is covered with solid water, methane, and ammonia. When a comet approaches the sun, these materials vaporize. As the comet interacts with the solar wind, the coma and the tail are formed. The low-density tail is pushed away from the sun by the pressure from the solar wind.

The most accepted theory of the origin of comets is that a collection of them left over from the early nebula now

What produces meteor showers?

Describe a comet.

FIGURE 16–12. The Barringer Crater in Arizona formed as a meteorite collided with the Earth more than 20 000 years ago. The crater measures 1.3 kilometers in diameter.

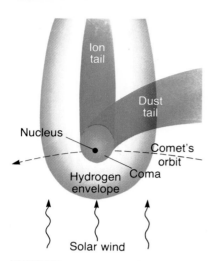

FIGURE 16–13.   Most comets have two types of tails that result when the nucleus interacts with solar wind and other radiation emitted by the sun.

Describe a space shuttle.

exists far from the sun. (On a scale of the distance from the Earth to the sun equal to two centimeters, the cloud of comets would be one kilometer from the sun.) When a star passes by the solar system at a distance, a slight tug pulls some of the comets away from the cloud. They move closer to the sun and eventually enter an orbit around it. The most famous comet is Halley's Comet. Halley's Comet moves in a narrow ellipse, taking 76 years for one revolution. In 1910, the Earth passed through the tail of Halley's Comet with no harmful effect.

16:9 Exploring Space

The first spacecraft was a small artificial satellite, Sputnik I, launched in 1957. Since then astronauts have landed on the moon. Spacecraft without people have visited many places in the solar system. Table 16–1 shows a number of the historically important space missions. Spacecraft have landed on Venus and Mars. Pioneer 11 became the first spacecraft object to leave the solar system in 1983.

The space shuttle is the main space vehicle used by the U.S. National Aeronautics and Space Administration (NASA). The shuttle consists of a reusable orbiter, two reusable solid rocket boosters, and an expendable fuel tank. The orbiter is covered with tiles of silicon finished with a ceramic glaze. During re-entry from outer space to the Earth's atmosphere, the tiles protect the orbiter from a plasma at about 1400°C that engulfs it. A typical shuttle crew consists of a mission commander and mission pilot (to fly the orbiter), two mission specialists, and two or three payload specialists.

A major science laboratory, Spacelab, may be carried in the space shuttle orbiter's cargo bay. Many experiments fit within the 18.1-meter Spacelab. Frequently science projects designed by high school students are carried in the Spacelab. Satellites such as the Hubble Space Telescope can be launched from the cargo bay by people working in the Spacelab.

Now a small space station is planned by NASA. A small crew will remain on the station, which will orbit the

Earth. The design will contain separate modules for working and living. Separate platforms for experiments will be placed in orbit near the station modules. The station is expected to be built by the early 1990s.

TABLE 16–1. SOME IMPORTANT SPACE MISSIONS

Spacecraft	Launched	Description
Sputnik I, U.S.S.R.	1957	First artificial satellite
Ranger 7, U.S.A.	1964	First close-up photographs of the moon before a crash landing
Luna 9, U.S.S.R.	1966	First soft landing on the moon
Venera 4, U.S.S.R.	1967	First probe to descend through Venus's atmosphere
Mariners 6 and 7, U.S.A	1969	First spacecraft flybys of Mars
Apollo 11, U.S.A.	1969	First astronauts land on the moon and return with lunar rocks
Pioneer 10, U.S.A.	1972	First spacecraft flyby of Jupiter
Apollo 17, U.S.A.	1973	Last of six astronaut landings on the moon
Pioneer 11, U.S.A.	1973	First spacecraft to leave the solar system (after studying Jupiter and Saturn)
Mariner 10, U.S.A.	1973	First close-up photographs of Venus and Mercury
Vikings 1 and 2, U.S.A.	1975	First soft landings on Mars and photographs of the surface
Voyagers 1 and 2, U.S.A.	1977	Detailed studies of Jupiter and Saturn and many of their satellites; Voyager 2 on trajectory for flyby of Uranus (1986) and Neptune (1990)
Space Shuttle Columbia, U.S.A.	1981	First reusable spacecraft to return to Earth
Space Shuttle Challenger, U.S.A.	1984	First astronaut activity in orbit free from spacecraft

See Teacher's Guide.

REVIEW AND REFLECT

1. What are three sources of meteoroids?
2. When is Halley's Comet expected to pass close to Earth again?
3. How were the Viking missions different from the Voyager missions?

16:10 Choices: Funding Space Exploration

How important is learning about the solar system? People disagree. Exploring space is very costly and usually financed by national governments. Some people think that government funds should be used for health, education, and defense projects. They feel spending money for space exploration is wasteful.

However, a number of citizens point out that space projects provide many jobs. Many people are needed to prepare and carry out the projects. The money paid to these workers is spent in the nation and supports the economy. The money value of a space project, like the Apollo missions to the moon, is multiplied many times in the products it has provided. These products, called "spinoffs" of the space program, help people in a number of ways. For example in medicine, electrical diagnosis of weak muscles has changed the lives of people who are paralyzed and could not have been helped in the past. In transportation, safer and more efficient airplanes are the result of devices and testing procedures developed for the space program. A cost-saving flat electrical cable is now widely used in the building industry. Miniaturized circuits and a large number of new lubricants and protective coatings are major technological advances. Recreation is safer with a new type of foam used in football equipment.

What are some spinoffs of the Apollo program?

FIGURE 16–14. Space technology has led to the development of microcomputers and communication systems widely used to help treat diseases and injuries (a). Freeze-dried processing was first used to prepare food for early NASA astronauts (b).

a

b

Scientists note that exploring the solar system will provide a new perspective of Earth. For instance, if we can understand the changes that made Venus become hotter, we might somehow be able to prevent a drastic change in Earth's climate. By studying the moon, planets, and radiation in space, we may prepare for a time when resources and living space on Earth become scarce. If the specific conditions and hazards of space travel and planetary surfaces are known, better space vehicles and space colonies can be designed. Improved procedures for mining and using resources can be developed.

How might studying the moon and planets lead to a better future for people?

Some people who acknowledge these benefits still feel that government funds should not be used for space exploration. They suggest that private industry and citizen's groups could finance the projects. For example, the Planetary Society has over 100 000 members. It is currently providing the money for a radio telescope search for life on other worlds. The Viking Fund raised money that kept a Viking lander on Mars turned on to send back data when the United States government was ready to turn it off. Similar groups might fund other projects. Industry and communications companies eagerly have funded research projects for the Space Shuttle. Perhaps the participation of these groups in space exploration could be expanded and coordinated by governments.

What are some alternatives to government funding of space exploration?

In summary, there are three options available when considering space exploration. The first one is simply not to explore space. The second option is not to use government funds for space exploration. Instead, allow industry or private groups to provide the money. We could also allow the government to coordinate and expand industrial involvement in space. The third option is to let the government continue to finance space exploration.

BACKGROUND   In the United States, NASA's entire budget is not used for space exploration. NASA applies funds to aeronautics and other projects also.

See Teacher's Guide.

REVIEW AND REFLECT

1. Why is all of the money for a space project, such as Apollo, not really "sent into space"?
2. Name three products that you use or affect you that were developed with the space program.
3. What is your opinion about funding space exploration? Give reasons for your opinion.

CHAPTER 16 REVIEW

SUMMARY

1. The nebular theory is currently used to explain the origin of the solar system. 16:1

2. The objects of the solar system revolve about the sun. All planets also rotate on their axes. 16:1

3. The Ptolemaic theory and the Copernican theory are models once used to describe the solar system. 16:2

4. The barycenter for Earth and moon moves in an elliptical orbit about the sun. 16:3

5. The movements of the Earth and the moon in relation to the sun result in the phase cycle of the moon. 16:3

6. Eclipses occur only when the moon is new or full and in the plane of the ecliptic. 16:3

7. Although Venus and Earth are about the same size, their atmospheres and surface temperatures are very different. 16:4

8. The surface of Mars has more different features than the moon or Mercury. 16:5

9. Jupiter and Saturn are much like miniature solar systems. 16:6

10. Uranus, Neptune, and Pluto are visible from Earth only with the use of telescopes. 16:7

11. Meteoroids and comets are believed to be left over from the formation of the sun and planets. 16:8

12. Many experiments in space are done within Spacelab, which is a portable laboratory that fits inside a shuttle orbiter. 16:9

VOCABULARY

comet 10	meteorite 8	phase cycle 3
ecliptic 2	meteoroid 7	revolution 11
lunar eclipse 4	minor planets 9	rotation 1
meteor 12	nebular theory 6	solar eclipse 5

Choose the correct word from the list to answer each question.

1. What describes the spinning motion of an object on its axis?

2. What is the imaginary plane in which the planets orbit the sun called?

3. What is a complete set of changes, from new moon to new moon called?

4. When the full moon lies in the plane of the ecliptic, what occurs?

5. When the new moon lies in the plane of the ecliptic, what occurs?

6. What describes the probable origin of the solar system?

7. What is an object that is smaller than a minor planet and revolves about the sun?

8. What kind of object formed most of the craters on the moon and Mars?

9. What objects are larger than meteoroids but smaller than planets and orbit the sun like planets do?

10. What is a mass of frozen materials such as water, methane, and ammonia along with bits of rock and dust?

11. What is the motion of an object in its orbit around another object called?

12. What is a rock fragment from space that becomes hot and glows called?

QUESTIONS

MAIN IDEAS

Choose the correct answer to complete each sentence.

1. Before the Renaissance in Europe, the *(nebular theory, Ptolemaic theory, Copernican theory)* was the most accepted model of the solar system.

2. Kepler discovered that planets *(revolve in ellipses about the sun, travel fastest when farthest from the sun, move due to gravitation)*.

3. Day and night are a result of *(revolution, rotation, phase cycles)*.

4. A lunar eclipse *(occurs when the moon is full, happens every month, happens once a year)*.

5. The planets with the most moons are *(Mars and Jupiter, Jupiter and Saturn, Saturn and Uranus)*.

6. An object that is made of rocks and gases that form a tail is a *(minor planet, meteoroid, comet)*.

7. The planet with the hottest atmosphere is *(Mars, Venus, Earth)*.

8. Meteorite craters are found on *(Mercury, Jupiter, Saturn)*.

9. The planet most distant from the sun is *(usually Neptune but sometimes Pluto, usually Pluto but sometimes Uranus, usually Pluto but sometimes Neptune)*.

10. Spacecraft have landed on and returned pictures from *(Mercury, Mars, Saturn)*.

See Teacher's Guide.

APPLICATIONS

Answer each question in one or more paragraphs.

1. What may have happened to the liquid water thought to have produced stream channels on Mars?

2. Explain why the rocks taken from the lunar highlands by Apollo astronauts are older than the rocks found in the maria.

3. How is the lack of liquid water on the surface of Venus related to the amount of carbon dioxide gas in Venus' atmosphere?

4. Explain why although Jupiter and Saturn are more massive than Earth and Venus, they are less dense.

5. How does a lunar eclipse provide evidence for Earth's shape?

6. How does the tail of a comet change as the comet moves around the sun?

7. How do the surface features on Mars provide evidence for the existence of a mantle within the planet?

FURTHER STUDY

INVESTIGATIONS

1. Prepare a possible future travel brochure for a planet or another place in the solar system. Be creative about possibilities, but apply information correctly.

2. Learn the origin of the names of the days of the week. Prepare a report of your research.

3. Construct a scale model of the sun and the planets.

READINGS

0 Chapman, Clark A. *Planets of Rock and Ice: From Mercury to the Moons of Saturn.* Scribner's: New York, 1982.

+ Cooper, Henry S. F. *The Search for Life on Mars.* Holt, Rinehart and Winston: New York, 1980.

− Lauber, Patricia. *Journey to the Planets.* Crown Publishers: New York, 1982.

You need air to breathe, but you probably do not think about it much. You need air to talk and hear, too. On a sunny day the sky looks blue because air scatters sunlight. Clouds and snow occur due to moisture in the atmosphere. Even though the weather is cold sometimes, the atmosphere protects you from extreme temperatures. How did the atmosphere get here? Of what is it made? What causes weather and climate?

WEATHER AND CLIMATE

INTRODUCING THE CHAPTER   Discuss the current weather at your location. Show a newspaper surface map of the country, which gives weather predicted for a particular time. Note the differences in weather due to occur at different locations at the same time. Discuss the value of knowing what the weather will be at another location if you are traveling.

17:1 Earth's Atmosphere

According to the nebular theory, when the earth formed 4.5 billion years ago, a first atmosphere probably was slowly created from the release of gases, including water vapor from inside the new planet. Most of the water vapor in the original atmosphere condensed to form the oceans. Simple life forms that produce oxygen, such as algae, took carbon dioxide from the first atmosphere and gave off oxygen.

Today, the earth's atmosphere is a mixture of mostly nitrogen and oxygen and suspended particles. The amounts of carbon dioxide and other components, such as water vapor and dust, vary depending on the location. For example, concentrations of carbon dioxide and dust are greater near erupting volcanoes and places where coal and oil are burned.

Figure 17–1 on page 360 shows how the atmosphere is divided into layers based on temperature differences. The air you breathe is part of the **troposphere** (TROP uh sfihr). Most weather occurs in this layer.

Throughout the troposphere temperature decreases as altitude increases. At an average altitude of 10 kilometers above the earth's surface, the steady decrease in temperature with height stops. The altitude at which temperature begins to level off marks the **tropopause**, the upper boundary of the troposphere. The jet streams, high-velocity winds often cited in weather reports, occur in the upper troposphere and the tropopause.

GOAL   You will learn major properties of the atmosphere and what causes different weather and climates.

How was oxygen in the atmosphere produced?

Describe the troposphere.
BACKGROUND   Ozone (O_3) is an important component of the upper atmosphere, since it forms an effective shield against most ultraviolet light. Oxygen, produced by plants, is concluded to have become abundant enough to produce the shield by about 1.5 billion years ago. Ozone near the ground, a product of complex chemical reactions in photochemical smog, is a pollutant.

359

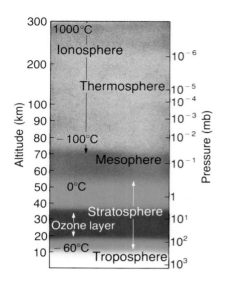

FIGURE 17–1. The atmosphere consists of layers arranged like shells around the earth. The layers are distinguished by their physical and chemical properties.

SUGGESTION   Review types of radiation (the electromagnetic spectrum), chapter 13.

FIGURE 17–2. The atmosphere permits short-wave electromagnetic radiation from the sun to strike the earth's surface. The atmosphere is heated as the surface reradiates the energy as long-wave radiation.

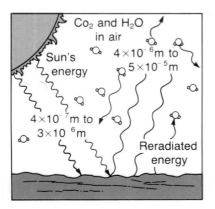

More than half of the mass of the earth's atmosphere is below the tropopause. The atomic masses of nitrogen and oxygen are greater than the atomic masses of the less abundant atmospheric elements. According to Newton's Law of Gravitation, gravitational attraction is directly proportional to mass. Because gravity holds the atmosphere to the earth, the majority of the gases in the atmosphere are near the earth's surface.

As a result of earth's gravitational attraction, the atmosphere has weight and exerts a pressure on the earth's surface. At sea level, the average air pressure is 101 kilopascals. Meteorologists, scientists who study weather, commonly use the millibar, mb, as the unit of pressure. One millibar is equal to 0.1 kilopascals. At sea level, standard air pressure is 1013 millibars. Pressure decreases with height.

BACKGROUND   As atmospheric gases absorb infrared radiation from the earth's surface, their average kinetic energy and thus their temperature is increased.

17:2   Heating the Atmosphere

Most of the energy in the atmosphere comes from the sun. The sun radiates a great deal of energy. However, only about 50 percent of the radiation that reaches the top of the earth's atmosphere filters down to the surface. About 20 percent is absorbed by the atmosphere. The rest is reflected by clouds or the earth's surface or scattered by atmospheric molecules back into space.

The gases in the atmosphere do not absorb the visible wavelengths very well. Most of the solar radiation that reaches the earth is in the form of light energy. The earth's surface is warmed as it absorbs the energy. The energy is re-radiated by the earth in the infrared wavelengths as heat. Water vapor and carbon dioxide in the atmosphere are good absorbers of infrared radiation. After they absorb energy from the earth, they radiate it eventually. The energy is reabsorbed by other air molecules or by the earth. This heating process, as shown in Figure 17–2, is called the **greenhouse effect.** Note that the troposphere is heated from the ground up.

Remember from the last chapter that the earth rotates on its axis daily as well as revolves around the sun annually. Due to the variation in the earth's orientation to the sun, the amount of solar radiation received at the earth's surface differs. As shown in Figure 17–3a, the earth's axis of rotation is tilted $23\frac{1}{2}°$ from the perpendicular to the plane of revolution. If it were not tilted, we would have no seasons.

When the sun is directly overhead, the rays strike the earth at a 90° angle. Solar radiation is most intense. The intensity of the radiation that reaches the earth decreases as the angle of the sun's rays decreases. See Figure 17–3b. Keep in mind that the earth is almost a sphere. As a result, lower latitudes receive more radiant energy than higher latitudes.

If the angle of the sun's rays were the only factor affecting temperatures on earth, you would expect all locations along a particular latitude to have the same seasonal temperatures. Although incoming solar radiation is the most important factor controlling temperatures, another factor is the nature of earth's surface. Water heats up and cools off much more slowly than land. The reason for this property is that the specific heat of water is much greater than that of land. As a result, a continent heats and cools more quickly than an ocean at the same latitude.

See Teacher's Guide.

REVIEW AND REFLECT

1. What is the significance of the tropopause?
2. Why do we have seasons?
3. Explain how the troposphere is heated.
4. Why does air pressure decrease with height?

What factors affect temperatures on earth?

FIGURE 17–3. Seasons result because of the tilt in earth's axis. The solstices occur when sunlight strikes the tropics at 90°. The sun is directly over the equator at the equinoxes (a). The intensity of the sun's radiation that strikes the earth depends on the latitude. The intensity of radiation at 60° is only one half the intensity at the equator (b).

Activity: What affects heating of the earth?

See Teacher's Guide.

MATERIALS

3 thermometers in rubber stoppers
   CAUTION: *Moisten thermometers with glycerine before inserting into rubber stoppers.*
beaker of room temperature water

lamp	ring stand
pan of soil	metric ruler
pan of water	graph paper
pan of salt	3 clamps
stirring rod	clock or watch

PROCEDURE

1. Attach three thermometers to a ring stand with clamps. Position the thermometers vertically so that each is about 3 cm deep in a pan of soil, salt, or water.
2. Set up a lamp about 25 cm above the pans. Adjust the lamp so that it shines on the pans at about a 90° angle. See Figure 17–4a.
3. Record in a data table the temperatures on the thermometers.
4. Turn on the lamp. Record the temperature of each material every minute for 10 minutes.
5. Remove the thermometers. Place them in a beaker of water to return their temperatures to room temperature.
6. Stir each of the materials with a stirring rod. Do not stir with thermometers.

FIGURE 17–4.

7. Replace the thermometers in the clamps and reposition them 3 cm deep in the pans.
8. Reposition the lamp so that it shines on the pans at about a 45° angle. See Figure 17–4b. Repeat steps 3 and 4.
9. Graph your data.

DATA AND OBSERVATIONS

Lamp angle:

Time (min)	Temperature (°C)		
	Soil	Water	Salt
0			
1			
2			
3			
4			
5			
6			
7			
8			
9			
10			

QUESTIONS AND CONCLUSIONS

1. What effect did changing the angle of the lamp have on how each material heated?
2. Why did the thermometers need to be about vertical, rather than horizontal, in the pans?
3. Predict differences in how the three materials differ in their cooling rates. How would you check your predictions?
4. How do your observations in this activity help to explain differences in temperature at the same latitude?
5. What two factors account for low annual temperatures at the poles?

17:3 Water in Air

Water vapor in air is a solution. Recall from chapter 7 that a saturated solution contains the maximum amount of solute that can be dissolved in a solvent. Saturated air contains the maximum amount of water vapor it can hold. **Relative humidity** is the ratio of the actual amount of water vapor in the air to the maximum amount the air can hold at a certain temperature. It is expressed as a percentage.

Recall from chapter 7 that solubility depends on temperature. Cold air can hold less water vapor than warmer air. Therefore, in winter even though the relative humidity may be high, the air contains less water vapor than summer air with the same relative humidity.

As the temperature of air decreases, the air approaches saturation. If air is cooled below the temperature at which it is saturated, the water vapor in it changes state. Perhaps after you have taken a shower you have noticed that the bathroom mirror was "steamed up." As you showered, the air in the bathroom became warm and humid. When the warm air touched the cool mirror, the water vapor condensed on the mirror. The temperature at which water vapor condenses is called the **dew point.**

Dew forms outdoors when air touches surfaces with temperatures at the dew point or below. If the dew point is below freezing, frost forms instead of dew. The direct change of state from a gas to a solid, in this case from water vapor to ice, is **sublimation** (sub luh MAY shun). The change of a solid to a gas is called sublimation, also.

Clouds form from saturated air. From an airplane window, you may have seen a flat layer of clouds that looked like snow-covered ground. The height of those clouds was the height at which rising air reached its dew point. In the atmosphere, water vapor condenses or sublimes on tiny particles, such as salt and dust. Clouds consist of millions of small water droplets or ice crystals. Clouds are classified generally according to their height as high, middle, or low clouds. The heights, types, and characteristics of clouds are shown in Figure 17–5. Note that some types of clouds produce precipitation. Rain and snow are the most familiar forms of precipitation. Some other forms of precipitation include hail and sleet.

SUGGESTION Discuss what "50 percent relative humidity" means—that air contains half of the amount of water vapor it would contain if it were saturated.

Describe relative humidity.

SUGGESTION Discuss what happens to hair in damp (high relative humidity) weather: naturally curly hair gets curlier and straight hair gets limp. Water molecules, trapped in pore spaces in hair, cause the effects. Curly and straight hair have different structures, so the effects are different.

Under what conditions does frost form?

ACTIVITY For a few days, observe and identify clouds at your location several times each day. Students could draw or even photograph clouds and later add labels. A reference with more detailed discussions of cloud types will show some not given in Figure 17–5.

Which types of clouds produce precipitation?

HIGH CLOUDS (above 6000 m)	**Cirrus** Thin white patches or strands composed of ice crystals Associated with fair weather but may indicate approaching precipitation
	Cirrocumulus Small rounded white clouds, may be in the form of ripples or small waves Usually associated with fair weather
	Cirrostratus Feathery sheets that sometimes cause halos to appear around the sun or moon Associated with fair weather but may follow cirrus and indicate approaching precipitation
MIDDLE CLOUDS (2000–6000 m)	**Altocumulus** Appear like higher and thinner stratocumulus clouds, but in smaller patches Often precede rain or thunderstorms
	Altostratus Gray or bluish fibrous clouds through which the moon or sun appear blurred Associated with continuous precipitation or approaching warmer weather
LOW CLOUDS (below 2000 m)	**Stratocumulus** Light gray clouds in patches or rolls that may form a continuous layer Occasionally produce light rain or snow showers
	Stratus Low layer of gray clouds that may cover entire sky May be associated with light drizzle
	Nimbostratus Thick layer of dark gray clouds that usually block out the sun Associated with steady, long precipitation
VERTICAL CLOUDS (500 – 18 000 m)	**Cumulus** Big, puffy clouds with flat bases and dome-shaped tops Usually associated with fair weather but may produce precipitation if they develop very high
	Cumulonimbus Tall, puffy clouds with tops that spread out like cirrus Associated with thunderstorms, hail, and severe weather

FIGURE 17–5. Classification of clouds

Raindrops are much larger than cloud droplets, rather like watermelons compared with peanuts. Slight air currents can keep small droplets suspended as clouds. However, once the droplets grow in size, they become too heavy for the air currents, and fall as precipitation.

Normally, air near the surface of the earth is warmer than air at higher altitudes. Therefore, air near the surface tends to rise. As air rises, it cools. Unstable air is the air that keeps rising. As long as the surrounding air is cooler, the air keeps rising. When the rising air cools to the same temperature as the surrounding air, it stops moving upward and becomes stable. Stable air near the earth's surface usually means fair weather, because the air does not rise and therefore is not cooled to produce clouds and precipitation. Air that is unstable often leads to clouds and rain.

Explain the relationship between air stability and weather.

See Teacher's Guide.

Career Profile

Grace Swanson is a meteorological technician or "met tech." She works at the National Weather Service Forecast Office near Cleveland Hopkins Airport in Ohio. Grace's main job is observing weather conditions. She notes and records data about clouds, visibility, precipitation, relative humidity, and temperatures. Weather forecasters depend on her timely and accurate observations. Grace was trained on duty to be a radar specialist. In a dark room, she studies incoming radar images and analyzes them for precipitation. Radar observations help forecasters determine the amount and intensity of rain or snow. Grace also makes recordings of weather summaries and forecasts. The recordings are broadcast on radio and television. An additional responsibility includes providing airplane pilots with immediate information about both surface and upper air conditions.

Grace was always interested in science. She planned to become an optometrist. However, while in college she took a course about climate. That course got her interested in both climate and weather. Grace rethought her career goals. Eventually she became a met tech.

One does not have to have a college degree to be a met tech. Each met tech is trained on the job. A number of books and manuals must be studied on subjects such as pilot briefing, radar use, and taking weather observations. A test on each of these subjects is required to be certified for this particular work.

What causes air to move?

FIGURE 17–6. If the earth were not rotating, warm air rising at the equator would flow directly toward the poles and would be replaced at the surface by cold air from the poles (a). Because of the earth's rotation, the path of an airplane traveling from the North Pole toward City A will appear to curve toward City B (b).

17:4 Air Circulation

You have learned that lower latitudes on earth receive more solar radiation than higher latitudes. Also, different surfaces on earth absorb and reflect the sun's energy differently. The uneven distribution of energy results in the movements of air we know as winds.

From your study of motion in chapter 9, you know that forces are responsible for motion. Gravity, for example, causes cool, dense air to descend in the process of convection. Also, air moves from areas of higher to lower pressure. Temperature and humidity affect air pressure.

Due to differences in air density and pressure, certain circulation patterns between the equator and the poles can be expected, as shown in Figure 17–6a. However, the earth's rotation upsets this expected pattern of large convection cells. The **Coriolis** (kor ee OH lus) **force,** a force caused by the effect of earth's rotation, tends to break each convective cell into three smaller cells. The cells are not completely independent, however. Air must mix between cells to transfer heat to the poles and cold air back to the equator.

The Coriolis force, unlike gravity, is an apparent force. To understand this force, see Figure 17–6b. Air moving from the North Pole to the equator appears to curve to the west on the rotating earth. In reverse manner, air moving northward from the equator appears to be deflected eastward. Therefore, the Coriolis force results from the fact that the earth is rotating, and the force acts only on air moving horizontally.

Note the major pressure belts and wind systems that result from the general circulation shown in Figure 17–7. Note the doldrums, a band near the equator. Here air rises, producing cloudy, rainy weather. Air that rises from the surface develops into areas of low pressure. At about 30° latitude, air sinks producing calm, dry belts. Areas of high pressure develop where air descends to the surface. A zone of changeable weather exists where warm air from lower latitudes meets cool air from higher latitudes. This zone is called the polar front.

There is a worldwide eastward upper air wind in middle latitudes called the **jet stream.** It is a riverlike band, mov-

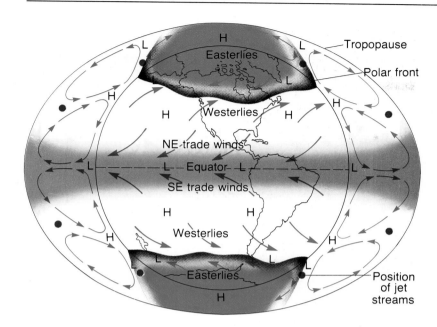

FIGURE 17-7. The general circulation of earth's atmosphere

ing eastward and weaving northward and southward at heights between about 6 and 15 kilometers. The jet stream changes height and latitude depending on what happens at the polar front. Because the jet stream flow is between 160 and 400 kilometers per hour, pilots can make use of the flow to save time and fuel.

Some winds do not move within the earth's major wind belts. These winds result from the differences in the absorption and reflection of thermal energy by different earth surfaces, such as mountains and lakes. One important example is a **monsoon,** a seasonal wind that blows between a continent and an ocean. In summer, a continent is hotter than surrounding ocean. Therefore the air pressure over the continent is less than that over the ocean. A steady wind blows toward the land during warm months. Because the wind comes from the ocean, it brings moisture and rain. In winter, a continent is cooler and has higher air pressure than a nearby ocean. The winter monsoon that blows toward the ocean during cold months is dry.

Small-scale versions of monsoons are land and sea breezes. Land and sea breezes reverse direction daily rather than seasonally. Daily wind changes also occur on mountain slopes. During the day, warm air rises from val-

Describe monsoons.

BACKGROUND   The world's best-developed monsoons are in India and southeast Asia, although monsoons also occur on other continents. Since the summer monsoon of southeast Asia makes land and roads very muddy, the monsoon was a significant factor in war strategies used in recent times there.

SUGGESTION Discuss student experiences with daily wind changes near large bodies of water and in the mountains. Many people go to the shore on a hot day to enjoy cool sea breezes. Skiers and mountain climbers must take caution with strong downhill mountain breezes.

What conditions create a cold, dry air mass?

Describe the air masses formed over the Gulf of Mexico.

SUGGESTION Discuss how the prevailing winds of the earth's general circulation carry air masses within them. Note how the prevailing southwesterlies carry air from the Pacific in a northeast direction across North America.

leys along mountain slopes. A valley breeze blows up the slopes. At night, cool dense air settles into the valleys from the mountains producing a mountain breeze.

17:5 Air Masses and Fronts

Sunglasses usually are thought of as summer apparel. However, if you ever have been outdoors on a sunny day after a heavy snow, you may have wished you had your sunglasses! Fresh snow reflects 90 percent of the sun's energy. In winter, vast snow-covered regions, such as northern Canada, reflect most of the sun's energy. Very little is absorbed. Air settling over this region for a period of time becomes cold and dry. Any body of air that acquires properties of the surface over which it lies is called an **air mass.**

Northern Canada is an example of a source region where cold dry air masses form. The Gulf of Mexico and nearby Atlantic Ocean are a source region where warm moist air masses form. Here, slowly circulating air is warmed by the ocean water. The air also absorbs large amounts of water vapor. After these air masses form, they begin to move into the flow of the westerlies in the middle latitudes.

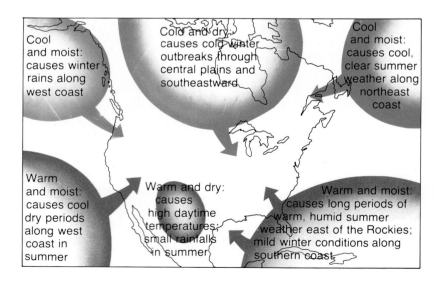

FIGURE 17–8. Air masses that affect North America

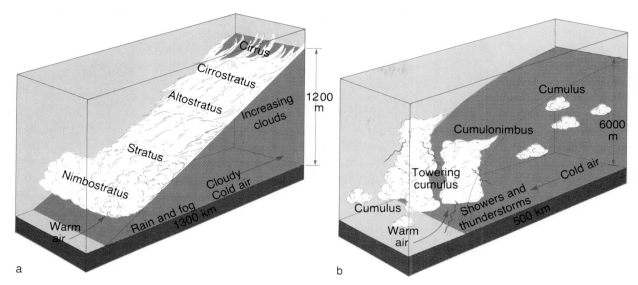

When air masses move, their properties affect the weather of the land over which they pass. Figure 17–8 shows source regions of air masses that commonly affect weather in North America. Observe that most of the United States and parts of Canada do not lie in an air mass source region. Most of the weather is produced in a zone along the polar front that is invaded continually by air masses from the north and south. A knowledge of air masses and the paths they follow is important in understanding our day-to-day weather. For example, an air mass that develops over the eastern Pacific may spread northward in winter, bringing heavy rains to the southern California coast.

In studying Figure 17–8, you also may notice how air masses frequently can collide in middle latitude regions. When different air masses meet, they do not mix. Instead, a boundary forms similar to a boundary between layers of water and oil. The boundary separating air masses is called a **front**. Along a front, warmer, less dense air slides over a sloping wedge of more dense, colder air. As warm air is lifted along the front, similar to the movement of air up a mountain slope, clouds and precipitation are likely to form. Figure 17–9 shows a warm front and a cold front and their associated weather.

FIGURE 17–9. Along a warm front, clouds and precipitation are usually widespread and cover a large area (a). Warm air is forced to rise rapidly along a cold front, producing thunderstorms and showers that start and stop quickly (b).

Name the source regions of air masses that affect weather in North America.

What causes fronts to form?

See Teacher's Guide.

REVIEW AND REFLECT

1. Why does saturated air at 25°C contain more water vapor than air at 12°C?
2. What determines the height at which clouds form?
3. Why does stable air near the surface usually mean fair weather?
4. What causes a zone of low pressure to form along the equator?
5. What effect does earth's rotation have on winds?
6. What are differences between the patterns of weather brought by cold fronts and warm fronts?

See Teacher's Guide.

Skill Inquiry

Surface weather maps are useful for showing weather systems that affect various world regions or continents. The maps are prepared using data taken from hourly observations. As you know, surface maps show the positions of pressure systems and fronts, as well as areas of precipitation. In order to determine where areas of high and low pressure are located, lines called isobars are drawn to connect points of equal atmospheric pressure. Meteorologists also may connect points on a weather map that have the same temperature. These lines are called isotherms. See the figure. Weather maps also may be analyzed to determine cloud cover and visibility. Study the map, which shows the weather conditions for Saturday, March 24, and answer the following questions.

1. What type of weather is associated with the low pressure area?
2. In general, where are the coldest isotherms on the map?
3. In what direction is the low most likely to move in the next 24 hours?
4. What kind of weather is associated with the areas of high pressure?
5. How do the isotherms indicate the position of the warm front?

Activity: How are clouds related to atmospheric conditions?

See Teacher's Guide.

MATERIALS

Figure 17–5, page 364

PROCEDURE

Part A

1. Study Figure 17–10. Identify the types and relative heights of the clouds shown in the photographs. Record this information in a data table.

FIGURE 17–10.

2. Refer to Figure 17–5, page 364. Review the weather associated with each cloud type.
3. In your data table, write a brief description of the atmospheric condition that may have produced each type of cloud.

Part B

1. Identify the types and relative heights of the clouds (if any) at your present location. Determine the atmospheric conditions that may have produced the types of clouds.
2. Record other information related to current weather conditions at your location.
3. Based on current weather information, write a forecast for the weather that will occur within the next three hours at your location.
4. After three hours note the weather that actually occurred.

DATA AND OBSERVATIONS

Location	A	B	C
Cloud Type			
Cloud Height			
Condition			

QUESTIONS AND CONCLUSIONS

1. In which picture do atmospheric conditions appear to be least stable? Explain.
2. How could you distinguish fog from a stratus cloud?
3. In your location, what weather conditions did you also use to predict the weather for the next three hours?
4. How accurate was your forecast?
5. What factors other than clouds should be considered in forecasting weather?
6. What changes occurred in your location that you did not forecast? Give some possible reasons these changes occurred.

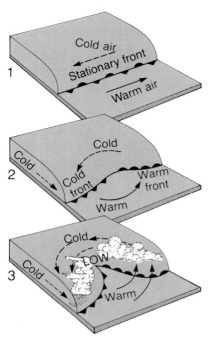

FIGURE 17–11.   A cyclone develops between two air masses. It begins as a small wave along a stationary front (1 and 2). A front that does not show much movement is stationary.

What is a cyclone?

BACKGROUND   A severe thunderstorm is defined as a storm with winds of over 95 km/hour or hail 2 cm or more in diameter. Hail forms in updrafts within cumulonimbus clouds, where successive layers of ice are deposited on an ice core.

What is the difference between a weather watch and warning?

17:6   Extreme Weather

Perhaps your school has been closed for a few days during winter because of snowstorms. Snowstorms and other extreme weather often are produced by what meteorologists call cyclones. A **cyclone** is a large area of low pressure that develops between air masses. Figure 17–11 shows the development of a cyclone along a frontal boundary. Note how the air spirals into the center of the low pressure system. Recall that rising air within a low pressure usually produces clouds and precipitation.

In winter, cyclones may bring heavy snowfall as well as freezing rain. Intense cyclones may produce blizzards. A blizzard is a system of strong winds carrying powdery snow.

During other seasons, cyclones often are responsible for the formation of thunderstorms. Thunderstorms are produced as unstable air rises quickly, forming cumulonimbus clouds. The stages of thunderstorm development are shown in Figure 17–12.

Occasionally, two vastly different air masses may meet along the polar front. For example, a rapidly moving cold air mass may invade a very warm, moist air mass. As a result, some severe thunderstorms will develop ahead of the cold front. The conditions that lead to severe thunderstorms also may produce tornadoes, particularly during spring and early summer, frequently late in the afternoon.

A tropical cyclone, sometimes called a hurricane, is different from a normal mid-latitude cyclone. Although a hurricane has a low pressure center, there are no fronts. At a very low pressure center, there is a clear region where air descends. The fastest winds whirl around this "eye" at about 30 kilometers from it. However, the destructive diameter of the hurricane is about 800 kilometers. Typically, a hurricane forms over an ocean in the tropics. In the northern hemisphere, it slowly moves northeast with the trade winds. When the hurricane reaches land, it moves faster, usually veering back toward the ocean along a path within the westerlies. Winds cause high waves that may cause damage to coastal cities. Further inland, heavy rainfalls from the storm may cause flooding.

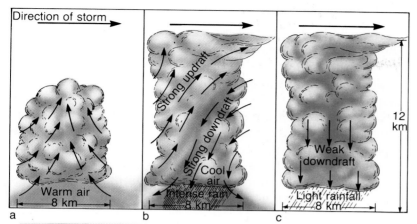

FIGURE 17–12. A typical thunderstorm begins to develop during the cumulus stage (a) where warm air rises. Strong updrafts prevent rain from falling. The mature stage (b) begins as rain falls, which produces a downdraft. The mature stage is the most intense period. The downdrafts finally cut off the updrafts (c).

Listening to weather reports is important during extreme weather conditions. A **watch** indicates that conditions in the atmosphere could produce a severe thunderstorm, tornado, or hurricane. A **warning** indicates that severe weather is occurring or is expected to occur.

17:7 Forecasting Weather

Maybe you listen to a radio in the morning for a weather forecast so you know how to dress for school. Weather forecasts are important to almost everyone. Consider the importance of weather information to farmers, airline pilots, construction workers, and truck drivers. Industries also depend on weather information. For example, clothing buyers for retail stores may order more wool items when advised of a cold winter.

Many nations cooperate in observing, reporting, and making predictions about the weather. The World Meteorological Organization, with headquarters in Geneva, Switzerland, coordinates weather services. Over 10 000 land stations, hundreds of ships, and weather satellites make frequent observations. Also, most countries have weather analysis centers. The centers prepare maps and tables that show current weather conditions. The centers also prepare weather forecasts. Because weather changes quickly, speed is important in the communication of data to and from centers. Teletype® and computer networks are essential in the sharing of weather data.

What are some reasons for forecasting weather?

How do nations cooperate in observing, reporting, and forecasting weather?

BACKGROUND There are three other locations that serve as centers for data analysis: Washington, D.C., Moscow, USSR, and Melbourne, Australia.

BACKGROUND Meteorologists make extended and long-range forecasts, as well as daily forecasts. An extended forecast is a set of general conditions predicted for a few days or a week. A long-range forecast is a description of how weather is expected to vary from normal conditions for a month or more. The flow of upper air is studied in making extended and long-range forecasts.

Why are weather forecasts often inaccurate?

In each city or town, the local meteorologist uses data from world and national centers to predict local weather. The particular needs of the people of an area are considered. Farming, outdoor industries, and special community outdoor activities are some things that the local forecaster keeps in mind.

Normally a forecast is made after the meteorologist examines both surface maps, like those you see in the newspaper, and upper air maps. Surface maps show the locations of fronts and pressure systems. Meteorologists note the rate at which air masses and fronts move. By understanding the weather that may result from particular conditions, the forecast can be made. Because there are so many variables in weather, a forecast is not always accurate. Often forecasters speak of the probability of an event, such as rain or snow. High-speed computers are used to relate the weather variables to help make forecasts.

17:8 Climate

SUGGESTION Discuss why people could be interested in climate, in ways other than the text examples. For example, when traveling to distant locations, climate information is important. Most travel brochures give climate data.

What factors affect climate?

BACKGROUND Cities are often slightly warmer than surrounding countryside, since the greater amount of CO_2 from vehicles and industry absorbs more heat. Also, particles of smoke and dust in cities act as condensation nuclei for water vapor, increasing cloud formation and precipitation.

How do people affect climate?

People are interested in more than just weather. You might want to know the average number of days of sunshine in a place if, for instance, you want to construct a home heated by solar energy. **Climate** is the average range of weather conditions at any particular location.

Many factors affect climate. Latitude is the most important overall factor in climate differences. Whether a place is on or near an ocean or lake makes a difference in temperature range. Areas near water have more equal yearly temperature than land locations. The presence of hills, mountains, and valleys influence climate because temperature drops with elevation. Winds on windward and leeward sides of mountains produce different moisture and temperature patterns.

Climate, as well as weather, may be slightly different within a city or in the same region. Roads, buildings, ponds, grassy land, and different crop fields absorb heat differently, stop or modify wind flow differently, and receive different amounts of direct sunlight. People have been responsible for many small-scale, or local climate changes because they have cut down forests, plowed and planted land, and constructed buildings.

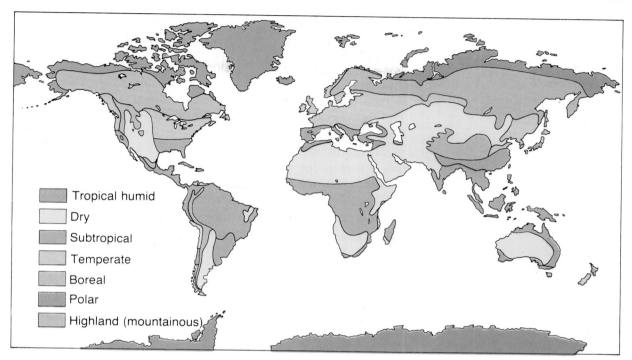

Tropical humid

Dry

Subtropical

Temperate

Boreal

Polar

Highland (mountainous)

FIGURE 17–13. Tropical humid climates have a small yearly temperature change. Some tropical climates have dry seasons. Dry climates include deserts and semi-arid regions. Subtropical climates have a definite cool season. Temperate regions experience seasonal changes. Boreal climates have very cold winters. Polar climates have very short summers. Highland climates vary.

During the past two million years, climates have changed due to the gradual thickening of huge ice sheets on continents. At the same time, smaller glaciers developed in high mountain ranges all over the world. As glaciers grew, wind systems were disrupted. Sources of moisture, such as the Arctic Ocean, froze solid. Rainfall increased in some inland regions. Wide shallow lakes formed. Water from the oceans that formed glacial ice on land lowered sea level hundreds of meters. Climates changed locally around the edges of every continent. When the great ice sheets melted, wind systems changed again. Some regions became more arid and lakes evaporated. Eventually shorelines were flooded as sea level rose.

See Teacher's Guide.

Describe how some major climate changes have occurred.

REVIEW AND REFLECT

1. How is a mid-latitude cyclone different from a hurricane?
2. Why are rain or snow forecasts given as a probability?
3. How are weather forecasts important to pilots?
4. How do bodies of water affect the climate of an area?

17:9 Information: Weather Modification

For about 40 years, scientists have known that spraying certain substances into clouds can change weather. Dry ice (solid carbon dioxide) causes supercooled water in clouds to freeze instantly. Millions of tiny ice crystals are formed. The ice crystals serve as nuclei on which more water freezes. If the crystals become large enough, they will fall as precipitation. Silver iodide crystals also make good nuclei for ice. The procedure of placing these compounds in clouds is known as cloud seeding.

Why are scientists studying cloud seeding?

Cloud seeding is being investigated to modify weather for several reasons. A primary interest is to increase precipitation in drought regions. Other interests include dispersing clouds, suppressing hail, and modifying hurricanes. Cloud seeding is currently used at some airports to disperse fog.

An important scientific experiment with cloud seeding was done in Israel between 1961 and 1975. A mixture of silver iodide and sodium iodide was used. There were rainfall increases of 15 percent in one stage of the experiment and 46 percent in another stage. Downwind of the area targeted for seeding, rainfall was judged to have increased about 20 percent. These are statistically convincing results that cloud seeding can increase rainfall.

Why is cloud seeding not a sure method of rainmaking?

However, another recent carefully-controlled experiment has produced inconclusive results. In the Florida Area Cumulus Experiment (FACE), a mixture of silver iodide and silver chloride was used. On some days, clouds were seeded with sand, which should have had no effect. The decision to use the silver iodide–silver chloride mixture was made randomly. The overall results showed only a five percent increase in rainfall. There was a 40 percent probability that this increase was due to chance. In other words, some very rainy days occurred when the clouds were seeded with sand. So, the rain that occurred on those days was from natural causes.

Another way to learn about cloud seeding is to use cloud chambers rather than doing outdoor experiments. With cloud chambers, scientists are able to control many conditions and find important relationships in what makes particles form and grow. Experimenters at Colorado State

FIGURE 17–14. The most common method of cloud seeding is to drop or eject the material from airplanes. Fog may be dispersed with material emitted from a ground sprayer.

University (CSU) have obtained results that may show why the Israeli experiment was successful and FACE was not. When the relative humidity is slightly more than 100 percent, as could have been true in Israel, there is a 30-times-faster rate of condensation on crystals. Also, the number of ice particles increases by a factor of 100. The FACE mixture of silver iodide and silver chloride was found to attract water relatively slowly. The CSU research team discovered that these particles must collide with a cloud droplet before it freezes. When the researchers added sodium chloride to the mixture, condensation rate increased 10 times.

Scientists have a lot of work to do before they know just how rain forms. Someday cloud seeding may be a useful way of modifying weather. Then people will have to decide where and when it should be used.

What are some advantages of using cloud chambers to investigate cloud seeding methods?

See Teacher's Guide.

REVIEW AND REFLECT

1. What is cloud seeding?
2. Describe the Israeli and FACE experiments.
3. Suppose scientists learn how to increase rainfall in most seeded clouds. Describe under what conditions you think cloud seeding should be permitted and recommended.

CHAPTER 17 REVIEW

SUMMARY

1. The atmosphere is a mixture of gases and suspended particles. The composition is fairly uniform in the lower layers. 17:1

2. Seasons result because the earth's axis is inclined with respect to the plane of its orbit. 17:2

3. Because of the high specific heat of water, oceans are warmed and cool more slowly than land. 17:2

4. Stable air usually means fair weather, while unstable air often produces clouds and precipitation. 17:3

5. The general circulation of earth's atmosphere produces major wind belts. 17:4

6. Monsoons, land and sea breezes, and mountain and valley breezes are caused by local heating and cooling conditions. 17:4

7. Fronts form between different air masses and move in the direction the air masses are moving. 17:5

8. Severe weather may be produced by intense low pressure cyclones. 17:6

9. A forecast for a city or town is made by a local meteorologist using data from national and world weather centers. 17:7

10. Climate is produced by a number of factors. Climate can vary within the same local area. 17:8

VOCABULARY

air mass 11	front 12	sublimation 7
climate 10	greenhouse effect 5	tropopause 2
Coriolis force 4	jet stream 14	troposphere 8
cyclone 1	monsoon 9	watch 6
dew point 3	relative humidity 13	warning 15

Match each definition with the correct word from the list.

1. Area of low pressure that may produce severe weather in the mid-latitudes and hurricanes in the tropics

2. Upper boundary of the troposphere

3. Temperature at which water vapor changes state

4. Due to the earth's rotation winds are deflected

5. Process by which infrared radiation is absorbed by water vapor and carbon dioxide

6. Indication that conditions in the atmosphere could produce severe weather

7. Change of state from a gas directly to a solid or a solid to a gas

8. The layer of the atmosphere in which we live

9. Seasonal wind that blows between a continent and an ocean

10. The average annual weather condition for a particular location

11. A large body of air having the same temperature and moisture properties as the surface over which it lies

12. Boundary between differing air masses

13. Ratio of the actual amount of water vapor in air to the greatest amount it can hold at a particular temperature

14. High-velocity winds in the tropopause

15. Indication that severe weather is occurring or is expected to occur

QUESTIONS

MAIN IDEAS

Choose the correct answer to each question.

1. Where do changes in weather mainly take place? *(troposphere, tropopause, stratosphere)*

2. Of what does the earth's atmosphere mostly consist? *(oxygen and carbon dioxide, carbon dioxide and nitrogen, nitrogen and oxygen)*

3. Heating of the troposphere is possible because of the presence of what in the air? *(O_2 and H_2O, CO_2 and H_2O, N_2 and O_2)*

4. Where is the sun's energy most intense? *(along the equator, at the poles, in the mid-latitudes)*

5. What is a process by which ice particles in clouds form? *(condensation, evaporation, sublimation)*

6. Because of the Coriolis force, air moving toward the equator from the North Pole is deflected in which direction? *(toward the earth's center, to the east, to the west)*

7. What is a cloud type that does not produce precipitation? *(cirrostratus, cumulonimbus, nimbostratus)*

8. A mass of cold air is replaced by warm air along what? *(cold front, warm front, jet stream)*

9. What is true of a cyclone in the mid-latitudes? It may *(develop along fronts, increase the stability of air, produce hurricanes in the tropics)*.

10. What is atmospheric pressure at sea level? *(1 kP, 101 millibars, 101 kP)*

See Teacher's Guide.

APPLICATIONS

Answer each question in one or more paragraphs.

1. Explain why the interiors of continents experience a wide annual temperature range.

2. Explain why warm, humid air is less dense than cold, dry air.

3. Why do spring bulbs bloom two weeks earlier five kilometers south of Lake Ontario in the United States than near the shore of Lake Ontario?

4. Explain the rush of cool air that precedes an approaching thunderstorm.

5. How might earth's climate change if the amount of carbon dioxide increased a lot?

6. A weather satellite photograph shows a buildup of cumulus clouds over islands during the day. Explain the development of these clouds.

FURTHER STUDY

INVESTIGATIONS

1. Find out how to set up a small weather station at home or school. Keep weather records and make weather predictions based on the information you collect.

2. Learn the types of hazardous weather that take place in your area. Mark the times of year severe weather is expected on a calendar. Write safety rules to follow in the severe weather.

READINGS

+ Allen, Oliver E. *Atmosphere.* Time-Life Books: Alexandria, VA, 1983.

− Lampton, Christopher. *Meteorology.* Franklin Watts: New York, 1981.

0 Long, Marion. "The Man Who Chases Tornadoes." *Science Digest.* May, 1984. pp. 66–69, 98–100.

0 McFall, Christie. *Wonders of Dust.* Dodd, Mead & Co.: New York, 1980.

HAVE you ever gone cave exploring? These students are learning about the geologic processes that formed the caves in this park. Many parks have been built around interesting geologic features. Perhaps you have visited a park near where you live that has deep valleys or high plateaus. You may have wondered how they formed. What produces geologic features? How are rocks formed? How do they change?

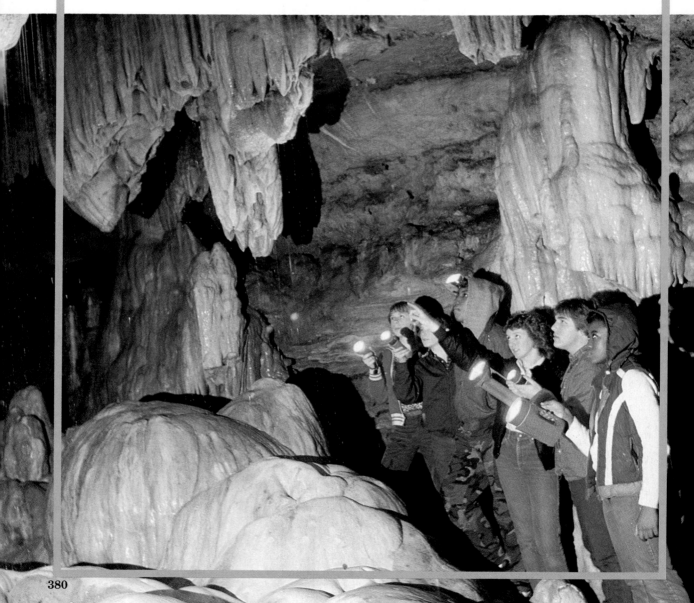

EARTH'S STRUCTURE

INTRODUCING THE CHAPTER   Many students have heard of Jules Verne's science fiction stories. Introduce a summary (or have a student introduce it) of Verne's *Journey to the Center of the Earth*. Discuss whether such a set of conditions is possible. A brief synopsis and discussion is given in the Teacher's Guide at the front of this book.

18:1   Rocks and Minerals

Recall from chapter 16 that the earth formed from a rotating cloud of gas and dust. When the cloud collapsed, the earth melted throughout. Lighter elements stayed near the surface. Heavier elements sank to the center. Scientists are unable to make direct observations of the earth's mantle and core. However, evidence from meteorites and earthquakes indicates that the core probably is composed mainly of iron and nickel. Evidence from volcanic eruptions indicates the mantle contains rock composed of iron and magnesium silicates.

Of the more than 100 elements known, eight—oxygen, silicon, aluminum, iron, calcium, sodium, potassium, and magnesium—make up more than 98 percent of the earth's continental crust. These elements combine in many different ways forming a variety of compounds. Oxygen and silicon are the most abundant elements in the crust. The chemical combination of these two elements plus others yields silicates. Silicates make up many minerals. **Minerals** are natural, inorganic solids that have a definite chemical composition and molecular structure. A few minerals, such as gold, are not compounds but consist of only one element. Minerals have distinctive physical and chemical properties that are used to identify them. The properties of some minerals make them economically valuable.

Combinations of minerals form rocks. Rocks are classified into three groups according to how they are formed. The groups are igneous, sedimentary, and metamorphic. The set of changes that forms the different kinds of rocks is called the rock cycle, Figure 18–1.

GOAL   You will learn about the materials that make up the earth and the processes that change them.

How do scientists learn about the earth's mantle and core?

DEMONSTRATION   Pour syrup into water in a clear container and observe the syrup settle to the bottom. The syrup represents elements with greater atomic weight. The water represents the lighter elements.

Describe minerals and rocks.

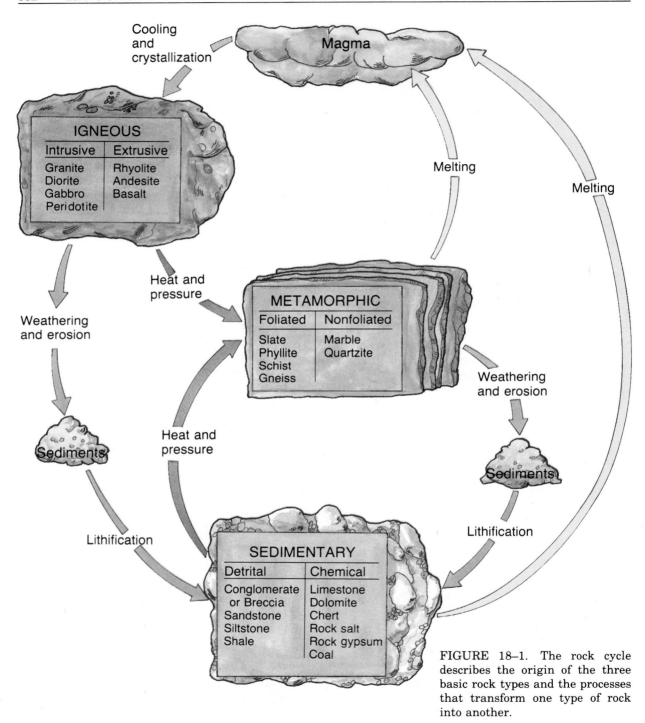

FIGURE 18–1. The rock cycle describes the origin of the three basic rock types and the processes that transform one type of rock into another.

18:2 Igneous Activities

When a volcano erupts, lava pours onto the earth's surface. Eventually the lava hardens forming rock. In a volcanic eruption, magma moves to the earth's surface through openings called vents. Magma is a hot mineral solution below the earth's surface that crystallizes as it cools, forming igneous rock. When magma reaches the surface, such as when volcanoes erupt, it is called lava. Igneous rocks also form from magma that cools beneath the earth's surface.

The composition of magma and the rate at which it cools affect the texture and type of igneous rocks that form. Magma that remains beneath the surface cools slowly. As a result, large mineral grains have time to form. Rocks with large mineral grains, such as granite, are called intrusive rocks. **Intrusive** rocks form as magma is forced into rocks and spaces between rock layers and then slowly cools. The continents are mostly granite, an intrusive rock.

When magma is exposed at the earth's surface as lava, it cools quickly. The igneous rocks that form contain very small mineral grains. Frequently, the lava cools so rapidly that elements harden without forming crystals. Igneous rocks that form at the earth's surface are called **extrusive** rocks. The earth's crust beneath the oceans consists mostly of basalt, which is an extrusive igneous rock.

What is magma?

Compare intrusive and extrusive igneous rocks.

FIGURE 18–2. Volcanoes are a result of extrusive igneous activity. This crater near Flagstaff, Arizona, is a cinder cone volcano consisting mostly of ejected lava fragments (a). Shield volcanoes, such as Mauna Ulu in Hawaii, are built primarily of quiet basaltic lava flows (b). Mt. Hood in Oregon is a composite volcano, which has periods of violent eruptions alternating with quiet lava flows (c).

a

b

c

ACTIVITY   Obtain examples of granite and basalt. Use a hand lens to study the distribution and sizes of mineral fragments.

What is the probable origin of magma?

One way extrusive igneous rocks are formed is by means of volcanoes. However, most extrusive igneous rocks are formed from fissure eruptions. Extensive areas of continents, such as the Snake River Plain of North America, were formed when lava was expelled through narrow cracks in the earth's crust. The basalt, which makes up the oceanic crust, also was produced by fissure eruptions, but beneath the sea. Much of the large amount of magma that forms both extrusive and intrusive rock probably comes from within the continents and in the crust just beneath the continents. However, slow currents within the mantle bring minerals from the lower mantle to the surface in some locations, such as the Hawaiian Islands.

FIGURE 18–3. Soil consists of weathered rock particles, organic matter, water, and air, which support plant growth. Soils in most areas have distinct layers called horizons. The A horizon is the topsoil, which contains the most organic matter. Many of the minerals dissolved by rainwater in the topsoil accumulate in the B horizon. The C horizon contains mostly fragments of the parent rock.

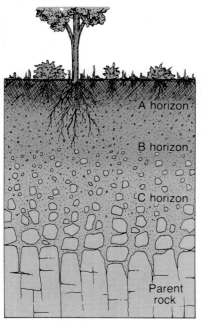

A horizon

B horizon

C horizon

Parent rock

18:3 Weathering and Sedimentary Rocks

Sedimentary rocks form from deposited fragments or particles of other rocks that have been weathered and eroded. The weathering of some rocks is due to the acids in rainwater and from decaying organic material in soil. Other rocks are broken when pressure between rocks changes. **Weathering** leaves crumbled or chemically changed rock in place or near the original rock formation.

Mechanical weathering breaks rocks into smaller pieces without changing their composition. Chemical weathering changes the chemical composition of rocks. For example, iron minerals in granite are oxidized as the rock is weathered chemically. In the same way, a bicycle becomes rusty when left outdoors. The presence of water in an environment speeds up chemical weathering. In deserts where there is little water, chemical weathering occurs very slowly.

Weathered rock particles that remain in place may form soil eventually. See Figure 18–3. However, products of weathered rocks frequently are removed by running water or by wind. These products range in size from small clay particles, silt, and sand to larger gravel and boulders. Eventually, the particles are deposited as sediment. A river, for instance, transports sediment to the ocean. There the sediment accumulates forming horizontal layers. If layers of sand, silt, clay, and other particles accumulate long enough, they will become sedimentary rock.

Sedimentary rocks may form in a number of ways. Clay particles become shale when the weight of overlying sediment squeezes out water and compresses the particles. Larger particles, such as sand, are cemented together by minerals that were originally dissolved in the water. Other rocks, such as rock salt, form when minerals dissolved in water are precipitated from the water. Some types of limestone result when shells of some marine animals are ground up by waves and deposited on the ocean floor. Coal is formed when a large number of dead plants are buried in a swampy environment.

ACTIVITY   Display a collection of sedimentary rocks. Determine which are precipitates and which are formed from particles compressed and/or cemented together (called elastic rocks). Learn the names of the rocks.

How are sedimentary rocks formed?

SUGGESTION   Many students have studied animal metamorphosis in previous science courses. Compare the life science meaning with the way the term is used with rocks.

18:4 Metamorphic Rocks

Igneous and sedimentary rocks may change if the rocks are subjected to heat and pressure within the earth's crust. The process by which rocks undergo changes in composition and texture is called **metamorphism** (met uh MOR fizm). One type of metamorphism occurs when magma is intruded within an existing body of rocks. Because of the magma's heat, the minerals that make up the surrounding rock are changed. This change that takes place within a narrow zone around the magma is called contact metamorphism. See Figure 18–4.

A much more extensive type of metamorphism is called regional metamorphism. Regional metamorphism is a result of the large-scale forces in the earth's crust that compress and distort the original rocks. The best examples of regional metamorphism can be seen within mountain ranges. Mountains such as the Appalachians in North America were formed as the earth's crust was compressed. The rocks were squeezed and pushed upward. During mountain building processes, some sedimentary and igneous rocks hundreds of meters thick are changed to metamorphic rocks.

As shown in Figure 18–1, metamorphic rocks are classified as foliated (FOH lee ayt ed) or unfoliated. Most rocks that undergo regional metamorphism are foliated. Foliated rocks have mineral grains arranged in parallel layers. Some of the softer foliated rocks break, or cleave, easily along these layers. Slate is a foliated rock. It forms from shale, a sedimentary rock.

What is metamorphism?

FIGURE 18–4. During metamorphism the mineral grains in granite (a) are realigned due to pressure, becoming gneiss (b).

a

b

What is the difference between foliated and unfoliated rocks?

ACTIVITY   Display a collection of metamorphic rocks. Determine which are foliated and which are unfoliated. Learn the rocks' names.

Unfoliated rocks are dense rocks in which mineral grains cannot be seen or shown to be arranged in layers. Most unfoliated rocks occur near contact metamorphic zones. Marble is an unfoliated rock. It can be formed from limestone.

See Teacher's Guide.

REVIEW AND REFLECT

1. What properties do you think are useful for identifying rocks? Explain.
2. How do extrusive rocks differ from intrusive rocks?
3. The sand along most beaches consists of weathered rock particles. How would the color of beach sand be used to identify the original rock from which the sand was formed?
4. Why are foliated rocks associated mostly with regional metamorphism?
5. Why are there more potholes in roads in New York City than in Los Angeles?

See Teacher's Guide.

Career Profile

How did Beverly Martinez, watchmaker and jewelry store owner, get into the jewelry business? "By snooping over someone's shoulder," she replies. Beverly did bookkeeping in a jewelry store when she was just out of high school, but she found that she was more interested in watching the watchmakers than in doing the books. Soon, Beverly was doing simple repairs. Her skill convinced Beverly's supervisor to send her to school to be a watchmaker.

Beverly took courses in basic watch repair, and spent four years gaining on-the-job training as a watchmaker's apprentice before she was certified as a watchmaker. In Albuquerque, New Mexico, she became partners with a local jeweler. Now she is sole owner of a jewelry store. Beverly re-

pairs watches in the evening. During the day, she runs the store.

Being a jeweler, Beverly needs to know geology and geography. How and where a gem is formed determines its quality, color, and price. Beverly also must know how climate affects gems. Beverly plans to become a certified gemologist and appraiser, which requires even more knowledge of science.

18:5 Erosion and Mass Movement

The earth's surface changes rapidly compared to the surfaces of other planets, such as Mercury and Mars. Many of the changes on the earth's surface are the result of erosion. Erosion is the process of transportation of weathered surface material. Agents of erosion include gravity, running water, wind, and ice. The rate at which erosion of the earth's surface occurs depends on factors such as climate and topography. Mountains in warm, rainy climates are subject to rapid chemical weathering, for example. Abundant rainfall then tends to remove weathered material quickly as water rushes down the slopes.

Gravity plays a direct role in erosion through a process called mass movement. A landslide is a familiar type of mass movement. A **landslide** results when weathered rock and soil are suddenly loosened from a hillside and slip rapidly down the slope. Landslides are most common where rock layers are parallel to the slope. If stream erosion or human activity cuts away the lower layers, the upper layers will collapse. Earthquakes may vibrate rocks and trigger a slide along weak boundaries between layers. In 1925 near Yellowstone National Park in Wyoming, a massive landslide occurred. Over 40 million cubic meters of rock and other debris rushed down one side of a river valley and about 115 meters up the opposite side. In the process, the river was dammed and a lake more than 13 kilometers long was created.

What is erosion and what causes it?

SUGGESTION   Compare erosion and weathering.

What causes landslides?

FIGURE 18–5.   An earthquake in 1984 caused a landslide near Morgan Hill in central California (a). Mudflows in the Toutle River Valley were caused by eruptions of Mt. St. Helens in 1980 (b).

a

b

Another type of mass movement occurs in dry mountain regions. Extended periods of heavy rains saturate loose sediments. The sediments move down slope like a mass of wet concrete. The material resulting from this mass movement is called a **mudflow.** Much damage was caused by mudflows in nearby stream valleys when Mt. St. Helens erupted. The heat from the volcanic explosions melted the snow. The snow mixed with thick layers of ash covering the slopes, and flowed downstream as mudflows.

What is mudflow?

The most common type of mass movement is creep. **Creep** is slow particle-by-particle mass movement that takes place on most slopes. The results of creep may be recognized by tilted fence posts and broken walls on a hillside. Creep is thought to result from seasonal or daily changes in moisture and temperature in the ground. Alternate periods of freezing and thawing, for example, cause particles to expand and contract. Each cycle moves the particles down the slope a short distance, so that in time, the surface of the hillside creeps down slope.

What is creep and what is thought to cause it?

ACTIVITY   Locate examples of creep in your area, if possible. Even where land is fairly flat, creep can often be found along river banks.

18:6   The Work of Rivers

Running water is the most significant agent of erosion, even in deserts. Rivers change landscapes more than any other agent of erosion. Mountains are worn down and eventually eroded to low plains. In time, rivers carry the weathered rock fragments to the oceans. The lowest level to which a stream can erode its channel is sea level.

The sediments that a stream carries are called its load. Part of a stream's load is dissolved materials. Most of a stream's load is small particles carried in suspension. Larger fragments, such as pebbles, are carried along the bottom of the stream.

When a stream's flow is slowed, its ability to carry particles is reduced. Thus, sediments are deposited. For example, when a river flows into an ocean, the velocity of its flow is suddenly reduced. Sediments accumulate in a fan-shaped deposit called a delta. A large delta is located where the Mississippi River flows into the Gulf of Mexico.

Rivers and streams produce valleys through erosional processes. Valleys that are narrow and V-shaped indicate stream flow is rapid. The stream's energy is concentrated

FIGURE 18–6.   A delta forms as a stream's load is deposited in order of decreasing weight. Suspended particles are the last to settle out, some distance from the river mouth.

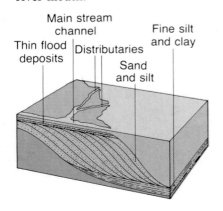

Main stream channel
Thin flood deposits
Distributaries
Fine silt and clay
Sand and silt

V-shaped valley results as
stream is mostly downcutting

Floodplain

Oxbow lake

Levees

Erosion occurs more laterally
as stream channel approaches
sea level

FIGURE 18–7. The patterns of erosion in a stream valley change as the elevation of the stream channel decreases.

on deepening the valley. Waterfalls and rapids are common. Notice the characteristic V-shaped valley of the river in Figure 18–7. As the stream channel is eroded to sea level or the slope is nearly flat, the flow slows down. More erosion now occurs laterally (from side to side) than downward. The river develops a wide floor with sediment on it. This flat floor is a floodplain. See Figure 18–7. On the floodplain, the river flows from side to side producing wide bends or meanders. As the water continues to flow, the meanders are cut off by sediment. The stream bypasses the meander forming an oxbow lake.

One river is part of a larger network of streams. The land that supplies water for this network is called a watershed. A **watershed** contains a main stream with its system of tributaries. Two watersheds are separated by a divide.

An understanding of watersheds is essential to human safety and protection of property that may be threatened by floods. Flooding occurs during periods of high rainfall and rapid melting of snow. To control flooding, dams temporarily store extra runoff. Another way to control flooding is to dig "back" channels parallel to main streams. These channels can relieve the high water in the main channel for a while. People also build up river banks with sandbags or concrete. These artificial levees help keep floodwater from flowing onto farmland or property on the floodplain.

Describe the changes that occur in a stream valley as the stream is eroded to sea level.

What are watersheds?

ACTIVITY   Find in what watershed your school location is situated. Locate it and neighboring watersheds on maps. Locate the continental divide on a map of North America.

Activity: How are rocks weathered?

See Teacher's Guide.

MATERIALS

3 samples of rock fragments
limestone fragments
7% HCl solution
5 glass jars, 1 with lid
stirring rod
pH paper
labels
large zip-lock bag
water
goggles
apron

PROCEDURE

Part A

1. Place each sample of rock fragments in a separate jar. Label each jar with the kind of rock it contains.

2. Place limestone in another labeled jar.

3. Determine the pH of the HCl solution. **CAUTION:** *HCl may cause burns. If spillage occurs, rinse with water.*

4. Carefully pour HCl solution down a stirring rod into each of the jars. Fill the jars enough so that the rock fragments are covered.

FIGURE 18–8.

5. Record your observations of each jar. Let the jars stand overnight. Then record your observations of the jars again.

Part B

1. Fill an empty jar to the top with water. Place a lid on the jar.

2. Seal the jar inside a zip-lock bag.

3. Place the bag in a freezer overnight.

4. Record your observations the next day.

DATA AND OBSERVATIONS

Rock	Observations	
	Day 1	**Day 2**
Limestone		

QUESTIONS AND CONCLUSIONS

1. In which part of the activity did you demonstrate chemical weathering? physical weathering?

2. The pH of normal rainwater is about 5.6. What effect might rain have on rocks?

3. The pH of acid rain is less than 5.6. What effect might acid rain have on rocks?

4. Cement, which is used to make concrete, contains calcium carbonate. Limestone is mainly calcium carbonate. What effect might acid rain have on concrete structures?

5. How can freezing water weather rocks?

6. In what climates (see Figure 17–13 on page 375) would you expect a lot of weathering to occur? Explain.

18:7 Groundwater

Rivers and streams are formed by runoff from rain or melted snow. Some of the water that does not become runoff soaks into the ground. Water that fills the pores within soil and layers of some types of rocks becomes groundwater. Rocks like fractured limestone and sandstone are permeable (PUR mee uh bul). Permeable rocks contain pores, fractures, and joints that allow the passage of groundwater. Any rock layer that allows water to flow through is called an aquifer.

When precipitation enters the ground, water passes down through permeable soil and rock until it reaches impermeable rock. The rock above the permeable layer becomes saturated. The top surface of this saturated zone is called the **water table**. The height of the water table varies with the season. The water table also is affected by topography. Lakes and springs occur where the water table intersects the earth's surface along a hillside.

In many regions of the world, thick layers of limestone make up the earth's surface. In humid climates, some of this limestone is dissolved by groundwater. Carbon dioxide dissolved in groundwater forms weak carbonic acid. Over thousands of years, the carbonic acid reacts with the limestone. Groundwater carries away the dissolved limestone. Caves and caverns form as a result. Occasionally, the roof of a cavern may suddenly collapse forming a sinkhole at the surface.

Describe permeable rocks.

BACKGROUND Where aquifers are found between impermeable layers, the system is called an artesian formation. The word artesian comes from the city of Artois in France.

What affects the height of the water table?

FIGURE 18–9. The water table may occur at various depths depending on the nature of the earth's surface. A spring or lake may form where the water table intersects the surface.

Rainwater infiltrates soil and upper rock layers

Permeable sandstone

Water table

Spring

Aquifer

Lake

Impermeable shale

What causes a geyser to eject water and steam?

BACKGROUND   Old Faithful in Yellowstone National Park is probably the most famous geyser in North America, erupting somewhat irregularly, but in intervals that average a little more than one hour.

Geysers (GI zurz) are hot springs in which water and steam is ejected with great pressure. At various time intervals, geysers erupt with a loud roar sending water 30 to 60 meters into the air. Geysers occur where groundwater collects in large openings near hot igneous rocks. At greater depths, the pressure increases the boiling point of the water. As water closer to the surface is heated, however, it expands out the opening. The release of pressure makes the hot water underground turn instantly into steam, which bursts out as a geyser. Geysers are common in the western United States, New Zealand, and Iceland.

See Teacher's Guide.

REVIEW AND REFLECT

1. In what ways does gravity affect the processes of erosion?
2. How is a river valley at a higher elevation different from a river valley near sea level?
3. What affect would an igneous rock intrusion have on the water table?
4. Why do people who live in areas where shale is the surface rock often have trouble with flooded yards and basements?

FIGURE 18–10. The McBride Glacier in Alaska is a valley glacier. The dark stripes within the glacier are moraines.

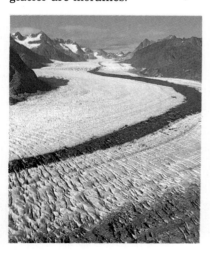

18:8 Glaciers

Glaciers are masses of flowing ice. They form wherever more snow falls than melts. When new snow falls and melts, the water trickles down filling the pores of old snow underneath it. This, plus the pressure of new snow on top, changes old snow beneath into ice. Glacial ice ranges from about 35 meters to more than three kilometers thick.

Glaciers have covered much of the earth's surface many different times in the past. Today, they cover about 20 percent of the land. Glaciers exist in the mountains of all continents except Australia. Glaciers in mountains are called valley glaciers. Glaciers that cover large areas of continents are continental glaciers. Continental glaciers are found on Antarctica, Greenland, and parts of Canada and Iceland today.

Both valley and continental glaciers erode and deposit rocks. With the rocks they carry, glaciers polish, scratch, and groove the rocks they pass over. A continental glacier tends to scrape and pluck at everything in its path. So, the landscape features caused by this erosion may not be very obvious. The overall result of continental glaciation is the smoothing of land.

A valley glacier erodes a large bowl-shaped depression called a cirque (SIRK) in the mountain where it begins. Gravity is responsible for glacier movement. Valley glaciers often flow in the paths of old river valleys. A series of basins may be carved along a mountain valley as the glacier moves down. A valley glacier also changes the cross-sectional shape of a river valley from a "V" to a "U." After the glacier melts, waterfalls may drop from tributary streams, which then hang high above the deepened valley floor.

When a glacier melts, its load of boulders and rock fragments is deposited. Ridges of such glacial deposits are known as **moraines.** Moraines may form below each valley wall as well as around the edges of valley glaciers. Very long moraines sometimes form where continental glacier edges do not move for a while.

FIGURE 18–11.   Most of Antarctica is covered by a continental glacier.

How are landscapes changed by glaciers?

18:9   Deserts and Wind Action

A desert receives about 10 centimeters or less of precipitation each year. Rain, when it does come, has a different effect on the landscape than in a humid climate because deserts have so little plant life. The rainwater moves across the desert floor in sheets and produces a system of temporary "braided" streams. This sheet flow erodes, transports, and deposits for a few hours after any rainfall. The water may empty into flat low regions of the desert where it evaporates forming hard mud or salty surfaces until the next rain.

In deserts, steep cliffs are eroded by streams. The eroded material is deposited on the slopes below the cliff, since not enough water is present to carry it away. These flat-topped hills with gentle slopes are mesas (MAY suz). The flat tops of mesas usually are due to hard rock layers capping soft layers below.

SUGGESTION   In the 1930s, a combination of over-cultivation and drought led to the erosion of much topsoil in the Great Plains. Use the "Dust Bowl" as an example of the importance of vegetation in reducing erosion.

Describe stream erosion in deserts.

Why are the effects of wind erosion most obvious in deserts?

DEMONSTRATION   Explain how dunes migrate by lining up a few students facing toward a hypothetical wind. When the "wind" blows against the first person facing it, this person moves to the back of the line. Continue this activity with each person, and the "dune" of people will move across the room away from the wind.

FIGURE   18–12. Mesas and buttes are desert landforms resulting from erosion. The flat tops of these structures are capped by horizontal rock layers that resist weathering and erosion by water (a). Sand particles moved by wind are deposited in large mounds called dunes. The dunes in large desert regions, such as Death Valley, may reach heights of 250 meters (b).

Wind is an important agent of erosion in both deserts and humid regions. The products of wind erosion are best seen in deserts, though, where vegetation covers less of the land. Sand carried by wind smoothes rocks by eroding them. As wind blows across soft or loose material, shallow basins are scooped out of the desert floor. The effect of both of these processes against unequally resistant rock produces the odd-shaped rocks often seen in deserts.

Perhaps the most spectacular wind deposits are sand dunes. Some dunes are as tall as skyscrapers. Others are less than a meter high. Sand dunes take different forms depending on how fast the wind blows. Crescent-shaped dunes face into the wind. Other dunes face in a downwind direction or in long parallel ridges. In a sandstorm, a dune migrates downwind. Sand is lifted from a dune's windward side and redeposited in the quiet zone on the leeward side.

Another deposit caused by wind is loess (LESS). Loess is a tan-colored silty deposit consisting of angular mineral fragments. Sometimes it is blown great distances from its original source. Large areas along the valley sides east of the Mississippi River are covered by loess. It came from glacial deposits on the floodplain that were later eroded by wind. Loess also blankets some large areas of northern China. Loess makes the soils in these areas very fertile.

a

b

18:10   Rock Deformation

Changes caused by erosion of the earth's surface occur gradually and become noticeable over many years. Some changes also occur within the crust. Sudden movements that cause earthquakes produce noticeable effects immediately. However, most other changes occur more slowly.

Scientists have learned that when large forces are applied gradually over a long period of time, rocks are folded. Some uplifted areas and "down-dropped" areas may be formed by folds called anticlines and synclines, as shown in Figure 18–13. Also, forces push flat rock layers slowly upward to form plateaus.

A **fault** is a fracture in a mass of rock in which movement occurs. Movement may be vertical, horizontal, or a combination of both. A scarp, or small cliff, is formed when faults occur at the earth's surface. Frequently, the sudden slippage of rock along a fault plane produces an earthquake. Shock waves accompany this sudden movement. These shock waves travel outward in all directions from the point of slippage. The shock waves produce the vibrations that we know as earthquakes.

The San Andreas fault in western North America is one example of a fault in which horizontal movement occurs. Some of the sudden movements are disastrous. One major earthquake occurred in 1906. It severely shook and partially destroyed the city of San Francisco.

FIGURE 18–13. Some surface features are formed as folded rock layers are eroded.

How are anticlines and synclines formed?

What causes earthquakes?

BACKGROUND   The forces within the earth that produce rock deformation and those that produce volcanoes are known to geologists as constructive processes. Although most people consider them destructive in general terms, these processes help build up the earth's surface. They counteract the destructive processes of weathering and erosion.

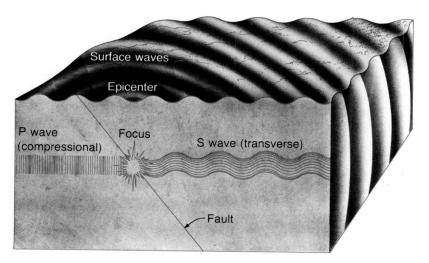

FIGURE 18–14. The energy released by an earthquake is transmitted away from the focus through rocks as waves. P and S waves penetrate deep into the earth. Surface waves travel mostly through the crust.

Rock deformations, such as faults and folds, may be seen in the rocks of many mountain ranges. The Appalachian Mountains and many ranges in the western United States were formed by internal forces that folded and uplifted thick layers of rock in the earth's crust. The Sierra Nevada and Grand Tetons were formed by forces that uplifted the crust along a series of faults.

Describe some places where landscape features have been formed by rock deformations.

See Teacher's Guide.

REVIEW AND REFLECT

1. What is the difference between a valley glacier and a continental glacier?
2. Why is the weathering of rock in deserts not as great as weathering in more humid regions?
3. What are some factors that may determine whether rocks will fold or fault when subjected to forces in the crust?

See Teacher's Guide.

Skill Inquiry

The Richter scale is used to compare earthquake magnitudes based on motion recorded by seismographs. The magnitude of an earthquake is a measure of the amount of energy released from the focus. Waves of energy radiate from the focus, vibrating the earth's crust.

Each number on the Richter scale is a magnitude representing the release of a certain amount of energy. Each increase of one magnitude indicates about 30 times more energy released. For example, an earthquake with a rating of 2.0 on the Richter scale releases 30 times more energy than an earthquake with a rating of 1.0.

The Richter scale is not a measure of earthquake intensity. The intensity of a quake is based on the damage it causes. Intensity depends on many factors, including location, geography, and population density. The table correlates the Richter scale with the effects of earthquakes.

TABLE OF EARTHQUAKE EFFECTS

Richter Magnitude	Effects
2.5	Generally not noticed
4.5	Local damage
6.0	May be destructive in populated areas
7.0	Major, serious damage
8.0	Great or total destruction to nearby communities

1. About how many times more energy is released by a major earthquake than one that is barely noticed?
2. In 1915, an earthquake with 7.8 magnitude occurred in a remote part of Nevada. Why was this earthquake less intense than the 1906 San Francisco quake, which had a magnitude of 8.3?

Activity: How are earthquakes located?

See Teacher's Guide.

MATERIALS

drafting compass
map of North and South America

PROCEDURE

1. Figure 18–15 shows seismograph data recorded at three locations. The vertical lines indicate minutes. Calculate and record the times between the arrival of P and S waves at each location.

2. Use Table 18–1 to determine how far each location is from the focus of the earthquake. Record each distance in the data table.

3. Using the map scale, determine the distance from the earthquake for each city. Mark the distances on the map.

4. Draw a circle around each city with a radius equal to the scale distance. (Put the compass point on the location.)

5. The point where the three circles intersect marks the source of the earthquake.

Augusta, Georgia
P wave   S wave

Seattle, Washington
P wave S wave

Santiago, Chile
P wave   S wave

FIGURE 18–15.

TABLE 18–1. DISTANCE AND TIME INTERVAL RELATIONSHIPS	
Distance From Earthquake (km)	Interval Between S and P Waves
2000	3.3 min
4000	5.6 min
6000	7.6 min
8000	9.4 min
10 000	10 min 59 s
11 000	11 min 39 s

DATA AND OBSERVATIONS

Seismograph Location	Augusta, Georgia	Seattle, Washington	Santiago, Chile
Time Between Arrival of P and S Waves			
Distance From Earthquake			

QUESTIONS AND CONCLUSIONS

1. The source of an earthquake is called its focus. The surface location directly above the focus is called the epicenter. Where was the epicenter of this earthquake?

2. Why is determining the epicenter of an earthquake important?

3. Why is it necessary to have data from at least three seismographs to determine the epicenter?

4. How might seismographic data from other locations be useful to geologists?

18:11   Information: Environmental Geology

Describe the importance of consulting geologists when planning major construction projects.

Whenever a building, a highway, or other construction project is planned, geologists need to help with proposed land evaluation. If they do not, results can be disastrous. For example, construction of a nuclear power plant began at a site on the California coast very close to the San Andreas fault. After managers realized that an earthquake could disrupt plant operation and release hazardous wastes, construction plans had to be changed.

When skyscrapers and other large buildings are erected, geologists first drill at the sites for rock samples. Engineering stress tests are done on the samples to help architects design appropriate foundations.

To judge a route for a highway, geologists map the types of soils and rocks and folds and faults along the way. The slope of the land and the position of the water table at every point are also important. Such information is needed to judge whether flooding, landslides, mudflow, and creep will occur.

Wherever a tunnel is needed, geologists must evaluate the earth and rock structure with particular care. Closely-spaced fractures in rocks lead to a lot of rubble in tunnels. Geologists recommend routes through the least-fractured rock where a tunnel is needed. Faults usually cause problems because groundwater moves down the fractures into the tunnel, Figure 18–16a. Geologists recommend that tunnels be constructed at right angles to faults whenever possible. In synclines, water tends to drain through aquifers, flooding tunnels. In addition, tunnels through syn-

a

b

FIGURE 18–16. Tunnels are built at right angles to faults. This design keeps the length of a tunnel in contact with the fault at a minimum (a). Tunnels that are built through synclines may have water problems because groundwater naturally drains into the tunnel (b).

a

b

clines require a great deal of support, Figure 18–16b. Tunnels through anticlines are recommended when possible. Soils and groundwater are considerations when constructing tunnels through earth, as well as rock.

Geological analysis is important when projects are planned. It is also important throughout construction. Sometimes original plans are changed when unexpected problems are encountered. For example, construction of a dam or highway may take a year or more. River deposition of sediments or creep along a slope may create a need for revising plans during these projects.

In general, the cost of construction projects is reduced by considering geological features. Long-term costs are reduced too, because the projects are more likely to last. A plan that recognizes the importance of rocks, soil, slopes, and water in construction and use is more successful than a plan that does not.

See Teacher's Guide.

FIGURE 18–17.   The structure of rock is an important consideration in tunnel construction (a). Undercutting by water caused the damage shown (b).

Why is geological analysis important throughout a construction project?

What are the economic advantages of considering geologic features' effects on construction projects?

REVIEW AND REFLECT

1. Why do geologists recommend that tunnels be built, when possible,
   a. at right angles to faults?
   b. through anticlines rather than synclines?
2. What might happen if geologic studies were not made before a skyscraper was built?
3. Suppose that you are going to purchase a lot on which to build a home. List at least five geological factors that should be learned about the land before purchase and construction.

CHAPTER 18 REVIEW

SUMMARY

1. Almost all of the rocks and minerals in the earth's crust are made up of only eight elements. 18:1
2. Changes in rocks and the processes that make the changes are represented by the rock cycle. 18:1
3. The texture of igneous rocks depends on the rate at which the magma cooled. 18:2
4. Mechanical and chemical weathering break down rocks and make soils. 18:3
5. Layers of sediment that accumulate long enough become sedimentary rock. 18:3
6. Unfoliated rocks are associated with contact metamorphism. Foliated rocks are associated with regional metamorphism. 18:4
7. The earth's surface changes rapidly due to erosion. The agents of erosion include gravity, running water, wind, and ice. 18:5
8. Rivers change landscapes more than any other agent of erosion. 18:6
9. Permeable rocks have small openings through which groundwater can flow. Rock layers that allow groundwater to flow through are aquifers. 18:7
10. Both continental and valley glaciers produce erosional and depositional features. 18:8
11. The products of wind erosion and deposition are best seen in deserts. 18:9
12. Pressures within the earth's crust cause rocks to fold and fracture. 18:10

VOCABULARY

creep 12	landslide 8	mudflow 11
extrusive 7	metamorphism 1	watershed 9
fault 3	minerals 5	water table 10
intrusive 6	moraines 4	weathering 2

Choose a word from the list to complete each sentence correctly.

1. Rocks undergo changes in composition and texture by _____.
2. _____ breaks rocks into smaller pieces or changes their chemical composition.
3. A(n) _____ is a fracture in a mass of rock in which movement occurs.
4. Ridges of boulders and rock fragments deposited by a glacier are called _____.
5. Solid earth materials that have a definite chemical composition and molecular structure are classified as _____.
6. Rocks formed from magma that cooled slowly have large mineral grains and are called _____.
7. Rocks formed from magma that cooled quickly have fine mineral grains and are called _____.
8. When weathered rock and soil are suddenly loosened from a hillside and slip rapidly down the slope, a(n) _____ results.
9. The land that supplies water for a large network of streams is called a(n) _____.
10. The top of the saturation zone in permeable rock is the _____.
11. A type of mass movement that occurs in dry mountain regions when heavy rains saturate loose sediments and cause them to move down slope is _____.
12. The slow mass movement that takes place on most slopes is _____.

QUESTIONS

MAIN IDEAS

Choose the correct answer to each question.

1. How are most extrusive rocks formed? *(by volcanoes, fissure eruptions, metamorphism)*

2. What is an example of slow mass movement? *(landslide, mudflow, creep)*

3. What kind of rock is granite? *(extrusive, intrusive, foliated, unfoliated)*

4. What is not likely to be produced by a river at a high elevation? *(wide floodplain, waterfalls, rapids)*

5. What kind of glaciers are found today on Antarctica and Greenland? *(continental, alpine, valley)*

6. What helps make the soil in northern China fertile? *(groundwater, loess, dunes)*

7. What kind of rocks were the first rocks on earth? *(igneous, sedimentary, metamorphic)*

8. What may form when groundwater dissolves limestone? *(mesas, caverns, moraines, cirques)*

9. How were the Grand Teton mountains formed? *(by folding, faulting, contact metamorphism)*

10. What kind of rock might form as a precipitate when water evaporates? *(basalt, limestone, granite)*

See Teacher's Guide.

APPLICATIONS

Answer each question in one or more paragraphs.

1. During the Middle Ages, many of the castles in Europe were built on the eroded necks of ancient volcanoes. Why do you think castle builders selected these locations?

2. Explain why oil should or should not be considered a mineral.

3. Sediments pressed together on the ocean floor become sedimentary rocks. How did these rocks come to be exposed on high land?

4. A type of igneous rock called a porphyry consists of large crystal grains imbedded within a mass of very tiny crystal grains or glassy material. How do you think a porphyry is formed?

5. Rocks as old as the earth are found easily on the moon. Why are rocks of that age difficult to find on earth?

6. How would the erosion of a stream change if the floodplain near sea level were uplifted?

7. Describe good preventive measures to take in a region
   a. near an active fault.
   b. where there are occasional landslides.
   c. where flooding may occur.

FURTHER STUDY

INVESTIGATIONS

1. Prepare a travel brochure describing national parks that have interesting rock features.

2. Learn more about the effects on people and property of a particular earthquake or a volcanic eruption. Write a short story based on the facts you learn.

3. Make a mineral or a rock collection. Label each sample and tell how it was formed.

READINGS

0 Gore, Rick. "The Dead Do Tell Tales at Vesuvius." *National Geographic.* May, 1984. pp. 557–613.

0 McPhee, John. *Suspect Terrain.* Farrar, Straus, Giroux: New York, 1983.

+ Matthews, W. H. *Geology Made Simple.* Doubleday & Company: Garden City, NY, 1982.

0 Young, Louise B. *The Blue Planet.* Little, Brown and Company: Boston, 1983.

THROUGHOUT history people have been fascinated by the oceans. Breaking waves, salty breezes, sandy beaches, and the unusual organisms of the sea seem to have special appeal. Perhaps you have enjoyed sailing, swimming, or collecting shells on a beach. Maybe you wondered how far away is the next shore? Why is seawater salty? What makes waves? What lies deep in the ocean?

THE OCEANS

INTRODUCING THE CHAPTER Oceanography incorporates all of the basic sciences (physics, chemistry, and biology), as well as other earth sciences and engineering. Recently, satellites and scientists on the space shuttles have studied the oceans, so the frontiers of space and the oceans have come together. Point out to students that whether or not they live near an ocean, the oceans affect them in many ways. Make a class list of students' ideas. Many of these ways will be discussed in the chapter.

19:1 The Earth's Water

Mars is often called the Red Planet because its iron-rich soil gives it a red appearance. Saturn is the Ringed Planet. The Water Planet is a good name for Earth. Seventy-one percent of earth's surface is oceans. The oceans are continuous, although continents divide the water. Therefore, we refer to different sections as oceans.

Most of the water of the oceans probably formed when the earth was young, about 4.5 billion years ago. Many volcanoes produced water vapor, which condensed when the earth cooled. Water filled the basins, the lowest regions of the planet. During the long period after the oceans formed, the ocean basin shapes have varied. The depth of the water also has varied due to worldwide periods of glaciation.

The earth's water constantly leaves and returns to the oceans in a water cycle. Water evaporates from the oceans. The water vapor condenses to form clouds and precipitation. Most of the precipitation that falls on the continents eventually flows back to the ocean and the cycle starts again.

Table 19-1 shows the concentration of the major elements found in oceans. Sodium and chlorine are the most abundant elements in seawater. Sodium is common in certain igneous rocks, and chlorine gas is supplied by gaseous volcanic eruptions. The chlorine gas combines with water in the atmosphere and eventually falls to earth as dilute hydrochloric acid. The acid dissolves the minerals in certain igneous rocks and joins with the sodium. Then, the chlorine and sodium combine, eventually reach the sea, and become the salt in the sea.

GOAL You will learn the characteristics of the ocean water and sea floor and also about ocean resources.

Describe the probable origin of the oceans.

What is the water cycle?

SUGGESTION Have students imagine that they are water molecules early in earth history. Explain that for more than four billion years, they would have existed somewhere in the oceans.

What are trace elements?

BACKGROUND   The trace elements may be present in varying ratios in different samples of sea water. This is unlike the major chemicals, which are found in the same ratio everywhere. As the elements silicon, nitrogen, and phosphorus are used by plants and animals (mainly tiny plants called phytoplankton) in shallow water, these elements are found in low concentrations.

Elements present in very tiny amounts in seawater are called trace elements. Trace elements are important to many forms of life. One trace element important to people is iodine. A balanced diet should include sources of iodine to help prevent goiter. Iodine and other trace elements are concentrated in sea life. So, certain types of seafood are good dietary sources of iodine. However, when heavy elements such as mercury become concentrated in fish, people who eat the fish may develop mercury poisoning, an illness that can cause death. Some industries along ocean shores pollute the water with mercury.

TABLE 19–1. COMPOSITION OF SEAWATER (%)	
Water	96.5
Chloride	1.9
Sodium	1.0
Magnesium	0.1
Sulfate	0.3
Other	0.2

FIGURE 19–1. Major bodies of water and land masses

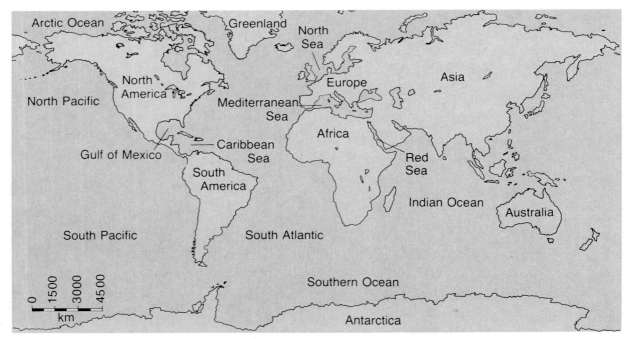

19:2 Structure of Ocean Water

The amount of solid materials in ocean water is measured in terms of salinity. **Salinity** is defined as the amount of solid material dissolved in one kilogram of water when certain conditions exist. As the salinity of water increases, its density increases also. Above 4°C, the density increases as temperature decreases.

Variations in the salinity, temperature, and density of ocean water result in the formation of water layers. In the tropics, for example, the upper layers of ocean water are warmer and more salty than the lower layers. The lower layers are more dense because they are colder. Mixing of layers occurs due to diffusion and ocean currents, but different layers still can be identified. In the central Atlantic Ocean, the upper 50 meters of water are about 27°C. At 400 meters, a sharp drop to about 10°C occurs. The temperature is about 1°C below 5000 meters.

The density of surface ocean water depends on location. Water at the poles is colder, and thus, more dense than ocean water at lower latitudes. Ocean water near the equator is less dense not only because it is warm, but also because abundant precipitation dilutes it, decreasing its salinity. Likewise, water near the mouth of a river is less dense because fresh water is flowing into the ocean.

Variations in salinity, temperature, density, and pressure affect the organisms that live in the oceans. Each species of organism requires certain conditions for survival. Two important factors that affect the distribution of organisms in the ocean are nutrients and sunlight. In general, the majority of organisms are found near the continents in the upper layers. Nutrients are most plentiful near the continents. Sunlight sufficient for organisms to make food by photosynthesis can penetrate only the upper layers of the oceans. Photosynthesis generally does not occur below about 100 meters. Plants, animals, and other organisms are restricted by this factor. The turbidity of ocean water may reduce the depth of sunlight penetration. Turbidity is the presence of suspended materials that reduce the clarity of the water. The more turbid water is, the more suspended materials it contains and the less clear it is.

What factors affect the density of water?

SUGGESTION   Review the concept of density. An understanding of density is important to comprehension of this section and to the activity on page 406.

Describe the layers in ocean water.

FIGURE 19–2.   The graph shows the average surface temperature, salinity, and density of ocean water at different latitudes (a). Plankton (b) are organisms, mostly very small, that drift in the oceans. Plankton are nutrients for larger marine organisms.

a

b

Activity: What is the relationship between floating and density?

MATERIALS

small empty juice can
graduated cylinder
600 mL beaker
water
table salt
string

scissors
six metal washers
marking pencil
balance
metric ruler
stirring rod

FIGURE 19–3.

PROCEDURE

1. Find the mass of a 600 mL beaker. Then fill the beaker with 300 mL of water. Find the mass of the beaker with the water in it. Find the mass of the water alone by subtraction.

2. Calculate and record the density of the water. (Density = mass/volume)

3. Punch two holes in the top of a juice can and loop string through the holes, Figure 19–3.

4. Place three metal washers in the can. Call the can with three washers "can A." Find the density of can A. (Volume = $\pi r^2 \times$ height of the can, r is the radius of the can.) Record the results.

5. Carefully lower can A into the beaker of water until it floats.

6. Remove can A and mark the water level. Dry off the can. Measure the depth that the can was submerged, and record the value.

7. Add three more washers to the juice can. Call this heavier can "can B." Find can B's density. Record your results.

8. Slowly dissolve 30 g of salt in the water, using a stirring rod. Find the density of this salt water. (Use a procedure similar to step 1. You already know the mass of the empty beaker.)

9. Repeat procedure steps 5 and 6 with can A, using the salt water.

10. Repeat procedure steps 5 and 6 with can B, using the salt water.

DATA AND OBSERVATIONS

Can	Density	Depth in Water Fresh D =	Salt D =
A			
B			

QUESTIONS AND CONCLUSIONS

1. What relationship exists between an object's density and how low it floats in fresh water? in salt water?

2. What relationship exists between how low an object floats and the density of the fluid in which it floats?

3. Seawater has a density between that of the fresh water and the salt water you used in this activity. (See Table 19–1.) Describe the depth you would expect cans A and B to sink to in seawater.

4. In which would a person float lower, a swimming pool or ocean water? Explain.

5. If an unknown object floats in a liquid, what do you know about the relative densities of the object and the liquid?

19:3 The Ocean Floor

All scientific study pertaining to the sea is called oceanography. Marine geologists are oceanographers. They study the rocks and topography of ocean basins. Marine geologists frequently use echo sounders to measure the depth of the basins. A sound signal is emitted, travels downward through water, bounces off the bottom, and travels back to a receiver. The depth is calculated by multiplying the velocity of sound in water by one-half the time between signal and echo.

If all of the water were drained from the oceans, the earth would appear somewhat like it does in Figure 19–4. The depressions between the continents are the ocean basins. The mountain ranges extending along the middle of the basins are known as **mid-ocean ridges.** In the center of each ridge are zones of deep cracks called rifts where fissure eruptions occur. The ridges are offset by faults in the ocean crust, which cut across the ridges.

Deep flat areas in the basins are **abyssal plains.** Abyssal plains have an average depth of five kilometers. Rows of huge submarine volcanoes cross some abyssal plains. Eroded volcanoes have flat tops and are called guyots (GEE ohs). Seamounts are not eroded as much and so have peaked tops. Islands found in ocean basins, such as the Canaries in the Atlantic, are the tops of large volcanic cones.

BACKGROUND Marine geology and geophysics are major subfields of oceanography. Others are oceanographic engineering, physical oceanography, and marine biology (biological oceanography).

How do scientists measure the depth of ocean basins?

Describe mid-ocean ridges.

SUGGESTION Point out that one would need to be viewing the waterless ocean basins from a vantage point in space (such as from a space shuttle) in order to get this wide view.

FIGURE 19–4. Structure of the ocean floor showing major features

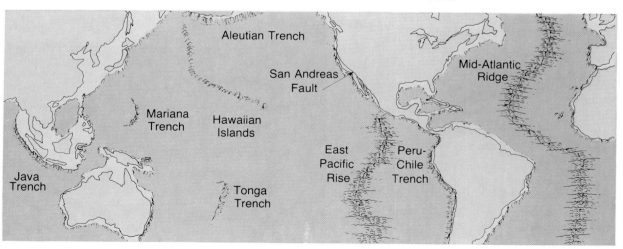

Aleutian Trench

San Andreas
Fault

Mid-Atlantic
Ridge

Mariana
Trench

Hawaiian
Islands

East
Pacific
Rise

Peru-
Chile
Trench

Java
Trench

Tonga
Trench

BACKGROUND   Mount Everest is almost nine kilometers above sea level.

Describe continental shelves and continental slopes.

SUGGESTION   Point out that if students were standing on an exposed continental shelf, the slope is so gentle that they would think they were on flat land. Compare the continental shelf to the lobby of a theater and the continental slope to the auditorium with sloped aisles and tiers of seats.

FIGURE 19–5. Along the western coast of South America, there is no continental shelf (a). In some regions of the ocean floor, water seeps down through fractures and is heated by magma. The hot water containing dissolved minerals is then ejected through vents (b).

a

The deepest places in the oceans are long narrow **trenches.** The Mariana trench is the deepest. Its depth is more than 11 kilometers below sea level, which is deeper than the height of the tallest land mountain, Mt. Everest.

Except where there are trenches offshore, the ocean basins near the continental edges slope up to the land. First there is a surface called the continental slope. Then the ocean floor flattens near the land. The ocean floor nearest the land is the **continental shelf.** The **continental slope** is defined by a marked increase in slope at the edge of the continental shelf. The continental shelves are actually extensions of the continental crust. Along some coasts, little or no continental shelf exists. Instead a trench occurs offshore. Along most continents, however, the continental slope drops down gradually to the deep ocean basin. In some places, the continental shelves and slopes are cut by submarine canyons formed by erosion. The erosion results when a soupy mixture called a turbidity current occasionally pours down the slopes from the continental shelves. Turbidity currents consist of a dense suspension of silt and clay in the ocean water.

In the last decade, scientists have discovered a new feature of ocean basins known as **deep sea vents.** Near the Galapagos Islands, a set of vents 2.5 kilometers deep was discovered. In a submersible diving craft called ALVIN, oceanographers found that deep sea vents release a hot solution containing hydrogen sulfide and water. It was learned that the hydrogen sulfide is a source of food for certain bacteria, which are a basis for a food chain.

b

Activity: How can the ocean floor be mapped?

See Teacher's Guide.

MATERIALS

rectangular
   waterproof container
   with low sides
modeling clay
graph paper
2 metric rulers

masking tape or
   indelible marker
water
string
washer

PROCEDURE

1. Mark off both long sides of the container in 1 cm units.

2. Use clay to construct a model of part of the ocean floor. Do this in the waterproof container. Make islands by allowing some of the clay to extend above the top of the container.

3. Fill the container with water up to 3 cm below the top.

4. Place a ruler across the container aligning the edge of the ruler that has unit markings with the 1 cm marks on each side of the container. See Figure 19–6a.

5. Tie a washer to one end of a length of string. Drop the washer into the container.

6. Line up the string with the 1 cm mark on the ruler. Keeping the string straight, let the washer rest on the clay as shown in Figure 19–6b.

7. Grasp the string between your fingers at the water level. Lift the washer out of the water without moving your fingers. Determine the water depth by measuring the length of the string from your fingers to the washer with another ruler. See Figure 19–6b,c.

8. Repeat steps 6 and 7 at 2 cm, 3 cm, and so on across the container.

9. Repeat steps 4–8 for each pair of marks on the sides of the container.

FIGURE 19–6.

10. Using one row of data in your data table, make a profile of your model on graph paper.

DATA AND OBSERVATIONS

Ruler Position	Depth Measurements (cm)				
	1	2	3	4	5
1 cm					
2 cm					
3 cm					

QUESTIONS AND CONCLUSIONS

1. How accurately did your profile represent your model ocean floor?

2. How could your profile be made more accurate?

3. How would changing your units of measurement from 1 cm to .5 cm change your profile?

4. What problems might arise if a smaller unit of measurement were used?

5. How is what you did in this activity like some work of marine geologists?

What are coral reefs?

Describe three types of reefs.

FIGURE 19–7. Coral reefs are characterized by colorful marine life (a). A fringing reef surrounds the island of Moorea near Tahiti in the Pacific Ocean (b).

19:4 Coral Reefs

Another feature of ocean basins is the calcium carbonate deposits called coral reefs. Coral reefs are formed by animals and plants that remove calcium carbonate from ocean water. Corals are animals that secrete calcium carbonate to make body structures. As generations of corals live and die, these body structures accumulate and become cemented together. Certain species of algae secrete calcium carbonate that also helps bind the skeletons together. The whole mass is known as a coral reef.

Coral reefs are found only where climate permits them to grow. The water temperature must be at least 20°C. They grow only in shallow water not more than 50 meters deep. Sunlight can penetrate to this depth enabling plants, which provide food and perform other functions, to grow. Because corals do not move about, they depend on circulation of near-surface water for nutrients.

There are several types of coral reefs. Fringing reefs such as those around Florida and Bermuda grow close to shores. Large reefs separated from large islands or the continents by some distance are barrier reefs. The largest barrier reef, the Great Barrier Reef of Australia, is almost 2000 kilometers long. A third type of reef is the atoll. An atoll is an elliptical or doughnut-shaped coral island with a lagoon in the center. Most atolls are found in the middle of the Pacific Ocean. They were probably built up around cones of sunken volcanoes.

a

b

Career Profile

George Billiris is an international sponge merchant whose Greek immigrant family helped build the sponge industry in the United States. George began diving for sponges at the age of 14. He worked hard and saved his income. When he was 18, George became captain of his own vessel. At the age of 30, George became a buyer of sponges, a trade taught to him by his father. Today, George divides his time between the sponge marketplace and diving for sponges on the continental shelf.

A sponge diver wears special equipment, including a full face mask with an air line attached to the boat and spiked shoes for traction. A diver gathers sponges with a "potato rake." The sponges are placed in a hand-held net bag that can hold about 50 sponges.

After the sponges are brought on deck, they are laid out in the sun and covered with burlap. Occasionally they are turned and sprinkled with water. Over a period of two to three days the skin of the sponge dies and decomposes. The sponge is then strung up to dry. A sponge that initially had a mass of 2700 grams will have a dry mass of 170 grams after this process is completed.

With 1400 recorded uses for the natural sponge, demand is still much greater than the supply. Synthetic sponges made of rubber, wood fibers, or nylon are used for many domestic needs. However the natural sponge, because of its texture and durability, is still preferred for commercial use.

George hopes to maintain his family's business by passing down his knowledge and expertise to his family members. He wants to be sure the ancient art and tradition of sponge diving remains alive.

19:5   Ocean Circulation

Ocean currents are movements of masses of water, much like movement of water in rivers. There are two main types of currents—surface and subsurface. Surface currents are mainly controlled by the prevailing wind system. The currents are also affected by the Coriolis force and the arrangement of the continents. The major surface currents

What controls surface ocean currents?

FIGURE 19–8. Ocean surface circulation consists of both cold and warm currents.

BACKGROUND The North Atlantic Sargasso Sea gets its name from large masses of floating seaweed, different species of sargassum.

Describe the Sargasso Sea of the North Atlantic Gyre.

BACKGROUND The Gulf Stream meanders across the ocean. Eddies, formed of warmer water with few nutrients, form frequently. Scientists estimate that as much as 99 percent of all the oceans' kinetic energy may be in the meanders and eddies of the Gulf Stream and other ocean currents.

are shown in Figure 19–8. Notice that the circulation pattern in most basins is a loop. These loops are known as **gyres** (JIRES). The gyre of the North Atlantic Basin includes the Gulf Stream, Canary Current, and the North Equatorial Current. Currents like the Gulf Stream carry heat away from the equator and are called warm currents. Currents like the Canary Current move cold water from higher latitudes. They are cold currents.

In the center of each gyre is a relatively calm area. The best known of these areas is the Sargasso Sea of the North Atlantic Gyre. At the center, the Sargasso Sea is about one meter higher than the surrounding circulating gyre. The outward force of this small "hill" of water balances the Coriolis force acting on the circulating water.

The Gulf Stream in the North Atlantic Gyre has a far-reaching effect on climate. The Gulf Stream transports warm water northward from the equator. Some of the warm water then moves eastward to form the North Atlantic Current. This current eventually flows past the British Isles and warms the air. Due to the shallow circulation of water in the English Channel, the British Isles have a climate similar to that of Spain.

Many subsurface currents are produced by differences in water density. Water that is more dense sinks, flowing below less dense water. Off the Antarctic coast, very dense, cold water flows down the continental slope. The water then moves horizontally, going eastward and then northward as the Antarctic Bottom Water.

Vertical upward currents called **upwellings** increase nutrients in surface water. Along the coasts of Peru, southwest Africa, and California, constant winds mix the surface water with deeper water. Coastal upwellings are formed. Important fishing areas are found where coastal upwellings occur.

See Teacher's Guide.

REVIEW AND REFLECT

1. Why is ocean water salty?
2. Why do layers form in ocean water?
3. How are continental shelves different from abyssal plains?
4. What factors are important to the growth of coral reefs?
5. What surface currents make up the South Pacific gyre?
6. How does sunlight limit the distribution of organisms in ocean water?

19:6 Tides

Tides are the rise and fall of the ocean's surface that takes place periodically. Tides are caused by the gravitational pull of the sun and moon on the earth. According to Newton's law of gravitation, the attraction between two objects is directly proportional to the product of their masses and inversely proportional to the square of the distance between them. Although the sun has a greater mass than the moon, the moon is much closer to the earth. Therefore, the moon has a greater influence than the sun in causing tides.

In Figure 19–10, notice the bulges of water on opposite sides of the earth. On the side of earth closest to the moon, the distance between the moon and water is less than the distance between the moon and solid earth. The water is pulled more toward the moon than the solid earth beneath

a

b

FIGURE 19–9. Along some coasts, the prevailing wind transfers energy to the coastal waters, which are then deflected offshore because of the Coriolis force. The water that moves away from shore is replaced by water from 50 to 300 meters below the surface (a). Because of coastal upwellings, fishing off the coast of South America is very productive (b).

Why does the moon have more influence on the tides than the sun?

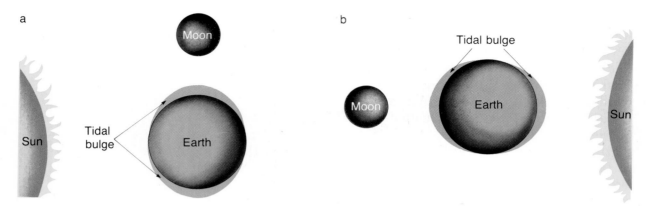

FIGURE 19–10. Neap tides are produced when the sun and moon are at right angles (a). Spring tides result during new moon and full moon phases when the moon and sun are aligned (b). Note the tidal bulges on opposite sides of the earth.

BACKGROUND   In addition to the bulge caused by the gravitational attraction of the moon, the revolving earth-moon system creates a centrifugal force that adds to the tidal bulge on the side of the earth farthest from the moon.

Why do places have two high tides and two low tides daily?

Why are high tides not exactly 12 hours apart?

it is. The gravitational attraction between the moon and water is greater than between the moon and solid earth. On the side of earth farthest from the moon, the solid earth is closer to the moon than the water. As a result, the earth is pulled more toward the moon than the water. A bulge of water also appears on the side of the earth opposite the moon.

When the moon and sun are in line with the earth, their combined gravitational attraction on the earth produces the highest tides of all. These tides are called spring tides. Spring tides occur twice each month, and they are not related to seasonal changes.

As the earth rotates, different locations on the earth are moved under or opposite the moon. So twice each day places near bodies of water experience a period of high tides and a period of low tides. If you lived near the ocean anywhere along a line connecting the highest point of the tidal bulges, you would experience two high tides each day as the earth rotates. The tides would be about 12 hours apart. If you lived at any point some distance from that line, you would still experience two high tides, but the tides would not be as high. You would cross the slopes of the bulges instead of the highest points as the earth rotates.

Because the moon moves eastward in its orbit each day, high tides are not exactly half a day apart. Each high tide is about 12 hours and 25 minutes later than the previous high tide. Other factors also affect the amount of rise and the times when tides occur. The size and shape of ocean basins and coastlines are important considerations in predicting tides.

19:7 Waves

Most ocean waves are produced by winds. Winds blow across water creating ripples. Ripples produced by strong winds develop into waves. Most waves are produced during storms. Local winds produce some of the waves seen at shores. Often one sees waves in calm weather. Such waves are the result of distant storm winds in open seas.

Energy in the winds is transferred to ocean water. Large waves are produced by winds that have blown long distances across water. The size of a wave is influenced by the speed and duration of the wind. Ocean waves have all the same features—height, length, and frequency—as transverse waves you studied in chapter 13. The wavelength of an ocean wave is usually about 20 to 30 times its height.

Earthquakes produced along faults on the floors of the ocean basins cause very long, high waves. These waves are called seismic sea waves or tsunami, first named by the Japanese. Typical tsunami have wavelengths of 150 kilometers and periods of 12 minutes. Tsunami travel at speeds of about 12.5 kilometers per minute, more than eight times normal highway speed limits.

The depth of water does not affect a wave as long as the water is deep. Near shore, the water becomes shallow. As the wave trough begins to touch bottom, the wave slows down. The wave crest steepens as shown in Figure 19–11. When the wave becomes too steep to support itself, the crest folds over and breaks into bubbly surf.

DEMONSTRATION Blow across a pan of water, producing "waves" (ripples).

What causes shore waves seen in calm weather?

BACKGROUND A Seismic Sea Wave Warning System provides tsunami reports. Normally a report gives people about an hour to evacuate before the tsunami hits the shore.
What are tsunami?

FIGURE 19–11. As waves approach the shoreline, they come in contact with the ocean bottom. The wave height increases and eventually breaks onto the beach (a). Waves with curling crests, called plunging breakers, form along beaches with steep slopes (b).

a

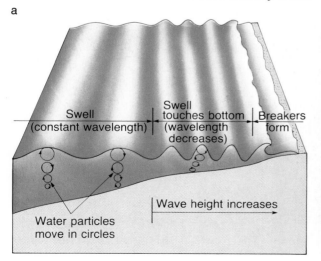

Swell (constant wavelength) | Swell touches bottom (wavelength decreases) | Breakers form

Water particles move in circles

Wave height increases

b

Most waves strike shores at angles producing currents with a net movement of water parallel to shore. These currents are **longshore currents.** The water of the wave that breaks against the shore flows back to the ocean. Most of the water flows back under the next breaking wave forming a sheet of backflowing water. Sometimes the water flowing back to the ocean creates a strong current below the water surface. Such flow is called an undertow.

When a large amount of water is piled up along the shore by waves, a rip current may form. A **rip current** is a strong, narrow surface current that moves swiftly out from the shore for a short period of time. Rip currents can be dangerous to swimmers. If caught in a rip current, you should swim parallel to the shore until you are out of the rip current.

See Teacher's Guide.

Skill Inquiry

Most animals have a characteristic called symmetry. Symmetry is a particular arrangement of body parts. An animal with *radial symmetry* can be divided lengthwise through its center in any direction and two equal halves will be produced. An animal with *bilateral symmetry* can be divided lengthwise through its center along only one axis to create equal halves. A sand dollar has radial symmetry. A clam has bilateral symmetry. See Figure a.

a

Each type of symmetry offers certain advantages. Radial symmetry may allow an animal to sense food or the approach of an enemy from all sides. Bilateral symmetry allows an animal to use muscles and appendages for movement in a specific direction.

Decide whether each marine organism in Figure b has symmetry. If an organism has symmetry, tell whether it is radial or bilateral. If the symmetry is bilateral, redraw the organism and show the position of the axis.

b

FIGURE 19–12. Features of a typical coastal region

SUGGESTION Compare the features produced by erosion with those produced by deposition shown in Figures 19–12 and 19–14.

19:8 Shorelines

Waves exert a tremendous amount of energy against shores. Waves erode coasts and deposit sediments where wave motion stops. Notice the features of a coastal region in Figure 19–12. Shores and coasts are made up of features caused by erosion and deposition.

The energy of waves is concentrated on land that juts into the ocean. These headlands are eroded into wave-cut cliffs. The wave-cut cliffs form as waves erode rock at the water level, and then the overhanging rock collapses. Wave-cut cliffs are seen in many places along the coasts of the western United States.

Wave erosion produces a lot of sediments. In addition, sediments resulting from erosion by rivers on the continents are transported to and along the shores. The sediments are distributed by longshore currents. Beaches usually form by deposition in the quiet water of bays. Deltas form if the sediment load of a river is greater at the river mouth than the longshore current can distribute. Some other depositional features of shores are shown in Figure 19–14 on page 418.

Because most waves strike beaches at angles, sediments, such as sand, are carried diagonally along the

Describe the features of a coastal region.

FIGURE 19–13. As waves strike a beach at an angle, they cause the movement of sand particles in a zigzag manner along the beach.

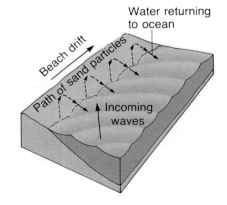

Water returning to ocean

Beach drift

Path of sand particles

Incoming waves

FIGURE 19–14. The erosion of headlands by currents and waves produces sediments, which are deposited in a variety of ways along a coastline. Some depositional features, such as deltas, are made by streams flowing into the sea.

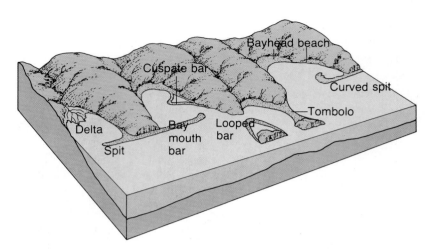

How do shoreline levels change?

beach. Gravity forces the backflow of water straight down toward the beach. The resulting zigzag movement of sand along beaches is called beach drift.

Shoreline levels change. Some are sinking, while others are rising. Shoreline levels may change for one or a combination of reasons. The water level of the ocean may change or the continents may rise or fall. Rising or emerging shorelines can be recognized by wave-cut cliffs and beaches that are higher than the present shorelines. Submerging shorelines can be recognized by submerged wave-cut cliffs and beaches. Submerging shorelines move onto the edge of a continent, drowning the lower parts of river valleys and producing deep bays. New York Bay on the Hudson River and San Francisco Bay on the Sacramento River are good examples of harbors formed by the drowning of river valleys.

FIGURE 19–15. One example of mariculture is oyster "farming" off the coast of Maryland.

19:9 Ocean Resources

Fish and other marine animals are sources of protein for many people. Currently, about 70 million metric tons of fish are removed from the ocean and used for food annually. However, many species of fish are not used as food, though they are good nutrition sources. Some ocean areas, such as the Indian Ocean, have not yet been well-explored for fishing potential. Taking the greatest yield of fish from oceans requires complete understanding of the life cycle, food sources, migrations, and predators of each species.

Scientists have not been able to learn enough to allow particular species to be fished at ideal levels, however.

In spite of some difficulty in establishing the best methods for catching fish, technology has made great strides to improve catching and processing. Echo sounders are now used on fishing trawlers to locate fishing grounds. Canning and freezing facilities on board special ships within trawler fleets help to ensure against loss due to spoilage.

In some countries, notably Japan, fish and shellfish are raised in seawater pools and cages. This industry is called mariculture. However, because of the expense, only species that are highly prized can be economically farmed. In the United States and Canada, for example, salmon and rainbow trout mariculture is profitable.

Other types of ocean resources are mineral deposits and petroleum. As land resources become exhausted, many nations will begin to obtain mineral ores buried within the continental shelves. Nations will also turn more and more to petroleum and natural gas that is trapped within the sedimentary rocks of the continental shelves for sources of energy. Ores and petroleum are believed to be absent from the sediments of deep-ocean basins. However, nodules of manganese, nickel, copper, and cobalt lie along the deep ocean floor. Some minerals found in seawater can be extracted economically.

Although off-shore petroleum deposits can supply some energy, most of the ocean's energy will probably come from nonpolluting sources. The oceans store a lot of heat because they are so large. A thermal energy device like that shown in Figure 19–16 may use the ocean's heat to produce electricity. Other nonpolluting energy sources may also come from currents, tides, and waves.

See Teacher's Guide.

FIGURE 19–16. A thermal energy device may produce electricity using the temperature differences in ocean water. Warm water near the ocean surface is used to vaporize ammonia. Electricity is produced as the ammonia gas passes through a turbine. Cold water from deeper ocean is then used to condense the ammonia so it can be used again.

Describe the resources of the oceans.

BACKGROUND   The most widely used mineral resources of the ocean floor now are sand and gravel, found on continental shelves. Bromine and magnesium are currently extracted from seawater.

REVIEW AND REFLECT

1. Why do tidal bulges appear on opposite sides of the earth?
2. What three factors influence the size of ocean surface waves?
3. How do the features of a submerging coastline differ from the features of an emerging shoreline?
4. How could an ocean current, such as the Gulf Stream, be used to produce electricity?

19:10 Choices: Ocean Ownership

For most of the time since civilization began, the oceans have been thought of as belonging to everyone. However, as technology has developed, people have harvested more ocean resources and polluted more ocean water. The question of ownership has become more important.

Parts of the ocean near land are considered territorial waters belonging to the country that owns the nearest land. Territorial waters are usually defined by the continental shelves. The central parts of the earth's oceans between continental shelves are called the high seas. About 60 percent of ocean area is high seas.

For a long time, there was no agreement among nations about the high seas. Rules governing activities in the high seas had been made by only a few nations. Actions by some nations created problems that were not addressed by any ruling body. For example, in 1972 Iceland extended its ocean boundary to 80 kilometers from shore and again in 1975, to 320 kilometers from shore. This action was protested by countries such as the United States and Germany, who had been fishing in these waters. Also, in 1967, Great Britain bombed the Liberian oil tanker, *Torrey Canyon,* when it ran aground within a few kilometers of Great Britain's territorial waters. The bombing was meant to set fire to all the oil before it escaped into the ocean and polluted the water. The oil company lost a valuable oil cargo and a ship.

In 1973 more than 100 nations began a United Nations conference to decide how the high seas should be governed.

What is the difference between territorial waters and high seas?

BACKGROUND   For many years, use and control of space was discussed by United Nations members. Although a treaty was formulated, major nations did not ratify it.

Why was a Law of the Sea treaty developed?

FIGURE 19–17. Although there is not international agreement, the petroleum drilling rights have been divided among the countries bordering the North Sea.

FIGURE 19–18. The treaty of the ISA gives nations economic rights out to 320 kilometers from their shores.

The conference met annually for nine years. It was the largest and longest of all international conferences. In 1982 a Law of the Sea treaty, which is like an international constitution, was signed by representatives of 119 nations.

The treaty created an International Seabed Authority (ISA). Articles of the treaty give nations economic rights out to 320 kilometers from their shores. Nations also have control of marine research and pollution within these zones. The high seas are considered the Common Heritage of Mankind, which means that they belong to all nations. Passage on the high seas and within the economic zones of nations is a right of every person and ship. The treaty creates a system that empowers the Seabed Authority to explore and direct the use of high seas resources and to grant licenses to nations. A supreme court, the International Tribunal of the Law of the Sea, is designed to settle international ocean disputes.

See Teacher's Guide.

BACKGROUND   The U.S.A. and U.S.S.R. did not sign the treaty, probably for military and economic reasons.

What does the "Common Heritage of Mankind" mean?

What are the provisions of the Law of the Sea treaty?

REVIEW AND REFLECT

1. Why are more countries interested in the oceans today than they have been in the past?
2. Describe the outcome of the United Nations conference on oceans that met from 1973 to 1982.
3. Suppose a country that did not sign the Law of the Sea treaty extended its ocean boundary beyond the limit recognized by the Law, much as Iceland did in 1972 and 1975. What pressures could be created by the Seabed Authority and other nations to have the country withdraw its claim?

CHAPTER 19 REVIEW

SUMMARY

1. The oceans probably were formed from water that condensed from volcanoes early in the earth's history.   19:1

2. The oceans mix slowly, but water tends to stay in layers due to differences in temperature and salinity.   19:2

3. Main features of the ocean basins are abyssal plains, continental shelves, continental slopes, mid-ocean ridges, and trenches. 19:3

4. Coral reefs are ocean basin features built up by marine organisms in warm, shallow areas of oceans.   19:4

5. In oceans there are surface currents that move in gyres, and subsurface currents that move horizontally and vertically.   19:5

6. Surface currents are controlled by trade winds, the Coriolis force, and the arrangement of oceans and continents. Subsurface currents are controlled by water density and surface circulation.   19:5

7. Due to the gravitational effects of the moon and sun on the earth, locations near large bodies of water experience two periods of high and low tides each day.   19:6

8. Winds cause most ocean waves. Faulting of the sea floor causes tsunami.   19:7

9. Shorelines are made up of features caused by wave erosion and deposition of sediments by longshore currents.   19:8

10. Oceans are sources of food, minerals, and energy.   19:9

VOCABULARY

abyssal plain   12
continental shelf   1
continental slope   2
coral reef   3
deep sea vent   10

gyre   5
longshore current   6
mid-ocean ridge   13
rip current   8

salinity   4
tide   11
trench   9
upwelling   7

Choose the correct word from the list to answer each question.

1. What ocean basin feature is closest to a shore?

2. What ocean basin feature is found between a continental shelf and an abyssal plain?

3. What ocean feature is formed by marine animals and plants that secrete calcium carbonate?

4. What is a measure of the amount of solid material dissolved in 1 kg of water?

5. What is the looplike circulation of surface currents called?

6. What current flows parallel to a shore?

7. What process brings nutrient trace elements to the ocean's surface?

8. What is a strong, narrow surface current that moves swiftly out from a shore for a short period of time?

9. What is the deepest ocean feature?

10. What ocean feature with hot solutions of hydrogen sulfide was recently discovered?

11. What is a periodic rise and fall of ocean water caused by the moon and the sun?

12. What is the deep flat area of an ocean basin called?

13. What is an ocean mountain chain from which submarine lava flows?

QUESTIONS

MAIN IDEAS

Choose the correct answer to complete each sentence.

1. The most abundant compound dissolved in ocean water is (MgCl$_2$, *NaCl*, NaBr).

2. Because the moon moves eastward in its orbit each day, high tides are (exactly, *a little more than*, a little less than) 12 hours apart.

3. In the Northern Hemisphere, surface currents (run along latitudes around the earth, *turn in large clockwise loops*, turn in large counterclockwise loops).

4. The depth of ocean floor is found by (finding the buoyant force on the ship, *using sonar and the known velocity of sound in water*, finding the center of a gyre).

5. The highest tides occur (*when the moon and the sun are in a line with the earth*, once per month, once per day).

6. Shorelines are mainly shaped by (tides, *waves*, gyres).

7. Nodules of manganese and other metals are found (on continental shelves, in ocean water, *along deep ocean floor*).

8. Turbidity is the presence of suspended materials that reduce the (density, pressure, salinity, *clarity*) of water.

9. An atoll is a type of (*coral reef*, barrier island, surface current).

10. The zigzag movement of sand along beaches is called (upwelling, longshore current, *beach drift*, undertow).

See Teacher's Guide.

APPLICATIONS

Answer each question in one or more paragraphs.

1. The average temperature of all ocean water is only 3.8°C. Why is the average so low?

2. What ways, other than by rivers, are materials added to oceans?

3. See Figure 19–8. Why is there a surface current that goes completely around the earth in the Southern Hemisphere but not in the Northern Hemisphere?

4. Why is the climate of Great Britain warmer than the climate of Canada's Labrador, since both are at about the same latitude?

5. Why does it cost more to remove minerals and oil from continental shelves than from land areas?

6. Within ocean layers, sound becomes enclosed, as in a pipe, traveling up to 10 000 km from the source. What value might this be to ocean animals?

FURTHER STUDY

INVESTIGATIONS

1. Prepare a chart comparing the chemical composition of blood with the chemical composition of seawater.

2. Visit a museum of sea life aquariums. Classify the organisms you observe as plankton, nekton, or benthos. Prepare a report including drawings of some organisms.

3. Plan and prepare a meal featuring different foods from the ocean.

4. Find out who or what Argo and Jason are. Prepare a report for your class about them.

READINGS

– Cardozo, Yvette. "Diving the Bottomless Pit." *Oceans.* March, 1984. pp. 40–45.

0 Polking, Kirk. *Oceans of the World.* Philomel Books: New York, 1983.

+ Ruggieri, George D. *The Healing Sea.* Dodd, Mead & Company: New York, 1978.

As these people ride down the Grand Canyon, they are passing through layers of rock. The farther down they go, the older the rocks become. Rocks contain a record of how the earth has changed and how it is still changing. How has the earth changed? What do rocks reveal about past life on earth? How does knowledge of earth history help us understand the earth today?

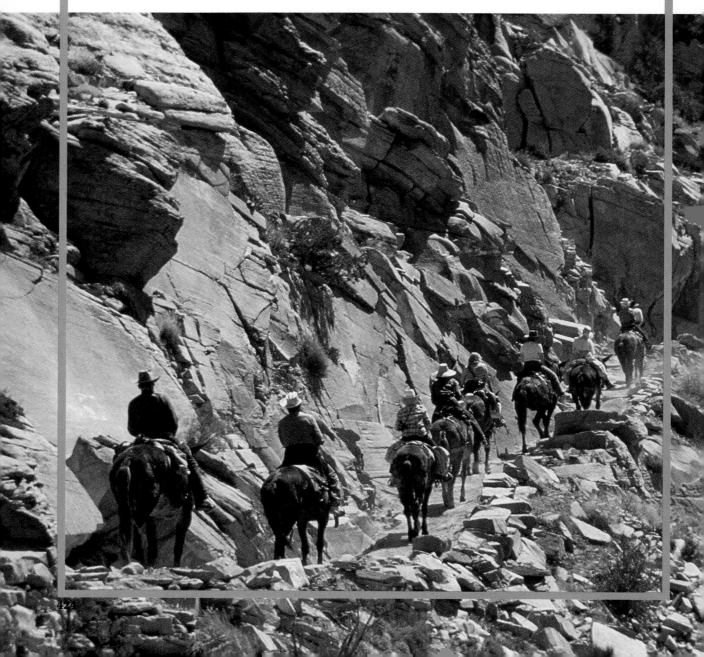

EARTH HISTORY

INTRODUCING THE CHAPTER   Compare the study of human history with the study of geologic history. Note the similarities and the differences. Discuss why methods of finding information are usually different and what some of the differences are. Note that some methods of studying geologic history will be developed within the chapter.

20:1   Fossils

Where ocean sediments become rock, scientists have found outlines and minerallike fragments that look like organisms. The shapes are often smashed and broken but are clearly different from the surrounding rock. The shapes are **fossils,** evidence or records of ancient life. Currently on continental shelves and abyssal plains, present-day organisms are collecting and becoming fossils.

Fossils form when organisms are buried in sediments. Hard parts of organisms, such as bone, shell, and wood, resist decay more than fur, feathers, skin, or soft internal organs. Quick burial prevents decay of many hard parts. Quick burial also hinders scattering and the breakup of dead organisms by weathering processes.

Some fossils are parts of animals or plants that have been preserved with little or no chemical change. Examples are entire mammoths and mastodons buried by Ice Age glaciers. Complete preservation is limited to a few hundred thousand years, a relatively short time in geologic history.

In older rocks, hard body parts of past organisms have been partly or completely changed to some other mineral material. This change happens slowly as each cell's structure is replaced by silica or calcium carbonate. The dinosaur bones shown in Figure 20–1a are a mixture of bones and minerals. In wood, cell walls usually are completely filled in by some new mineral. When the fish in Figure 20–1b was buried in an ancient lake in Wyoming, heat and pressure eliminated all elements but the carbon from it.

GOAL   You will learn how the earth has changed and learn a theory that explains many of these changes.

What are fossils?

ACTIVITY   Examine a collection of fossils. Some students may have fossils they could bring for this activity. A local rock/gem store or a collector might lend a set of examples. Determine the type of each, as discussed in this section. Use library sources to learn as much as possible about the organism, when it lived, and its environment.

How do fossils form?

BACKGROUND   Many scientists say that to be called a fossil the trace must be at least 10 000 years old.

a

b

c

FIGURE 20–1. A fossilized skull of a dinosaur was formed by mineral replacement (a). The carbon remains of a fish formed a thin layer between rock layers (b). Dinosaur tracks were found in Colorado (c).

SUGGESTION Apply superposition to everyday activities. For example, the bedspread on a bed was placed there last, while the sheets were put down first.

Describe two important principles that help scientists understand relative ages of rocks.

Heat and pressure cause chemical reactions that change most tissue into gases, which escape. However, the element carbon stays behind.

Some fossils are molds or objects formed in molds, called casts. A muffin pan is actually a mold. The muffins formed in the pan are casts. Animal tracks are a natural mold. When a dinosaur stepped in mud and sand covering a lake bottom, it made the tracks shown in Figure 20–1c. In time, the mud and sand were changed to rock. The tracks became fossils. The place where a shell makes a depression in sediments is a natural mold. When minerals fill the natural mold, a fossil cast of the shell is produced.

Fossils provide information about past ocean temperatures and climates. For example, fossil corals in sedimentary rocks indicate a past environment of shallow, warm water. Fossil ferns in coal show that the past environment was once a warm swamp.

Some fossils indicate a certain period in geologic history because the organisms from which they formed lived only during that certain time. These fossils are called **index fossils.** Trilobites are index fossils. Trilobites were small sea animals that lived only during a time called the Paleozoic Era.

20:2   Early Ideas

Throughout history natural scientists have contributed to an understanding of the earth's history. In the fifth century B.C., Greeks and Romans studied fossil fish and shells found on high hills. These early scientists concluded that an ocean once covered the hills. Much later, in the 1700s, scientists discovered that many organisms they saw in ancient rocks were not present in more recent rocks. Some scientists concluded that many species had been destroyed in sudden catastrophes, such as floods or volcanic eruptions.

Two important principles that help scientists understand the relative ages of rocks were also identified during the 1700s. The first principle is that rock layers are usually deposited horizontally. Rocks that are found in a dipping or folded form must have been disturbed in some way. The second principle is that younger layers are laid on top of older layers. This principle is known as **super-position.**

In 1788, the Scottish geologist James Hutton put forth another principle. He had observed rates of weathering and erosion and the features of landscapes. He concluded that all features were formed by processes that are occurring currently. The Grand Canyon is slowly becoming deeper by downward cutting of the Colorado River. The canyon was produced by continuous slow cutting by the river over a very long time. The idea of continuous changes creating the earth's geologic features is called the principle of **uniformitarianism.**

In 1912 Alfred Wegener proposed a theory to explain the earth's present geography. Wegener noticed that continental coastlines seem to fit like pieces of a puzzle. Perhaps you have noticed that the shapes of South America and Africa appear to fit together. Wegener found that those continents do fit together roughly, particularly along continental shelf boundaries. Wegener also called attention to coal deposits on opposite sides of the present oceans' basins. The coal deposits have the same kinds of fossil ferns. Ferns always grow in warm climates, but similar coal deposits also are found in Antarctica. Wegener proposed that Antarctica once must have been closer to the equator, where the climate is warmer. He concluded finally that the continents were once together in a supercontinent called **Pangaea** (Pan JEE uh). Pangaea, he decided, started to break up about 200 million years ago. Little by little, the continents moved or drifted to the positions they have today.

FIGURE 20–2. Sediments that become rocks are deposited in horizontal layers. The oldest deposits are at the bottom (a). The sequence of layers may later be disrupted by geological processes such as erosion, folding, and faulting (b).

Describe the ideas of Hutton and Wegener.

20:3 Dating Rocks

Throughout earth's history, the Grand Canyon region has been above and below sea level many times. Layers of sedimentary rocks formed on an ancient seafloor. Each layer contains information about ancient environments. The Grand Canyon's rocks are a vertical record of the events of earth history that occurred at that location. Perhaps you have heard of people who are finding out about their family histories. They study records of past events,

Where did the sedimentary rocks of the Grand Canyon form?

BACKGROUND   The study of family history is called genealogy.

such as births, marriages, and deaths. Scientists study rocks to find out about the earth's history.

The ages of rocks help establish when the events recorded in them occurred. There are two ways of measuring rock age. **Relative age** is a rock's age compared to other rocks. Relative age can be determined from a rock's position in a rock column. A person's relative age may be given by saying she or he is older than a brother or younger than a sister. Relative age does not indicate how much older or younger a person is than a brother or sister. Relative age simply specifies a position in a sequence.

Parts of the rock record may be missing from some locations. Earth forces may lift a region high above sea level. Weathering and erosion then usually remove some of the exposed rocks. Later, the region may become submerged again. New rocks form on top of the uneroded rocks. Geologists can tell if layers are missing in the rock record by looking for unconformities. An **unconformity** is a buried erosion surface. In one type of unconformity, sedimentary rocks lie on top of folded or faulted rocks. This formation shows that earth forces changed older rocks before they were exposed to erosion and that new sediments then were deposited on top and changed to rock.

Absolute age is the actual age of a rock in years. A method for finding the absolute age of a rock using radioactivity is **radiometric dating**. Small amounts of radioactive elements are present in some rocks. A rock's absolute age can be found by measuring the amount of a radioactive element and the amount of the stable isotope

How can relative age be determined?

SUGGESTION   To continue with the idea of comparing geologic and family history, compare removed rock layers to family members who leave home.

What do unconformities show?

FIGURE   20–3.   Unconformities are gaps in the rock record as a result of erosion or a period of time when sediments were not deposited. Figure (a) shows three types of unconformities. Note the angular unconformity visible in this formation in the Grand Canyon (b).

a

1. Nonconformity

2. Angular unconformity

3. Disconformity

—— Unconformity

b

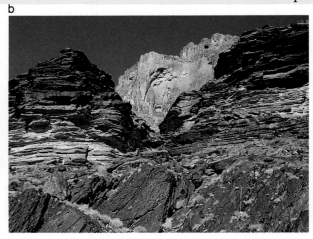

element into which the radioactive element decays. Table 20–1 shows the half-lives of some radioactive elements found in rocks. For example, a rock in which half of the U^{238} has decayed to Pb^{206} would be 4.49 billion years old. A basic assumption of radiometric dating is that nuclear decay occurs at a constant rate.

TABLE 20–1. HALF-LIVES OF SOME RADIOACTIVE ELEMENTS		
Radioactive Element-Isotope	**Stable Element-Isotope**	**Half Life (years)**
Uranium-U^{238}	Lead-Pb^{206}	4.49 billion
Uranium-U^{235}	Lead-Pb^{207}	0.71 billion
Thorium-Th^{232}	Lead-Pb^{208}	13.9 billion
Rubidium-Rb^{87}	Strontium-Sr^{87}	47.0 billion
Carbon-C^{14}	Nitrogen-N^{14}	5730.0 ± 30

For a variety of reasons, some rocks cannot be radiometrically dated. Indirect methods may be used to date these rocks. For example, the shale layer shown in Figure 20–4 was dated indirectly. The two igneous intrusions shown have been radiometrically dated. By studying the formation, you can see that the shale layer must have formed after the older intrusion and before the younger intrusion. Therefore, the approximate absolute age of the shale layer can be found.

Besides radioactive minerals, some igneous rocks contain the mineral magnetite, which is an iron oxide. As the magma cooled, the magnetite grains became aligned with the earth's north and south magnetic poles. By studying the grains, geologists are able to calculate the past position of the igneous rocks relative to the magnetic poles. Determining rocks' ages by studying the alignment of magnetite grains is known as **paleomagnetic dating.**

See Teacher's Guide.

REVIEW AND REFLECT

1. How does the principle of uniformitarianism explain the expression, "The present is the key to the past"?
2. What could cause quick burial in the formation of fossils?
3. Describe your relative age and your absolute age.

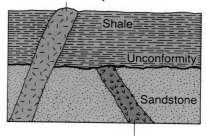

Radiometrically dated at 295 m.y.

Shale

Unconformity

Sandstone

Radiometrically dated at 300 m.y.

FIGURE 20–4. The absolute age of a shale layer is determined by using the principle of cross-cutting relationships.

Describe radiometric dating.

BACKGROUND Dating with radiocarbon differs in some aspects from dating by other radioactive elements. In radiocarbon dating, gamma rays are measured instead of amounts of parent and daughter isotopes. Gamma ray count decreases as carbon-14 decays.

What is paleomagnetic dating?

Activity: How can rock ages be determined?

MATERIALS

paper and pencil

PROCEDURE

1. Study the geologic cross section of the rock layers in Figure 20–5. Read the caption, which lists known rock ages as determined from radiometric and fossil data.
2. Identify the unconformities in the cross section.
3. Determine the ages of each rock layer.

DATA AND OBSERVATIONS

Relative Age	Rock Layer	Age
Oldest	Granite A	
↑	Limestone A	
	Shale A	
	Limestone B	
	Coal	
	Sandstone	
	Limestone C	
	Shale B	
↓	Granite B	
Youngest	Basalt	

QUESTIONS AND CONCLUSIONS

1. The "basement" rocks are defined as the oldest recognized igneous and metamorphic rocks in a given area that underlie all sedimentary rocks. Which rock layer can be called the basement rocks?
2. How much time passed between the cooling of the basement rocks and deposition of limestones that contain fossil trilobites?

FIGURE 20–5. Rock samples taken from a large body of granite have been dated at 3.7 to 3.4 billion years. A limestone containing fossil trilobites was deposited between 590 and 515 million years ago. Several species of fish known to exist between 515 and 415 million years ago were found in two sedimentary rock layers. A thin layer of coal was formed between 325 and 280 million years ago. Oil and natural gas are pumped out of sandstones deposited 280 to 240 million years ago. Several species of dinosaurs known to exist between 240 and 135 million years ago were found in two sedimentary layers. Samples of granite rock that cut across all sedimentary rock layers have been dated at 135 to 65 million years. Surface basalts from fissure eruptions have been dated at 22 to 3 million years.

3. Which layer of limestone was originally the thickest? (Hint: Erosion has removed most of the layer.)
4. How much time had lapsed between intrusion of the cross-cutting granite B and eruption of the surface basalts?
5. How much time had lapsed between deposition of the oil-bearing sandstone and fish-bearing shale?
6. How could you determine that granite A and granite B are not the same age, without using radiometric data?

Career Profile

When Jack Pullen refers to his day's work as "a real grind," he means it literally. As a physical science technical assistant at the University of Illinois, Jack specializes in making thin sections of rocks for use in teaching and research.

Thin sections are an average of 30 microns thick. (A micron is about one millionth of a centimeter.) They are secured on a slide for microscopic examination of the crystalline structure of the rock. Identifying the minerals and other components of rocks helps scientists understand the metamorphic experience that occurred during their formation.

When making thin sections, Jack uses a diamond saw to cut a chip about 0.5 to 1.0 centimeter thick from a rock. The inside and outside edges of the chip are then ground until two flat parallel surfaces are achieved. The chip is cleaned thoroughly with water or alcohol and dried at 100°C in an oven for one hour. Next, the slide is bound to the chip at a high temperature.

Jack removes any residue from the slide and checks the mount for air bubbles. The chip is finely ground until the entire structure of the crystals is visible and minerals appear at their proper identification colors. The thin section is complete once a coverslip is glued to the surface for protection.

Except for a few geology courses, Jack had little college preparation for his present career. However, Jack took a job after college with a large oil company. There he obtained valuable training for his work at the university. Jack works with students at the university on a one-to-one basis teaching the thin section technique.

20:4   Correlation

Studying and dating the rocks of a certain region helps scientists develop a geologic calendar of events for the region. To develop a geologic calendar for the whole earth, scientists use a method called correlation. **Correlation means finding out how rocks at different locations compare in age.**

The main rock unit used for correlation is called a **formation.** A formation may be one or several distinctive kinds of igneous or sedimentary rocks grouped together. A formation should be picked out easily from different rocks above and below it. It also should be recognized at some place distant from the place where it was first described.

What is correlation?

BACKGROUND   Correlation also means the degree to which two sets of data match. The term is used in statistical procedures with this meaning.

FIGURE 20–6. Note how the Green River splits the rock formation visible in this view of "Split" Mountain in Utah.

What is the Geologic Time Scale?

A number of procedures are used to correlate rocks. A formation gradually may change into another formation in the same horizontal layer. For example, sandstone may grade into silty sandstone, which grades into shale. Based on knowledge of sediment deposition, scientists know that the sediments were deposited at the same time. Sometimes a formation is interrupted. Rocks that are identical, although unconnected, are part of the same formation. Therefore, they are known to be the same age. Formations above and below an unknown formation may be known. Then the conclusion can be made that the unknown formation became rock at a time between the times that the known formations became rock. Fossils are particularly valuable in correlation work. Index fossils in two different unconnected rock formations show that the formations were formed at the same time. Paleomagnetic dating also is used to correlate rocks.

Scientists have correlated many formations from one place to another. This information was used to build an imaginary column of the earth's rocks according to their relative ages. A sequence of geologic events based on the rock record and related to absolute ages is known as the **Geologic Time Scale**. The Geologic Time Scale at first was a relative scale based on correlation. Later, radiometric and paleomagnetic dating were used to establish absolute ages of formations.

The Geologic Time Scale shown in Table 20–2 is divided into eras, periods, and epochs (EP uhks). Eras are the larg-

FIGURE 20–7. Rock samples taken from location A and location B can be correlated based on the information obtained from the blue shale formation. Location A contains relatively younger rocks than location B. Column C shows a more complete rock record when column A and column B are correlated.

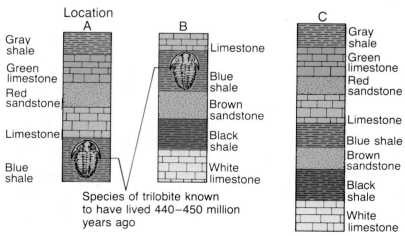

Location A | B | C

Gray shale
Green limestone
Red sandstone
Limestone
Blue shale

Limestone
Blue shale
Brown sandstone
Black shale
White limestone

Gray shale
Green limestone
Red sandstone
Limestone
Blue shale
Brown sandstone
Black shale
White limestone

Species of trilobite known to have lived 440–450 million years ago est divisions. The Cenozoic Era is the most recent. More information is known about it than the other eras. Periods are smaller time units within eras. Periods are separated into epochs. Eras, periods, and epochs are divided on the basis of large-scale metamorphism and igneous activity and the appearance or disappearance of many species of life.

BACKGROUND The Archeozoic and the Proterozoic Eras together cover most of geologic time. The two eras together are called Precambrian time. Periods last about 100 million years or less. Epochs last about 10 million years or less.

TABLE 20–2. GEOLOGIC TIME SCALE

Era	Period	Millions of Years Ago	Major Events
Cenozoic	Quaternary	0.011	End of glaciation
		1.8	Glaciation begins in Northern Hemisphere
	Tertiary	26	Andes Mountains develop
		37–38	Africa and Eurasia collide
		53–54	Himalayas grow as India and Eurasia collide
		65	Beginning of Rocky Mountains
			First mammals appear
Mesozoic	Cretaceous	136	Domination and eventual extinction of dinosaurs
	Jurassic	190	Pangaea breaks up
			First birds
	Triassic	225	First reptiles
Paleozoic	Permian	280	Asia and Europe collide forming the Ural Mountains; Pangaea forms
			Appalachian Mountains are born
	Carboniferous	345	Extensive fern forests; large-winged insects
	Devonian	395	Europe and North America collide
	Silurian	440	First land animals, amphibians
	Ordivician	500	First fish
	Cambrian	570	First animals with skeletons and shells (trilobites)
Precambrian		650	Extensive glaciation
		1500	First soft-bodied animals (jellyfish)
		3200	Single-celled algae, bacteria
		3800	Oceans begin forming
		4000	Earth's crust begins to solidify
		4500	Earth forms from early nebula

See Teacher's Guide.

Skill Inquiry

Geologists have divided the past into eras, periods, and epochs of time as shown in the Geologic Time Table, Table 20–2. As the table shows, the divisions are marked by noticeable changes in life forms. In fact, the names of the eras mean recent life (Cenozoic), middle life (Mesozoic), and ancient life (Paleozoic) in Greek. Little is known about life before the Cambrian period of the Paleozoic Era. So, the time before this period often is simply called Precambrian time.

Geologic time is hard to imagine. The difference between one, two, or three million years is difficult to comprehend. You just know that each of them is a very long time.

Sometimes relating the Geologic Time Scale to a time scale with which you are familiar can help you understand geologic time. For example, imagine that geologic time began one month (30 days) ago instead of 4500 million years ago. Precambrian time lasted for 3930 of those 4500 million years. So, 87.3 percent of geologic time passed during Precambrian time.

$$(3930 \div 4500) \times 100 = 87\%$$

If geologic time began one month ago, 26 days would have passed before the Cambrian period began.

$$30 \text{ days} \times .87 = 26 \text{ days}$$

1. How many years did each of the geologic eras last?
2. What percentage of geologic time passed during the Paleozoic Era? the Mesozoic Era? the Cenozoic Era?
3. If geologic time began one month ago, how long ago did the Mesozoic Era begin? the Cenozoic Era?
4. If geologic time began one month ago, when were dinosaurs roaming the earth?

20:5 Plate Tectonics

BACKGROUND The term *plate tectonics* translates as plate construction. It became popular in the 1960s. Alfred Wegener's theory was described as continental drift.

What is plate tectonics?

Recall that Alfred Wegener proposed a theory of continents drifting away from a single supercontinent, Pangaea. Wegener based his idea on various evidence. For example, continental margins of South America and Africa seemed to fit together. Also, rocks on opposite sides of the Atlantic Ocean were similar. In the 1930s, most scientists thought Wegener was wrong. There was no force known to push or pull continents across the earth's surface.

Now most scientists realize that sufficient evidence for movement of the continents has been found. The theory of continental movement is known as **plate tectonics**. According to the theory, the earth's crust and upper mantle are composed of rigid sections called plates. As the plates move, the earth's geography changes. In the 1960s, scientists Harry Hess and Robert Dietz proposed a process called **seafloor spreading** to explain how the plates move. They said that magma moves upward through the

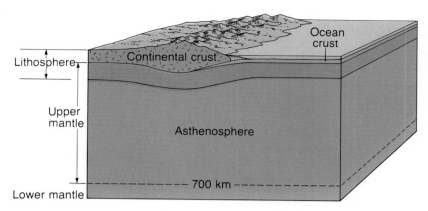

FIGURE 20–8. Earth's lithosphere consists of the crust and part of the upper mantle. The plasticlike zone of the upper mantle is called the athenosphere.

oceans' crust to the seafloor. It forms long chains of submarine volcanoes in the oceans' basins. Magma spreads out on both sides of the chain, thus adding new rock and new seafloor. Hess and Dietz concluded that old ocean floor, far from places where magma wells up, is pushed under continental crust material, forming deep trenches. Also, at the place of collision, high mountains and rows of volcanoes form.

Much evidence supports the idea of seafloor spreading. If the idea is correct the oceans would be relatively young while the continents would be very old. Radiometric dating of ocean sediments shows that all ocean floors are not more than 200 million years old, much younger than the continents. Paleomagnetic dating of ocean floor rocks on both sides of the mid-ocean ridges shows that rocks at the same distance out from the ridges have the same magnetic properties. The rocks are therefore the same age, as would be expected according to the seafloor spreading model.

What evidence supports the idea of seafloor spreading?

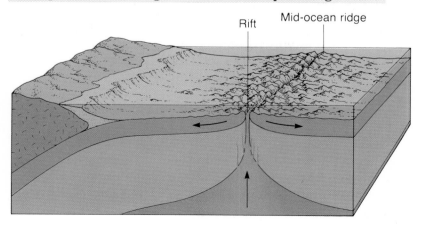

FIGURE 20–9. Magma from the mantle moves to the surface along the mid-ocean ridges, forming new ocean crust.

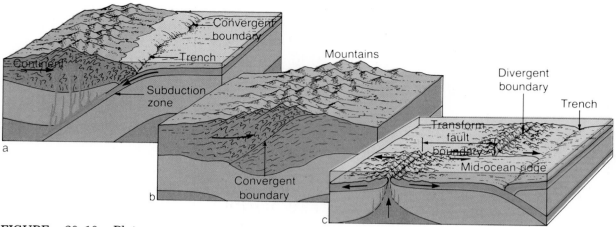

FIGURE 20–10. Plates move apart at divergent boundaries. A trench forms along convergent boundaries when an ocean plate collides with a continental plate (a). A trench may also develop when two ocean plates collide. When two continental plates converge, mountain ranges usually form (b). Two plates slide past one another along a transform fault (c).

What is thought to cause plate movements?

In addition to seafloor spreading, apparent wandering of the positions of the poles is evidence for plate tectonics. The earth's north and south magnetic poles are assumed to have always been close to the north and south geographic poles. Using paleomagnetic data for numerous times throughout geologic history, scientists find that the locations of the poles seem to have moved or wandered about compared to the present locations of the continents. However, the poles have not actually wandered, so the continents must have changed their positions.

Plate tectonics includes three types of boundaries of places where plates meet as shown in Figure 20–10. Slow movement of material in the upper part of the earth's mantle is thought to power the process of plate tectonics. Although the mantle is solid, in some ways it behaves as a thick fluid. Scientists theorize that as the lower mantle is heated in the earth's interior, material rises and sinks like convection currents. Near the earth's surface, horizontal plate movements occur as part of this convection that takes place in the mantle.

See Teacher's Guide.

REVIEW AND REFLECT

1. How is a rock formation different from a rock layer?
2. Why were scientists at first reluctant to accept Wegener's idea of continental drift?
3. How does the concept of seafloor spreading support the theory of plate tectonics?

Activity: How are rock formations interpreted?

MATERIALS

modeling clay,
  3 colors

pencil
cake knife

PROCEDURE

Part A

1. Use different colors of clay to make a three layer model of undisturbed sedimentary beds that formed underwater.
2. Fold the model to form an anticline and a syncline.
3. Assume that uplift occurs, raising the beds above sea level. Cut off the top of your model to represent erosion.
4. Assume that the formation again sinks below sea level and another layer of sediments is deposited. Add another layer of clay to the top of your model.
5. Cut the model in half and offset each side slightly, representing a fault.
6. Stick a pencil into the model from the bottom to represent an igneous intrusion.

FIGURE 20–11.

7. Draw a cross-section of the rock formation represented by your model.
8. Summarize the sequence of events that created the formation.

Part B

1. Study the rock formation shown in Figure 20–11.
2. Identify each labeled feature.
3. Rank the features from 1 to 6 in order of their occurrence.
4. Explain the sequence of events that created the formation.

DATA AND OBSERVATIONS

Feature Label	Feature	Rank
A		
B		
C		
D		
E		
F		

QUESTIONS AND CONCLUSIONS

1. Unconformities are gaps in the geologic record of an area, and are usually the result of erosion. How would a period when sediments were not deposited be classified as an unconformity?
2. What processes may cause the formation of anticlines and synclines?
3. What processes may cause the formation of a fault?
4. How can you determine when an igneous intrusion occurred relative to other features of a rock formation?
5. Where might you view cross-sections of rock formations that could be interpreted like your model or Figure 20–11?

20:6 Precambrian Time

What are shields?

Plate tectonics was probably in effect early in the earth's history. Near the beginning of Precambrian time, small continents were present. These continents, called shields, formed from granite and are now the centers of the much larger continents.

Volcanic activity is thought to have added water vapor, along with other gases, to the atmosphere. The water vapor condensed forming the oceans very early in Precambrian time. Using correlation techniques and radiometric dating, geologists find that the small continents came together and split apart a number of times during the Precambrian. The oldest rocks discovered are only 3.8 billion years old, so it is not possible to know what happened before then. However, during Precambrian time, shields probably split and joined a number of times. Whenever the shields came together at convergent boundaries, the shields were enlarged. Ocean floor material was lifted and folded up against the shield margins. Throughout geologic history, the continents have been enlarged in this way.

What are shields?

How have geologists learned what happened to land during Precambrian time?

Many valuable minerals have been found in shield rocks. Ores are abundant in the Canadian shield, the original land around which North America was formed. Although the location of the minerals and shield boundary are now far inland, both were once along a coastline. When ocean crust converged on the shield during plate movements, minerals became dissolved in hot sea water.

Describe Precambrian life.

Fossils of algae and bacteria in rocks radiometrically dated as 3.2 billion years old are the earliest evidence that has been found of life. Iron-bearing minerals were concentrated in the bodies of most bacteria during early Precambrian time. About two billion years ago, algae had increased the amount of free oxygen (O_2) in the atmosphere by photosynthesis, so other events became possible. Oxidized iron-bearing minerals began forming beds of red or orange rocks in warm, moist climates. More complex forms of life, all with soft bodies that breathed oxygen, developed next. The oldest radiometrically dated rocks containing definite animal fossils are between one and two billion years old. In late Precambrian rocks, the earliest fossil evidence for organisms with many cells appears.

FIGURE 20–12. A fossil of a Precambrian organism, *Dickinsonia costata,* is about 600–650 million years old and was found in South Australia.

20:7 The Paleozoic Era

Metamorphism and igneous activity separates Precambrian time from the Paleozoic Era. After that activity, seas moved inland on most continents. Many sea animals, including trilobites, became fossils in the rocks of this era. Thick layers of both sedimentary and igneous rocks were formed on the margins of the shields during the early Paleozoic. Later in the era, these were transformed into mountains.

Folded, faulted, and metamorphosed rocks below unconformities show that three sets of Appalachian Mountains were created along the southeast coast of North America during the Paleozoic Era. From this and other data, scientists conclude that the African Plate converged with the North American Plate. The ocean between them was narrowed as a result. Each set of Appalachians was eroded nearly flat. Then new ocean floor and thick continental shelf sediments were pushed against and over the North American Plate making new mountains. The Appalachians seen today were formed near the end of the Paleozoic Era. However, they are small remnants of their former great heights. Sediments from a continental shelf of the Paleozoic were shoved up over other rocks. Now they are about 250 kilometers from the present coast at high elevation. Other mountains in the United States, Europe, Asia, and West Africa formed as other plates converged. Deformation resulted from repeated collisions as Pangaea, the supercontinent identified by Wegener, formed at the end of the Paleozoic.

Also by the end of the Paleozoic, the land had changed from areas without life to places teeming with plants and animals. Plants included scouring rushes, conifers, and ferns. Many ferns grew as tall as trees, and some still do in New Zealand and other tropical islands today. Land animals included both amphibians and reptiles. Fish were abundant in the oceans. The trilobites, along with many other sea animals without backbones, became extinct at the end of the Paleozoic Era. The widespread extinction, determined by the disappearance of fossils of many organisms, helped define the boundary between the Paleozoic and the Mesozoic Eras.

b

FIGURE 20–13. The Appalachian Mountains began forming during the late Paleozoic Era as the continental shields of Africa and North America collided (a). Many fossil plants of the Carboniferous Period of the Paleozoic Era have been found (b).

Describe how the Appalachian Mountains formed.

Describe Paleozoic life.

What happened to many organisms at the end of the Paleozoic Era?

a

b
FIGURE 20–14. During the Jurassic about 135 million years ago, Pangaea was breaking up as the North Atlantic Ocean was beginning to form between North America and the old continent of Gondwana (a). *Stegosaurus* was a dinosaur of the Mesozoic Era. It lived about 135 million years ago (b).

Briefly describe the Mesozoic Era.

20:8 The Mesozoic Era

The Mesozoic Era began about 225 million years ago. The Mesozoic Era began with all known continental plates joined in the supercontinent of Pangaea. Paleomagnetic data and other evidence show that the continents started breaking apart from Pangaea about 190 million years ago, near the close of the Triassic Period. North America and Eurasia pulled apart in the north. Africa and South America separated. Then India, Australia, and Antarctica broke off. North America and Europe as well as South America and Africa have been separating ever since the early Mesozoic Era.

Present western North America was shaped mainly by events during the late Mesozoic Era and the following Cenozoic Era. At the end of the Cretaceous Period, plate movements squeezed thick sections of sedimentary rocks that had formed in a large inland sea. The rocks were folded and thrust up many kilometers forming the first set of Rocky Mountains. Erosion almost flattened these Rocky Mountains, but recent uplifting of western North America has rejuvenated them. Also late in the Mesozoic Era, western North America was enlarged by joining with fragments of a continent that originated in a tropical region.

Dinosaurs and related reptiles were found on land, in oceans, and even flying in the air during the Mesozoic Era. Fossils of early flowering plants appear in rocks of the late Jurassic and Cretaceous Periods. Small mammals are found in Mesozoic rocks. At the close of the Mesozoic, the fossil record shows that more than 75 percent of all species living at that time became extinct.

20:9 The Cenozoic Era

At the beginning of the most recent era, the Cenozoic, evidence shows that the continents and oceans looked similar to the way they do today. Plate movements within the Cenozoic included the separation of Australia and Antarctica (about 50 million years ago). Also, a separate India collided with southern Asia pushing up the Himalayan Mountains. Only recently, geologically speaking, some

In what positions were the plates during the Cenozoic Era?

separations began occurring. Saudi Arabia began separating from Africa, forming the Red Sea about 13 million years ago. Also Baja, California, began separating from Mexico, creating the Gulf of California, about five million years ago.

During the Quaternary Period (the Pleistocene Epoch), major glacial periods occurred. These were times of widespread glaciations and cool climates. Throughout the Cenozoic, a gradual cooling of climate took place as Australia moved southward over the south polar region and North America and Europe moved northward. The glacial ages were a climax to this trend of continents moving into the polar regions.

Throughout the Cenozoic Era, mammal fossils show an increase in diversity, size, and particularly brain size. Most species of Tertiary mammals and large Pleistocene mammals have become extinct. However, the species show resemblances to present-day mammals. By the beginning of the Pleistocene Epoch, especially during warm interglacial ages, elephants, rhinoceroses, cows, and one-toed horses were found. Evidence exists of humans and their tools and weapons. So, it is concluded that people lived at the same time as these animals and hunted them. The land bridges that formed during the Pleistocene allowed animals to travel freely between continents. The glacial ages and interglacial ages also contributed to large scale animal migrations in this epoch. The latest epoch, called Recent, began about 10 000 years ago. The boundary is set at the time the oceans were in the middle of a warming trend after the last major glaciation.

See Teacher's Guide.

REVIEW AND REFLECT

1. Through what processes have continental shields been enlarged throughout earth's history?
2. How was the formation of mountains in Europe, Asia, and West Africa during the Paleozoic related to the development of the supercontinent, Pangaea?
3. When in geologic history did the present Atlantic Ocean begin to form?
4. Name the eras of the Geologic Time Scale. Describe one type of life and a geologic event that took place in each.

a

b

FIGURE 20–15. The Himalayas formed when the Indian plate collided with Asia during the last 50 million years (a). The Red Sea formed recently when the Arabian Peninsula split away from Africa (b).

Describe Cenozoic life.

SUGGESTION   Students may be familiar with the Flintstones cartoon series. Discuss what species are incorrectly shown together in the cartoon. Dinosaurs became extinct by the end of the Mesozoic Era. Humans lived only within the Pleistocene Epoch.

What does the Milankovitch theory explain?

BACKGROUND Currently the eccentricity of the orbit is small, making the orbit shape almost a circle.

FIGURE 20–16. The tilt of the earth's axis changes about three degrees during a period of 41 000 years (a). Precession of earth's axis has a cycle of about 22 000 years (b).

20:10 Information: The Ice Ages

During the Pleistocene Epoch, ice ages alternated with periods of warmth. Continental glaciers up to three kilometers thick covered most of the land in the Northern Hemisphere at times. Glaciation took place in the Southern Hemisphere, too. However, it had less effect because there was less land in the Southern Hemisphere.

Scientists have tried to find out what caused these ice ages to occur. In 1920, a scientist from Yugoslavia named Milutin Milankovitch proposed a theory. The Milankovitch theory, also called astronomical forcing, is now widely used to help explain the ice ages. According to the theory, the distribution of solar energy over the earth varies as a result of three factors. The first factor is the axial tilt of the earth. Axial tilt is the angle that the earth's axis makes with the plane of the earth's orbit. Axial tilt changes about three degrees over 41 000 years. The second factor is precession. Precession is a slow wobbling of the earth's axis. Precession has a 22 000 year cycle. The third factor is eccentricity. Eccentricity is a change in the shape of the earth's orbit. The elliptical orbit becomes more elongated and then less elongated over 100 000 years.

Milankovitch calculated variations in the distribution of solar energy over the earth as a result of these cycles. He tried to correlate the variations with the ice ages that occurred during the Pleistocene. Some people accepted his theory that the climate changes were related to the astronomical cycles. Some people did not accept the theory be-

a

b

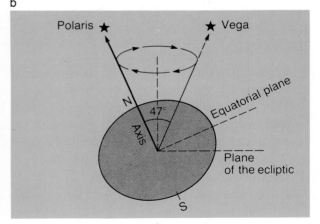

cause no one was sure of the dates of the ice ages. Also, evidence from the geologic past shows that glaciation did not occur very often. However, the astronomical cycles would have been occurring throughout the earth's history. If Milankovitch's theory is correct, why have glaciers been absent during most of the earth's past?

The development of the plate tectonics theory helped answer this question. Because glaciers occur only on continents, land masses would have to be in high latitudes before an ice age could occur. The astronomical cycles would not cause great enough temperature variations to create glaciers nearer the equator. So, the ice ages could only occur when the movement of the crustal plates shifted the continents from the tropics to the poles.

In 1976, studies of ocean sediments provided information that enabled scientists to determine more specifically when the ice ages occurred. The scientists used this information to make a time scale of climate changes during the last 500 000 years. The scientists found that there were major changes in the amount of ice at intervals of about 20 000 years and 40 000 years. They also found an even greater change about each 100 000 years. The scientists found that the ice decreased rapidly after a slow buildup each 100 000 years. This new information has led more people to accept the Milankovitch theory.

Now scientists are trying to predict when the next ice age will occur. According to the Milankovitch theory, the earth will cool off again in about 15 000 years. Peak ice coverage will occur in about 25 000 years. Other factors besides the three astronomical cycles will be operating then, though. Particularly, people have increased the carbon dioxide content of the atmosphere. More carbon dioxide content should greatly modify the effect of the astronomical cycles.

See Teacher's Guide.

REVIEW AND REFLECT

1. What is the theory of astronomical forcing (Milankovitch theory)?
2. What evidence supports the Milankovitch theory?
3. Why can scientists not predict with certainty when the next ice age will occur?

High eccentricity

Low eccentricity

FIGURE 20–17. Earth's orbit becomes more elongated and then less elongated over a 100 000-year period.

How does recent research support the idea of astronomical forcing?

BACKGROUND Before Milankovitch, other scientists suggested some type of astronomical cause. Alfred Wegener, who also proposed continental drifting, was one such person. James Croll thought orbit eccentricity and precession were important, but he was not aware of axial tilt. Milankovitch worked out a very detailed astronomical theory with the three cycles.

CHAPTER 20 REVIEW

SUMMARY

1. Hard body parts and quick burial help to produce fossils. 20:1
2. Horizontal rock layers, superposition, and the principle of uniformitarianism help geologists learn about geologic events. 20:2
3. Rocks may be radiometrically or paleomagnetically dated to determine their ages. Some rock ages are found indirectly. 20:3
4. The Geologic Time Scale is divided into eras, periods, and epochs. The boundaries are based on evidence of physical events and changes in life. 20:4
5. A theory of plate tectonics, which was extended from an earlier theory of continental drift, helps to explain many observations about the earth. 20:5

6. For Precambrian time, only soft-bodied life fossils are found. Shields were present and growing during Precambrian time. 20:6
7. During the Paleozoic Era, continents moved close together, forming Pangaea. Fossils of trilobites, fish, amphibians, reptiles, and land plants mark the era. 20:7
8. Within the Mesozoic Era, continents broke apart from Pangaea. Fossils of dinosaurs and reptiles, early mammals, and early flowering plants mark the era. 20:8
9. Throughout the Cenozoic Era, the shapes of continents and oceans have been similar to what they are today. Major ice ages occurred. Plant and animal life resembled present forms. 20:9

VOCABULARY

absolute age 3	index fossils 7	relative age 9
correlation 14	paleomagnetic dating 10	seafloor spreading 11
formation 15	Pangaea 1	superposition 6
fossils 2	plate tectonics 5	unconformity 8
Geologic Time Scale 4	radiometric dating 13	uniformitarianism 12

Choose the correct word from the list to answer each question.

1. What is the supercontinent formed at the end of the Paleozoic Era called?
2. What are records of ancient life called?
3. What is the actual age of a rock?
4. What is the sequence of events on earth based on the rock record?
5. What is the present theory of continental movement?
6. Younger rock layers are deposited over older layers according to what principle?
7. What are fossils of organisms that lived only at a particular time but in many places called?

8. What is a buried erosion surface called?
9. What is a rock's age stated in terms of other rocks called?
10. What is based on using the direction and inclination of iron minerals to date rocks?
11. What process creates new ocean plate material at mid-ocean ridges?
12. What principle shows that the present is the key to the past?
13. What technique is based on using radioactive minerals to absolutely date rocks?
14. What is the general term for finding out how rocks from different locations compare in age?
15. What rock unit is used for correlation?

QUESTIONS

See Teacher's Guide.
MAIN IDEAS

Complete each sentence with the correct word or phrase.

1. The theory that continents change positions on the earth due to both the formation and destruction of parts of the crust is called _____.

2. People have lived in the _____ Era(s).

3. North America has had roughly its present boundaries since the beginning of the _____ Era.

4. Two factors that are important to the formation of fossils are quick burial of organisms and _____.

5. A fossil formed when animal tracks in mud were changed to sedimentary rock would be a(n) _____.

6. Wegener's idea of continental drift was not originally accepted because _____.

7. Rocks that cannot be dated radiometrically or paleomagnetically may be dated _____.

8. An important index fossil of the Paleozoic Era is _____.

9. Scientists have used the processes of _____ to develop the Geologic Time Scale.

10. The largest divisions of the Geologic Time Scale are called _____.

11. Scientists theorize that horizontal plate movements occur near the earth's surface due to _____ in the mantle.

12. Much of the earth's history occurred during Precambrian time, which ended _____ years ago.

See Teacher's Guide.
APPLICATIONS

Answer each question in one or more paragraphs. Show how to solve each problem.

1. Some rare fossils are found in igneous rock. Explain how such fossils might have formed.

2. Why was preparing the Geologic Time Scale a project that required a lot of effort?

3. How does the theory of plate tectonics illustrate the scientific method at work?

4. Why is carbon-14 not used for radioactive dating of rocks? See Table 20–1.

5. Early geologists tried to absolutely date the age of the oceans by using present salinity and rate of salts added. Why does this method not work to show ocean age?

6. North America and South America are separating at the rate of about 2 cm/year. How long will it take before the two continents are one kilometer farther apart? 100 kilometers farther apart? What assumption is made in these calculations?

FURTHER STUDY

INVESTIGATIONS

1. Prepare a model of the rocks of your area. Place names of some buildings, lakes, or other well-known features on the top. Show side views of the structure of the rocks.

2. Visit a place where fossils are found. Collect or photograph samples.

3. Do a report on the theory that plate tectonics destroyed the Chimu civilization of Peru.

READINGS

0 Fortley, Richard. *Fossils: the Key to the Past.* Van Nostrand Reinhold Company: New York, 1982.

+ Halstead, L.B. *Search for the Past.* Doubleday & Company: Garden City, NY, 1982.

+ Miller, Ron, and William Hartmann. "Catastrophes That Shaped the Earth." *Science Digest.* April, 1984. pp. 64–69, p. 101.

THE PATTERNS OF LIFE

UNIT 5

Unit Five focuses on patterns of characteristics in living things and in their relationships. All living things have some common characteristics. For example, both people and trees are made of cells. Yet each is different from the other. Although all trees are alike in some ways, they are not exactly the same. In this unit, you will learn how the characteristics of living things and their relationships form patterns of life.

1. How are living things different from nonliving things?
2. What are the parts of cells?
3. How are living things classified?
4. How do the major human body systems function together?
5. What can a person do to maintain a healthy body?
6. How are traits inherited?
7. What are the roles of organisms in environments?

YOU probably have looked at some object through a microscope. What did you see that you could not see without the microscope? Scientists use microscopes to look at very tiny things, such as cells that they cannot see with the unaided eye. The students in the picture are looking at cells through microscopes. How big are cells? What are they made of? What do they do?

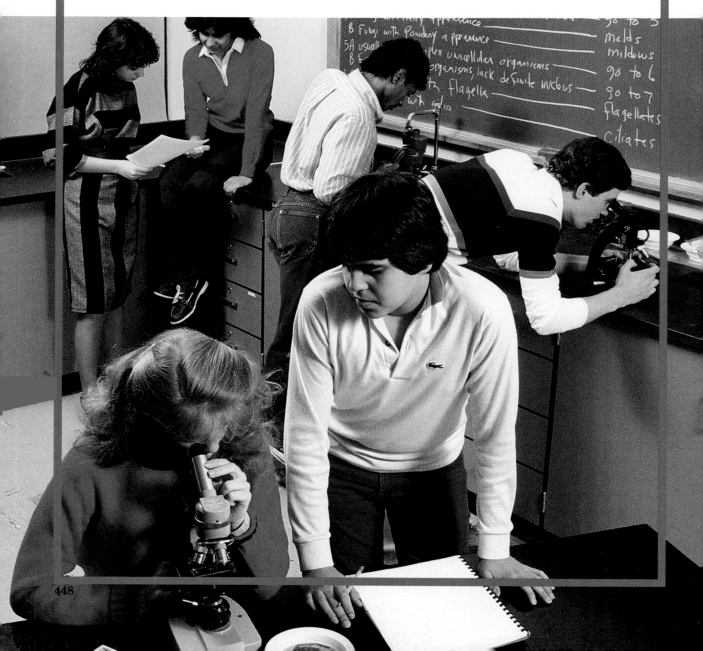

CELLS

INTRODUCING THE CHAPTER   Students are already familiar with the word *cell*. However, the word has many different meanings and is used in many different contexts. Have students suggest examples of cells, such as batteries (a group of electrolytic cells), plant and animal cells, cells in a honeycomb, prison cells, and so on. Discuss reasons why each of these things is called a *cell*. Lead students into a discussion of the characteristics of living cells, how they are similar and different.

21:1 The Nature of Life

If you look at Figure 21–1 on page 450, you see that none of the items pictured are living. How do you know that? Living things have certain characteristics that make them different from nonliving things. Organisms from bacteria to people, consist of one or more units called cells. They reproduce. They respond to conditions around them. They take in certain chemicals and give off other chemicals. Many chemical reactions that use or produce energy occur in organisms.

Each of the nonliving things in Figure 21–1 has one or more of the characteristics of organisms. For example, papers are "reproduced" by a copy machine, a building is made of smaller units, and a thermometer "responds" to conditions around it. How are a factory and a lamp like organisms?

Even though the items in Figure 21–1 are like organisms in some ways, you know that they are not living. Some characteristics are missing in each example. One main characteristic of organisms is cells. None of the items in Figure 21–1 is made of cells.

GOAL   You will learn what is found within cells and how each main part functions.

What are five characteristics of living things?

SUGGESTION   A factory and a lamp take in something in one form (raw materials, electric energy) and release it in another (products, light). Use this paragraph to promote a class discussion of the characteristics of living and nonliving things. Make a list on the chalkboard.

449

FIGURE 21–1. Nonliving things may have some, but do not have all of the characteristics of living things.

SUGGESTION   Discuss and illustrate nonliving systems in which specialized parts work together (such as a motor or other machine).

How are the cells of many-celled organisms different from cells that are complete organisms?

FIGURE 21–2. The bacteria that cause milk to spoil are single-celled organisms. Each cell shown is one bacterium.

21:2 Kinds of Cells

Organisms are made of cells. Some cells are large enough to be seen by the unaided eye. If you had an egg for breakfast, you have seen a cell today. An egg is a single cell! Most single cells are too small to be seen without a microscope.

Some single cells, such as the bacteria shown in Figure 21–2 are complete organisms. Trees and people are many-celled organisms. In many-celled organisms, cells are specialized. Specialized means that each kind of cell in an organism works in different ways. The cells in a many-celled organism are like students playing instruments in a school band. Each kind of instrument has a different part to play. When all of the parts are played together correctly, the band makes music. Each kind of cell in a many-celled organism has a different job. When all of the cells work together, they make a complete organism.

Scientists use many instruments and procedures of chemistry, physics, and biology to learn about the organization of chemicals in cells. Electron microscopes have been very useful in cell studies. An electron microscope can magnify cell parts hundreds of thousands of times. Many tiny cell parts can be seen by using an electron microscope.

See Teacher's Guide.

Skill Inquiry

Throughout this chapter you will observe several pictures of cells. The pictures show cells many times larger than their actual size. For each picture, a magnification is given. For example, in Figure 21–4a on page 453 the magnification is 120×. The number and multiplication sign indicate that in the picture the cell is shown magnified 120 times, or 120 times larger than it really is.

1. What is the magnification of the cell shown in Figure 21–4b?

You can find the actual length of the cell shown in Figure 21–4a. Measure the length of the cell in the picture. It is about 3 centimeters long. Divide the length by the magnification. From the picture you know that the magnification is 120×. Therefore the actual length of the cell is .025 centimeters.

2. What is the actual length of the cell shown in Figure 21–4b?

You can compare the sizes of cells shown at different magnifications by dividing the actual size of one by the actual size of another. For example, the actual length of the cell shown in Figure 21–4a is .025 centimeters. The actual size of the cells shown in Figure 22–8a on page 479 is about .005 centimeters. Notice that the cell in Figure 21–4a looks shorter than the cells in Figure 22–8a. By dividing .025 by .005, you find that the cell in Figure 21–4a is actually five times larger than the cell in Figure 22–8a.

3. Compare the sizes of the cells in the following pictures. Tell which cells are larger and how much larger they are.
   a. Figure 21–4a and Figure 21–4b
   b. Figure 22–8a and Figure 22–8b

4. Compare your height with the length of the cell shown in Figure 21–4a. How many times taller are you than the actual cell is long?

21:3 Cell Parts

Notice the cell parts in Figure 21–3. The outermost living part of a cell is the **cell membrane.** The cell membrane controls the movement of materials into and out of a cell. All materials that go into or come out of a cell must pass through the cell membrane.

The **nucleus** is a cell's control center. It directs the activities that occur in the cell. Inside the nucleus are strands of DNA, a compound that is important in cell reproduction. The DNA in the nucleus also helps to manufacture other compounds that cells use. The nuclear membrane surrounds the nucleus and controls the movement of materials into and out of the nucleus. The nuclear membrane separates the nucleus from the cytoplasm (SITE uh plaz um).

What is the function of the cell membrane?

BACKGROUND   An egg yolk is not an egg's nucleus. The yolk is a sac of concentrated nourishment that would furnish a developing embryo with food. The egg nucleus is very tiny.

What are the main cell parts and their functions?

The **cytoplasm** is a fluid within the cell membrane. It is the site of many chemical reactions. Note in Figure 21–3 the many structures in the cytoplasm. For example, **mitochondria** (mite uh KAHN dree uh) are structures that provide energy for a cell by oxidizing food.

The **endoplasmic reticulum** (en duh PLAZ mihk · rih TIHK yuh lum) is a system of tubelike structures that transport materials within a cell. Some endoplasmic reticulum has small spheres on its surface. The spheres are ribosomes. Some ribosomes are scattered in the cytoplasm, too. Proteins are manufactured in **ribosomes**. Proteins from the endoplasmic reticulum and the ribosomes are released into the cytoplasm by Golgi (GAWL jee) bodies. Golgi bodies are involved in the storage and release of chemicals in cells.

BACKGROUND   Some cells lack one or more parts discussed here. For example, red blood cells in mammals lose their nuclei while they form.

BACKGROUND   When a cell is injured, lysosomes break open and digest the cell. Unrefrigerated meat deteriorates quickly because lysosomes are acting. This is an illustration of the interaction of cell parts.

BACKGROUND   There also are structures called microbodies. Some types are responsible for the elimination of toxins produced by chemical reactions within cells. Some microbodies in plant cells assist in photosynthesis.

ACTIVITY   Have students construct and label 3-dimensional models of cells. A variety of materials can be used creatively.

FIGURE 21–3. Some parts of cells are made of living matter called protoplasm. Although each part of the cell shown is characteristic of animal cells, not all animal cells have all of these parts.

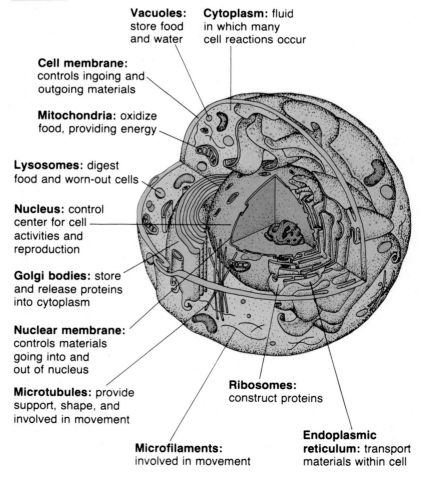

Vacuoles: store food and water

Cytoplasm: fluid in which many cell reactions occur

Cell membrane: controls ingoing and outgoing materials

Mitochondria: oxidize food, providing energy

Lysosomes: digest food and worn-out cells

Nucleus: control center for cell activities and reproduction

Golgi bodies: store and release proteins into cytoplasm

Nuclear membrane: controls materials going into and out of nucleus

Microtubules: provide support, shape, and involved in movement

Microfilaments: involved in movement

Ribosomes: construct proteins

Endoplasmic reticulum: transport materials within cell

Vacuoles (VAK yuh wohlz) are fluid-filled spaces in a cell where food and water are stored. Some vacuoles squeeze water out of a cell with a pumping action. These vacuoles help rid cells of excess water and waste. Some cells have small structures called lysosomes (LI suh sohmz) that contain chemicals. The chemicals help digest food and worn-out cell parts.

Microtubules are structures that provide support and shape to cells. They are thin hollow rods found throughout the cell membrane. They also are involved in cell division and movement. Microfilaments are involved in cell movement, too. They are long threadlike structures that are narrower than microtubules.

Some cells look as if they have hair. The hairlike structures are cilia (SIHL ee uh). Other cells seem to have tails. The taillike structures are flagella (fluh JEL uh). Cilia and flagella extend out from the cell membrane. Notice how the cilia and flagella of the cells shown in Figure 21–4 are different. Many single-celled organisms have cilia or flagella. As the movement of oars makes a rowboat move, the movement of cilia or flagella makes the organisms move.

The cells of plants and some simpler organisms have structures called chloroplasts (KLOR uh plastz). **Chloroplasts** contain the compound chlorophyll. Chlorophyll is needed for photosynthesis (foht oh SIHN thuh sus). Photosynthesis occurs in chloroplasts.

Plant cells, some protists, and some monerans have **cell walls**. Cell walls are nonliving material surrounding cell membranes. Cell walls protect the softer living material within the cells. Adjacent cell walls are connected. The cell walls provide stiffness that helps support the organism.

See Teacher's Guide.

FIGURE 21–4. Some one-celled organisms have special structures for movement. For example, a paramecium (a) has cilia; a euglena (b) has a flagellum. A light microscope was used to produce these photographs.

How do some cells move?

BACKGROUND Animal cells do not have cell walls.

What are the functions of cell walls?

REVIEW AND REFLECT

1. What part of a cell is like
   a. a power plant?
   b. a screen door?
   c. an air traffic control tower?
   Explain your answers.
2. Suppose you encountered an object you had never seen before. How would you judge whether it was living or nonliving?

21:4 Homeostasis

What is homeostasis?

BACKGROUND   In animals, overall homeostasis is maintained by operation of both the nervous system and endocrine system (hormones). In plants, overall homeostasis is maintained mainly by hormones.

Homeostasis (hoh mee oh STAY sus) is a state of balance that is maintained by a system of controls within a cell or an organism. Organisms respond when changes occur in their environment. Adjustments occur within an organism that keep it alive and healthy. For example, your body makes adjustments to maintain a constant temperature. Perspiration has a cooling effect on your body. Shivering causes heat to be produced. These processes are examples of homeostasis.

A shoe factory is an example of a system that consists of input, processing, and output. Leather and other materials are the input. They are processed in the factory into shoes. Shoes are the output.

Some systems also involve feedback. A system that maintains homeostasis involves feedback. In body systems, information about what is happening in the environment is sensed. This information is the input. The information is processed and an adjustment to restore balance is the output. As a result of the adjustment, the sensor gets new information called feedback. The new input varies depending on the feedback received. As shown in Figure 21–5, this system of input, processing, output, and feedback is called a feedback loop.

What does a feedback loop include?

FIGURE 21–5. Cells and organisms maintain homeostasis by means of feedback loops. A simple example of a feedback loop occurs when nerves in the eyes sense light dimming. This information (input) is sent to the brain where it is processed. Information (output) is sent to muscles in the eyes. They adjust the size of the pupils to allow more light in. Feedback occurs when the nerves in the eyes sense the change. Then new information (input) is sent to the brain. A feedback loop is a continuous system.

Learning to drive a car is an example of how feedback loops work. The balance to be maintained is to keep the car in the lane. When a driver sees that the road curves, the hands turn the steering wheel into the curve. If the steering wheel is turned too far, the car goes out of the lane. The eyes sense the car is out of the lane. The brain processes this input and sends information to the hands to turn the wheel back the other way. Feedback helps the driver know just how far to turn the steering wheel into a curve and still keep the car in the lane.

In a cell, maintaining homeostasis involves keeping many factors in balance. Changing one part of a system brings about changes in other parts of the system. When changes occur outside a cell, sensors within the cell send feedback to a processor. Information is sent from the processor to cell parts that make the adjustments needed to maintain homeostasis. After action is taken, sensors detect whether the adjustments were just right, too much, or too little. Then further adjustments may be made.

Sometimes feedback loops within a cell or organism do not work as they should. For instance, the temperature outside a cell may become extremely high or low. Adequate adjustments may not be possible to maintain the correct temperature within the cell. Or if sensors fail to detect a temperature change, no adjustment is made. If feedback loops do not work properly, homeostasis is not maintained. Without homeostasis, the cell dies.

What happens to cells if feedback loops do not work as they should?

See Teacher's Guide.

Career Profile

A small child, the victim of a serious car accident, is rushed into the Emergency Room of the Toronto Sick Children's Hospital in Toronto, Canada. Louise Smith receives the emergency order for a blood test. She rushes to produce the results within minutes.

Louise is a medical laboratory technologist. Louise's work in the routine hematology lab includes doing blood counts and analyzing the various types of cells she finds present in a sample.

During her two year study at the Toronto Institute of Medical Technology, Louise acquired these and many other skills. In the hematology lab, Louise examines between 30 and 40 blood samples a day. She types her findings for each patient onto a computer terminal. The doctor in charge then reads the results to determine an appropriate treatment.

In the future, Louise hopes to advance her career by attending more classes. She would like to achieve a supervisory position in the laboratory or perhaps try more specialized hematology work. But for now Louise finds her present job very rewarding.

Activity: What can you learn from a feedback loop?

See Teacher's Guide.

MATERIALS

self-standing, adjustable angle mirror
10 pieces tracing paper
pencil
masking tape

PROCEDURE

1. On a piece of tracing paper, trace shape A. Label the paper A_1.

2. On another piece of tracing paper, trace shape B. Label the paper B_1.

3. Repeat this procedure for shapes C, D, and E.

4. Set up the mirror at a slight angle to your desk top, as shown in Figure 21–6.

5. Put paper A_1 in front of the mirror so that the shape is completely visible in the mirror. Tape the paper to the desktop in this position.

6. Label another piece of tracing paper A_2. Place this piece of paper on top of paper A_1.

7. WHILE LOOKING ONLY IN THE MIRROR, trace completely over shape A. Do not look at the paper until your tracing is complete.

8. Repeat steps 6 and 7 for shapes B, C, D, and E.

FIGURE 21–6.

DATA AND OBSERVATIONS

Shape	Tracing	
	1	2
A	■	
B	◆	
C	●	
D	✳	
E	🐰	

QUESTIONS AND CONCLUSIONS

1. When you tried to trace shape A, what happened? Why?

2. Compare your second tracings of shapes A and B, both of about equal difficulty. Does your work show improvement?

3. Compare your second tracings of shapes, C, D, and E. What is the evidence that you learned or did not learn how to trace while looking in a mirror?

4. How is this activity a controlled experiment to judge if learning took place?

5. Diagram the feedback loop that exists when you learn to trace while looking in a mirror. Label the input, processing, output, and feedback.

21:5   The Cell Membrane

Every material needed by cells must move into the cell through the cell membrane. All wastes must move out through the same membrane. If all materials could move through the cell membrane at all times, the cell could not maintain homeostasis. But cell membranes are selectively permeable. That means only certain materials can move in and out. You might think of a gate at a football game as selectively permeable. People with tickets can come through the gate. People without tickets are kept out.

There are two ways that materials can pass through the selectively permeable cell membrane. One way requires no energy from the cell; the other way requires energy from the cell. In each way, materials are thought to squeeze through tiny spaces between molecules of the cell membrane. Notice the structure of a cell membrane shown in Figure 21-7.

One way that materials pass through the cell membrane is diffusion. Diffusion takes no energy from the cell. Materials that are in greater concentration on one side of a

Why must cell membranes be selectively permeable?

DEMONSTRATION   Place a small amount of dye such as potassium permanganate or a food color tablet in water in a clear container. Observe color changes in the water at intervals within a class period.

Protein-carbohydrate

Phosphate

Fatty acid

Protein

FIGURE 21-7.   The molecules of a cell membrane are believed to be arranged like a phosphate and fatty acid "sandwich" as shown. Protein and carbohydrate molecules are also part of the structure. Materials entering and leaving cells are thought to move through tiny spaces between molecules.

Describe diffusion processes.

BACKGROUND Diffusion occurs because water (solvent) and dissolved material (solutes) are in constant motion, a process called Brownian movement.

What is osmosis?

BACKGROUND Cells, such as red blood cells, will burst if the solution has high osmotic pressure due to excess water. In reverse, cells will shrivel if they are placed in solution with low water concentration, so that water moves out of cells. An isotonic solution is one in which osmotic balance is reached so cells neither burst or shrivel.

Describe active transport.

ACTIVITY Observe *Elodea* cells with a microscope first in distilled water and then in a concentrated solution of sugar and water. Students should note the plasma membrane and cytoplasm reach to the cell walls in distilled water. In the sugar solution, they will see blobs of cytoplasm surrounded by cell membranes (green) that do not reach the colorless cell walls. Osmosis causes water to pass from the cytoplasm into the sugar solution.

cell diffuse across the cell membrane to the other side. In this way, food that is in greater concentration outside the cell diffuses into the cell through the cell membrane. Waste products that are in greater concentration inside a cell than outside diffuse out of the cell through the cell membrane.

Many different materials diffuse into and out of cells through cell membranes. When the diffusing material is water, the process is called osmosis. Since over half of the mass of every cell is water, osmosis is a very important form of diffusion.

Sometimes unwanted molecules such as carbon monoxide diffuse into cells. Carbon monoxide poisoning happens in this way. Carbon monoxide diffuses into red blood cells, preventing the cells from getting enough oxygen. Without enough oxygen in the red blood cells, a person may suffocate. Carbon monoxide can build up inside closed cars or inside homes with gas heaters and furnaces if they are not used properly or kept in good condition. One part of carbon monoxide per 100 parts of air can cause death in a few minutes.

Sometimes cells need materials from outside that cannot diffuse through the cell membrane. Or cells may need to get rid of wastes that cannot diffuse through the cell membrane. A second way that materials can pass through a cell membrane is **active transport.** Active transport requires energy from the cell. In active transport, certain molecules act as carriers to move materials across the cell membrane. Some materials that require active transport are molecules of sugar and ions of potassium and sodium. Sodium ions can diffuse into a cell, but they must be "pumped" out by active transport.

See Teacher's Guide.

REVIEW AND REFLECT

1. How does an organism maintain homeostasis?
2. How is a cell membrane selectively permeable?
3. What are the two main ways that materials are transported across a cell membrane? Explain each of the processes and how they differ.
4. What can be done to prevent carbon monoxide poisoning in a car and a home?

Activity: What can pass through a membrane?

See Teacher's Guide.

MATERIALS

dialysis tubing   graduated cylinder
(10 cm length)   Lugol's solution
scissors   Benedict's solution
thread   starch solution
dropper   water
2 250-mL beakers   hot plate
2 test tubes   test tube holder
corn syrup–water   apron
mixture

PROCEDURE

Part A

1. Fill a 250 mL beaker about two thirds with water. Heat to boiling.

2. Fill a test tube about half full of starch solution. Add a few drops of Lugol's solution. **CAUTION:** *Do not breathe this solution or get it on your skin.*

3. Fill another test tube about half full of corn syrup–water mixture. Add 5 mL of Benedict's solution. Place the test tube in the boiling water bath.

Part B

1. Tie one end of the dialysis tubing tightly with thread to make a "bag", Figure 21–8a.

2. Pour corn syrup–water mixture into the bag until it is about one third full. Pour starch solution into the bag until it is about two thirds full.

3. Tie the top of the bag tightly with another piece of thread. Make sure that you leave a large air space above the liquid, as shown in Figure 21–8b.

4. Fill a 250 mL beaker about half full of water. Place the bag in the water. Let it sit undisturbed for 24 hours.

5. After 24 hours, observe the bag.

a   b

FIGURE 21–8.

6. Pour water from the beaker into another test tube, about half full. Add a few drops of Lugol's solution.

7. Pour water from the beaker into another test tube, about half full. Add 5 mL Benedict's solution. Place the test tube in a boiling water bath.

DATA AND OBSERVATIONS

Liquid	Solution Added	Observation
Starch solution	Lugol's	
Corn syrup– water mixture	Benedict's	
Beaker water	Lugol's	
Beaker water	Benedict's	

QUESTIONS AND CONCLUSIONS

1. What moved out of the bag into the water? What did not move out of the bag into the water? What moved into the bag? How do you know?

2. By what process did materials move?

3. Why is dialysis tubing said to be selectively permeable?

FIGURE 21–9. High energy bonds exist between the three phosphate groups of adenosine triphosphate, ATP.

Describe photosynthesis.

Where does photosynthesis occur?

Which photosynthesis reactions require light and which do not?

BACKGROUND During photosynthesis a large number of chemical reactions occur. One set requires light and is known as light reactions. Another set is called dark reactions because light is not needed. Dark reactions are not the same in all plants. Each set of reactions includes oxidation and reduction.

21:6 Energy for Cells

Energy is needed for the activities constantly taking place in cells. They need energy to move, to keep homeostasis, and to reproduce. Organisms that contain chlorophyll manufacture food that supplies energy. The food is manufactured by a process called photosynthesis.

In **photosynthesis,** light energy from the sun is trapped by chlorophyll molecules and converted into chemical energy of adenosine triphosphate. Energy is released when certain bonds in adenosine triphosphate, called **ATP** for short, are broken. Light energy is also used to split molecules of water into hydrogen ions and oxygen. The oxygen is released into the air. The hydrogen ions combine with carbon dioxide from the air to form glucose. Energy is transferred from ATP to the glucose molecules. Glucose is a simple sugar that cells can break down to release the energy stored in its molecules.

The many chemical reactions of photosynthesis can be summarized in an overall equation.

$$\text{water + carbon dioxide} \xrightarrow{\text{light energy}} \text{glucose + oxygen}$$
$$6H_2O + 6CO_2 \xrightarrow{\hspace{2cm}} C_6H_{12}O_6 + 6O_2$$

Photosynthesis takes place in chloroplasts. Remember that chloroplasts contain chlorophyll. In plant chloroplasts, structures that look like stacks of coins are filled with chlorophyll. In the presence of light, ATP is produced in the stacks. In the protoplasm that surrounds the stacks, glucose is formed from carbon dioxide and hydrogen ions. The hydrogen ions from water are formed in the presence of light. Carbon dioxide combines with the hydrogen ions using energy from ATP. This reaction can occur in darkness as well as in light.

Figure 21–10 shows how photosynthesis in a plant is like a production line in a factory. In a factory, a production line changes raw materials into finished products. In a plant, photosynthesis changes sunlight, water, and carbon dioxide into glucose. The glucose is food for the plant cells. By eating plants, animals also use the food made by plants.

FIGURE 21–10. In a plant, light energy is changed to chemical energy in the form of ATP. Some of the energy is used to split water molecules into H^+ ions and oxygen molecules. The oxygen is released into the air. Along with carbon dioxide from the air and energy released from ATP molecules, H^+ ions are used to form glucose.

For organisms to get usable energy from glucose, their cells must oxidize glucose molecules. A series of chemical reactions are involved in this biological oxidation, which is called **cell respiration.** In cell respiration, glucose molecules are combined with oxygen, forming carbon dioxide and water. Energy is released. The energy is used to form ATP. ATP supplies cells with energy for life activities. This overall equation summarizes the many chemical reactions of this type of cell respiration.

glucose + oxygen → energy + water + carbon dioxide
$$C_6H_{12}O_6 + 6O_2 \rightarrow energy + 6H_2O + 6CO_2$$

ATP supplies the energy for the oxidation of glucose molecules in cell respiration. Cell respiration is very efficient. For each glucose molecule oxidized, enough energy is released to form more ATP. So, a net gain of ATP results from each glucose molecule oxidized.

What are the overall reactants and products in cell respiration?

BACKGROUND As in photosynthesis, there are a large number of chemical reactions in cell respiration. The overall effect is oxidation. None of the reactions of cell respiration require light.

21:7 Enzymes

Both cell respiration and photosynthesis are complex and involve hundreds of individual chemical reactions. Other cell functions also require many chemical reactions. The reactions occur in cells, in fractions of seconds. Normally, many fast reactions require high temperatures to get them started. Such high temperatures would kill cells. Cells contain special compounds called **enzymes** (EN zimez) that allow the chemical reactions to take place at temperatures below 45°C.

Each enzyme is a protein, a large coiled molecule made up of smaller organic molecules called amino acids. Each enzyme has a unique three-dimensional shape. The shape of an enzyme has a very specific fit with only one kind of molecule. When an enzyme touches another molecule, the other molecule is rejected if it does not fit. If it fits, it is joined to the enzyme. When a molecule is joined to an enzyme, a chemical reaction can occur at normal cell temperatures.

When you eat a cookie, you are consuming sucrose, which is table sugar. Sucrose is a complex molecule made with two simpler molecules. Sucrose combines with water in your digestive system and breaks down into the simpler molecules. The enzyme sucrase makes this reaction possible at cell temperatures. The shape of the enzyme sucrase just fits the sucrose molecule. When a sucrose molecule touches the enzyme sucrase, they join. When a molecule of water is added, the reaction yielding the simpler molecules takes place. When the reaction is complete, the sucrase is released and can be used again to break down other sucrose molecules. Enzymes also work in reactions that combine simple molecules into complex molecules. Figure 21–11 shows how enzymes are involved in the breakdown and formation of complex molecules.

Coenzymes are nonprotein molecules that join with some enzymes temporarily during chemical reactions in cells. Without coenzymes, the chemical reactions would not occur. Like enzymes, coenzymes remain unchanged during reactions and can be used again.

Several of the substances we call vitamins are used by cells to form coenzymes. If a person does not get enough of

How are cell reactions possible at low temperatures?

Describe enzymes.

ACTIVITY The three-dimensional shape of each enzyme is not seen well in a flat drawing. However, the three-dimensional aspect is an important factor in the joining of enzymes with other molecules. Use a 3-dimensional puzzle to illustrate the importance of 3-dimensionality in fitting together.

How do enzymes work?

What are coenzymes?

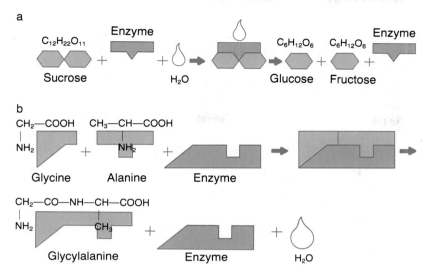

FIGURE 21–11. When sucrose, $C_{12}H_{22}O_{11}$, combines with water and an enzyme, sucrase, a bond is broken and two simpler molecules, $C_6H_{12}O_6$, are formed (a). When the amino acids glycine and alanine combine with an enzyme, peptide polymerase, a more complex molecule, glycylalanine, and water are formed (b). In both reactions (a and b), the enzymes are released unchanged.

one of these vitamins, the coenzyme does not form, and important cell reactions will not take place. For example, lack of vitamin B (thiamine) causes a disease called beriberi, which can result in slow growth, loss of appetite, paralysis, and heart disease.

Sometimes enzymes do not work right if molecules similar to the ones they normally fit jam into them. These "impostor" molecules squeeze into the spaces where the correct molecules should go. The medical use of penicillin is a good example of what happens when an impostor molecule jams an enzyme. Penicillin in people acts as an impostor molecule. It jams certain enzymes in the infecting bacteria. The bacteria die because chemical reactions needed to keep the cells alive do not occur.

BACKGROUND There are two types of vitamins, those that form coenzymes, also called water-soluble vitamins, and a group called fat-soluble vitamins. The water-soluble group is so-called because they are excreted easily. The fat-soluble vitamins must be processed by body enzymes (metabolized) before they can be excreted.

See Teacher's Guide.

REVIEW AND REFLECT

1. How do cells get energy for cell homeostasis?
2. Write the balanced chemical equations for the overall reactions of photosynthesis and cell respiration. How are the reactions related?
3. Why can chemical reactions occur quickly and at low temperatures in cells?
4. What foods have you eaten today that supply vitamin C to your body?

What is cryobiology?

What is the main problem with freezing cells?

21:8 Information: Life Below Zero

On a cold winter day, you may be concerned about life below zero, but you probably do not think about it the rest of the year. Cryobiologists think about life below zero all year round. "Cryo" comes from the Greek word, *kryos,* which means icy cold. Thus, cryobiology is the study of life at very low temperatures. Cryobiologists are concerned with freezing cells without destroying them. Frozen cells are especially useful for medical purposes.

A main problem with freezing cells is the water that cells contain. When the water freezes, it expands and that often breaks the cell membranes. As more water freezes, chemicals get crowded into a smaller amount of remaining water. The remaining solution gets very concentrated. Homeostasis cannot be maintained.

Cryobiologists have experimented with freezing cells at different rates. They have found that freezing cells quickly or slowly affects whether the cells survive or die. Cells frozen at certain rates stay alive. Notice in Figure 21–12 how different freezing rates affect yeast cells. The best rate for freezing cells depends on the kind of cell. Cryobiologists experiment to find the rate that causes the least damage to each kind of cell. Adding chemicals, such as glycerol and sodium chloride, also helps keep cells alive. Such compounds help freezing to occur more evenly.

By changing freezing rates and by adding chemicals, cryobiologists have learned how to freeze many kinds of cells without destroying them. For example, red blood cells can be frozen without destroying them. In the past, donated blood could be preserved for up to three weeks. Any blood that was not used by that time had to be thrown

a   b

FIGURE 21–12. Ice forms within yeast cells cooled at between 10° and 100°C per minute (a). When ice forms within cells, the survival rate of the cells is low. Ice does not form in yeast cells cooled at 6°C per minute (b). If cells are cooled at a sufficiently slow rate, their survival rate is higher.

away. Now, red blood cells can be saved for 10 years or more. Red blood cells are separated from whole blood by a spinning process. Then they are mixed with water, glycerol, and sodium chloride. The mixture is frozen at a certain rate and stored at $-85°C$. When the blood is needed, the cells are thawed, washed with salt water, and spun to remove the glycerol. A mixture of water, sugar, and salt is added to them. Then the "remade" blood can be used for transfusions.

Frozen blood has other advantages in addition to a long storage life. Some diseases that may be passed from blood donors to recipients are not passed on in blood that has been frozen. Another advantage of frozen blood is that it can be shipped to hospitals more easily than fresh blood.

Cryobiologists are trying now to freeze very large groups of cells, such as kidneys, hearts, bones, and skin. A problem with freezing whole organs is that they are made of many different kinds of cells. The freezing rates that keep each kind of cell alive are different. If cryobiologists can learn to freeze whole organs, the organs could be stored for transplants. Frozen skin cells could be stored for use as skin grafts for patients with severe burns.

What cryobiologists have learned about the destruction of cells by freezing has led to the field of cryosurgery. In cryosurgery, low temperatures are used to kill unwanted cells by instant freezing. Surgeons remove tumors using a probe with a silver tip that contains cold nitrogen gas (colder than $-100°C$). The surgeon touches tumor cells with the tip and they die. Doctors find that tumors removed by cryosurgery are less likely to grow back than tumors that are cut out with a knife. Also, patients recover more quickly after cryosurgery.

FIGURE 21–13. Cryosurgeons use special instruments containing liquid nitrogen to destroy tissues by freezing.

What is an important application of what cryobiologists have learned about freezing cells?

See Teacher's Guide.

REVIEW AND REFLECT

1. a. How is blood frozen?
   b. Describe two advantages of frozen blood.
2. What is cryosurgery? What are the advantages of cryosurgery?
3. Explain what you think the following terms mean.
   a. cryoprobe
   b. cryoprotective
   c. cryotherapy

SUMMARY

1. Organisms are made of one or more cells. 21:1

2. Scientists use special tools, such as microscopes, to learn about cells. 21:2

3. Some cell parts are common to all types of life. Some types of life have cell parts that are unique. 21:3

4. To remain alive, cells must maintain homeostasis. Homeostasis is maintained by feedback loops. 21:4

5. Materials and wastes move through cell membranes. 21:5

6. Photosynthesis, which takes place in cells that contain chlorophyll, makes use of energy from sunlight to form ATP and glucose. 21:6

7. Cell respiration is an oxidation process that releases the energy stored in glucose. 21:6

8. ATP supplies the energy for the formation and oxidation of glucose. 21:6

9. Enzymes fit in an exact way with other molecules, allowing chemical reactions in cells to take place at low temperatures. 21:7

VOCABULARY

active transport 2	chloroplasts 3	mitochondria 15
ATP 5	cytoplasm 6	nucleus 4
cell membrane 7	endoplasmic reticulum 9	photosynthesis 13
cell respiration 14	enzyme 11	ribosomes 12
cell wall 10	homeostasis 1	vacuoles 8

Choose a word from the list to complete each sentence correctly.

1. _____ is a balance maintained by a system of controls within a cell or an organism.

2. The method of movement of materials through a cell membrane by carrier molecules is called _____.

3. Photosynthesis occurs in the _____ of plant cells.

4. The _____ is the control center of a cell.

5. Energy in cells is stored in a molecule called _____.

6. Respiration in cells occurs in the _____.

7. The _____ is the outermost living part of a cell.

8. Food and water are stored in _____ in cells.

9. The part of a cell that carries proteins is _____.

10. A cell part called the _____ surrounds the cell membranes of some cells, such as plant cells.

11. A(n) _____ is a protein molecule that enables chemical reactions in cells to occur at low temperatures.

12. Proteins are produced in cell _____.

13. _____ is the production of food using energy from sunlight.

14. Another name for biological oxidation in cells is _____.

15. Structures that provide energy for a cell by oxidizing food are _____.

QUESTIONS

MAIN IDEAS

Choose the correct answer to complete each sentence.

1. Every type of life *(moves from place to place, shows energy changes, has cell walls)*.

2. All cells *(are about the same size, vary so that the largest is about 10 times larger than the smallest, vary so that the largest is more than 10^4 times bigger than the smallest)*.

3. Cell parts found in all forms of life include *(mitochondria, chloroplasts, lysosomes)*.

4. In every feedback loop, a sensor is connected to something that *(changes an action, performs photosynthesis, performs active transport)*.

5. Movement of carbon monoxide into cells is an example of *(diffusion, active transport, osmosis)*.

6. The products formed in photosynthesis are *(water and carbon dioxide, glucose and oxygen, enzymes and coenzymes)*.

7. Compounds needed for the formation of coenzymes are *(vitamins, carbon monoxide and carbon dioxide, carbon dioxide and water)*.

8. The temperatures at which cell reactions can take place are lowered by *(ATP, enzymes, chlorophyll)*.

9. Cell respiration requires *(sunlight, carbon dioxide, oxygen)*.

10. All cells have *(nuclei, cell walls, cell membranes, chlorophyll)*.

See Teacher's Guide.

APPLICATIONS

Answer each question in one or more paragraphs.

1. How is a cell nucleus different from an atomic nucleus?

2. Imagine that typical cells are enlarged to be the size of the solar system in comparison to you. What two cell parts (like planets) would you choose to explore first with spaceships? Explain why.

3. Describe the feedback loops that occur when you pick up a pencil and write the answer to a question.

4. Recall what you learned about color in chapter 14. Why does chlorophyll in green plants appear green?

5. Since scientists have not found oxygen (O_2) in the atmospheres of other planets, what can be said about photosynthesis on those planets?

FURTHER STUDY

INVESTIGATIONS

1. Construct a three-dimensional model of a plant or animal cell. Display the model in class with labels.

2. Prepare a report about differing opinions on the value of taking vitamin supplements.

3. Prepare a report on how certain narcotics interfere with diffusion and active transport across the cell membrane.

READINGS

0 Brown, M. and J. Goldstein, "Receiving Windows for the Cell." *Science Year, 1980.* pp. 42–55.

+ Pines, Maya. *Inside the Cell.* Enslow Publishers: Hillsdale, NJ, 1980.

– Shih, Gene, and Richard Kessel. *Living Images.* Science Books International: Boston, 1982.

0 Snyderman, Ralph. "Cell Wars." *Science Year, 1981.* 1980. pp. 56–69.

How do you organize your school papers? Some students have notebooks with pockets for each subject. The students classify their papers according to subjects. Scientists classify organisms according to likenesses and differences. What organisms do you see in the picture? How do scientists classify organisms? Why do scientists classify organisms?

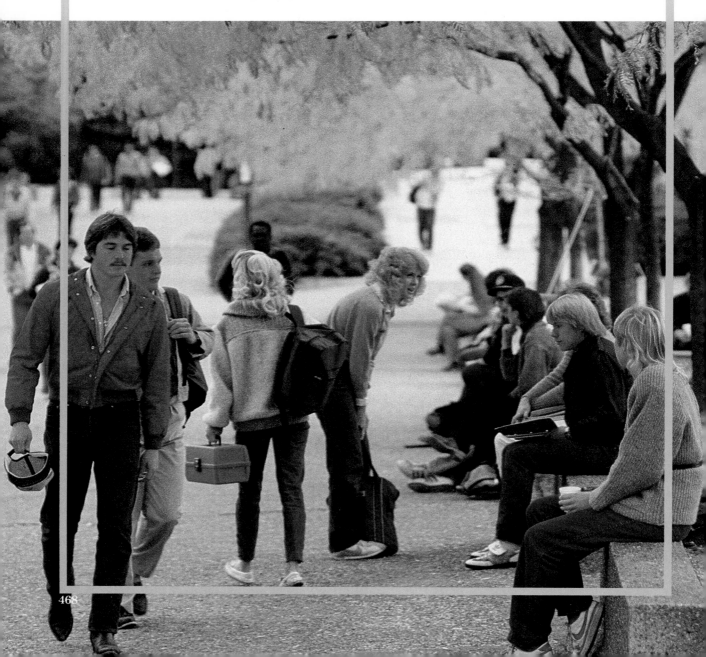

CLASSIFICATION

INTRODUCING THE CHAPTER   In earlier chapters, ways of differentiating between elements, compounds, and mixtures were studied. The properties of elements were used to organize the elements into the periodic table. Review the classification concepts with which students are already familiar from unit 2. Discuss the similarity of the scientific development of the periodic table and the development of biological classification systems. On a bulletin board, make a biological classification table with pictures of organisms. (See Figure 22–3.) As you proceed through the chapter, refer to the bulletin board and add to it.

22:1   Two Types of Cells

The simplest classification of organisms is based on the structure of their cells. Compare the two basic types of cells, eukaryotes (yew KER ee ohts) and prokaryotes (pro KER ee ohts), in Figure 22–1. **Eukaryotes** are cells that have nuclei. They also have distinct structures, such as mitochondria or chloroplasts, within the cell membrane. Plants and animals have eukaryotic cells.

Some simple organisms, such as bacteria, are prokaryotes. **Prokaryotes** are cells that do not have nuclei. They have no distinct structures within the cell membrane. A prokaryotic cell has nuclear material, but it is not defined by a nuclear membrane. Some prokaryotes contain chlorophyll, but it is not located in chloroplasts as it is in eukaryotic cells. In prokaryotes, chlorophyll is located in the cytoplasm.

GOAL   You will investigate the main properties of different forms of life and how organisms are classified.

What are eukaryotes and prokaryotes?

ACTIVITY   Carefully observe similarities and differences in photographs of eukaryote cells and an electronmicrograph of a bacterium.

FIGURE 22–1. Eukaryotes have distinct cell structures within their cell membranes. Note the nucleus, chloroplasts, and other structures in the plant cell (a). Prokaryotes lack distinct structures within their cell membranes. Note the simple cell structure of the blue-green alga cells (b).

a   b

22:2 Five Kingdoms

The structure of cells is just one feature that is used to classify organisms. Information about other body structures, chemistry within organisms, reproduction and development, complexity, and behavior is used to classify organisms, too. When new information becomes available, the way an organism is classified may change. Sometimes biologists disagree. Some biologists may think an organism should be classified in one group, while other biologists think the organism belongs in another group.

In general, biologists classify organisms into one of five main groups called **kingdoms.** The animal and plant kingdoms are the two best-known kingdoms. All of the organisms in these kingdoms are many-celled organisms with eukaryotic cells. The fungus kingdom is another kingdom of organisms with eukaryotic cells. Some fungi, such as mushrooms, are many-celled organisms. Some, such as yeasts, are single-celled organisms. The protist kingdom includes other single-celled organisms that are eukaryotes, such as paramecia and amoeba (uh MEE buh). Prokaryotes are classified in a separate kingdom called the moneran (muh NIHR uhn) kingdom. Bacteria and blue-green algae (AL jee) are examples of monerans.

Kingdoms are like the subject pockets in a student's notebook. The organisms in a kingdom are not exactly alike, just as the papers in each pocket of a student's notebook are not exactly the same. A student may divide the papers in each pocket into subgroups. Tests may be paperclipped together as one subgroup, class notes another,

What are the five life kingdoms?

FIGURE 22–2. Until the 1950s, most biologists classified all organisms as either animals or plants. In the 1960s, biotechnology provided new information about organisms that resulted in new systems of kingdom classification. Today most scientists classify all organisms into five kingdoms.

and so on. Biologists divide kingdoms into subgroups. Each subgroup, called a **phylum** (FI lum), is in turn subdivided a number of times. Note the subdivisions shown in Figure 22–3. Each subdivision is smaller and more specific than the one before it. Biologists define **species** as a group of organisms that are able to produce fertile offspring when they breed.

The **scientific name** of each kind of organism is the **genus** (JEE nus) and the species. Most of these names come from Latin and Greek words. *Homo sapiens* is the scientific name for people. *Homo* is the genus; *sapiens* is the species. In a scientific name, the genus is capitalized, but the species is not. Scientific names are printed in italic type or underlined when written.

Although scientific names might confuse people who are not familiar with classification, scientific names are very important. Common names may not mean the same organism in every language or even in different parts of a country. For example, a "gopher" is a land turtle to many people who live in the southern United States. In midwestern states, "gopher" is a name for a ground squirrel. In the west, a large snake is called a "gopher." Each of these organisms has a different scientific name. Referring to organisms by their scientific names helps biologists understand each other. Each species of organism has a particular scientific name. Scientific names are usually the same in every language.

How are organisms within each kingdom classified?

How is a scientific name written?

ACTIVITY   Obtain a book of Greek and Latin roots, prefixes, and suffixes from a library. Prepare a list of scientific names and let students use the book to figure out common names.

FIGURE 22–3.   As levels of classification become more specific, the size of the group decreases. Note that all seven organisms shown are classified in Kingdom Animalia. However, only six are classified in Phylum Chordata, five in Class Mammalia, and so on. The organisms left out of each descending level are classified in other phyla, classes, and so on.

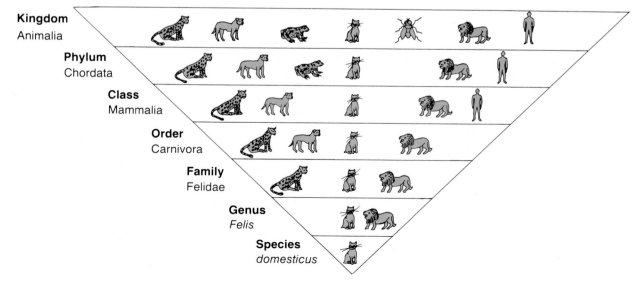

Kingdom
Animalia

Phylum
Chordata

Class
Mammalia

Order
Carnivora

Family
Felidae

Genus
Felis

Species
domesticus

See Teacher's Guide.

REVIEW AND REFLECT

1. How are eukaryotes and prokaryotes different?
2. How do biologists classify organisms?
3. Why is it important that biologists use scientific names when discussing organisms?

22:3 Animals

What are some characteristics of animals?

Animals are many-celled organisms that obtain food from other sources. Most animals can move about seeking food. In complex animals, specialized cells are organized into tissues, organs, and systems of organs that work together.

What is a vertebrate?

Animals are classified as vertebrates (VURT uh brayts) or invertebrates. A **vertebrate** is an animal with a backbone. Vertebrates also have internal skeletons and organ systems. All vertebrates belong to one phylum (Chordata) in the animal kingdom. The phylum is subdivided into classes. Some classes of vertebrates include bony fish, amphibians, reptiles, birds, and mammals. Some characteristics of these classes are listed in Table 22–1.

BACKGROUND   Three classes of fish are included in Phylum Chordata. Bony fish, or Class Osteichthyes, are discussed here. The other classes are jawless fish (Class Agnatha), such as lamprey, and cartilaginous fish (Class Chondrichthyes), such as sharks.

ACTIVITY   List a number of common names of vertebrate animals. Using Table 22–1, let students determine the class of each.

TABLE 22–1.	SOME CHARACTERISTICS OF VERTEBRATES
Class	**Characteristics**
Bony fish	Cold-blooded, have covered gills, hinged jaws, scales, fins, live in water
Amphibians	Cold-blooded, smooth skin without scales, young have gills but develop lungs as they grow, most adults live on land but eggs are laid in water
Reptiles	Cold-blooded, have scales, live on land, eggs have tough covering, are laid on land
Birds	Warm-blooded, have feathers, wings, beaks, live mainly on land
Mammals	Warm-blooded, have hair, mothers feed young milk from mammary glands, live on land or in water

An **invertebrate** is an animal with no backbone. Invertebrates are classified in a number of phyla. The major phyla include sponges, coelenterates (sih LENT uh raytez), worms, mollusks, arthropods, and echinoderms (ih KI nuh durmz). Examples of these phyla are shown in Figure 22–4.

You have probably observed the body segments of an ant. Perhaps you have noticed that spiders have jointed legs. The hard outer covering of a lobster is an exoskeleton. Segmented bodies, jointed legs, and exoskeletons are characteristics of all arthropods. About three fourths of all animals, or more than 800 000 species, are arthropods. Scorpions, bees, ticks, centipedes, crabs, and shrimp are some other arthropods. Trilobites, common during the Paleozoic period of earth history, were arthropods too.

What are some examples of invertebrates?

FIGURE 22–4. Some common examples of invertebrates and their phylum classifications are sponges (a) in Phylum Porifera; coral (b) in Phylum Coelenterata; earthworms (c) in Phylum Annelida; snails (d) in Phylum Mollusca; spiders (e) in Phylum Arthropoda; starfish (f) in Phylum Echinodermata.

a

b

c

d

e

f

22:4 Plants

What are the characteristics of plants?

Plants are organisms that produce food by photosynthesis. Their cells are eukaryotic and have chloroplasts. Most plants are many-celled, but some species of algae are one-celled plants.

Plants are classified as vascular (VAS kyuh lur) or nonvascular. A **vascular** plant has "true" roots, stems, and leaves. These structures contain tissues that move food and water throughout the plant. Ferns and seed plants are vascular plants. **Nonvascular** plants, such as algae and mosses, may have structures that look like roots, stems, and leaves. But these structures do not contain food- and water-conducting tissues, so they are not true vascular structures. Nonvascular plants are classified in four phyla. Vascular plants are classified chiefly by the nature of their reproduction.

What is the difference between vascular and nonvascular plants?

BACKGROUND   The word *division* often is used for phylum in the plant kingdom. There are three divisions for algae (not to be confused with blue-green algae, which are monerans)—red algae, brown algae, and green algae. Mosses, liverworts, and hornworts are in a fourth division together. All vascular plants are in a fifth division.

Ferns reproduce by spores. Spores are a kind of reproductive cell. The small brown spots on the underside of fern leaves are spore cases that release spores. When distributed in moist areas by wind, some spores eventually will form young fern plants.

In seed plants, reproduction results in seeds that grow into new plants. An important feature of seed plants is pollen. Some people are allergic to pollen. Hay fever is a common allergy. A pollen grain is several male sex cells enclosed in a tough, tiny sac. Pollen grains are produced in male reproductive structures of seed plants. They are transferred by wind, water, or insects to a female reproductive structure called an ovule. The ovule contains eggs, which are female sex cells. In the ovule, the female and male sex cells unite to form a fertilized egg. A seed is the fertilized egg and stored food. It is surrounded by a protective covering. Pines and other cone-bearing plants are called "naked" seed plants because their seeds are exposed. The cone simply anchors the seeds. In flowering plants, seeds are enclosed in fruits. All of the fruits you eat are nature's containers for seeds.

What is the function of pollen?

BACKGROUND   Pollen is an adaptation of seed plants that makes fertilization without water possible. In some species, the pollen has sperm with flagella that must "swim" to the egg, but in such instances the fluid is secreted by the plant with the egg and the sperm does not swim far.

What are some uses of flowering plants?

Flowering plants are the most numerous plants on earth. Some have great economic importance. Particularly important to people are food crops, fibers, spices, and drugs derived from flowering plants.

Activity: How do flowering plants differ?

See Teacher's Guide.

MATERIALS

bean, corn, peanut,
pea, oat, squash,
and barley seeds
(4 of each)
paper towels
scalpel

potting soil
tap water
4 250-mL beakers
labels
wax paper
hand lens

Bean   Corn

Cotyledons   Cotyledon

FIGURE 22–5.

PROCEDURE

Part A

1. Carefully study one corn seed and one bean seed. Flowering plants are classified as monocots or dicots, depending on the structure of their seeds. Corn is a monocot; a bean is a dicot.
2. Place 4 corn seeds in a wet paper towel overnight. Repeat with 4 bean seeds.
3. The next day, dissect a corn seed and a bean seed. **CAUTION:** *Use care with a scalpel.* Use a hand lens to study the internal structures.
4. Record your observations of the characteristics of each kind of seed.
5. Fill a beaker half-full of potting soil. Add water to make the soil moist but not wet.
6. Plant the other 3 bean seeds on one side of the beaker. Plant the other 3 corn seeds on the other side of the beaker. Label each side. Plant the seeds so they are about 1 cm deep and next to the side of the beaker.
7. Cover the beaker with a piece of wax paper. Daily remove the paper and moisten the surface of the soil.
8. Record daily observations for a week.

Part B

1. Carefully study a pea, peanut, oat, squash, and barley seed.
2. Place 4 of each kind of seed in a separate wet paper towel overnight.
3. The next day, dissect one of each kind of seed. Record the characteristics of each.
4. Predict whether each seed is a monocot or a dicot.
5. Plant the other 3 seeds of each kind, using the procedure in steps 5–8 of Part A.

DATA AND OBSERVATIONS

Seed	Type or Prediction	Character-istics
Corn	Monocot	
Bean	Dicot	
Pea		
Peanut		
Oat		
Squash		
Barley		

QUESTIONS AND CONCLUSIONS

1. Which seeds were similar to the corn? the bean? Explain.
2. How are monocots and dicots different?
3. Which seeds are monocots? dicots?
4. Were your predictions correct?

22:5 Fungi

Fungi are plantlike organisms that do not contain chlorophyll. Therefore, they cannot make their own food. Most fungi get food from dead or decaying organic matter. Some fungi are parasites (PAR uh sitez) that get food from other living things. Fungi release substances that digest food. The food is absorbed along with water and minerals into the organism.

Fungi are classified primarily according to their reproductive structures. Some fungi are many-celled and some are one-celled. They are both helpful and harmful to people. For example, mushrooms are many-celled fungi that you may enjoy eating on a pizza or in a salad. But many species of mushrooms are poisonous. There is no simple way to tell an edible mushroom from a poisonous one. You should never eat a wild mushroom unless you are certain it is safe for eating. One kind of fungi is a mold that spoils fruits and bread but is used to produce penicillin. Many kinds of fungi are used to make certain foods, such as cheeses, bread, and beer. Other fungi destroy crops. In the 1840s in Ireland, a fungus destroyed the potato crop and a million people died of starvation. Some fungi cause diseases or annoying skin conditions, such as athlete's foot. Molds and mildews are fungi that may be problems in damp places.

The fungus kingdom includes a group of organisms that are not individual organisms. A combination of a fungus and an alga is a lichen (LI kun). The two partners in a lichen probably help each other. The fungus may provide water and minerals. The algae produces food by photosynthesis.

See Teacher's Guide.

REVIEW AND REFLECT

1. What is the difference between a vertebrate and an invertebrate? Give three examples of each.
2. How are reptiles different from amphibians?
3. Compare reproduction in seed plants and ferns.
4. Since arthropods have exoskeletons, how can they grow?
5. If no fungi existed, how might the world be different?

Why can fungi not produce food?

Describe the beneficial and harmful effects of fungi.

BACKGROUND Fungi, along with bacteria, perform the important function of decomposing dead organisms.

FIGURE 22–6. Lichens are sensitive to air pollution. Their decline in an area may indicate declining air quality. Also, they take in metals and other elements from rainwater and dust. So around pollution sources lichens can be chemically analyzed to determine the extent of the pollution.

Activity: How are fungi different from plants?

See Teacher's Guide.

MATERIALS

3 250-mL beakers
graduated cylinder
green algae culture
table sugar
spoon
2 packets of yeast
warm water
labels
microscope
2 microscope slides
2 coverslips
dropper

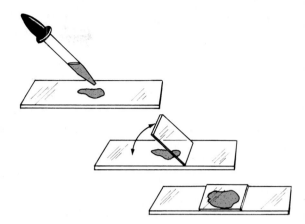

FIGURE 22–7.

PROCEDURE

Part A

1. Label three beakers A, B, and C.
2. Fill each beaker with 100 mL of warm, not hot, water.
3. Add a spoonful of sugar to beakers A and B.
4. Add 5 mL of algae culture to beaker A. Add a packet of yeast to beaker B. Add a packet of yeast to beaker C.
5. Record your observations in a data table.

Part B

1. Place a drop of yeast culture (from beaker B in Part A) on a microscope slide. Add a coverslip. Observe under high power.
2. Draw one of the fungus cells. Label any parts you can identify. (Review Figures 21–3, 21–4).
3. Place a drop of green algae culture on a microscope slide. Add a coverslip. Observe under high power.
4. Draw one of the plant cells. Label any parts you can identify.

DATA AND OBSERVATIONS

Beaker	Contents	Observation
A	Sugar, water, and algae	
B	Sugar, water, and yeast	
C	Yeast and water	

QUESTIONS AND CONCLUSIONS

1. In which beakers did you observe evidence of growth? What is the evidence?
2. What is the source of energy for the growth?
3. How are yeast different from algae?
4. How are yeast and algae similar?
5. Why do you think scientists classify green algae as plants?
6. Why do you think scientists do not classify yeast as plants?

See Teacher's Guide.

Career Profile

Imagine groping your way down an underground corridor as wide as a highway with steep walls. It is very dark and damp as the corridor narrows. Suddenly you find yourself in a huge open area like a field. Scattered lights move slowly about. The lights seem to be attached to human figures carrying large metal trays. Upon closer examination, you notice these figures picking something from large wooden flats. The scene is almost otherworldly. It is a mushroom farm near Worthington, Pennsylvania.

Jean Chemelli has been a mushroom farmer for nearly 20 years. From 7:00 A.M. until sometimes 7:00 P.M. each day, several hundred men and women pick between 50 and 60 metric tons of mushrooms in the abandoned limestone mine.

The mushrooms start growing in a laboratory where microscopic spores are nourished in test tubes. When the spores have matured, they are transferred to trays filled with organic matter and are covered lightly with soil. Once in the mine they are watered daily. The constant darkness, high humidity, and consistent temperature (16°C) of the mine create ideal growing conditions for the mushrooms.

Jean, who worked as a picker for many years, now oversees a crew of 15 people plus a mushroom hauler. Two days a week she also works as a section leader whose responsibility is to supervise four crews or 64 people. Jean's job is to motivate and encourage the pickers. She must know how to deal fairly with any problems that arise. Her work is a challenge because each day brings new management situations. She also likes the satisfaction of seeing a job well done. Jean requires the pickers to leave the floor around each tray clean.

On Jean's crew, the work runs smoothly and the job gets done fast. Pickers talk casually as they work. The most frequently asked question is, "What's the weather like outside?"

22:6 Protists

Describe characteristics of protists.

Protists are simple organisms. Most are one-celled and microscopic. They are eukaryotic. Most live in water. Some protists contain chlorophyll, like plants, so they can make their own food. Other protists are more like animals and cannot make their own food. They are parasites, or organisms that feed on other organisms.

FIGURE 22–8. Diatoms (a) are golden algae classified as protists. Because they contain chlorophyll, they can make their own food. Amoebas (b) are protists with pseudopods, which are fingerlike projections used for getting food and movement. Flagellates (c) are protists with more than one flagellum and most are parasites. Slime molds (d) are protists that resemble fungi.

Protists are classified according to their structure and means of movement. Most protists move by themselves. Some, like euglena, move by whipping flagella. Amoeba move by the flowing of their cytoplasm. Paramecium have many beating cilia.

Some protists cause diseases. A certain species of mosquito carries protists that cause malaria. When infected mosquitoes bite people, the people experience periodic chills and fever caused by the protists in their blood. It is estimated that about 1.5 million people today, mostly in tropical countries, have malaria.

How are protists classified?

BACKGROUND Protists include simple algae, protozoa, and slime molds. The algae are mostly one-celled and contain chlorophyll in chloroplasts. Protozoa are one-celled and animallike. Slime molds have one-celled and many-celled stages. They have features of protozoa and fungi.

22:7 Monerans

Monerans are prokaryotes. The moneran kingdom is divided into two main groups: blue-green algae and bacteria.

Blue-green algae make their own food by photosynthesis. They have chlorophyll in their cytoplasm. Remember, prokaryotes have no chloroplasts. Blue-green algae are found as individual cells, in chains, filaments, or colonies. They are important producers of food and oxygen for animal life in lakes, ponds, and streams. Blue-green algae are the earliest life form of which fossils have been found. Some fossils of blue-green algae are believed to be almost four billion years old.

What are monerans?

BACKGROUND Recently a green algae called *Prochloron* has been discovered and added to the moneran kingdom.

a

b

c

FIGURE 22–9. Bacteria may be spherical (a) called cocci, rod-shaped (b) called bacilli, or spiral (c) called spirilla.

How do bacteria get food?

BACKGROUND On sea floors at deep sea vents, bacteria that produce food have been found. Instead of sunlight, these bacteria use H_2S at high temperatures to obtain energy. The process is known as chemosynthesis.

ACTIVITY Try making yogurt with and without a yogurt culture. The culture contains bacteria needed to make yogurt.

Bacteria depend on organic matter or other living things for food. They are one-celled but often are found in chains or clusters. Notice the three shapes of bacteria shown in Figure 22–9. Many bacteria do the helpful job of decaying dead organisms. Some bacteria live in plant roots and make nitrates needed by plants as nutrients from nitrogen in the air. Other bacteria are important in the production of cheese, butter, vinegar, yogurt, sour cream, and some solvents used in industry.

Many bacteria cause disease. For example, some cause food poisoning. An often fatal food poisoning called botulism (BACH uh lihz um) can occur when people eat food that has not been canned properly. Canning foods at very high temperatures destroys botulism bacteria. However, if canning temperatures are not high enough, botulism bacteria may reproduce in the cans. Cans may bulge from the pressure of carbon dioxide produced by the bacteria's respiration. Cans of food should be inspected for swelling before they are opened or for a foamy appearance inside when they are opened. If either is observed, the food should not be eaten because it is likely to contain harmful bacteria.

See Teacher's Guide.

REVIEW AND REFLECT

1. How are fungi and protists similar? In what ways are they different?
2. How are some protists like animals? How are some protists like plants?
3. How are prokaryotes helpful to people? How are they harmful?

22:8 Viruses

When was the last time you had a cold or the flu? These illnesses are caused by viruses (VI rus uz). A **virus** is composed of a molecule of nucleic acid surrounded by a coating of protein. Viruses invade and reproduce inside other cells. In some cases, the nucleic acid of a virus destroys the nucleic acid of a cell it invades. In other cases, the nucleic acid of a virus combines with the nucleic acid of a cell. The nucleic acid of the virus may be replicated with the nucleic acid of the cell for many generations. For example, viruses inject DNA into bacteria cells. Thus, more viruses may be produced within the cell. Eventually the cell breaks and the viruses are released to infect other cells. Some viruses are less active at first. The DNA they inject into bacteria cells is reproduced each time the bacteria reproduces. Environmental conditions at a later date may cause viruses to start forming in the cells.

What is a virus?

See Teacher's Guide.

Skill Inquiry

Usually when you view an organism, the internal structures are not visible. Scientists have observed the internal structure of many organisms by dissection. Often, drawings in textbooks show dissected views of organisms so that students can learn about the internal structures.

A cross-section is a view of a flat surface cut vertically or horizontally through an object.

1. Draw a vertical cross-section of an apple.
2. Draw a horizontal cross-section of a stalk of celery.
3. Draw a vertical and a horizontal cross-section of an orange.

Cross-sections are two-dimensional. A dimension is a measure in one direction. Consider the diagram. In a, only two dimensions, height and width, are apparent. In b,

a third dimension, depth, is apparent. The square a is a cross-section of the box b. When viewing cross-sections, also try to picture a three-dimensional view of the objects.

4. What three-dimensional objects are represented by the cross-sections shown in c, d, and e?

22:9 Variety of Life

Classification is a useful tool of scientists who study the variety of organisms on earth. How the species of today developed is a question scientists have tried to answer.

Fossils indicate that species of organisms have changed over time. The change of a species over time is called evolution. The **theory of evolution by natural selection** is an explanation of how species have changed with time. It is based on the following observations.

What is evolution?

1. Organisms produce many offspring. Offspring compete for food, places to live, and mates.
2. Organisms pass on their traits to their offspring, but there are slight differences in the many offspring of a species.
3. The offspring with differences that help them to get food, places to live, and mates are the ones most likely to survive and reproduce.

Fossil evidence shows that horses were once much smaller and had more toes than the horses of today. Compare the horse foot fossils in Figure 22–10 with the foot of the living horse. Gradually, over a period of 50 million

FIGURE 22–10. *Eohippus* (a), horses that lived about 60 million years ago, had four toes on their forefeet and three toes on their hindfeet. *Mesohippus* (b), horses that lived about 35 million years ago, had three toes on each foot. *Merychippus* (c), horses that lived about 30 million years ago, had three toes on each foot, but two were not used. *Equus* (d), modern horses, have one toe on each foot and pairs of splinterlike bones that are traces of two other toes on each forefoot.

a

b

years, larger horses with fewer toes have been naturally selected. That means they have survived while smaller horses with more toes have not. Perhaps the larger horses could run faster than the smaller horses to escape predators, so the larger horses were more likely to survive and reproduce, passing on their traits.

Many biologists conclude that differences and similarities in living things are the result of evolution by natural selection. Organisms that are closely related, like several species in the same genus, probably evolved from common ancestors. There were some differences in the offspring within the genus. Environmental conditions made some differences more helpful than others. The offspring best suited to their surroundings survived.

See Teacher's Guide.

REVIEW AND REFLECT

1. How do most scientists account for the variety of life on earth?
2. Why are viruses difficult to classify?
3. Ancestors of giraffes had shorter necks. How does the theory of evolution by natural selection explain the present longer necks?

How does the evolution of the horse support the theory of evolution by natural selection?

BACKGROUND   This general theory of evolution by natural selection is attributed jointly to Charles Darwin and Alfred Wallace (1858). The fossil record indicates that changes in life did not occur at a consistent rate, so recently Stephen Jay Gould and other scientists have put forth a modification called the punctuated equilibrium hypothesis. At certain times, they say, when conditions made competition keener, evolution would proceed at a rapid rate.

c

d

BACKGROUND Extinct means that a species no longer exists. Endangered means that a small enough number of a species exists that its continuing existence is questionable.

What are some human activities that endanger species directly and indirectly?

FIGURE 22–11. Saguaro cacti grow only in the deserts of southern Arizona, southeastern California, and northwestern Mexico. They may grow as tall as 15 meters and produce flowers and fruit. Many desert animals depend on the cacti for food and shelter.

22:10 Choices: Endangered Species

Throughout earth's history, species have become extinct by natural causes. However, in recent times, human activities that interfere with natural processes are causing species to become endangered. An endangered species may become extinct because only a few members of the species are alive.

Illegal hunting is one human activity that can directly endanger a species. Wild animal furs, alligator shoes and purses, and elephant ivory items are some of the products people buy that may have come from illegally hunted animals.

Cactus rustling in the southwestern United States' deserts has endangered certain species of cacti. Cacti are popular among people who like desert landscaping or who collect rare plants. Cacti grown and sold legally are expensive to buy. Rustlers illegally dig up cacti in deserts and sell them at lower prices. However, since cacti require special growth conditions, few survive for more than a short time.

Activities such as these have harmful indirect effects too. For example, cacti are necessary for the survival of many bird and animal species in the Southwest. About half of the bird species in the deserts depend on saguaro cacti for their food and nesting. As rustlers deplete the number of saguaro cacti, they not only endanger the species but also the birds and animals that depend upon the cacti.

Lumbering in eastern Texas has nearly destroyed a shrub called *Sterwartia malachodendron*. Sewage is killing wild rice along river banks in California. Housing projects and roadbuilding are destroying the natural homes of many species. Pesticides, fertilizers, and industrial wastes affect many species of animals and plants.

Laws have been passed in some places to protect endangered species from extinction. In 1973, the Endangered Species Act became a law in the United States. However, the laws are difficult to enforce. "Cactus cops" in the Southwest have difficulty catching cactus rustlers. Illegal hunting and trade is not easy to prevent.

Sometimes economic situations result in exceptions to the laws. In the 1970s, a large dam was planned in Tennessee. An endangered fish species, the snail darter, was likely to become extinct if the Tellico Dam was built. Building the dam would have violated the Endangered Species Act, so construction was stopped. Some people thought saving the snail darter was not important. They said the fish had no economic value. Tennessee citizens who wanted the benefits of the dam convinced lawmakers to make it exempt from the Endangered Species Act. In 1978 the Act was amended with a provision that allows a project to be completed if the economic benefits outweigh the benefits of preserving the species. Eventually the Tellico Dam was built. However, some snail darters were relocated to another stream and are reproducing there.

Often the true value of a species is not always recognized. For example, in the 1950s, many country sparrows in China were killed because they were eating rice. After the birds were gone, more rice was lost than before. The rice was being eaten by insects that would have been eaten by country sparrows. Many plants are sources of medicine. If the cinchona plant had been wiped out, quinine which is used in the treatment of malaria, would not have been discovered.

FIGURE 22–12. The Tellico Dam on the Little Tennessee River was completed in 1980 and is operated by the Tennessee Valley Authority for flood control, hydroelectric power, and recreational uses.

Why is it not always easy to weigh environmental risks and benefits before taking action?

See Teacher's Guide.

REVIEW AND REFLECT

1. How is an endangered species different from an extinct species?
2. How does cactus rustling affect animal species in deserts?
3. What are some of the problems and benefits of
   a. building a dam?
   b. preserving an endangered species?
4. Suppose you are faced with the problem of whether to build a highway connecting a major airport in a city suburb with the city center. The highway is planned in an area where a rare plant species grows. The plant is not known to grow anywhere else. What would your solution be? Explain.

SUGGESTION   Learn which species are considered endangered in your region. Discuss the possible reasons for their endangered status and the benefits and costs of trying to maintain or increase their numbers.

CHAPTER 22 REVIEW

SUMMARY

1. Organisms are classified simply according to the structure of their cells. 22:1
2. Many biologists use a classification system of five kingdoms: animals, plants, fungi, protists, and monerans. 22:2
3. Kingdoms are subdivided into more and more specific divisions. 22:2
4. Animals are classified as vertebrates or invertebrates. Vertebrates are classified in one phylum. Invertebrates are classified in several phyla. 22:3
5. Plants are classified as vascular or nonvascular. Vascular plants are classified according to their reproductive processes. 22:4
6. Fungi cannot make their own food. They are classified primarily according to their reproductive structures. 22:5
7. Protists are classified according to their structure and means of movement. 22:6
8. All monerans are prokaryotes. 22:7
9. Many organisms cause diseases in people. 22:7
10. Viruses have some characteristics of living and nonliving objects. 22:8
11. Most scientists accept the theory of evolution by natural selection as an explanation of how species have changed with time. 22:9

VOCABULARY

eukaryote 1	nonvascular 5	theory of evolution by
fungus 14	phylum 7	natural selection 15
genus 9	prokaryote 6	vascular 16
invertebrate 8	protist 11	vertebrate 12
kingdom 2	scientific name 13	virus 3
moneran 10	species 4	

Match each definition with the correct word from the list.

1. A cell with a nucleus and distinct structures
2. One of five main groups into which scientists classify organisms
3. An object that is difficult to classify biologically
4. A group of organisms that can breed and produce fertile offspring
5. A plant without "true" roots, stems, and leaves
6. An organism that has cells with no nuclear membrane or distinct structures
7. One of the main subdivisions of a kingdom
8. An animal without a backbone
9. The first part of a scientific name
10. The only kingdom containing prokaryotes
11. A kingdom of simple organisms with eukaryotic cells
12. An animal with a backbone
13. The genus and species of an organism
14. A plantlike eukaryote that does not contain chlorophyll
15. An explanation of how species have changed with time
16. A plant with "true" roots, stems, and leaves

QUESTIONS

See Teacher's Guide.
MAIN IDEAS

Complete each sentence with the correct word or phrase.

1. Viruses are difficult to classify because _____.
2. Prokaryotes do not have _____.
3. Three fourths of all animals are classified as _____.
4. The five kingdoms are _____.
5. _____ are organisms that get food from other living organisms.
6. Most colds and flu are caused by _____.
7. All vertebrates have _____.
8. Three observations on which the theory of evolution by natural selection is based are _____.
9. A combination of a fungus and alga is a(n) _____.
10. Unlike plants, the cells of fungi contain no _____.
11. Some algae are classified as plants or monerans, and some are classified as _____.
12. The seven main classifications scientists use for all organisms are _____.

See Teacher's Guide.
APPLICATIONS

Answer each question in one or more paragraphs.

1. Although all animal phyla are found in oceans, a lot more variation is found in animal life on land. Why do you think this is so?
2. How might each of the following characteristics aid in survival?
   a. many cells instead of one cell
   b. vascular tissues in plants
   c. an internal skeleton
   d. lungs instead of gills
   e. eggs with tough coverings
3. Why are sponges, of which many are attached to the bottom of an ocean or lake, not classified as plants?
4. Suppose an unclassified form of life is discovered. How do you think biologists would proceed to classify it? Describe what they would do first, and so on.
5. Think of the rates at which different kinds of plants grow. Why do you think that flowering plants are the most numerous plants on earth?

FURTHER STUDY

INVESTIGATIONS

1. Visit a zoo. Make lists of animal species that have physical characteristics in common.
2. Visit a greenhouse, conservatory, or horticultural garden. Look for the scientific names of different plants and sketch or photograph the plants.
3. Find out if there is any relationship between car and industry air pollution and the locations of lichens in your area.
4. Prepare a report about Charles Darwin and Alfred Wallace.

READINGS

0 Graf, Joan Stephenson. "All in the Family." *Science Digest.* November, 1983. pp.60–63, 117.

+ Margulis, L., and K. V. Schwartz. *Five Kingdoms.* W. H. Freeman and Co.: San Francisco, 1982.

0 Patent, Dorothy Hinshaw. *Sizes and Shapes in Nature–What They Mean.* Holiday House: New York, 1979.

– Rose, Kenneth Jon. *Classification of the Animal Kingdom.* McKay: New York, 1980.

IMAGINE you are involved in this scene. Where would you like to be—among the dancers or the crowd? Many people enjoy dancing as a form of exercise. Exercise is important to good health. What forms of exercise do you enjoy? What else is important to good health? How can understanding the human body help you maintain good health?

THE HUMAN BODY

INTRODUCING THE CHAPTER   Compare the smooth operation of a complex physical machine with the body. Discuss similarities between the machine and the body: both have systems, the systems function together, both require proper maintenance, including preventive maintenance. Discuss differences between the machine and the body: different sources of energy, different methods of communication between parts, and different types of malfunction.

23:1   Body Homeostasis

To be healthy, your body needs to maintain a set of balanced conditions. Just as individual cells must keep homeostasis, the body as a whole must keep homeostasis, too. Food has to be taken in and broken down to supply needed materials and energy to cells. Oxygen must get to individual cells for cell respiration. Wastes must be eliminated. Internal activities must be regulated. External movements must be controlled. The systems of the human body work together like a team to maintain the body's homeostasis.

Feedback from each body system is needed to keep homeostasis. Each system is influenced by the others. For example, when you swim the muscle movement of your body increases. This information is received by sensors, sent to your brain, and processed. Your body needs more oxygen to deal with the increase. Your brain sends instructions to adjustors. They increase your respiration and heart rate to supply more oxygen. The amount of adjustment is fed back to the sensors. This new information is input and processed. New instructions for adjustments are made. The sensors receive new feedback and the loop continues. (See Figure 21–6, page 454.)

GOAL   You will learn the major systems of the human body and relate their functions to good health.

How does the body as a whole maintain homeostasis?

BACKGROUND   The use of "input" and "output" applied to body organs and systems further emphasizes the similarity of the body to a complex machine with many subsystems. Such terminology applied to biological functioning has become common with the widespread use of computers.

23:2 Food and Energy

In order for your body to maintain homeostasis, you need to eat a balanced diet. See Figure 23–1. A balanced diet contains proper amounts of carbohydrates, fats, proteins, vitamins, minerals, and water. The human body needs each of these materials for certain purposes. For example, carbohydrates and fats supply energy to the body. Proteins supply amino acids. You have already learned about the importance of vitamins. Minerals and water are also important in chemical reactions. Nutrition labels on foods include information about the carbohydrate, fat, protein, vitamin, mineral, and water content of foods. This information is useful in planning a balanced diet.

Nutrition labels also include Calorie information. Recall from chapter 11 that kilocalories, or Calories, are units commonly used to measure the energy foods supply. In chapter 21 you learned how cells get energy from food by respiration. The energy supplied by the foods you eat should balance the energy you need for your daily activities. Table 23–1 shows the Calorie requirements of people doing various activities.

Why is eating a balanced diet important?

BACKGROUND   Eight amino acids cannot be made within the human body and must be obtained from food. These essential amino acids are made in plants, and they are not found together in most individual plants. Soybeans, which contain all eight, are an exception. Therefore in a meat-free diet, it is important to choose vegetables and grains that complement each other.

FIGURE 23–1.   A balanced diet for teenagers includes the recommended number of servings shown from each of the four main food groups. Foods in the other group may complement but do not replace foods in the main groups.

Milk group
4 servings

Meat group
2 servings

Fruit-vegetable group
4 servings

Grain group
4 servings

Other

TABLE 23–1. AVERAGE ENERGY USED FOR SOME ACTIVITIES	
Activity	Calories Used
Sleeping 8 hours	664
Talking on the phone one hour	130
Eating lunch	33
Making your bed	55
Watching a half-hour TV show	43
Normal school activity for one day	714
Washing a sinkful of dishes	40
Walking for 15 minutes to school	63
Bicycling for 20 minutes	80
Dancing for an hour at a party	350
Getting ready for school	110

BACKGROUND Calorie use varies with body build and chemistry. At age 15, an average use is about 2900 C/day for boys and 2300 C/day for girls. The values for Calories used in this table are approximations. Many factors affect individual Calorie requirements and usage.

If the food a person eats supplies more Calories than are needed, the person gains weight. If a person does not eat enough food to balance the energy needed for daily activities, the person loses weight. When people diet to lose weight, they may eat less and exercise more. However, any weight loss plan should be supervised by a doctor. Fad diets sometimes produce weight loss too quickly and may cause illness. Drugs designed to assist weight loss also may cause problems. A doctor should be consulted about their use.

How does a person gain or lose weight?

23:3 The Digestive System

Like other animals, *Homo sapiens* cannot manufacture food. Therefore, energy must come from eating food. Food has to be digested so that it can be taken into body cells by diffusion and active transport. Digestion is the preparation of food in the body for movement into cells.

Hydrolysis (hi DRAHL uh sus), a chemical reaction in which water is combined with substances, is important in digestion. Water reacts with food, and smaller molecules are formed. Enzymes help speed up many of the hydrolysis reactions.

Figure 23–2 shows the human digestive system. Note the organs through which food passes. Even though food

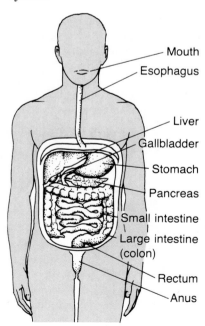

FIGURE 23–2. Human digestive system

Mouth
Esophagus
Liver
Gallbladder
Stomach
Pancreas
Small intestine
Large intestine (colon)
Rectum
Anus

FIGURE 23–3. A cross-section through a small intestine shows that villi are folds of the inner layer of the intestine wall. The surfaces of the villi also are folded, further increasing the surface area of the wall.

What is peristalsis?

DEMONSTRATION Peristalsis is a wave action in which the contractions are like compressions in a longitudinal wave. The movement along a slinky that has been pulled at one end is analogous to peristalsis. A review demonstration of longitudinal waves (chapter 13) may therefore be helpful.

Describe the path food follows in the digestive system.

does not pass through the liver and pancreas, they are still important organs in digestion.

The process of digestion starts in the mouth with the aid of water and an enzyme in saliva. Chewing increases the surface area of food exposed to the enzyme and water. Think of the difference in melting time of an ice cube and crushed ice. Which do you prefer in cold drinks? Ice cubes melt more slowly at room temperature than crushed ice since less surface area is exposed to the warmer beverage.

A reflex muscle motion called peristalsis (per uh STAHL sus) causes food to move from the esophagus to the stomach and on through the digestive system. Peristalsis is a series of wavelike muscle contractions and relaxations.

In the stomach, gastric juices are released. Gastric juices contain hydrochloric acid, water, and enzymes. The pH of gastric juices is between 1 and 2. Digestion continues as the acid mixture in the stomach churns food and digests protein.

Peristalsis in the stomach forces food into the small intestine. More enzymes are secreted in the small intestine. Bile made in the liver and pancreatic juice made in the pancreas enter the small intestine through separate ducts. Digestion continues as this mixture breaks down the food into droplets. The droplets enter the blood by diffusion through the walls of the small intestine. Fingerlike projections called villi line the inside of the small intestine. Notice in Figure 23–3 how the villi provide a large surface area for absorption.

Undigested food and water left in the small intestine are moved by peristalsis into the large intestine. More water and other materials diffuse into the blood from the large intestine. The remaining materials in the large intestine are a solid waste called feces (FEE seez). Feces is made up of water, worn-out cells, undigested cellulose, salts such as calcium phosphate, and many bacteria. The feces is stored in the rectum and leaves the body through the anus.

See Teacher's Guide.

REVIEW AND REFLECT

1. What is needed for a balanced diet?
2. What takes place in each organ of the digestive system?
3. Males and females differ somewhat in their Calorie requirements. Why do you think there is this difference?

23:4   The Cardiovascular System

Blood supplies digested food to body cells. Blood also carries away wastes from cells and supplies oxygen for cell respiration. The blood flows in a complicated network of blood vessels. The heart is a muscle that forces blood through the blood vessels. The blood, the blood vessels, and the heart are known as the **cardiovascular** system. *Cardio* means heart and vascular refers to the tubes that carry blood, the blood vessels.

Each minute the heart contracts about 72 times, pumping blood throughout the body. Note the four chambers of the heart shown in Figure 23–4. Trace the flow of blood through the heart beginning at the right atrium.

Valves between the heart chambers control the one-way flow of blood. Like automatic doors in a supermarket, the valves open in only one direction. Each heart chamber has an "in" valve and an "out" valve. Your heartbeat is the sound of the valves closing.

When you inhale, you take in air which contains oxygen. Oxygen diffuses from the lungs into blood in tiny blood vessels. Blood with oxygen moves throughout the body in blood vessels called arteries. Arteries become subdivided into tiny blood vessels called capillaries. Oxygen diffuses from blood in the capillaries into cells. Carbon dioxide, a cell waste, diffuses from the cells into blood in

What makes up the cardiovascular system?

Describe the path of blood through the heart chambers.

BACKGROUND   A heartbeat begins in the wall of the right atrium at a position frequently called the "pacemaker." In some patients with heart disease, artificial pacemakers are implanted in the chest just beneath the skin, to give electrical impulses like those induced by the natural pacemaker.

DEMONSTRATION   Use a three-dimensional model of the heart to trace the flow of blood through the heart.

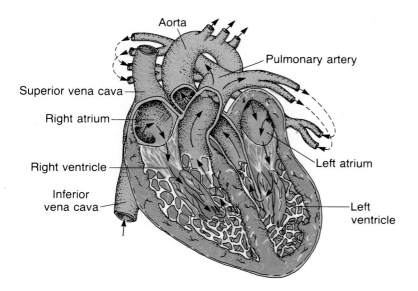

Aorta

Pulmonary artery

Superior vena cava

Right atrium

Right ventricle

Inferior vena cava

Left atrium

Left ventricle

FIGURE 23–4.   Blood enters the heart in the right atrium. Contractions force the blood into the right ventricle. From there, it flows through the pulmonary arteries, into lung capillaries, and back to the heart in the pulmonary veins. The veins empty into the left atrium. Then blood is forced into the left ventricle. From the left ventricle, it is pumped through the aorta and throughout the body. It returns to the heart in the superior and inferior vena cavae, which empty into the right atrium.

BACKGROUND CO_2 does not dissolve well in blood plasma. CO_2 is transported in blood as HCO_3.

What composes blood?

What is hemoglobin?

FIGURE 23–5. Heart disease is a major killer. Arteries may become blocked with fatty tissue. Then the heart muscle does not get enough oxygen so it is less efficient at pumping blood. Stress, alcohol, smoking, and diets high in animals fats contribute to heart disease. A program of aerobic exercise and a healthy diet may help prevent it.

capillaries. Blood with carbon dioxide moves back to the heart in blood vessels called veins. The blood enters the heart at the right atrium. When the blood flows through the blood vessels to the lungs, the carbon dioxide is exchanged for oxygen through the walls of capillaries. The carbon dioxide in the lungs is eliminated when you exhale. Then the cycle repeats.

The pumping of blood creates pressure within the heart and blood vessels. If blood pressure is too high, there is a risk of damage to the heart and other organs. If blood pressure is too low, a person may faint. Prescribed medication can help both high and low blood pressure.

A person with a mass of 70 kilograms has about five liters of blood. About 55 percent of a person's blood is plasma. **Plasma** is an almost colorless blood fluid that is mostly water. It also contains small amounts of salts, ions, proteins, carbohydrates, vitamins, and amino acids. The remaining 45 percent of blood consists of three types of cells that are suspended in plasma: red blood cells, white blood cells, and platelets.

A cubic millimeter of blood contains about five million red blood cells. Red blood cells contain hemoglobin, a compound of iron and protein. The hemoglobin in red blood cells gives blood its color. The hemoglobin transports oxygen from the lungs to body cells.

For about every 650 red blood cells, there is one white blood cell in normal blood. White blood cells are important for protection against disease. When a part of the body is infected by microorganisms, white blood cells collect there. Lysosomes in white blood cells help to break down and destroy the microorganisms. The pus that forms around skin infections is what remains of the destroyed microorganisms, damaged cells, and white blood cells.

Blood **platelets** (PLAYT lutz) are cell-like parts shaped like discs that control blood loss from broken blood vessels. When a blood vessel is injured, such as when you cut your finger or scrape your knee, platelets help the clotting of blood. For about every 20 red blood cells, there is one platelet.

Normal weight is important for proper heart function. For every extra 10 newtons of body weight, the heart must pump blood through an additional 1.7 kilometers of blood vessels. Thus, extra weight puts a greater burden on the cardiovascular system.

Exercise is important for maintaining a healthy body. Regular exercise strengthens the heart. Sports, aerobic dancing, and walking normally are helpful, but some people with heart problems cannot withstand such exercise. A doctor should be consulted before any active program is started. Relaxation, like exercise, also must be included in a daily routine for proper health.

How is exercise important to good health?

See Teacher's Guide.

Skill Inquiry

A help wanted ad says a company that makes drugs by *biosynthesis* needs people to work in *microbiology* labs. Would you know what the company does and what kind of work the job would involve? Recall the meanings of the words *biology, photosynthesis,* and *microscope.* Knowing these words should help you make a fairly accurate guess.

Many scientific and technical words are put together from similar roots. Knowing the meanings of some of these words often can help you understand unfamiliar terms. Look at the list of words and their descriptions. Try to determine the meanings of the roots that make up each word. Most are words you have already learned.

adrenal gland—a gland located just above the kidney
arthritis—an inflammation of the joints
cardiac—of the heart
cytoplasm—the liquid inside a cell
echinoderm—an animal with spiny skin
gastric juice—digestive juice found in the stomach
hemophilia—a blood disease

hypotension—low (blood) pressure
osteology—the study of bone structure
leukemia—a disease characterized by too many white blood cells
porifera—having many pores or tiny holes; sponges
static—not moving; stopped
thermometer—an instrument that measures temperature
vascular—having small tubes

Use your knowledge of the words in the list above to rewrite each of the following sentences. Replace the italicized technical word with a phrase made up of more common words.

1. Using this drug to treat *dermatitis* may cause the skin to become *photosensitive.*
2. Careful attention to diet can help reduce *osteoporosis* and *cardiovascular* disease in elderly people.
3. Besides having *gastritis,* the patient shows signs of *renal* damage.
4. Several motorists stranded by the blizzard were taken to hospitals to be treated for *hypothermia.*
5. During the operation, the surgeon used *hemostats* and asked the lab to do a *leukocyte* count the next day.

Activity: How does blood pressure vary?

See Teacher's Guide.

MATERIALS

stethoscope
sphygmomanometer kit
clock or watch

PROCEDURE

1. Time your partner sitting quietly for five minutes.
2. Wrap the cuff of a sphygmomanometer around your partner's upper arm so it surrounds the brachial artery. See Figure 23–6. The cuff should be secure but not tight.
3. Place the bell of the stethoscope over the brachial artery firmly so the entire bell contacts the skin.
4. Under your teacher's supervision, pump up the cuff. Then slowly release the pressure. **CAUTION:** *Always begin releasing the pressure immediately after pumping up the cuff.*
5. Listen with the stethoscope for a sharp sound. Note the measurement on the meter when you hear the sound. This value is the systolic pressure, SP. Systolic pressure is the maximum pressure reached when the ventricles contract.

6. As the pressure continues to drop, you will hear a series of increasingly louder sounds. When the sounds abruptly become muffled, note the measurement on the meter. This value is the diastolic pressure, the minimum pressure reached when the ventricles relax.
7. Record your partner's SP, DP, and blood pressure (SP/DP) in a data table.
8. Time your partner lying still for five minutes. Then repeat steps 2 to 7.
9. Time your partner running in place for five minutes. Immediately repeat steps 2 to 7 while your partner is sitting.

DATA AND OBSERVATIONS

Position	SP	DP	Blood Pressure
Sitting			
Lying still			
Sitting after exercise			

QUESTIONS AND CONCLUSIONS

1. Why must the cuff and bell of a sphygmomanometer be placed over an artery when taking blood pressure?
2. How does the pressure of blood in the arteries relate to the contractions and relaxations of the ventricles?
3. In what units is blood pressure read?
4. How are systolic and diastolic values indicated when writing blood pressure?
5. Do position (sitting or lying still) or exercise affect blood pressure? Explain.
6. Compare the blood pressures of your classmates. What other factors may affect blood pressure?

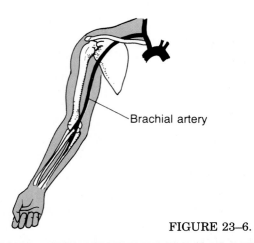

Brachial artery

FIGURE 23–6.

23:5 Immune Response

Skin, mucus, tears, stomach acid, and white blood cells are some of the body's first lines of defense against pathogens (PATH uh junz). **Pathogens** are organisms that cause infections. For example, your tears contain an enzyme that helps prevent eye infections.

The body's second line of defense against disease is the immune system. The immune system consists of a type of white blood cell called lymphocytes (LIMH fuh sites) that help defend the body against disease. Lymphocytes are produced in lymph (LIMF) nodes and other tissues.

Lymph nodes are part of the lymphatic system. They also filter lymph, removing bacteria and other unwanted particles. Lymph forms from blood plasma. Some plasma diffuses out of blood capillaries into tissues. This tissue fluid generally lacks the large protein molecules of plasma, though. As shown in Figure 23–7, when tissue fluid diffuses into lymph capillaries, it is called **lymph.** The lymph capillaries merge into larger lymph vessels. As lymph flows through these vessels, it is filtered in lymph nodes. The lymph vessels have valves that allow only one-way flow of lymph back to the bloodstream.

Sometimes a pathogen gets past the body's first lines of defense. Then a person gets an infection. The body's immune response system takes over. Some lymphocytes begin producing antibodies (ANT ih bohd ees). An **antibody** is a protein that destroys pathogens and the poisons they produce, called toxins. A different antibody is produced for each type of pathogen. If you had chicken pox as a child, your body was infected by a virus. Your body produced antibodies to destroy the virus and you got well. Once an antibody is produced to destroy a certain type of pathogen, the antibodies stay in the body. The next time a person is infected with the same type of pathogen, the antibodies may prevent symptoms of the disease or weaken the effects. For this reason, once you have chicken pox, you are not likely to get the disease again.

Vaccinations are made up of weakened or dead pathogens that can be taken into the body usually without causing disease. Vaccinations cause the body to produce antibodies that keep a person from getting a disease. This process is called **immunization.** You probably have been

What are the body's first and second lines of defense?

SUGGESTION   Compare and contrast the body's lines of defense against disease with defense plays in football or another sport.

What is lymph?

FIGURE 23–7.   Some plasma diffuses out of blood capillaries into tissues. Some of this tissue fluid diffuses into lymph capillaries.

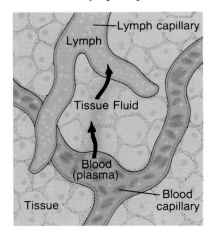

BACKGROUND If a person has
become infected, immunization
does not work. A substance called
an antitoxin, antibodies taken
from an immune person, are used
instead.

immunized against polio, diphtheria, tetanus, whooping
cough, measles, small pox, rubella, and mumps. Children
usually are required to be immunized before they begin
attending school.

23:6 The Respiratory System

The system that takes in oxygen and eliminates carbon
dioxide from the body is the respiratory system. Note the
parts of the respiratory system in Figure 23–8.

When you inhale, your lungs inflate like a blown-up balloon filled with air. When you exhale, your lungs deflate
like a balloon that has lost air. When you hold your
breath, the air pressure in your lungs is greater than the
air pressure outside your body. When you let your breath
go, the presssure in your lungs becomes the same as the
air pressure outside your body.

As you learned in section 23:4, the lungs and cardiovascular system work together. The lungs are lined with tiny
folds called **alveoli** (al VEE uh li). They look like a mass of
white foam. The surface area of the alveoli is large—more
than the floor area of two classrooms. As blood circulates
through the capillaries in the alveoli, carbon dioxide
wastes are released and oxygen is picked up. The large
surface area of the alveoli makes rapid exchange of these
gases possible. As blood flows away from the lungs, it
takes oxygen to cells throughout the body.

One way to help maintain a healthy respiratory system
is not to smoke cigarettes. Cigarette smoke contains harmful compounds that damage the body. Studies have shown
that smokers are more likely to develop lung cancer or
have heart attacks than nonsmokers.

See Teacher's Guide.

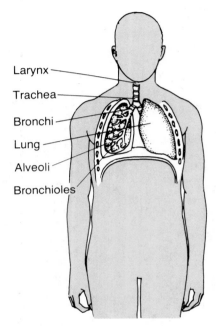

Larynx
Trachea
Bronchi
Lung
Alveoli
Bronchioles

FIGURE 23–8. Human respiratory system

**How does smoking cigarettes
affect the body?**

REVIEW AND REFLECT

1. Why are healthy heart valves important to the function
   of the heart?
2. What is the purpose of immunizations? What are three
   recommended immunizations?
3. How do the respiratory and cardiovascular systems
   work together?

Activity: How much gas passes in and out of your lungs?

See Teacher's Guide.

MATERIALS

2000-mL bottle	straw
water	crayon
trough or sink	graduated cylinder
35-cm rubber tubing	apron

PROCEDURE

1. Fill the bottle to the top with water. Put your hand over the opening, then overturn the bottle in a trough or sink filled with water. Try to get as small an air bubble in the bottle as possible.

2. Attach a straw to the rubber tubing. Insert the rubber tubing into the inverted bottle of water. Keep the straw above the water.

3. Breathe in and out normally. Notice the feeling of a normal pattern.

4. When you are aware of your normal intake and outflow, take a normal breath and hold it. Breathe out through your mouth into the straw. Make sure that your breath goes into the bottle.

5. After your breath has displaced some of the water in the bottle, use a crayon to mark the water level.

6. Pour the water out of the bottle. Set the bottle upright on a table.

7. Fill a graduated cylinder with water. Pour water from the graduated cylinder into the bottle until the water comes up to the crayon mark. Keep track of the total amount of water needed to fill the bottle up to the crayon mark. Record this volume as your tidal volume. Tidal volume is the volume of gas passed in and out of the lungs with each breath.

8. Repeat steps 1 to 7 twice for a total of three values of tidal volume.

9. Find your average tidal volume.

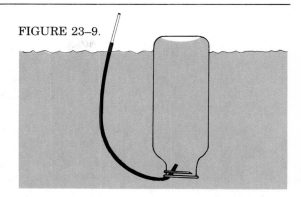

FIGURE 23–9.

10. Jog around the perimeter of your classroom 10 times. **CAUTION:** *Do not run.* Repeat steps 1 to 9.

DATA AND OBSERVATIONS

Trial	Tidal Volume	
	At rest	After exercise
1		
2		
3		
Average		

QUESTIONS AND CONCLUSIONS

1. Why do you think that tidal volume may vary slightly from trial to trial?

2. How did your tidal volume after sitting compare with your tidal volume after mild exercise? Why?

3. How might your tidal volume after vigorous exercise compare with your tidal volume after mild exercise?

4. How do the average tidal volumes of students in your class compare?

5. What are some factors that could also account for differences in average tidal volumes?

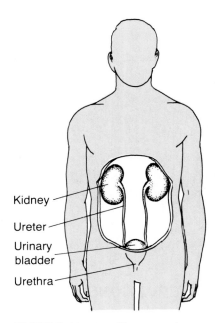

Kidney

Ureter

Urinary
bladder

Urethra

FIGURE 23–10. Human urinary
system

**What are the functions of
kidneys?**

BACKGROUND   Urea is the
name of an important constituent
of urine. Urea is the product
formed when amino acids break
down, first forming ammonia, and
then combining with carbon
dioxide. Urea is produced in the
liver. The kidneys collect urea
and get rid of it.

23:7   The Urinary System

The urinary system does several important tasks in the
body. It rids the body of wastes produced by chemical reactions in cells. It also helps control blood pressure, the
concentration of certain fluids and ions in blood, and the
pH of blood. Figure 23–10 shows the organs of the urinary
system.

The main organs of the urinary system are the kidneys.
Wastes are filtered from blood in the kidneys. Blood is
transported to the kidneys by the renal arteries. Each
renal artery divides into smaller arteries. Each smaller artery divides into many capillaries that come in contact
with a nephron (NEF rahn). **Nephrons** are tiny tubes in
the kidneys. The division of the renal arteries into smaller
arteries and then into many capillaries causes an increase
in blood pressure in the capillaries. The pressure causes
blood plasma to be filtered through the capillary walls into
the nephrons. The filtrate in the nephrons contains water,
wastes, and useful materials such as glucose, amino acids,
and important ions. As the filtrate moves through the
nephrons, water and useful materials are reabsorbed into
the blood by diffusion and active transport. The wastes
that remain in the nephrons are excreted as urine.

Another function of the kidneys is to maintain the constant pressure of body fluids. Osmosis is an important part
of this process that controls water volume. It also keeps a
balance between the many salt ions in blood. A small in-

FIGURE 23–11. A cross-section
of a kidney shows the relationship
between blood vessels and nephrons.

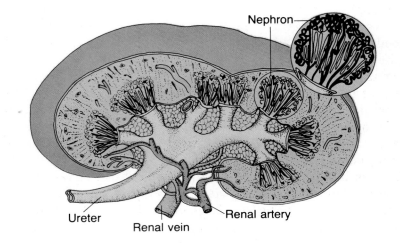

Nephron

Ureter

Renal vein

Renal artery

crease or decrease in the amount of certain ions may be fatal. For instance, too much potassium ion (K^+) can cause the heart to stop.

The kidneys also work to keep the blood slightly alkaline, with a pH between 7.3 and 7.4. Outside of this narrow range, death can result quickly. Alkaline blood helps to neutralize the hydrogen ions that are constantly produced in body reactions. As the kidneys make blood alkaline, urine is made acidic. This process is important to body homeostasis.

How do the kidneys help maintain body homeostasis?

SUGGESTION   Discuss kidney function in terms of homeostasis.

<u>23:8</u>   The Nervous System

The nervous system is the body's main control system. It controls all voluntary movements, decision-making, memory, and movements within body systems. Even when you are sleeping, your cardiovascular and respiratory systems stay active due to control by your nervous system. Figure 23–12 shows the parts of the nervous system.

Nerve cells are specialized cells that react to changes in the environment. They carry nerve impulses, which are like messages, throughout the body. The nerve impulses provide the feedback required for body homeostasis. The route followed by a nerve impulse through the nervous system is called a nerve pathway. All nerve pathways involve the central nervous system that consists of the brain and spinal cord.

Nerve cells, called **neurons,** (NOO rahnz) consist of a cell body and nerve fibers. The nerve fibers are extensions of the cytoplasm of the cell body. The fibers vary in length; some are as long as a meter. Nerves are bundles of the nerve fibers of many neurons. Nerve impulses are electrochemical changes that travel along nerves to the central nervous system from all parts of the body. Some nerves carry impulses to the central nervous system; others carry impulses away from the central nervous system. Think of nerves like two-way streets in a town that all lead to the town square. Nerve impulses are like the traffic on the streets. Some of the traffic is going to the town square; some is coming from the town square.

What does the nervous system do?

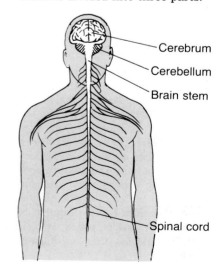

FIGURE 23–12.   The spinal cord and brain make up the central nervous system. The nerves throughout the body make up the peripheral nervous system. The brain is divided into three parts.

Cerebrum
Cerebellum
Brain stem
Spinal cord

How are nerve impulses transmitted from one neuron to another?

BACKGROUND   The chemical part of the transmission of nerve impulses involves potassium and sodium ions. When a neuron is triggered by a strong enough electrical impulse, the membrane around transmitting fibers becomes permeable to sodium ions that are outside. After they flow into the neuron, potassium ions flow out. The result is a change in the internal charge of the neuron from negative to positive and back to negative again, all in about one-thousandth of a second.

What are the functions of each part of the brain?

BACKGROUND   The chemicals released at the ends of transmitting fibers, called neurotransmitters, pass on a signal and then are either destroyed by enzymes or are regathered at the ends of nerve fibers.

Nerve impulses travel from neuron to neuron on their way to and from the central nervous system. The place where one neuron meets another is called a **synapse** (SIHN aps). At a synapse, the nerve fibers of two neurons do not actually touch each other. There is a gap between the nerve fibers. When an impulse comes to a synapse, it is released from the ends of the nerve fiber. The chemical stimulates an impulse in the nerve fiber on the other side of the synapse. You can think of the chemical like a fer- ryboat that carries traffic back and forth across a river.

Synapses are found throughout the nervous system. Most are found in the brain. It contains about one hundred billion (10^{11}) neurons. Each of the brain's cells meets at least 50 others. The nerve impulses that travel from neu- ron to neuron across synapses in the brain control a per- son's thoughts and behavior.

Note the main parts of the brain shown in Figure 21– 12. The cerebrum is involved in interpretation of nerve impulses, control of voluntary muscles, and thinking pro- cesses. Your personality, speech, thought, learning, mem- ory, and senses are controlled by your cerebrum. The cer- ebellum is involved mainly in muscle coordination. Your

FIGURE 23–13.   Reflexes are au- tomatic responses that involve simple nerve pathways, excluding neurons in the cerebrum of the brain. For example, if you burn your fingers, pain receptors in your skin are stimulated. Sensory neurons transmit impulses to your spinal cord where they are con- ducted to motor neurons. Motor neurons transmit the impulse to an effector that responds, in this case a muscle that withdraws your hand.

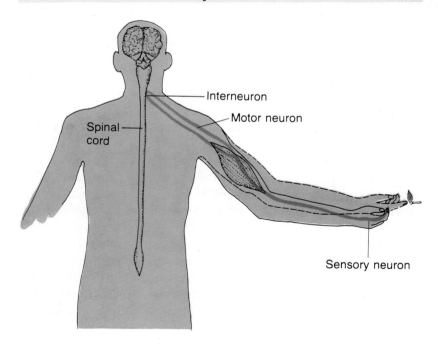

Interneuron

Motor neuron

Spinal cord

Sensory neuron

posture and balance are controlled by your cerebellum. The brain stem is a relay station for nerve impulses. Also, it is involved in maintaining homeostasis and controlling behavior.

After nerve impulses from the body travel through the spinal cord to the brain, they are interpreted. Some impulses are transferred to other nerves. The impulses are carried from the central nervous system to body parts that respond, such as muscles.

Suppose you sit near a burning fire on a cold evening. As the fire warms you, neurons in your skin detect a change in the environment. Impulses are sent along nerves from your skin to your central nervous system. When you begin to feel too warm, the impulses are interpreted as discomfort. Impulses are sent along nerves from your central nervous system to your muscles. So, you move away from the fire.

SUGGESTION   Sketch the nerve pathways for nerve impulses involved in sensing a too-warm fire and moving away from it.

The nervous system is affected by certain chemicals. Alcohol (ethanol, C_2H_5OH) is a drug that slows down the movement of nerve impulses across synapses in the front part of the brain. Since alcohol is absorbed into the blood very quickly, people feel its effect soon after drinking. After the alcohol reaches the brain, judgment is disrupted, muscular coordination is reduced, and vision and speech are affected. Marijuana may have similar or worse effects on the body.

How do alcohol and marijuana affect people?

ACTIVITY   Obtain additional information about the effect of drugs on the nervous system from medical authorities, police, or others. Have the authority make a presentation to the class and answer questions.

Drugs from various plants can upset the nervous system. Caffeine is a drug that stimulates the nervous system. Stimulants make some people feel "jittery." Caffeine is found in small amounts in coffee, tea, and many soft drinks. In large amounts, caffeine is poisonous. Nicotine, a compound in tobacco, also is a stimulant.

Morphine, heroin, methadone, barbiturates, amphetamines, codeine, cocaine, and PCP are very strong drugs. Some are useful as medicines because of their effects on the nervous system. However, unsupervised and nonmedical use of the drugs can be very dangerous. Drugs can be habit-forming or addictive. When addictive drugs are used, a person's body adjusts to the drug's presence and develops a need for the drug. If use of the drug is stopped, the person gets very sick until the body readjusts to the absence of the drug.

What effect do other drugs have on the body?

Career Profile

"It's sort of like a uranium prospector with a geiger counter." That is how Dr. Charlotte Otto describes the way physicians use the radioactive drugs she develops. Charlotte has a Ph.D in chemistry and is a professor at The University of Michigan–Dearborn. She teaches organic chemistry classes. She also does research in the development and study of radioactive pharmaceuticals. These special drugs are "tagged" with radioactive isotopes. Radioactive isotopes may be exchanged with stable isotopes in drug molecules. Or radioactive isotopes may be added to drug molecules.

Patients are injected with the radioactive pharmaceuticals. A doctor observes how the drug is absorbed by various tissues and organs in the body by analyzing the radiation emitted. This procedure often eliminates the need for X rays. X rays are most effective for studying hard tissue, such as bones. Use of radioactive pharmaceuticals provides better "pictures" of soft tissues. Tumors often can be detected in this way.

Charlotte is currently developing a drug to enable physicians to study a person's pituitary gland (section 23:9). The radioactive isotope commonly used is iodine-123 because it has a relatively short half-life. After a drug has been developed, Charlotte must test it on laboratory animals before it can be used on people.

Charlotte always wanted to study science. She began college intending to become an engineer. After about two years, she decided she was better at chemistry. So she became a chemistry major. Today Charlotte enjoys her research. She says, "It is challenging to try to develop something that has never been produced before and may help doctors save lives."

23:9 The Endocrine System

In addition to the nervous system, another body system helps control body functions. The **endocrine** (EN duh krun) system consists of glands that secrete chemicals called hormones. Figure 23–14 shows the glands of the endocrine system.

Some glands secrete fluids into tubes, called ducts, that transport the fluids to other organs. The liver is an example. Endocrine glands do not have ducts. They produce hormones that circulate through the blood.

BACKGROUND The stomach and kidneys also release hormones through ducts. Other glands, such as salivary and sweat glands, release other substances through ducts.

Hormones speed up or slow down different chemical reactions. They do not start chemical reactions in body cells. Some hormones are produced at irregular rates. Others are secreted in cycles, many on a daily basis.

The pituitary gland, at the base of the brain, releases hormones that directly control some body systems and all other glands. The adrenal glands, over the kidneys, release large amounts of the hormone adrenaline during times of stress. The adrenal glands also release hydrocortisone, a chemical that enables the body to recover from injury or illness. The thyroid gland, found in the neck, produces hormones that control the rate of chemical reactions within the body. Considered together, body reactions are called **metabolism** (muh TAB uh lihz um). If the thyroid gland is underactive, metabolism is slowed down and a person may feel very tired. If the thyroid is overactive, metabolism is speeded up. A person may feel jumpy and excited most of the time. Iodine is an important dietary mineral for normal thyroid function. When the thyroid produces the normal amounts of hormones, proper feedback for controlling metabolism helps maintain homeostasis.

See Teacher's Guide.

REVIEW AND REFLECT

1. What occurs in the nephrons? Where are they located?
2. Describe what happens at synapses.
3. Describe the function of the thyroid gland.
4. The liver is not part of the endocrine system.
   a. To what system does the liver belong?
   b. What fluid does it secrete?
   c. To what organ is the fluid transported?
   d. What is the fluid's function?

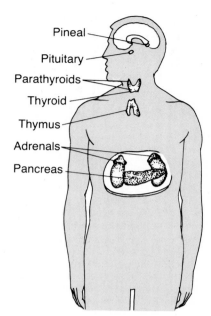

FIGURE 23–14. Human endocrine system. The ovaries in females and testes in males are also endocrine glands.

How do hormones affect chemical reactions in the body?

23:10 The Reproductive Systems

The male and female reproductive systems are both controlled by the endocrine system. Hormones control the development of sexual characteristics as people mature.

The female reproductive system produces egg cells. Females are born with thousands of immature eggs. Between

BACKGROUND The menstrual cycle is controlled by hormones from the pituitary gland, the ovaries, and the uterus.

FIGURE 23–15. The male and female reproductive systems

the ages of about 12 and 50, about one egg per month matures in an ovary and is released into the oviducts. This release of an egg is called **ovulation** (ahv yuh LAY shun).

Before ovulation, the uterus develops a thick lining in preparation for the egg. If the egg is not fertilized within 24 to 48 hours, the lining of the uterus breaks down. It is released through the vagina (vuh JI nuh) after about two weeks. This release of blood and tissues lining the uterus is called **menstruation** (men STRAY shun). After menstruation ends, another egg matures in an ovary. Then ovulation occurs again. This cycle of ovulation and menstruation is called the menstrual cycle. Ovulation occurs about midway between menstrual periods.

What is menstruation?

In the male reproductive system, sperm cells are produced in the testes (TES teez). Sperm may be released from a male's penis. If sperm are deposited in a female's vagina, they travel by a swimming action up the female oviducts. If a live egg is present in the oviducts, the sperm and egg may unite. This process is **fertilization.**

BACKGROUND   Sperm are released within semen, which is a mixture containing sugars that supply energy for the sperm to move, lubricants, and substances that regulate pH.

After fertilization, a fertilized egg continues down an oviduct to the uterus. In about a week, the fertilized egg becomes implanted in the uterus. Then a tissue called a placenta develops in the uterus. For the first eight weeks, the new life is called an embryo. After that, until birth, it is known as a fetus. The placenta is connected to the fetus by a tube called an umbilical cord. In the placenta,

Describe the development of a fertilized egg until birth.

nutrients and oxygen diffuse from the mother's blood into the fetus' blood. Also wastes diffuse out of the fetus' blood into the mother's blood. However, the blood supplies of the mother and fetus do not mix. At birth the umbilical cord is cut, and the baby must breathe on its own. After birth, the placenta is discharged from the uterus.

23:11 Health Management

The attention that you give to proper regular exercise, a balanced diet that maintains normal weight, and avoidance of cigarettes, alcohol, and drugs can build your resistance to disease. Reducing stress is important for good mental health as well as for maintaining healthy body systems. Adequate rest, cleanliness, good posture, and comfortable clothes and shoes help maintain good health, too. Today doctors and health care insurance directors promote these practices known as preventive medicine.

Preventive medicine includes regular checkups by doctors and dentists along with everyday good health habits. Immunizations for infants and for people exposed to particular diseases are very important. When a health problem develops, a person should obtain expert medical attention immediately. Otherwise the problem may grow more serious.

You should become an informed consumer of medical services, just as you become skilled at selecting clothes and food. Careful reading of labels and following directions that come with medicines help improve the chances that the medicines will work effectively without harmful effects.

Describe everyday health habits that help maintain good health.

ACTIVITY Have students obtain information about different health care insurance plans. Compare the advantages and disadvantages of each plan. Identify provisions that help to prevent illness or to detect illness at an early stage, both of which save money in the long run for the companies.

How can medicines be used wisely?

See Teacher's Guide.

REVIEW AND REFLECT

1. Describe the stages in the female menstrual cycle.
2. What is fertilization? Where does it occur?
3. Describe what is meant by preventive medicine.
4. If mothers are immune to diphtheria, whooping cough, and tetanus, do infants also need to receive immunizations for the diseases? Explain.

23:12 Choices: Organ Transplant Programs

Many people have body parts that do not work properly because of disease, injury, or malfunction. Some body parts, such as joints and heart valves, can be replaced with parts made by people. You learned about some of the medical benefits of technology in terms of prosthetics in chapter 8. The most reliable replacements of organs are transplants from other people. Figure 23–16 shows the eight types of transplants now performed.

About 20 000 people who die each year, mostly from traffic accidents, are possible donors of organs for transplants. However, at present, few of the organs are being donated. Family members generally are not aware of how the death of a loved one might make a life-saving transplant possible.

Why are many organs that could be used for transplants not available?

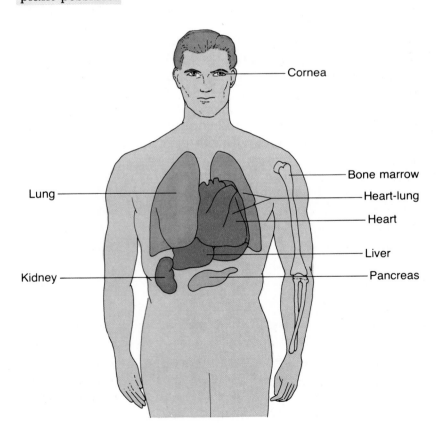

FIGURE 23–16. The success rates of transplants vary. However in recent years, the overall success rate has been increasing due to new drugs that help prevent organ rejection and improved surgical techniques.

Organs can be transplanted for only a short time after the death of a donor, so communication between donors' families and doctors of transplant candidates must be quick. Special legal permission must be obtained to use organs for transplants.

Grief often prevents families from making the quick decisions needed for organ donation. Prior arrangements for organ donation can avoid some of these problems. In many states, people can indicate on their drivers' license what organs they wish to donate for transplants if they die in an auto accident. Then their families are not faced with the decision in a time of grief.

You may have seen a plea in newspapers or on television for an organ donation. Sometimes the desperate parents of a child who needs a transplant ask the media for help. Later you may learn that the child received a transplant and survived. Meanwhile, other children who needed transplants probably did not get them.

There is a large gap between the need for transplants and the donation of organs. A number of concerned people are suggesting a transplant program managed by the United States government. A national program would match transplant candidates and organ donors all over the country. The program also could help pay some of the high costs of transplant operations. Critics of a government program say that supplying organs for transplants should be handled by a private business. They use the American Red Cross as an example. It is a private organization that for years has done an efficient job of obtaining and providing blood. Some people oppose spending government money for transplants. They say the money would benefit more people if it were spent on research to find cures for diseases.

FIGURE 23–17. Cornea transplants have the highest success rate. Ninety percent of transplant receivers have improved vision.

What are some advantages and disadvantages of a national transplant program managed by the government?

See Teacher's Guide.

REVIEW AND REFLECT

1. What eight types of transplants are done today?
2. What suggestions do you have for closing the gap between the need for transplants and organ donations?
3. Do you think people would vote for a slight tax increase if the money were to be used for a government transplant program? Explain.

SUMMARY

1. All body systems work together like a team to maintain body homeostasis. 23:1
2. Food is broken down and absorbed into the blood in the digestive system. 23:2, 23:3
3. Blood, pumped by the heart, carries oxygen to and wastes from all body cells. 23:4
4. The immune response system produces antibodies against pathogens and toxins. 23:5
5. The respiratory system takes oxygen into the body and gets rid of carbon dioxide waste. 23:6
6. The urinary system rids the body of some wastes, keeps the pressure of body fluids balanced, and keeps the pH of the blood controlled. 23:7
7. Nerve impulses travel from neuron to neuron on their way to and from the central nervous system. 23:8
8. Hormones affect different body reactions. Hormones are secreted at different rates at different times. 23:9
9. Fertilization occurs when a sperm from the male reproductive system penetrates an egg in the female reproductive system. 23:10
10. Good health management involves preventive medicine and being an informed consumer of medical services. 23:11

VOCABULARY

alveoli 4	immunization 6	ovulation 8
antibody 3	lymph	pathogen 2
cardiovascular 7	menstruation 14	plasma 1
endocrine 13	metabolism 16	platelet 10
fertilization 17	nephron 9	synapse 5
hormone 15	neuron 12	

Match each definition with the correct word from the list.

1. A colorless fluid containing water, salts, ions, proteins, carbohydrates, vitamins, and amino acids that makes up more than half of a person's blood
2. An organism that can cause an infection
3. A protein that destroys a certain pathogen or toxin
4. The tiny folds that line the lungs
5. A gap between neurons across which a chemical carries nerve impulses
6. The process of stimulating production of an antibody by vaccination
7. The body system consisting of the heart, blood, and blood vessels
8. The release of an egg from an oviduct
9. A tiny tube in a kidney through which materials are reabsorbed into the blood
10. A tiny disc-shaped cell in blood that helps control loss of blood
11. Tissue fluid that has diffused into lymph capillaries
12. A nerve cell
13. A type of gland that has no ducts
14. The release of tissue and blood from the female uterus that occurs when an egg is not fertilized
15. A chemical produced by glands that circulates in blood and affects reactions in cells
16. Chemical reactions in the body
17. The union of a sperm and an egg

QUESTIONS

MAIN IDEAS

Choose the correct answer to complete each sentence.

1. Peristalsis occurs *(only in the stomach, in the stomach and the small intestine, throughout the digestive system).*

2. The main components of blood are red and white blood cells, *(platelets and lymph, plasma and lymph, platelets and plasma).*

3. When a person is immunized, the body produces *(alveoli, hormones, antibodies).*

4. Inhaling causes *(gases to move both in and out of the lungs, air to move into the lungs, gases to move out of the lungs).*

5. Some processes that take place in the kidneys are *(peristalsis and digestion, filtration and reabsorption, storage and regulation of food).*

6. Synapses are found *(in both the central nervous system and the peripheral nervous system, only in the spinal cord and the brain, only in the brain).*

7. Fertilization occurs in *(an ovary, an oviduct, the uterus).*

8. The compound in red blood cells that transports oxygen from lungs to body cells is *(iodine, peristalsis, hemoglobin).*

9. The body maintains homeostasis by *(input and output, feedback loops, producing antibodies).*

10. Caffeine is a drug found in *(coffee, cigarettes, wine).*

See Teacher's Guide.

APPLICATIONS

Answer each question in one or more paragraphs.

1. List and explain five ways a person can maintain good health.

2. How do immunizations help to eliminate a disease?

3. Why might a pathogen be able to get past the body's first lines of defense?

4. Why can you get the flu or a cold again after you have had them once?

5. How are kidneys affected if a person uses a lot of table salt or does not drink enough water?

6. What makes a nerve impulse electrochemical, which is both electric and chemical?

FURTHER STUDY

INVESTIGATIONS

1. Prepare a report on the brain, including different activities of the right and left hemispheres, the nature of emotions, and brain development.

2. Learn about diseases of the immune system including AIDS.

3. Find out what euthanasia is. Have class debates about the issues it involves.

4. Learn about body cycles called biorhythms. Find out how sleep fits into the body's biorhythms.

READINGS

+ Corrick, James A. *The Human Brain.* Arco Publishing: New York, 1983.

– Daly, Kathleen N. *Body Words.* Doubleday: Garden City, NY, 1980.

0 Grady, Denise. "It Seemed Like He Might Die Before We Could Help Him." *Discover.* February, 1983. pp. 14–18.

+ Nourse, Alan E. *Hormones.* Franklin Watts: New York, 1979.

0 Ward, Brian R. *Food and Digestion.* Franklin Watts: New York, 1982.

HAVE you ever looked at animals in a pet store just for fun? What was special about the animal you liked best? You have learned about the classification of organisms according to similar characteristics. However, no organism is exactly like another, even if both are the same species. What makes one organism different from another? How are the traits of a species passed from parents to offspring?

HEREDITY

INTRODUCING THE CHAPTER   The study of inherited traits and genes, genetics, is an area of science that is mentioned frequently in the news. As you begin this chapter, it may be interesting to discuss topics that students have seen in newspaper and magazine articles and described on radio and TV. Examples are genetic diseases and treatments, cancer and treatments, biotechnical research and products, clones, and either known or suspected mutagens (agents that cause mutations).

24:1   Genetics

What kinds of fruit do you like to eat? Maybe you like navel oranges, the kind without seeds. Or perhaps you like nectarines or grapefruit. These fruits and many other foods we enjoy have been developed or improved by the study and application of genetics (juh NET ihks). **Genetics** is the study of inherited traits.

Much of the world's food supply depends on special varieties of plants and animals bred for high yields. For example, geneticists have developed varieties of wheat that are resistant to disease. Cows that produce more milk and chickens that produce more eggs have been bred with the help of geneticists.

Genes (JEENZ), from which the word genetics comes, are long molecules that contain DNA. As you know, DNA is found in every cell. The cells of organisms as simple as bacteria or as complex as people all contain DNA. When cells reproduce, DNA is passed from the parent cells to the offspring cells. DNA controls inherited traits.

In addition to the development and improvement of foods, genetics is important in medical science. Some diseases are inherited. Table 24–1 lists some of these genetic diseases. Such diseases are illnesses caused completely or in part by abnormal genetic material in cell nuclei.

GOAL   You will learn the nature of DNA, how DNA is passed to new cells, and the ways that DNA can change.

BACKGROUND   When Gregor Mendel (1822–1884) did his classic work on traits of different generations of pea plants, genetics was a very limited science. Now, with many techniques to study genes directly and even construct and change them, genetics has become an indepth science that is developing rapidly.

How are traits inherited?

513

BACKGROUND   Some other genetic diseases are thalassemia (a blood disease), phenylketonuria (PKU, the inability to metabolize a protein), and Huntington chorea (progressive degeneration of muscles and nerves in adults). There are more than 3000 genetic diseases.

TABLE 24-1. SOME GENETIC DISEASES

Disease	When Symptoms Appear	Description
Hemophilia	Birth	Blood does not clot, so minor injuries may cause severe blood loss; can be controlled with medication
Down syndrome	Birth	Severe mental retardation and other physical defects; usually results in death at a young age
Sickle-cell anemia	Birth	Lack of oxygen in blood and kidney infections; may result in death by heart failure
Tay-Sachs	Birth	Decline in mental ability, gradual loss of physical and mental control; usually results in death by age 3
Muscular dystrophy	Birth to adult	Slow weakening of muscles
Cystic fibrosis	Birth	Thick deposits of mucus in lungs; chronic lung infections
Diabetes mellitus	Any age	Body cannot produce insulin needed for cell respiration; can be controlled with medication, diet, and exercise

SUGGESTION   Arrange for a genetic counselor to speak to the class about the work he/she does.

Knowing the genetic history of each family can be important to people who plan to have children. Sometimes the parents may not have any genetic diseases, but they may be carriers. In other words, if they carry the genes for a disease, their children may inherit it. A genetic counselor can help people learn their genetic history and provide information about genetic diseases their children may inherit.

24:2 DNA

The traits of individuals are controlled by a complex molecule in cell nuclei: deoxyribonucleic acid, or **DNA.** Notice the spiral staircase structure of DNA shown in Figure 24–1. The arrangement of the base pairs in DNA molecules is a set of instructions for the making of proteins in cells. Every DNA molecule has the same four bases, but they are arranged differently. Just as billions of different compounds are formed from only about 100 different elements, many different DNA molecules are formed from only four different bases.

Many proteins are made according to the instructions in DNA molecules. Feedback between genes and environment influences when and how quickly proteins are made. The proteins that are made determine the traits of an organism. Differences in organisms, from bacteria to trees to people, are due to differences in the order of base pairs in DNA molecules.

Describe the structure of DNA.

FIGURE 24–1. DNA is a spiral-shaped molecule (inset) in cell nuclei. DNA is composed in part of base pairs: G, guanine, and C, cytosine; A, adenine, and T, thymine (a). When protein synthesis begins, DNA "unzips" (b). mRNA forms on one half of the DNA molecule (c). mRNA also has base pairs: G and C, A and U (c). After formation, the mRNA separates from the DNA and moves to the cytoplasm. In the nucleus, the DNA molecule halves rejoin.

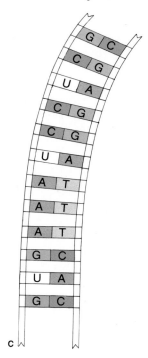

Describe the structure of genes.

One gene contains the DNA needed for a cell to make one protein. A human gene can be hundreds or thousands of base pairs long. Genes are arranged in coiled and folded strands called **chromosomes** (KROH muh sohmz) in cell nuclei. Chromosomes become distinctly visible in cell nuclei during cell division.

See Teacher's Guide.

REVIEW AND REFLECT

1. Name and describe three genetic diseases.
2. Describe the structure and functions of DNA.
3. How can many different DNA molecules be made up of only four bases?

See Teacher's Guide.

Skill Inquiry

DNA stores the information a cell uses to assemble amino acids into proteins. Scientists have calculated that the DNA in a bacterium stores about one million bits of information. An amoeba's DNA can store 400 times more. Each human cell's DNA can store 5.0×10^9 bits of information. Scientists are trying to find ways of using DNA-like molecules for computer information storage.

Computers store bits of information in a memory. One bit of information in a computer memory is like a light switch being on or off. The switch "remembers" the information since it stays in one position until changed. Suppose you had eight switches each controlling a different light bulb. How many different combinations of on and off could this set of eight switches remember? The answer may be larger than you think. Eight switches can remember one of 2^8 or 256 different combinations. If you do not believe it, draw several rows of eight circles and use x's to indicate switches that are on. You will soon see that many different combinations are possible.

1. How many different combinations of on and off could be remembered by 16 switches? by 32 switches?

In a computer, each group of eight memory switches is called a byte. In other words, 256 bits of information can be stored by one byte. Small computers may be able to store 64 000 bytes of information compared to 10 million or more by large computers. This information makes up the instructions that the computer follows in carrying out its program, just as DNA contains instructions for living things to carry on life processes.

2. How many bytes of information are stored in bacterial DNA? in human DNA?
3. Which is larger, the information storage capacity of human DNA or a large computer? How much larger?

Activity: How are proteins made in cells?

See Teacher's Guide.

MATERIALS

48 2 cm × 2 cm pieces of construction paper, 12 marked A, 12 marked G, 12 marked C, 6 marked T, 6 marked U

4 index cards marked Amino Acid A, Amino Acid G, Amino Acid L, Amino Acid P

stiff ribbon, 2 meters

scissors

cellophane tape

marker

metric ruler

PROCEDURE

Part A   In Cell Nucleus

1. Cut 3 strips of ribbon, each 39 cm long. Mark each strip in 3 cm units from one end to the other. Number the marks from 1 to 12 on each strip.

2. Construct a model of a DNA molecule as shown in Figure 24–1a on page 515. Use the strips of ribbon to form each side of the ladder. Tape 12 bases to each strip of ribbon in the correct order. Put the top base at mark number 1, the second base at mark number 2, and so on. Note that adenine and thymine always match and guanine and cytosine always match.

3. Unzip your DNA molecule. (Figure 24–1b).

4. Using the right half of your DNA molecule, make an mRNA molecule by attaching bases to another strip of ribbon. (Figure 24–1c). Match the bases as you did when you made the DNA molecule. However, this time match uracil instead of thymine with adenine.

5. Unzip the mRNA from the DNA.

6. Put the DNA molecule back together.

Part B   In Cytoplasm

1. Cut 4 strips of ribbon each 12 cm long. Mark each strip in 3 cm units.

2. Make a tRNA molecule with an amino acid attached as shown in Figure 24–2.

3. Make 3 more tRNA molecules. Use these combinations of bases and amino acids.

Amino Acid G	Amino Acid L	Amino Acid A
C A C	U U U	C G A

4. Correctly match the tRNA bases with the bases of your mRNA model. As you match the bases, tape together the amino acids that touch to form a protein.

5. Remove the tRNA molecules from the mRNA and the protein. Record the arrangement of amino acids in the protein.

DATA AND OBSERVATIONS

Amino Acid __	Amino Acid __	Amino Acid __	Amino Acid __

QUESTIONS AND CONCLUSIONS

1. Which pairs of bases fit together in a DNA molecule? in an mRNA molecule?

2. How does the structure of DNA account for the wide range of differences in life?

3. Use what you learned in this activity to write a step-by-step description of the way DNA controls protein production.

tRNA

FIGURE 24–2.

24:3 Mitosis

What is mitosis?

Mitosis (mi TOH sus) is the division of one cell into two cells just like the first cell. Although mitosis is a continuous process, it is usually studied in phases. Mitosis is divided into four phases as shown in Figure 24–3. Mitosis occurs about every 10 to 20 hours in most cells. The time when mitosis is not occurring is called interphase.

What is interphase?

During interphase, DNA molecules in the cell nucleus split between the base pairs. As the DNA splits, bases in the cell nucleus attach to the exposed bases of the DNA molecules. Two new DNA molecules are formed that have the same arrangement of base pairs as the original DNA molecule. See Figure 24–1 on page 515 again.

BACKGROUND   The set of four phases of mitosis together with the events that cause daughter cells to grow to the size of the parent cell is known as the cell cycle.

In prophase, the first phase of mitosis, chromosomes form in the nucleus from threadlike material that contains

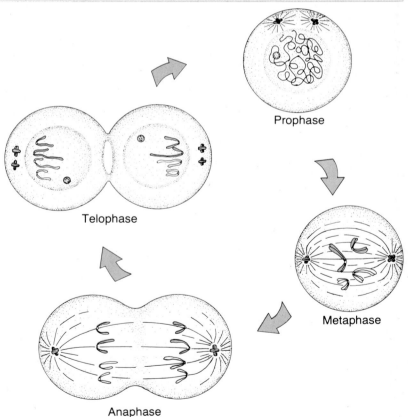

FIGURE 24–3. The stages of mitosis

DNA. Chromosomes appear as double-stranded structures. Each strand is a chromatid. Pairs of chromatids are joined at a special region called a centromere. Each chromatid contains identical DNA molecules that were formed during interphase. Later in prophase, the nuclear membrane disappears. In the cytoplasm, microtubules form as tiny fibers from one end of the cell to the other.

In metaphase, chromosomes move toward the center of the cell. The centromeres of each chromosome attach to a separate fiber. The chromatids move apart in anaphase.

The final phase of mitosis is telophase. In telophase, the chromosomes change back into threadlike material, becoming invisible. Two nuclear membranes form, the microtubules disappear, and the cytoplasm splits into two parts. Identify as many phases of mitosis as you can in Figure 24–4.

BACKGROUND   In animals, mitosis is completed as two daughter cells are pinched apart by a constriction at the middle of the original cell. In plants, a crosswall forms at the middle of the original cell, and new cell walls form about each daughter cell.

Describe the phases of mitosis.

FIGURE 24–4. Note the various stages of mitosis occurring in the cells of an onion root tip.

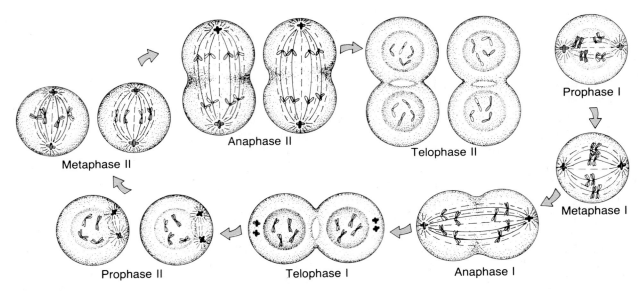

FIGURE 24-5. The stages of meiosis

24:4 Meiosis

What is meiosis?

Meiosis (mi OH sus) is another kind of cell division. Meiosis produces sex cells. In mitosis, two cells with the same number of chromosomes are formed from one "parent" cell. In meiosis, four cells, each with half as many chromosomes as the parent cell, are formed. Egg and sperm cells are formed in reproductive organs by meiosis.

Like mitosis, meiosis is a continuous process, but it also is studied in phases. Figure 24-5 shows the phases of meiosis. Notice that prophase I in meiosis is much like prophase in mitosis. As prophase I continues, pairs of similar chromosomes align and become intertwined.

BACKGROUND The orientation of members of chromosome pairs during metaphase I determines how the pairs will separate.

In metaphase I, the chromosome pairs line up across the middle of the cell along the thin tubes. In anaphase I, the chromosome pairs move apart. Telophase I is similar to telophase in mitosis. Notice that each cell formed in the first division of meiosis has only half as many chromosome pairs as the parent cell.

Describe the phases of meiosis.

A brief interphase occurs before the second division in meiosis begins. Prophase II, metaphase II, anaphase II, and telophase II are similar to the four phases of mitosis. The four resulting sex cells each have half as many chromosomes as the parent cell.

In humans, each body cell contains 23 pairs (46) of chromosomes. During meiosis, sex cells containing 23 chromosomes each are formed. When an egg and sperm cell combine in fertilization, the fertilized egg is called a zygote. As a result of fertilization, a zygote has 23 pairs (46) of chromosomes. A zygote divides by mitosis. Mitosis occurs repeatedly, and eventually the specialized cells of a many-celled organism are formed. Figure 24–6 shows the development of an organism from an egg and a sperm cell.

How many chromosomes does a human zygote contain?

See Teacher's Guide.

REVIEW AND REFLECT

1. Compare the cells produced by mitosis and meiosis. How are they similar? different?
2. Explain why a human zygote does not have 92 (2 × 46) chromosomes.
3. What is the relationship between DNA, genes, and chromosomes?

FIGURE 24–6. When a sperm fertilizes an egg (a), a zygote is formed. A series of cell divisions begins (b), forming an embryo (c). As growth continues, when the organism takes on the characteristics of its species, it is called a fetus (d).

a

b

c

d

24:5 How Traits Are Inherited

What controls the traits of an organism?

Remember that chromosomes contain genes. Genes contain the information that is responsible for an individual's traits. Traits are controlled by one or more pairs of genes. A sperm cell contributes one gene and an egg cell contributes the other gene in each gene pair. You have at least one pair of genes for every trait you have. Half of your genes came from your mother and half came from your father.

The two genes in a gene pair may be the same for a trait, or they may be different. If the genes in a pair are the same, the trait is called **pure.** If the genes in a pair are different, the trait is called **hybrid** (HI brud).

What is the difference between pure and hybrid gene pairs?

For example, notice the difference between attached ear lobes and free ear lobes as shown in Figure 24–7. You have two genes (one pair) that control whether you have attached or free ear lobes. You inherited one of the genes from your father and the other gene from your mother.

If you have free ear lobes, you may have inherited one gene for free ear lobes from each of your parents. Then you have a pure trait for free ear lobes. However, you may have inherited a gene for attached ear lobes from one parent and a gene for free ear lobes from your other parent. Then you have a hybrid trait for free ear lobes. You have free ear lobes because the gene for free ear lobes is dominant (DAHM uh nunt). In a hybrid trait, only the **dominant** gene is expressed.

In the hybrid trait for free ear lobes, the gene for attached ear lobes is recessive (rih SES ihv). **Recessive**

a

b

FIGURE 24–7. Attached ear lobes (a) and free ear lobes (b) are genetic traits determined by a single pair of genes.

genes are expressed as traits only when the gene pair for that trait contains no dominant genes. For example, if you have attached ear lobes, then you inherited one gene for attached ear lobes from each of your parents. You have a pure trait for attached ear lobes. You do not have any dominant free ear lobe genes.

When are recessive genes expressed as traits?

TABLE 24–2.   COMMON TRAITS

Dominant Traits	Recessive Traits
Full lips	Thin lips
Bridge of nose convex	Bridge of nose concave
Farsightedness	Normal vision
Extra fingers or toes (polydactyly)	Normal number of fingers and toes
Freckles	Lack of freckles
Ability to roll tongue into U-shape	Lack of ability to roll tongue into U-shape
Dimples in cheeks	Lack of dimples in cheeks
Feet with normal arches	Flatfeet

ACTIVITY   Have each student taste a small piece of clean PTC paper, which can be ordered from a scientific supplier. The ability to detect a distinct taste is a dominant trait. Let each student determine whether he/she has dominant or recessive genes for this trait.

When are dominant genes expressed as traits?

Some dominant and recessive traits are shown in Table 24–2. Dominant traits may be pure or hybrid. Recessive traits are always pure. If a dominant gene is present, the recessive gene is not expressed. In some hybrid gene pairs, both of the genes are incompletely dominant. As a result, both genes are partly expressed as traits. For example, two forms of a gene for making hemoglobin are incompletely dominant. One form causes normal hemoglobin development. The other form causes abnormal development that results in sickle-shaped red blood cells. A person with both genes develops both kinds of hemoglobin. The person does not have sickle-cell anemia, but is a carrier of the sickle-cell trait.

A geneticist uses a diagram called a **Punnett square** to show the probability of offspring inheriting certain traits. Figure 24–8 shows a Punnett square. Notice the shorthand that is used to represent pure dominant, hybrid, and pure recessive traits. The gene pairs of the parents are represented outside the square. The possible gene pairs of the offspring are shown in the boxes.

FIGURE 24–8.   Each child born to these parents has a one in four chance of having attached ear lobes. Twenty-five percent of the children are expected to have attached ear lobes and 75 percent free ear lobes. However, the traits of the actual offspring may vary.

See Teacher's Guide.

Career Profile

When Sharon Kruebbe of Port Orchard, Washington, looks at a purebred dog, she sees much more than most of us do. She notices whether the head is small, the coat uneven, or the legs thin and weak. Sharon has twenty years of experience breeding Weimaraners, large gray short-haired sporting dogs. In that time, Sharon has become a leading expert in her field.

Sharon grew up on a farm and learned about many different kinds of animals. After she finished high school, she became interested in dogs. She bought a female Weimaraner of average quality. As her interest in the breed increased, she contacted a well-known breeder of Weimaraners and purchased a well-bred male in hopes of breeding good offspring. From this hobbyist approach, Sharon slowly improved the line. Today, her kennel houses 25 Weimaraners. She boasts a record of having bred 50 show champions, one field champion, and one dual champion.

According to Sharon, a prospective dog breeder should begin with a purebred dog of the highest quality affordable. Magazines and kennel clubs have information about good breeders all over the country. One should also be familiar with the championship standards for the breed. This information helps a person know what characteristics to look for and develop. Breeders have a record of each dog's pedigree. Knowing the genetic history of a dog's ancestors is essential to improving the quality of its bloodline.

In breeding dogs, you must learn to be very critical of the offspring produced. Sharon keeps only the best females for breeding, which she takes to their championship. To improve the line, she then breeds these females to males whose ancestors carry complementary characteristics and have consistently produced outstanding offspring. In this way, Sharon eliminates undesirable characteristics in the offspring and strengthens desirable ones. She never sacrifices one characteristic for another. She always keeps in mind an outstanding image of the dog she is trying to develop. Sharon learned everything she knows about dogs through observation and reading. She finds dog breeding to be a challenging and creative profession.

24:6 Sex Chromosomes

The boys and girls in your class have the same number of chromosomes (46) in their body cells. However, males and females do not have exactly the same kinds of chromosomes. Look at the two sets of chromosomes shown in

Figure 24–9. If you compare both sets, you will see that all but one of the chromosomes are the same.

A person's sex is controlled by a pair of chromosomes rather than just a few pairs of genes. The sex chromosomes are called X and Y chromosomes. Females have two X chromosomes (XX). Males have an X chromosome and a Y chromosome (XY).

Remember that when meiosis takes place, four sex cells are produced from one body cell. In females, the sex cells (eggs) all have X chromosomes. In males, the sex cells (sperm) may have an X or a Y chromosome. If an X-chromosome sperm fertilizes an egg, a female (XX) is produced. If a Y-chromosome sperm fertilizes an egg, a male (XY) is produced.

Sex chromosomes contain genes for sex traits. Genes for nonsex traits also are located on the sex chromosomes. Traits controlled by these genes are called sex-linked traits. One example is hemophilia. Genes for hemophilia are found only on X chromosomes. The Y chromosome has no gene for either trait. Therefore, a male can inherit hemophilia only from his mother. Since the gene for hemophilia is recessive, a female would have to inherit a hemophilia gene from both parents in order to have the disease. If she inherits a hemophilia gene from one parent and a normal gene from the other, she will not have the trait, but she will be a carrier.

What chromosome combinations produce male and female offspring?

BACKGROUND   Queen Victoria of England (1819–1901) is thought to have been a carrier of hemophilia. Her many descendants had a high incidence of hemophilia.

BACKGROUND   A female inheriting a recessive trait for hemophilia (both X chromosomes containing the gene for hemophilia) dies before birth.

Why is hemophilia called a sex-linked trait?

a   b

FIGURE 24–9. Note that one pair of chromosomes is different if you compare the two human sets of chromosomes shown. A male (a) has an XY pair. A female (b) has an XX pair. These pairs are called the sex chromosomes. They control the sex of offspring.

Activity: Is red-green color blindness a sex-linked trait?

See Teacher's Guide.

MATERIALS

paper
pencil

PROCEDURE

1. Look at Figure 24–10. The number 86 is hidden in the figure. Can you see it? If you cannot, you may have red-green color blindness.
2. Think of 15 people (friends, family members, classmates, teachers, and so on) that you can interview.
3. Interview each person in the following way. Ask: "Do you know whether you are color blind?" Record the answer in a data table. Hold Figure 24–10 in front of the person. Ask if any number can be seen and if so, what it is. Record the result. Allow only about five seconds for a response. Record whether the person is a male or a female.
4. Give your data table to your teacher when you have completed all 15 interviews.

FIGURE 24–10.

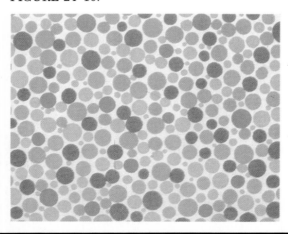

5. Your teacher will supply the following data for the sample population (the total number of people interviewed by your class): the number of males and females, the number of males who are color blind, the number of females who are color blind.
6. Make the following calculations for the sample population: the percentage of color-blind males, the percentage of color-blind females. Show your work.

DATA AND OBSERVATIONS

Person	Knows Whether Color Blind	Sees Number	Sex
1			
2			
3			
4			
5			

QUESTIONS AND CONCLUSIONS

1. What is the ratio of red-green color-blind males to red-green color-blind females in the sample population?
2. Do you think red-green color blindness is a sex-linked trait? Explain.
3. Can you determine to which chromosome the gene causing red-green color blindness is attached?
4. From which parent does a person inherit red-green color blindness? Explain.
5. Did anyone discover that they are red-green color blind from your interview?

<u>24:7</u> Mutations and Mutagens

Sometimes a gene is reproduced incorrectly during either mitosis or meiosis. A changed gene is called a **mutation** (mew TAY shun). Some mutations are beneficial and some are harmful. Beneficial mutations have produced disease-resistant grains and larger fruit. Since they have been produced, the world has had more and better food.

A beneficial mutation gives an organism an advantage in competition for survival. If a mutation helps an individual avoid getting killed or helps it find food or a mate, it will survive to reproduce more of its kind. Some scientists think that mutations over billions of years account for the great variety of life now.

Normally the rate of mutations in bacteria, humans, or any other life is fairly low. However, certain agents called mutagens (MEWT uh juns) cause greater mutation rates. Some mutagens are X rays, ultraviolet light, microwaves, chemicals, and extreme temperature.

Some people are concerned about common mutagens in our lives. These may include medical and dental X rays, nicotine from cigarette smoke, certain food additives, pesticides, cosmic rays, and radiation from radioactive decay of certain minerals in stone and brick buildings. Exposure to more mutagens increases the chance of mutations occurring. Some mutations may cause cancer and birth defects. Mutations are responsible for some genetic diseases. Each person is estimated to carry some recessive mutant genes that would produce genetic disease if the dominant normal genes were not present. The mutation that causes a genetic disease often is a change in just one base of a DNA molecule.

See Teacher's Guide.

REVIEW AND REFLECT

1. How are dominant and recessive genes different?
2. What determines the sex of a child?
3. Do males produce more sperm with X chromosomes, Y chromosomes, or about the same of each? Explain.
4. What is the difference between a beneficial and a harmful mutation?

FIGURE 24–11. Polyploidy is a condition in which an organism has more than the normal number of chromosomes. Larger fruit varieties have been produced by treating plants with a drug that causes sex cells with more than the normal number of chomrosomes to be formed. The plants that grow from these cells have more than the normal number of chromosomes in their cells.

BACKGROUND   A broad definition of a gene mutation includes not only changes in individual genes but changes in their positions in chromosomes as well.

How might mutations be beneficial or harmful to organisms?

SUGGESTION   Have students brainstorm a list of mutagens to which they are frequently exposed. Discuss which, if any, could be reduced in students' lives (e.g., cigarette smoke, frequency of dental X rays).

24:8 Choices: Ice Minus

Suppose there were a way to prevent billions of dollars of frost damage to crops each year. Would you think right away that it should be used? Biologists at the University of California at Berkeley believe they have found the procedure. Some groups oppose testing of it, though. These opponents have been able to stop or at least postpone the testing in the United States with court orders.

What is Ice Minus?

The Berkeley biologists sliced out a small section of DNA in a species of bacteria, *Pseudomonas syringae*. This bacteria had been found to cause frost damage. The new strain of bacteria that was formed is called "Ice Minus." Ice Minus does not have the ability to produce a substance that causes ice to form in plants. Normally, at a few degrees below 0°C, plants freeze because bacteria make nuclei that collect ice. The role of normal strains of bacteria is similar to the role of dust or salt spray, which are nuclei in the atmosphere for ice crystal formation. In the absence of normal bacteria strains on plant leaves, plants can remain unfrozen at −8°C for a few hours.

Why do plants normally freeze at a few degrees below 0°C?

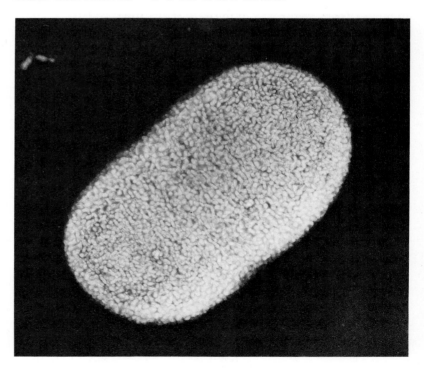

FIGURE 24–12. Ice Minus is a form of *Pseudomonas* bacteria.

Some citizen groups and scientists oppose testing of Ice Minus to prevent frost damage to crops. First, they say, ecological balance could be upset. That is, the Ice Minus might invade land everywhere, replacing the natural strains of bacteria. It has been suggested that present frost-resistant plants and insects that co-exist with normal bacteria might somehow not exist without them. Weeds and other harmful insects might take their places. Second, the opponents say that ice-nucleating bacteria might have an unknown role in cloud formation and precipitation. The bacteria exist within the atmosphere. If Ice Minus replaces normal strains, weather and climate could be affected.

FIGURE 24–13. Frost damage to crops is an agricultural concern.

Many scientists think that these fears are unfounded. They point out that mutations occur naturally in bacteria. Just because a mutation occurs in the laboratory, that is by removing a slice of DNA, does not make it a harmful mutation. The scientists say the worry about the bacteria spreading and invading the world's land and atmosphere is unfounded, too. The decrease of DNA in Ice Minus makes the bacteria less adapted rather than more adapted to its environment. The Ice Minus will tend to stay in one spot. Experiments with chemically modified bacteria show that the bacteria not only stay in test plots, but in a short time are replaced by normal strains.

In response to the opponents, the scientists in favor of testing Ice Minus also make the following points. In nature the normal bacteria is a kind of pathogen, or disease-causer, at cold temperatures. Ice Minus has no pathogen aspect and therefore is better for the plant, somewhat like a vaccine for people. Also, if experiments on a large number of genetically-engineered simple organisms had been blocked, we would not now have many valuable products produced with them. These products include hormones, antibodies, and vaccines.

What are some of the possible beneficial and harmful effects of using Ice Minus?

SUGGESTION Have students research the current status of testing and use of Ice Minus using science magazines and other recent sources.

See Teacher's Guide.

REVIEW AND REFLECT

1. What are two arguments for testing Ice Minus?
2. What are two arguments opponents have used for not testing Ice Minus?
3. Do you think that Ice Minus should be tested? Why or why not?

CHAPTER 24 REVIEW

SUMMARY

1. Understanding how traits are inherited is useful in agriculture and medicine. 24:1
2. Genetic counselors can provide information about testing and care for genetic disease. 24:1
3. The structure and functions of DNA control traits in all species. 24:2
4. Mitosis produces two cells like an original cell. 24:3
5. Meiosis produces sex cells, which contain only half the number of chromosomes as the original cell. 24:4
6. Many traits are controlled by pairs of genes. Some traits are controlled by multiple genes. 24:5
7. The probability of offspring inheriting certain traits can be predicted. 24:5
8. Males have one X and one Y chromosome (XY). Females have two X chromosomes (XX). 24:6
9. Sex-linked traits are due to genes found on X sex chromosomes. 24:6
10. Mutagens increase the rate of mutation in genes. 24:7

VOCABULARY

chromosomes 11
DNA 3
dominant 1
genes 6

genetics 8
hybrid 12
meiosis 2
mitosis 7

mutation 4
Punnett square 9
pure 5
recessive 10

Choose the correct word from the list to answer each question.

1. What kind of traits are always expressed in a hybrid gene pair?
2. What kind of cell division forms sex cells?
3. What molecules carry the instructions for making proteins in cells?
4. What is a gene that has been changed in some way?
5. What kind of gene pair is made up of two dominant or two recessive genes?
6. What are the long molecules that contain deoxyribonucleic acid called?
7. What kind of cell division produces offspring cells with the same number of chromosomes as the parent cells?
8. What is the study of inherited traits?
9. What kind of diagram do geneticists use to predict the probability of offspring inheriting certain traits?
10. What is the gene that is not expressed in a hybrid gene pair called?
11. What are the coiled strands that become distinctly visible during cell division?
12. What kind of gene pair is made up of a dominant and recessive gene?

QUESTIONS

MAIN IDEAS

Choose the correct answer.

1. A model of DNA looks a lot like a (*solar system, ferris wheel, spiral staircase*).
2. Diabetes mellitus is caused by the lack of (*DNA, an X chromosome, insulin*).
3. Hemophilia is caused by (*an extra chromosome, a sex-linked gene, mitosis*).

See Teacher's Guide.

4. Finding the probability that a child will have the disease hemophilia is a part of the study called *(mitosis, fertilization, genetics)*.

5. The process that makes two cells like the original cell is *(mitosis, meiosis, interphase)*.

6. The nuclear membrane disappears during prophase of *(mitosis, meiosis, both mitosis and meiosis)*.

7. A serious genetic disease in which muscles slowly weaken is *(cystic fibrosis, Tay-Sachs, muscular dystrophy)*.

8. If one parent has short fingers and toes (dominant) with a gene pair Ss and the other parent is ss (normal), the percentage of children expected to have short fingers and toes is *(50%, 25%, 100%)*.

9. An example of a mutagen is *(nicotine, vitamin C, DNA)*.

10. If the two genes in a gene pair are the same, the trait is *(pure, hybrid, dominant, recessive)*.

APPLICATIONS

Answer each question in one or more paragraphs.

1. Suppose that a color-blind man marries a color-blind woman. What percentage of their female children would be expected to be color blind?

2. Scientists conclude that most genetic diseases come from mutations of normal genes. If the number and strength of mutagens in the world increases, what is likely to happen to the number of genetic diseases and to the rate of change in species?

3. What if there were no mutations from now on. How might the world be different?

4. Let H_1 represent the gene for normal hemoglobin development. Let H_2 represent the gene for abnormal development. If a woman with an $H_1 H_2$ pair and a man with an $H_1 H_2$ pair have children, what percentage of their children are likely to develop sickle-cell anemia?

FURTHER STUDY

INVESTIGATIONS

1. Prepare a report on the blood groups A, B, AB, and O. Describe how parents with certain types of blood can have children with certain types of blood. Tell how knowledge of blood type is important.

2. Devise a Punnett square for considering two traits at one time. Use two pairs of traits that show a simple dominant-recessive nature, such as dimples and freckles, both dominant traits in people.

3. Investigate one or more traits in your family, such as eye color, attached or free ear lobes, or a genetic disorder/disease.

4. Using library sources and information from employees at a greenhouse and/or a seed supply store, prepare a report on the "green revolution" made possible by hybrid fertilization.

5. Prepare a report on Gregor Mendel.

READINGS

+ Harsanyi, Zsolt, and Richard Hutton. *Genetic Prophecy: Beyond the Double Helix.* Rawson, Wade Publishers: New York, 1981.

+ Preuss, Paul. "The Shape of Things to Come." *Science 83.* December, 1983. pp. 80–87.

+ Rosenfield, Israel. *DNA for Beginners.* Writers & Readers: London, 1983.

0 Solomon, Stephen. "Green Genes: Bioengineering New Foods." *Science Digest.* January, 1983. pp. 54–59, 103.

0 Watson, James D. *The Double Helix.* W. W. Norton: New York, 1980.

0 Weisburd, Stefi. "Dissecting the Dance in DNA." *Science News.* June 9, 1984. pp. 362–364.

IN a garden, many organisms interact. People plant and harvest vegetables and pull weeds. Bacteria cause overripe vegetables to rot. Fungi and protists live on garden plants. Rabbits, mice, worms, and insects nibble at the plants and burrow in the soil. How do the activities of each organism affect other organisms? How does the physical environment affect the organisms?

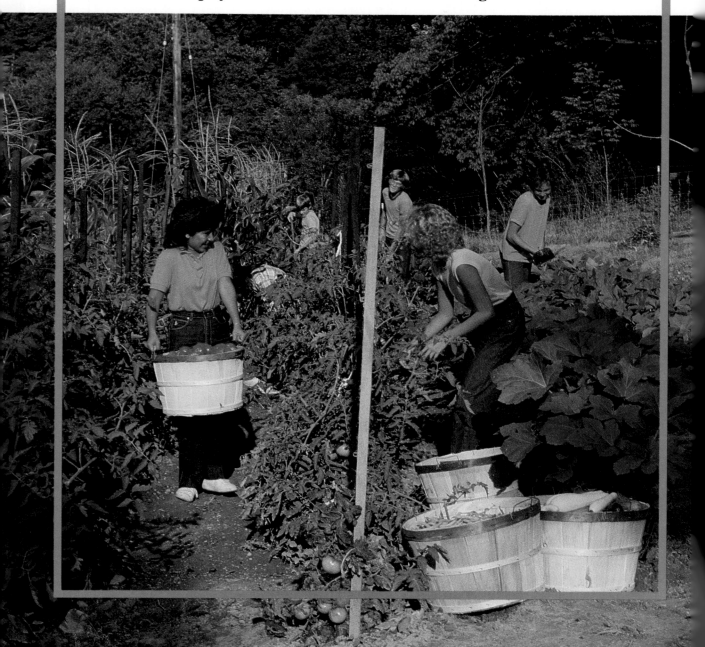

ECOLOGY

INTRODUCING THE CHAPTER   Students may have had experience
gardening. Encourage discussion of their experiences. Discussion of a
garden will prepare students for the concepts of the chapter. The
garden ecosystem can be brought up throughout the chapter for
purposes of comparison and illustration. You also may want to
investigate the possibility of planting a class garden somewhere in the
school yard or growing garden plants in the classroom.

25:1   Cycles in Ecosystems

A garden is a good place to learn about ecology. Many
interactions occur in a garden. Ecology is the study of interactions of living things and their environments. An
ecologist's unit of study is an **ecosystem** (EE koh sihs
tum). An ecosystem can be any size that suits an ecologist's purposes. A drop of water can be an ecosystem. Gardens, lakes, or forests can be ecosystems, too.

The physical environment of an ecosystem includes
many factors. Energy, water, and elements are needed in
a garden for photosynthesis, respiration, decomposition,
and other processes. Sunlight, air, rainfall, and organisms
supply these important factors.

The living part of an ecosystem is called a **community**.
The community of a garden includes organisms from every
life kingdom. Ecologists call a single species found in an
ecosystem a **population**. All the populations in an ecosystem make up its community.

The processes of the organisms in any ecosystem are
parts of cycles, such as the water cycle and the carbon
dioxide–oxygen cycle, Figure 25–1. Another important cycle is the nitrogen cycle.

GOAL   You will learn the
nature of ecosystems, how they
change, and how organisms
interact within them.

What is included in an
ecosystem?

BACKGROUND   About 20
elements are recycled again and
again by organisms and by
physical processes such as
evaporation, precipitation,
erosion, and deposition.

FIGURE 25–1. Individual organisms are members of populations which together make up a community. In ecosystems, water evaporates from the earth and returns from the atmosphere as precipitation. Plants and animals take in and give off water, also being part of the cycle. Plants take in carbon dioxide and give off oxygen as a byproduct of photosynthesis. Animals take in oxygen and give off carbon dioxide as a byproduct of respiration.

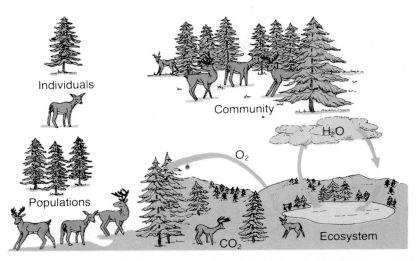

Describe the nitrogen cycle. How is "homeostasis" maintained in a garden?

BACKGROUND Different bacteria are responsible for different steps of change in the nitrogen cycle. Some use amino acids, releasing NH_3 or NH_4^+. Others change ammonia to nitrite (NO_2^-), while a third group oxidizes nitrite to nitrate.

Some bacteria live in the roots of certain plants, such as beans and clover. These bacteria change nitrogen gas in the air into ammonia, NH_3. Most of the ammonia is converted into amino acids which plants use to make proteins. Animals that eat the plants also get amino acids. When organisms in the garden produce waste or die, other bacteria cause the organic matter to decay. Some of these bacteria convert the complex organic compounds to ammonia. The ammonia combines with water in the soil of the garden forming ammonium ions, NH_4^+. Other bacteria change the ammonium ions to nitrite ions, NO_2^-. These ions are changed to nitrate ions, NO_3^-. Plants absorb nitrate ions from the soil and use them to make amino acids, which are used to make proteins and other nitrogen compounds. When you eat vegetables from the garden, you get some of the nitrogen compounds you need for your life processes.

Soil fungi are also important in breaking down and recycling dead materials. In fact, some plants cannot live unless certain fungi grow among their roots. Some fungi supply plants with needed water and elements.

A garden is always changing. People, rabbits, mice, birds, and earthworms come and go. Vegetables grow and are picked. Plants die and decay due to the action of decomposers. Weather changes throughout the growing period. Cycles of changes are important in maintaining an overall balance, a kind of homeostasis, in an ecosystem.

Activity: What is the density of a population?

See Teacher's Guide.

MATERIALS

outdoor location with trees or shrubs
field guide to trees or shrubs
meter stick
string
pencil
unlined paper
aquarium
reference books

PROCEDURE

Part A

1. Choose an outdoor ecosystem to study. It should have a rectangular shape. Draw a map that shows the boundaries of the ecosystem you chose.

2. Use string and a meter stick to find the length and width of the ecosystem. Record these measurements in a data table.

3. Calculate the area of the ecosystem by multiplying the length times the width. Record the area. Be sure to include the units.

4. Choose one tree or shrub population that you see in the ecosystem. Use a field guide to determine the scientific name of the species. Record the name.

5. Count all members of the population within the ecosystem. Record this number.

6. Find the population density by dividing the number of members by the total area. Record the population density.

Part B

1. Use a meter stick to measure the length, width, and height of an aquarium. Record these measurements.

2. Find the volume of the aquarium by multiplying the length times the width times the height.

3. Choose a population in the aquarium, such as a species of fish or plant.

4. Learn the scientific name of the species.

5. Count all the members of your chosen population in the aquarium. Record.

6. Find the population density. Divide the number of members by the total volume. Record.

DATA AND OBSERVATIONS

Ecosystem	Outdoor	Aquarium
Length		
Width		
Height	✕	
Area		✕
Volume	✕	
Population Name		
Population		
Population Density		

QUESTIONS AND CONCLUSIONS

1. Define population density.
2. What physical features were found in the outdoor ecosystem?
3. What physical features were found in the aquarium ecosystem?
4. In which ecosystem were boundaries most clear-cut? Why?
5. What are some populations that you did not see that probably existed in each ecosystem?
6. How do you think that knowing population density helps ecologists?
7. Why is it useful to find human population density in places like schools and cities?

Tundra

Grassland

Temperate forest

Desert

Tropical rain forest

Aquatic

FIGURE 25–2. Scientists agree that at least six major biomes exist. On this map, the temperate forest biome includes taiga, northern evergreen forests. Savannah and chaparral are included with the grassland and desert biomes. Tundra biomes include arctic and alpine tundra. Aquatic biomes include freshwater and marine environments.

25:2 Biomes, Habitats, and Niches

Some ecologists study very large ecosystems, called **biomes** (BI ohms), which cover large regions of the earth. Figure 25–2 shows some of the world's biomes and their important features.

Within each biome, similar organisms and climate are found. Climate influences what organisms live in a biome. For instance, the tundra biome has mosses, lichens, and a few species of grasses. These organisms can survive the cold climate of the tundra. The tundra is too cold and dry for large trees to grow. Animals such as reindeer and snow geese migrate to warmer regions during winter in the tundra. In the tropical rain forest biome, trees grow very well because the climate is warm and wet.

How does climate affect the life of a biome?

Each population in an ecosystem is "at home" in a certain type of environment. This home environment is called a **habitat.** A population's habitat provides things the organisms need to survive, such as shelter and food. For example, the earthworms that live in a garden burrow in the soil and eat organic matter. The soil is that population's habitat. The organisms in an ecosystem have specific roles in the processes that occur in the ecosystem. The role of an organism in its habitat is called its **niche** (NICH). For example, some animals eat meat, others eat plants. These characteristics are adaptations that help the organisms survive. Every organism has certain characteristics that help it survive. Each organism has its own niche.

What is a habitat?

What is a niche?

See Teacher's Guide.

Career Profile

When Lois Mittino Gray has a day off from work she usually spends it hiking, collecting flowers, or talking with people about nature. Lois could be considered a nature enthusiast because she spends her work days doing the same things!

Lois graduated from Michigan State University in 1973 with a degree in biology education. That summer she was a ranger-naturalist at the Blue Ridge Parkway in Virginia. Her responsibilities included developing workshops, leading hikes, writing a newsletter, and keeping inventories of natural relics.

Lois eventually accepted a position with the Indiana State Park system as a naturalist. Her first assignment was at Spring Mill State Park near Bloomington, Indiana. There, a restored pioneer village with 18 buildings set the stage for many historical plays that Lois produced and narrated. Lois also wrote a nature column in three local newspapers, did a daily radio show, and appeared regularly on a TV show called "Indiana Outdoors."

Today, as a naturalist at Harmonie State Park, Lois also serves as an educational consultant. She develops programs for school groups and writes articles about nature for local newspapers. She teaches noncredit nature study courses at nearby Indiana State University in Evansville, too.

A special pleasure for her is introducing young people from urban areas to the wonders of the outdoors. She recommends that a young person interested in work as a naturalist do volunteer work at a nature park.

25:3 Succession

Every ecosystem has a past and a future. A series of changes in the community of an ecosystem is called **succession.** You may have observed the first stages of succession in a vacant lot full of weeds. Perhaps you remember when the area was cleared for construction, and the soil was exposed. When nothing was built on that lot, weeds began to grow. If no one mows the weeds, shrubs may appear. Seeds that fall from nearby trees may begin to grow.

Two different kinds of succession are believed to occur. Primary succession begins when plant communities start to grow in places where no organisms live. In Hawaii, primary succession begins on volcanic rocks. First, physical weathering of the rocks occurs. Then lichens and mosses grow. This first life on the rock starts forming soil by both physical and chemical weathering. With soil, low vegetation like grasses and shrubs becomes established. Finally, a tropical rain forest may develop. Each community step in the succession prepares the ecosystem for the next community.

Secondary succession begins when a plant community starts to grow where another community once lived, but no longer does. Think of the vacant lot again. A community of organisms lived on the land before it was cleared for construction. Perhaps trees were cut down or weeds were burned to clear the land. The changes in the ecosystem, from barren soil to weeds to shrubs to trees, are an example of secondary succession.

What is succession?

BACKGROUND Primary succession takes a lot longer than secondary succession, because new soil usually must form.

Describe primary succession.
BACKGROUND Some other places where primary succession occurs are on a sand dune, where a lake filled in, where a glacier has been, and where a landslide took place. Sometimes a few organisms, such as bacteria, are present when primary succession begins.

Describe secondary succession.

FIGURE 25–3. Stages of secondary succession are shown at Indiana Dunes National Lakeshore. The first stages are beach and grasses (a), grasses are followed by a cottonwood stage (b), which is followed by an oak forest (c).

a

b

c
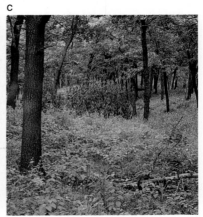

The final stable community that exists at the end of natural succession is called a climax community. Stable means that there are no major changes in populations, although small changes continue. For example, a fire may burn the trees in a small area of a forest. Some changes occur as the area goes through stages of regrowth. However, the populations within the ecosystem as a whole change very little.

Sometimes people change an ecosystem, so that natural succession is interrupted. The natural succession in the ecosystem is stopped before the climax community is established. For example, an area might be cleared for farming before secondary succession has formed a climax community. Intervention for farming or other purposes is called controlled succession. Lawns are examples of controlled succession. Many species of plants will grow, but most homeowners allow only certain species of grass to grow.

A community is usually named after the most plentiful plant species in it. The most plentiful plant species is called the dominant species. The beech tree *(Fagus grandiflora)* and the sugar maple tree *(Acer saccharum)* are the dominant species in the beech-maple forests of the northeast United States. The dominant species of the tall grass prairie of Illinois and Iowa is big turkey foot grass *(Andropogon gerardii.)* The redwood tree *(Sequoia sempervirens)* is the dominant species of the California redwood forests.

See Teacher's Guide.

REVIEW AND REFLECT

1. Describe the physical environment and community of a picnic area in a park.
2. How is homeostasis maintained in an ecosystem?
3. Use a diagram to explain how the "flow" of nitrogen in an ecosystem is a cycle.
4. What is the habitat and niche of a squirrel?
5. What climax community would you expect has occurred after natural succession on a plot of land in
   a. central Australia?
   b. eastern Canada?
   c. southeastern Africa?
   d. Greenland?

Describe a climax community.

How do people affect succession?

How are communities named?

BACKGROUND Succession occurs even in a climax community, such as when a fire or disease eliminate some areas of vegetation. Other changes can occur seasonally, such as when birds migrate. Occasionally communities on islands have "species turnover," which is a maintenance of the total number of species by new species replacing ones that become extinct.

FIGURE 25–4. In a garden, vegetable plants are producers. They provide food for many consumers, including people.

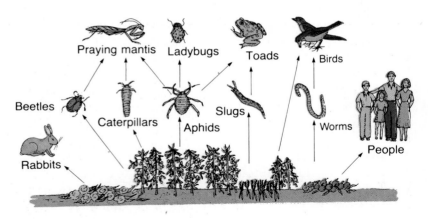

BACKGROUND Due to the great loss in mass and energy for each level (called trophic levels), five levels is the normal maximum in any ecosystem.

25:4 Community Interactions

Energy comes into a community from the sun. The organisms that make food using sunlight are the **producers** for the community. Organisms that eat other living organisms, including plants, are **consumers.** The organisms that eat producers are first-order consumers. The organisms that eat the first-order consumers are second-order consumers. The organisms that eat second-order consumers are third-order consumers.

Describe the relationship between producers and consumers in a community.

In a garden, the vegetable plants and weeds are producers. The people who eat the garden vegetables are first-order consumers. Rabbits, raccoons, grasshoppers, and caterpillars in the garden are first-order consumers, too. A bird that eats a grasshopper is a second-order consumer. A cat that eats the bird is a third-order consumer. The bacteria and fungi that break down the organic matter of wastes are **decomposers.** The decomposers make elements and compounds available for new plants.

FIGURE 25–5. The energy pyramid shows the loss of energy in a food chain. Note that many plants are required to indirectly support one cat. Only about 10% of the energy contained in each level of the pyramid is transferred to the next higher level.

Tracing energy flow from producers through consumers is called a food chain. The interactions of producers, consumers, and decomposers are part of an ecosystem's food web. A **food web** shows how populations in a community are involved in making and getting food. Figure 25–4 shows parts of the food web in a garden. Energy is transferred from producers to consumers to decomposers in a food web. Each time energy is transferred from one organism to another, some energy is lost as heat. Figure 25–5 shows that large populations of producers are needed to support small populations of consumers.

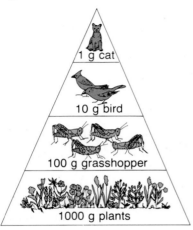

Activity: How does energy flow in ecosystems?

See Teacher's Guide.

MATERIALS

world map
reference books

FIGURE 25–6.

PROCEDURE

1. Refer to a world map. Choose one region of the world that interests you, such as the Sahara Desert, the Great Plains, the Australian outback, a tropical rain forest, or whatever you like.
2. Find out in which biome this ecosystem is. (Refer to Figure 25–2).
3. Using reference books, make a list of the most common organisms in the region. Record the information in a data table.
4. Determine whether each organism is a producer, first-, second-, or third-order consumer, or decomposer based on what they eat.
5. Draw and label at least two food webs that might exist in the region.
6. Draw and label an energy pyramid for each food chain.

QUESTIONS AND CONCLUSIONS

1. What are the main physical features of the ecosystem you chose?
2. What organisms in your food webs require the most producers to support them, directly or indirectly?
3. What consumers in your food webs require the least producers to support them?
4. Imagine that one of the first-order consumers in a food web was eliminated. How do you think that the missing population would affect the rest of this food web?
5. What roles, if any, do people have in each food web of the ecosystem?

DATA AND OBSERVATIONS

Region	
Biome	
Producers	
1st Order Consumers	
2nd Order Consumers	
3rd Order Consumers	
Decomposers	

25:5 Community Relationships

What are predators, scavengers, and parasites?

Populations in communities have different ways of getting food. One way is predation. **Predators** are second- or third-order consumers that kill animals for food. Cats that catch mice to eat and birds that eat insects are predators. Sometimes people are predators, when animals are hunted for food. The animals that predators eat are called prey.

Scavenging is another means of getting food. **Scavengers** eat dead organisms. A good example of a scavenger is a vulture. You may have seen vultures circling in the sky above animals that have been killed by cars on a highway. Some animals can be both scavengers and predators.

Some organisms are parasites that get food from other living organisms. Parasites can harm the host organism from which they get their food, but they usually do not kill it. Fleas and ticks on a dog are parasites. Bacteria that cause you to be sick are parasites, too. Some fungi are plant parasites that damage crops.

Mutualism (MYEW chuh lihz um) is an association of living organisms in which both organisms benefit. An example of mutualism is the action of *Escherichia coli* in your digestive system. *E. coli* is a bacteria that feeds on the undigested food in your large intestine. *E. coli* do not harm you. In fact, they help you. They fight disease bacteria. The relationship between you and *E. coli* in the ecosystem of your body is important to your health.

FIGURE 25–7. *Escherichia coli* is a bacteria found in human intestines that aids digestion.

5500 ×

See Teacher's Guide.

REVIEW AND REFLECT

1. Name an example of a producer, a first-order consumer, a second-order consumer, a third-order consumer, and a decomposer in a garden food web.
2. Describe three ways that animals get food.
3. Explain why a food web in which people eat corn is more efficient than a food web in which people eat beef from cows that eat corn.
4. Suppose there were no scavengers. How might this affect food webs?
5. How many orders of consumers include people? What are the benefits of having such a varied diet?

BACKGROUND   Another type of life strategy involving two species is commensalism. In this relationship, one member gets some benefit while the other apparently does not but is not harmed. An example is small fish that live between tentacles of sea anemones, getting protection but not providing any apparent benefit or harm to the anemones.

<u>25:6</u> Limiting Factors

Organisms compete for food. Since the amount of food for consumers is limited, the number of consumers also is limited. Food is said to be one of the limiting factors for a population. A **limiting factor** helps control the size of a population in a particular community. Besides food, some limiting factors for consumers are temperature, numbers of predators, and water. For producers, limiting factors include, temperature, sunlight, water, and nutrients.

Space is also an important limiting factor for organisms. Most animals have an area in which they move for their activities. The size of the area may be only a few square meters (for a mouse, for example) or thousands of square kilometers (for a reindeer). Within these ranges there are areas which the animal will defend against other members of the species. The defended area is called a territory. Defense of a territory aids in survival, because the animal is guarding a food supply or a space for a nest, burrow, or den. Sometimes territories are shared by a group of animals. An example of shared territory is found among prairie dogs. Black-tailed prairie dogs groom each other in order to help them recognize what individuals are part of the territory group.

Many characteristics and behaviors of organisms are adaptations that help them survive. For example, sometimes a predator threatens the young killdeer birds in a nest. Then the mother killdeer bird acts like her wing is broken. Predators tend to follow the mother away from the nest, since she appears to be easy prey. Some organisms use mimicry to protect themselves from predators. **Mimicry** (MIHM ih kree) is the characteristics or behaviors of an organism that make it appear like another organism or its surroundings. Some organisms use mimicry to attract other organisms. For example, a wasp orchid has the shape and scent of a female wasp. When male wasps try to mate with the orchid, the plant is pollinated. A walking stick is an insect that looks like a twig. When a walking stick stands still, predators do not recognize it as prey. Pigment cells in chameleons change so that the organisms blend in with their surroundings. Some rabbits' coats

BACKGROUND A useful concept related to limiting factors is "carrying capacity." This is the number of a species that the ecosystem can support for an extended time. Typically a population will grow until it reaches the carrying capacity of the ecosystem, and then fluctuations occur.

Name some limiting factors for producers and consumers.

BACKGROUND Animals may range over a wider area in their daily activities, called the "home range," than their territory.

FIGURE 25–8. This caterpillar has protective coloration, a kind of mimicry, that makes it less visible to predators because it blends with its background.

DEMONSTRATION Obtain one or more organisms that exhibit mimicry, such as a chameleon, a walking stick, the *Io* moth with eye markings on its wings, and caterpillars with head markings on their tails. Observe such organisms in backgrounds similar to their natural ones and in nonnatural ones.

What are "biological" clocks?

See Teacher's Guide.

change color with the seasons. They have white coats when snow is on the ground.

Many organisms seem to have "biological clocks" that control rhythmic behaviors. For example, most communities have two sets of populations: those active during the day (in the light) and those active at night (in the dark). Most birds and insects are inactive at night, since they are adapted to survival in light. However, owls can see well in the dark and catch the small mammals which are active then. Night moths eat the nectar of flowers that are open at night. Biological clocks are a kind of life strategy for most organisms that help them survive.

Skill Inquiry

The table shows the birth and death rates of people in different areas of the world. Refer to the table to answer these questions.

1. Which area has the highest birthrate?
2. Which area has the lowest death rate?

The growth rate of a population is expressed as a percentage. The word percentage comes from the Latin words, *per centum,* which mean for each one hundred. Each of the birth and death rates in the table can be expressed as percentages. A percentage is calculated by figuring how many births or deaths there were for each one hundred people. For example, in Africa there are 46 births per 1000 people. Since 1000 is 10 times 100, the birthrate for 100 people is 10 times less than for 1000 people. The birthrate in Africa is 46 divided by 10, which is 4.6. So the birthrate is 4.6 percent.

3. Which area has a birthrate of 3.4%?
4. What is the death rate (in percent) of North America?

Growth rate is determined by subtracting the death rate (in percent) from the birth rate (in percent). Calculate the growth rate of each area. Then answer these questions.

5. Which area has the highest growth rate? the lowest growth rate?
6. What is the average growth rate for the world?

TABLE OF BIRTH AND DEATH RATES

World Area	Birthrate per 1000 People	Death Rate per 1000 People
Africa	46	17
Asia	23	11
North America	16	8
Central and South America	34	8
Europe	14	10
Oceania	20	9

25:7 The Human Population

Most organisms adapt to the environment for survival. However, people often adapt the environment for their survival. Our intelligence helps us design ways to change our environment to help us survive. For example, farming supplies a more reliable food source than hunting and gathering. We build homes in which the temperature is controlled. As a result, we can survive in many different climates.

The technology we have developed often reduces the complexity of ecosystems. Modern farming methods enable us to control succession on farmlands. Only certain populations of plants are allowed to grow. The technology increases our food supply. However, the productivity of the soil may gradually decrease. Balance is important in any ecosystem. In natural ecosystems, limiting factors help maintain overall balance. In ecosystems in which people interact, natural processes may be upset. Sometimes the limiting factors are difficult to determine. However, a balance needs to be maintained among interacting factors in ecosystems involving people, just as in natural ecosystems.

Recently, many new sanitary and medical techniques have been developed. Along with reliable sources of food, they have prolonged human life. The natural controls on the human population, such as disease and famine, have been eliminated in many areas. Therefore, the human population has increased very rapidly. Food and energy needs and accumulation of wastes have become problems for the human population. These problems could become limiting factors for the human population if growth continues. As other populations adjust to environmental changes, so must people.

See Teacher's Guide.

How does intelligence promote human survival?

BACKGROUND   The world's total population was about four billion in 1974 and is expected to be almost eight billion by 2000. More than half of the world's population is now under age 25.

What effect does technology have on ecosystems?

Discuss specific advances in sanitary and medical procedures between times in the past (e.g., 1700, 1800, 1900) and currently. Use library sources as background for a detailed discussion.

REVIEW AND REFLECT

1. Name three limiting factors each for
   a. animals   b. plants   c. people
2. Give three examples of mimicry.
3. How is the human population like other populations? different?

25:8 Information: Antarctica

Antarctica is a unique region. It is the only polar continent. Ocean and ice cover the North Pole. A huge glacier, three kilometers thick at its center, covers the South Pole and most of the rest of Antarctica. The weight of the ice forces most of the continent below sea level. Most of the snow that formed the glacier fell thousands of years ago. Now Antarctica gets very little precipitation. The average temperature is below freezing. The wind blows constantly. If you have ever been caught in a cold wind, you know that the wind makes the temperature seem less than it really is.

BACKGROUND This effect is the so-called "wind chill."

Describe the organisms of Antarctica.

Relatively few kinds of life can live in this climate. The communities of plants and animals found in Antarctica are adapted to live in the cold, windy, and dry environment. About 400 kinds of lichens, 75 species of mosses, and 3 kinds of flowering plants live in snow-free nooks around mountains and places near the edge of the continent that are free of ice. The Antarctic organisms grow very slowly. Some may be earth's oldest organisms.

Fewer than 70 kinds of animals are found within the Antarctic Circle. Of these, most are insects, including a wingless mosquito. The most complex life forms to go far inland are birds, two of which are the short Adelie penguin and the tall Emperor penguin. The penguins stay together in groups called rookeries. There they mate, build nests, and raise their young during fall and winter. The penguins eat fish from the oceans. Parents make long trips to the ocean for food. They regurgitate some of their food to feed the young penguins.

FIGURE 25–9. Adelie penguins are residents of Antarctica.

The Atlantic, Pacific, and Indian Oceans surround Antarctica. Passing through the oceans, some hundreds of kilometers offshore, there is a clockwise current around Antarctica. In a 40-kilometer wide zone, upwelling occurs where cold water flowing north meets warmer water flowing south. This zone, known as the Antarctic Convergence, is one of the richest communities of life anywhere. Phosphates and other compounds from the sea floor provide food for phytoplankton, which are the base of Antarctic food chains. A small shrimplike animal called krill is abundant. Krill are eaten by fish and squids, which are eaten by penguins, seals, and some whales.

Since the beginning of this century, explorers and scientists have worked in small numbers in Antarctica. The human population there is still small, about 2000 during the summer and 100 during the winter. Since 1957, a group of nations, now numbering 16, have participated in decisions about human activity in Antarctica. These nations all agree to environmental protection, freedom of information, and interest in science. Science activities specifically are overseen by the Scientific Committee on Antarctic Research (SCAR). This committee was formed when the 1957 agreement of nations was made. SCAR has been responsible for observing and guiding the development of science and human involvement in Antarctica.

Many things have been discovered, but SCAR emphasizes that there is still much to learn about Antarctica. The Antarctic Convergence is probably responsible for much of earth's weather, but how this occurs is not completely understood. Much can be learned from the Antarctic glacier, because the ice shows a history of the earth's climate.

Scientific exploration has been about the only reason for people to go to Antarctica. However, that may change. A group of 77 developing nations are not satisfied with the management of the 16 controlling nations. They feel that the wealth of Antarctica, whatever it may be, should be available to all. The oceans hold fish, whales, and krill that could feed millions. Some desert nations think the icebergs could be possible sources of water. Many nations think oil and mineral resources may be buried in the land, although none have been found yet. Some people would like to promote tourism to this very different land. These pressures may change the scientific and environmental interest that has preserved the Antarctic ecosystem so far.

See Teacher's Guide.

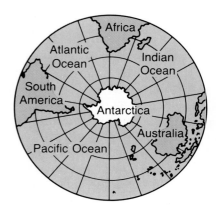

FIGURE 25–10. Antarctica is the only polar continent. It is surrounded by the Atlantic, Pacific, and Indian Oceans.

What pressures may change the Antarctic ecosystem?

ACTIVITY   Have some students adopt roles as delegates to developing countries, while others assume roles as delegates to the group of countries currently directing activities in Antarctica. Simulate a meeting of the two groups to discuss the future of the Antarctic ecosystem.

REVIEW AND REFLECT

1. Name five features of the Antarctic ecosystem.
2. What topics of scientific study in Antarctica can give important information about the entire earth?
3. What changes, if any, do you think should be made in the control and use of Antarctica? Give reasons for your recommendations of change or maintaining the present system.

1. Ecologists study the interactions of living things and the physical environments in ecosystems. 25:1
2. Cycles are important to the maintenance of a kind of homeostasis in ecosystems. 25:1
3. Major world ecosystems are called biomes, which are defined by climate and communities of organisms. 25:2
4. Organisms share habitats. Each organism has a particular niche. 25:2
5. A natural succession of communities occurs in ecosystems until the climax community is formed. 25:3
6. The food web in a community includes producers, consumers of different orders, and decomposers. 25:4
7. At each level of the food web, energy is lost as heat. 25:4
8. Organisms in communities get food by predation, scavenging, parasitism, and mutualistic relationships. 25:5
9. Limiting factors include food, water, temperature, and space. 25:6
10. Removal of natural controls has caused rapid increase in the human population. 25:7

VOCABULARY

biomes 4	habitat 10	predators 12
community 5	limiting factors 16	producer 6
consumers 7	mimicry 15	scavenger 13
decomposer 8	mutualism 14	succession 3
ecosystem 1	niche 11	
food web 9	population 2	

Choose a word from the list to complete each sentence.

1. An ecologist's unit of study is a(n) _____.
2. A single species found in an ecosystem is called a(n) _____.
3. _____ is a series of changes in the community of an ecosystem.
4. Large regions of the earth with similar organisms and climate are _____.
5. A(n) _____ is made up of all the populations in an ecosystem.
6. An organism that makes food using sunlight is called a(n) _____.
7. Organisms that eat other organisms, including plants, are _____.
8. An organism that breaks down organic matter is a(n) _____.
9. A(n) _____ shows interactions of producers and consumers in a community.
10. A population's _____ provides things the organisms need to survive.
11. The role of an organism in its habitat is called a(n) _____.
12. Consumers that eat animals for food are _____.
13. A(n) _____ eats dead organisms.
14. An association of living organisms in which both benefit is _____.
15. Adaptations that make an organism appear like another organism or its surroundings are _____.
16. Things, such as amount of food or living space, that help control the size of a population in a community are _____.

QUESTIONS

MAIN IDEAS

Choose the correct answer to each question.

1. What is the final stable community that exists at the end of natural succession called? *(niche, population, climax community, habitat)*

2. What main factor determines the organisms that live in any biome? *(trees, climate, sunlight)*

3. When succession starts on a barren rock, what is it called? *(primary, secondary, third-order, climax)*

4. What kind of consumer is a bird that eats a leaf-eating insect? *(first-order, second-order, third-order)*

5. The actions of *E. coli* in a human's large intestine is an example of what? *(scavenging, parasitism, mutualism, predation)*

6. What is not a natural cycle in an ecosystem? *(water, carbon dioxide–oxygen, nitrogen, ammonia)*

7. What is the most plentiful plant species in a community called? *(dominant, recessive, abundant, controlled)*

8. What usually is not considered a limiting factor for animals? *(temperature, water, predators, sunlight)*

9. The migration of birds is an example of what? *(mimicry, biological clocks, limiting factors)*

10. What is not part of the physical environment of an ecosystem? *(energy, rainfall, sunlight, plants)*

See Teacher's Guide.

APPLICATIONS

Answer each question in one or more paragraphs.

1. Explain in which major world ecosystem you would find
   a. the greatest total flow of energy.
   b. the least total flow of energy.

2. Name a type of producer other than plants.

3. Suppose there were no decomposers. How would this affect the rest of a garden community?

4. Compare the energy required to feed people who live mostly on rice, potatoes, and wheat with the energy needed to feed people with high-meat diets.

5. The viceroy butterfly looks like the monarch butterfly. The monarch butterfly has a bitter taste to birds. The viceroy butterfly does not have a bitter taste. Why do most birds not eat viceroys?

FURTHER STUDY

INVESTIGATIONS

1. Use library sources to prepare a report on some organisms with behaviors controlled by biological clocks.

2. Visit a zoo. Make a list of adaptations that help different animals survive in their natural habitats.

3. Select an animal which interests you. Prepare a report on its niche and habitat. Discuss the other organisms in its natural community.

READINGS

0 Croall, Stephen, and William Rankin. *Ecology for Beginners.* Pantheon Books: New York, 1981.

0 Levinson, Marc. "Nurseries of Life." *National Wildlife.* February/March, 1984. pp. 18–21.

+ Sheffield, Charles. *Man on Earth.* Macmillan: New York, 1983.

– Swenson, Allen A. *The World Within the Tidal Pool.* David McKay Company: New York, 1979.

THE INFLUENCE OF SCIENCE

UNIT 6

Unit Six focuses on the influence of science applied to the world in which we live. Technology has resulted in many changes in the environment. For example, better farming methods have been factors in increased population growth. As a result, communities have grown and open space has become more limited. In this unit, you will learn about positive and negative environmental effects of the influence of science.

1. What are energy alternatives?
2. What are sources of pollution?
3. How does technological change affect plants and animals?
4. How can natural resources be conserved?
5. What management practices can be used to maintain a healthy environment?

How did you get to school today? Maybe you walked or rode in a bus or a car. Would you walk or ride a bus home if you could drive? Every means of transportation requires a different amount of energy. How can the use of energy be compared? What factors affect energy use?

ENERGY RESOURCES

INTRODUCING THE CHAPTER   Review the concept of energy studied in chapters 10 and 11. Ask students to list different forms of energy, such as radiant energy and thermal energy. Discuss sources of these forms of energy. Also review how living organisms obtain energy. Point out that this chapter deals with sources of energy for transportation, heating and cooling buildings, and manufacturing and other industrial uses.

26:1   Energy Use

Think of all the ways you use energy in a day. Food provides energy to your body, but consider the energy used to grow, process, and prepare the food you eat. Energy was used to make your clothing and perhaps provided you with transportation to school. Energy is used to light your classroom and operate televisions and video games, too.

In the past, people did not use as much energy. As technology has advanced, people's standard of living has changed. Traditionally, more energy use has meant a better life. Automobiles made transportation faster and more convenient. Modern electrical appliances made many daily tasks easier. Entertainment devices provided new amusements.

As people's standard of living rises, energy use increases. Figure 26–1 shows that energy use increases as population increases. More people use more energy. While demand for energy continues to increase, our supply of many energy resources does not. The gap between our supply of energy and our demand for it is widening.

Conservation can reduce demand for energy. Technology may provide some alternative sources to increase the supply of energy. Deciding how to manage energy resources is not easy, but people—governments and individuals—must make these decisions. Our management of energy resources today will affect our future.

GOAL   You will learn different sources of energy and some problems related to energy use.

SUGGESTION   Have students make individual lists of all the ways they know they have used energy today, either directly or indirectly.

Why is more energy used now than in the past?

SUGGESTION   Make sure students understand the term "standard of living."

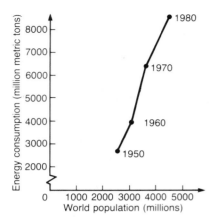

FIGURE 26–1. Population growth is the independent variable and energy use is the dependent variable. As the graph shows, energy use is directly proportional to population growth.

What are fossil fuels and how are they formed?

BACKGROUND   Crude oil is the liquid component of petroleum. Petroleum includes crude oil, natural gas, and asphalt and wax materials. Petroleum is produced over a long period where marine organisms are buried and contained.

SUGGESTION   Discuss possible problems of oil use and the rate of population growth, which affect how long the earth's oil will last.

26:2 Fossil Fuels

In 1973, many people first became aware of an energy crisis. In a political move, a group of middle-eastern nations called the Organization of Petroleum Exporting Countries (OPEC) stopped supplying oil to the United States and other countries for a short time. Gasoline suddenly became scarce and costly. Although the energy crisis got people's attention in 1973, it had been developing for a long time.

Oil is a fossil fuel. Most of the energy used in the United States comes from burning **fossil fuels,** which were formed from the organic matter of ancient plants and animals. Millions of years of heat and pressure changed the organic matter into oil, coal, and natural gas. Oil, coal, and natural gas are still forming, but at rates much slower than they are being used. Fossil fuel reserves are considered finite, which means the supply is limited. For this reason, fossil fuels are **nonrenewable** sources of energy.

People do not agree about how long fossil fuel reserves will last. Many scientists suggest that most of the earth's oil will be gone by the year 2000 if it continues to be used at the same rate as it is used now. If the rate of population growth changes, the amounts of fuels needed will probably change, too. The OPEC nations control much of the world's

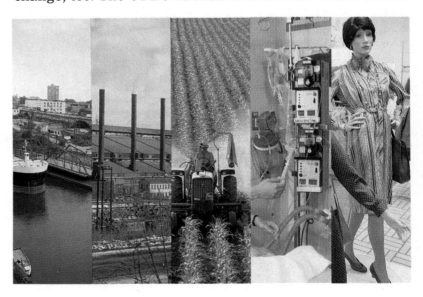

FIGURE 26–2. Petroleum products have many uses.

oil reserves. How OPEC decides to manage its oil will affect the whole world.

Reserves of natural gas are estimated to be as limited as those of oil. The same wells that produce oil often produce natural gas. Coal should last a much longer time than either oil or natural gas if it continues to be used at current rates.

Oil shale and tar sand are materials that contain oil, although it is not concentrated as in normal oil reserves. Oil shale is a brown rock. It does not look or feel oily. Chemical methods can be used to remove oil from oil shale. However, removing the oil is extremely costly, requires a great deal of energy, and is harmful to the environment. Although technology has provided a means to make use of this energy resource, deciding to use it may not be wise.

Tar sand is rock or rock particles with tar in the spaces between grains. Tar is a petroleum product that can be removed from tar sand to produce oil. It is easier and less costly to produce oil from tar sand than from oil shale. Production of oil from tar sand now takes place in Canada, particularly in northern Alberta.

There are problems with the use of fossil fuels. The natural landscape often is disturbed by mining equipment. When coal is mined and transported, harmful dust may be distributed over many kilometers. Transportation of oil may result in spills that kill wildlife and endanger people. Pipe transportation of natural gas and oil can produce fires and explosions where there are pipe failures.

Combustion is incomplete when fossil fuels are burned to produce energy. Particulates, such as smoke and ash, and harmful gases, such as carbon monoxide, pollute the air. Other compounds given off cause acid rain and smog when they react with atmospheric compounds. The air pollutants are health hazards, harm crops and livestock, and damage the environment.

We cannot depend on fossil fuels to supply all of our future energy demand because they are nonrenewable resources. In addition, because using fossil fuels causes land and air pollution, we need to carefully evaluate their use. Alternative sources of energy need to be developed to reduce our dependence on fossil fuels.

FIGURE 26–3. Tar sands are mined in Alberta, Canada, and used to produce oil.

BACKGROUND The solid petroleum material in oil shale is called kerogen.

What are oil shale and tar sands?

What are some problems with the use of fossil fuels?

SUGGESTION Review the effect of carbon monoxide on the human body, discussed in chapter 23. Review the mentioned compounds discussed in unit 2 and acid rain from the enrichment in chapter 6.

See Teacher's Guide.

REVIEW AND REFLECT

1. What brought an energy crisis to people's attention in the 1970s?
2. What are fossil fuels? Why do we need to consider changing our present use of fossil fuels?
3. What are the problems with obtaining oil from oil shale and tar sands?
4. Suppose the price of oil tripled. How might that affect your life?

See Teacher's Guide.

Career Profile

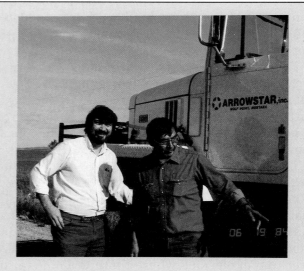

As a young student in the small town of Wagoner, Oklahoma, George Thomas developed an early interest in the mysteries of science. Though George did not grow up on a reservation, he gained a very strong sense of his Cherokee heritage. Today, George is a nuclear engineer, but he has not forgotten his heritage. Over the past decade, he has used his leadership abilities to help American Indians understand the sciences better.

As a graduate student at the University of Oklahoma, George helped plan a summer program for American Indian students in high school. It was George's hope to introduce these young people to others who had been successful in engineering and the sciences. About this same time, George also founded the American Indian Science and Engineering Society. The purpose of the organization has been to bring more American Indians into engineering.

In 1979, George took a job in Denver with the Council of Energy Resource Tribes. It is a group of more than thirty tribes with significant amounts of oil, gas, coal, and uranium on their lands. George served as director of human resource development and education. He helped develop training programs to further the American Indians' understanding of how their natural resources should be used.

Currently, George works with a large oil company. On a typical day he may oversee the work of seismic crews or drilling and petroleum engineers. He most enjoys meeting with the tribal leaders and assuring them of the care that will be taken with their land. George feels a duty to use his talents to help others and to encourage all young people to do the same.

26:3 Nuclear Energy

Nuclear energy is released from radioactive elements when certain changes occur in the nuclei of the atoms. Two types of nuclear reactions—fission and fusion—produce energy. **Fission,** which is the splitting of atoms, is currently used to produce electricity in nuclear power plants.

The nuclear reactor contains fuel rods, which are tubes filled with small pellets of uranium dioxide. The uranium dioxide contains radioactive uranium-235. Bombarding the fuel rods with neutrons causes the uranium nuclei to split. Energy and neutrons are released. These neutrons split more uranium nuclei, releasing more energy and more neutrons. A chain reaction results, with billions of nuclear reactions occurring every second.

Control rods of cadmium or boron are placed in the reactor core with the fuel rods. Operators adjust the control rods in or out of the core to keep the chain reaction going at a controlled rate. Water circulates around the rods in the reactor. The water's hydrogen atoms slow down the energetic neutrons and cool the rods.

A type of nuclear reactor is shown in Figure 26–4. A loop of water passes through this reactor. This water is contaminated with radioactive wastes from the reactor, so it must be well-contained and never come in contact with other parts of the power plant. The water in the loop is

What is the source of nuclear energy?

DEMONSTRATION
Demonstrate a chain reaction with a set of dominoes. Discuss how hitting the head pin in bowling sets off a similar chain reaction.

How is a chain reaction produced and controlled in a nuclear reactor?

BACKGROUND   Some reactors, particularly those in Canada, use water composed of deuterium atoms. These heavy water reactors can use less expensive uranium fuel than normal or light water reactors. Light water reactors, used in the U.S., require that natural uranium be treated to concentrate atoms of U-235.

FIGURE 26–4. The most common type of nuclear power plant in use is the pressurized-water reactor. Pressurized water flows through the reactor and heat exchanger. Heat from this water is transferred to secondary water, vaporizing it. Note that the two water supplies never mix. The steam powers the turbines that run the electric generator.

SUGGESTION   Review why very hot water under high pressure does not boil.

What are some advantages and disadvantages of nuclear power plants?

FIGURE 26–5. In 1979, Three Mile Island nuclear power plant in Pennsylvania was in danger of a meltdown. A bubble of hydrogen gas that developed above the reactor core could have exploded, shattering the building. Workers at the plant mistakenly had turned off the automatic safeguards that normally would prevent a meltdown. The bubble of gas was vented gradually into the atmosphere, so a meltdown did not occur. However, large amounts of low-level radioactive steam and gas were released into the air.

very hot, about 315°C, but it does not boil because it is kept under high pressure. The heat of the pressurized water is transferred to another water system at a lower pressure. This uncontaminated water boils, producing steam. The steam runs a turbine that makes electricity.

Nuclear power plants have some advantages over power plants that use fossil fuels. Much less fuel is needed to produce the same amount of energy, so the fuel costs are reduced. Fewer mines and less transportation of fuel are needed. Fewer harmful gases and particulates are released into the air by nuclear power plants.

A major problem with nuclear power plants is radioactive wastes. Low-level radioactive wastes come from leaks in the material that covers the water circulating through the nuclear reactor. Filters normally remove these wastes. Some low-level gas wastes are released into the air. Low-level liquid and solid wastes are burned. Small amounts of low-level radioactive wastes are not considered hazardous by most scientists.

High-level radioactive wastes are found within the used fuel rods. The rods contain radioactive fission fragments and nuclei made when uranium-235 atoms split. The reason for concern about high-level radioactive wastes is that they have long half-lives and radiation from them harms cells. The cells may die, may be damaged so that they will not reproduce, or may mutate. The mutations are usually harmful. Some mutations can cause cancer and birth defects. Most of the high-level radioactive wastes produced in nuclear reactors have half-lives of many years. Thousands of years must pass before the wastes can be considered safe. Safe locations for disposal of these products is essential. It is also necessary to have a safe way to transport the wastes to the disposal sites.

The largest amount of dangerous radiation that would be released from a nuclear power plant in a catastrophe is called a meltdown. In a meltdown, the core of a nuclear reactor would become exposed and high-level radioactivity would contaminate a large area. Nuclear power plants have safeguards to prevent the release of dangerous radiation. A meltdown is unlikely.

Nuclear fusion might someday produce energy in nuclear power plants. **Fusion** is the combination of lighter nuclei to form heavier ones. Fusion makes much more energy from the same mass of fuel than fission does. Also, fusion does not create large amounts of radioactive wastes.

In a nuclear fusion reactor, hydrogen isotopes would be combined to form helium isotopes or heavier hydrogen isotopes. Very high temperatures are required for a fusion reaction to occur. It occurs naturally in the sun and other stars. Scientists and engineers are trying to find ways to contain light hydrogen nuclei in the plasma state at a temperature of 40 000 000 K. The plasma must be dense and held together for a long time at the high temperature for the fusion reaction to occur.

FIGURE 26–6. One of three basic designs for nuclear fusion reactors is a tokamak, such as the one shown in California.

26:4 Solar Energy

Picture a car with black vinyl seats parked in the sun on a summer day. If you got in, the seats would be hot because they absorbed solar energy. Solar energy comes directly from the sun.

Two ways of using solar energy—passive and active—currently supply some of our energy demand. Generally, passive use of solar energy does not require special equipment. A building that uses a **passive system** is designed to take advantage of the sun's energy naturally. For example, buildings constructed with their longest sides facing north/south are more energy efficient than those facing east/west. The angle of the sun to the horizon is greater in summer than in winter (chapter 16). So, roof overhangs, which shade windows in summer, allow the sun's warmth to penetrate in winter. In cold climates, passive solar heating may be supplemented by other heat sources, such as electric heat, a furnace that burns fossil fuels, or a woodburning stove or fireplace. Passive use of solar energy to provide at least some energy in buildings reduces the demand for energy from fossil fuels and nuclear power.

Describe passive solar heating.

Construction of passive solar buildings generally costs no more than construction of conventional buildings, because the differences are basically in design. Any additional costs that may occur are usually quickly offset by reduced energy costs.

FIGURE 26–7. The solar radiation that comes through a collector is 46 percent infrared (heat). A black metal sheet absorbs the heat. The heat does not pass out through the glass cover over the sheet. (Recall the greenhouse effect, page 360.) Just below the sheet, tubes are bonded to absorb heat by conduction. Insulation is placed under the tubes. Water passes through the tubes, absorbing heat.

Glass cover

Black metal sheet

Insulation

Fluid tubes

How does an active solar heating system work?

SUGGESTION Discuss the general meaning of the terms active and passive, and apply them to other situations (for example, active and passive sports activities).

How are solar cells used?

BACKGROUND Solar cells vary in efficiency. Cadmium sulfide cells found in cameras have an efficiency of about five percent. Silicon cells used in space projects have an efficiency of about 15 percent. Research projects are under way to greatly improve the latter's value.

An active solar heating and cooling system is more expensive to build than a passive system. An **active system** for solar energy involves special collectors, storage units, and circulation systems. Figure 26–7 shows the structure of a solar collector. The heat absorbed by collectors is transferred by conduction to water or air passing over them. The hot water or air circulates in pipes throughout the building, radiating heat. Excess heat is stored in water tanks or rock bins. A supplemental heat source is used when solar energy does not supply enough heat.

Solar energy can be changed to electrical energy. Sometimes this is done with solar cells. A solar cell converts solar energy directly to electricity using a dime-thick sandwich of elements that are semiconductors. As the sun shines on one side of the cell, a small potential difference results between the top and the bottom of the cell. While the sun shines, the solar cell behaves like a battery. When no light strikes it, the solar cell cannot operate. The energy converted by solar cells can be stored in batteries for later use.

Solar cells are a common energy source in calculators, watches, and cameras. Solar cells can be connected together in arrays to supply large amounts of energy. Some homes have solar arrays that supply electricity. An irrigation system in Nebraska is operated by a solar array. An Indian reservation in Arizona receives its electricity from a solar array. Currently it costs about 10 times more to supply electricity with solar cells than it does with fossil fuels.

A solar thermal power plant produces electricity by focusing sunlight on collectors. This method of getting energy is similar to an active solar heating and cooling system. The collectors store the energy as heat, which is used to make steam. The steam runs a turbine that generates electricity. Figure 26–8 shows the first operating solar thermal power plant, Solar One.

Solar energy has many advantages over fossil fuels and nuclear energy. Solar energy is a continuous flow energy source. A **continuous flow** source is one that is always being produced. Solar energy will be available as long as the sun shines. Solar energy does not produce wastes like those of fossil fuels and nuclear fission. Solar energy often is called "free." However, it costs money to make the systems that collect, store, or change solar energy into electricity. Active solar energy systems are most useful in regions where the annual number of sunny days is high. See Figure 26–10 on page 564. The major problem with active solar energy is the cost of construction. However, as fuel prices rise, the building costs may become more economical. Another problem is that sometimes the energy needed to operate active solar energy systems is more than the useful energy the systems can provide. In such cases, using active solar heating is unwise.

See Teacher's Guide.

REVIEW AND REFLECT

1. How is energy produced in a nuclear power plant?
2. What are some problems with
   a. fossil fuels?
   b. nuclear fission power plants?
   c. nuclear fusion power plants?
3. Is nuclear energy a nonrenewable energy resource? Explain your answer.
4. What is the difference between active and passive solar heating?
5. Make a sketch of the building you live in. Was it designed with passive solar heating in mind? What do you think could have been done to improve passive solar heating effects?

FIGURE 26–8.   Solar One in California is a model for future commercial solar thermal power plants. An oil and rock heat storage system allows the plant to produce power for four hours without sunlight.

When is use of active solar energy systems wise?

BACKGROUND   While active solar heating and cooling may not be practical in many homes, an active solar hot water heating system is practical for many homes.

Activity: What factors affect passive solar heating?

See Teacher's Guide.

MATERIALS

shoe box
plastic wrap
tape
scissors
white and black
  construction paper
high-intensity lamp
paper towels

thermometer
metric ruler
beaker of room
  temperature water
colored cellophane
potted plant
clock or watch

FIGURE 26–9.

PROCEDURE

1. Make a model house out of a shoe box. Let the lid be the roof. Cut out a large window on one long side. Tape clear plastic over the window.
2. Cover the outside of the box with white paper, except the window.
3. Place the box with the window side facing a lamp. Place the lamp about 30 cm from the edge of the house. Direct the light on the house at an angle of 45°.
4. Dip the thermometer in water to return it to room temperature. Then dry it off. Put the thermometer inside the house and replace the roof (lid).
5. Check the temperature inside the house after 10 minutes. Record.
6. Turn the house so that the long non-window side is toward the lamp. Repeat steps 4 and 5.
7. Repeat step 2 with black paper. Then repeat steps 3, 4, 5, and 6.
8. Place a plant between the lamp and the house so that the plant casts a shadow on the window. Repeat steps 4 and 5.
9. Tape a white overhang above the long window. Repeat steps 3, 4, and 5.
10. Remove the overhang. Cover the window with colored cellophane. Repeat steps 3, 4, and 5.

DATA AND OBSERVATIONS

Color	Window Position	Other Factors	Temperature

QUESTIONS AND CONCLUSIONS

1. What effect did each of the following have on passive solar heating?
   a. position of window
   b. house color
   c. window overhang
   d. plant
2. From the standpoint of a scientific method, why was it necessary to test each house color in each position?
3. What other factors might affect passive solar heating?
4. Suppose that you could design a building and choose where and how to build it. Make a sketch of the building and its location. Tell why you chose different features.

26:5 Wind Energy

About one percent of the sun's energy reaching the earth is converted into wind. Wind-powered water pumps are common on farms and ranches in some regions. Once wind-powered electric generators were common, too. As fuel costs continue to rise, interest in wind power to produce electricity has been renewed. The U.S. National Aeronautics and Space Administration (NASA) maintains several large model wind-powered generators. Based on experiments with the NASA models, some cities have started using wind power to generate electricity. Places where wind energy could be used to supply electricity are shown in Figure 26–10. The largest wind generator, in the state of Washington, consists of 25 towers.

Like solar energy, wind energy produces no air pollution or radioactive wastes. However, wind power is not useful everywhere. The best sites for wind power are places where the wind blows fairly constantly and at a reasonable speed. Energy generated by wind power can be stored in batteries for use when the wind is not blowing.

BACKGROUND A wind turbine converts the wind's kinetic energy into rotational mechanical energy. About one fourth of the power is changed to electricity in a practical system.

Why is wind energy being considered more and more today?

What are some advantages and disadvantages of wind energy?

26:6 Geothermal Energy

Geothermal energy is heat from within the earth. Igneous intrusions in the crust, sometimes called hot spots, are places where magma rises close to the earth's surface. Water in the rock above the magma is heated. The heat from the geothermal source is transferred to a loop of fresh water. This hot water is used to power a steam turbine that produces electricity. The geothermal water is not used directly because it contains dissolved minerals that would corrode pipes.

Geothermal energy is useful where it is found. However, it is not widely available. Figure 26-10 shows places where geothermal energy is used. The dissolved minerals in the hot water corrode metal parts of geothermal power plants, which may require costly repairs. Releasing of the hot water into the environment after it has been used is also a problem.

What is geothermal energy?

BACKGROUND The source of heat in magma and deep within the earth is from the decay of naturally radioactive elements, U-238, Th-232, and K-40.

What are some problems with the use of geothermal energy?

c

FIGURE 26–10. The total solar radiation received at the earth's surface during the entire year is shown in kilojoules per square meter (a). As shown, the darker the shading, the greater the availability of wind energy for development (b). Locations of geothermal development for energy supply (c); Locations of major tidal power sites (d).

d

26:7 Water Energy

Falling water is used to supply some of the demand for energy. Electric energy produced when water falls from a high place to a low place is called **hydroelectric** energy. Hydro means water. Hydroelectric energy is related to the water cycle and solar energy. As water evaporates from oceans, condenses as clouds, and falls as precipitation over land, the water in streams is replaced. The sun provides the energy for evaporation and for wind to move clouds.

Many hydroelectric dams have been built on major rivers, such as the Colorado, Tennessee, and Columbia Rivers in the United States. The release of water held back by the dams is controlled. Water falling over the dams powers turbines that produce electricity.

Hydroelectric power is a clean source of energy. It does not cause much water or air pollution. Also, its cost is comparable to the cost of energy from fossil fuels or nuclear power. Hydroelectric power currently supplies some of the United States' energy demand. However, the river sites for hydroelectric power are limited, and the best sites have been developed already. So, hydroelectric power is not a major energy alternative for the future. In addition, the environmental effects of dams may be severe, even though pollution is slight.

Energy from ocean tides also can be used to generate power. Tidal energy is a result of gravitation between the moon and the earth. In a tidal electric power plant, water flows into a large bay or pool. The flowing water turns a turbine to make electricity. At high tide, the water gates are closed. As the tide starts to fall, the gates are opened again and the falling water turns the turbine.

The range in height from high to low tide limits energy available from tides. Sites where the total amount of water that can flow into a pool is large are the best locations for tidal power plants. Tidal power plants cost more to build than other kinds of power plants and few locations are suitable. In addition, tidal power plants are harmful to the marine environment.

See Teacher's Guide.

REVIEW AND REFLECT

1. Compare the advantages and disadvantages of solar, geothermal, wind, tidal, and hydroelectric energy.
2. Suppose that the sun stopped shining. What sources of energy would be eliminated? What energy sources would still be present?
3. What are the most promising energy alternatives for future large-scale use? Explain.
4. What are the most important factors in determining which energy source to use?

FIGURE 26–11. Ocean thermal energy conversion (OTEC) is a way of using the temperature difference between warm surface water and cold deep water to generate electricity. An experimental OTEC project is being tested near Hawaii. OTEC causes no pollution and, although costly at present, may one day be an economical source of energy.

Describe two types of water energy sources.

BACKGROUND/SUGGESTION
The sun, as well as the moon, causes tides. However, the effect due to the sun is much less than the effect due to the moon. Review the causes of tides, chapter 19.

How can people conserve
nonrenewable energy
resources?

BACKGROUND The study of
heat flow and energy changes is
called thermodynamics. The fact
that energy is always lost in an
energy-converting system is
known as the Second Law of
Thermodynamics. The First Law
of Thermodynamics is the Law of
Conservation of Energy.

What is efficiency?

How is efficiency expressed?

SUGGESTION Have students
check the rated efficiencies of
various energy-converting
devices, such as appliances. Have
students report their results and
compare them.

26:8 Energy Efficiency

Increased use of continuous flow energy resources (solar, geothermal, wind, and water) will help reduce demand for nonrenewable energy sources (fossil fuels, nuclear fission). However, continuous flow energy sources are limited by economics, geography, and available technology. People will need to accept and adapt to alternative energy sources.

Another important way to reduce demand for nonrenewable energy sources is to conserve energy. If we reduce the demand for nonrenewable energy sources by using less energy, our supplies of fossil fuels and nuclear fuels will last longer. Pollution and other problems, such as mining, transporting, and waste disposal, will be lessened.

One way to conserve energy is to improve efficiency. **Efficiency** is a comparison of the useful energy put out by a system and the energy put in to operate it. According to the Law of Conservation of Energy, the amount of energy put into a system is equal to the amount of energy put out. However, some of the energy output is not useful. It is lost as heat. For example, the gasoline put into a car has a certain amount of potential energy. When the fuel is burned in the car's engine, the car moves. The motion of the car is kinetic energy output. However, the car's engine gets hot after being driven for a while. Some of the potential energy in the fuel is changed to heat, another form of kinetic energy, instead of motion. So, the useful kinetic energy output, that is, the energy of motion, is less than the potential energy of the fuel.

Efficiency usually is expressed as a percentage. The percentage indicates the ratio of useful energy output to energy input. Percent efficiencies can be useful for making energy decisions. For example, an incandescent light bulb has an energy efficiency of five percent. A fluorescent bulb is 20 percent efficient. By comparison, a fluorescent bulb is more efficient than an incandescent bulb. In other words, a fluorescent bulb uses less energy to put out the same amount of light as an incandescent bulb. The efficiency of many energy-converting devices can be improved. Improving efficiency becomes more economical as energy costs increase.

See Teacher's Guide.

Skill Inquiry

Exponential growth is a change in which the rate of increase is a percentage of the current size. Many changes important to energy study are exponential. For example, population growth is exponential.

Population has been increasing rapidly in recent times because the growth rate of the human population has been increasing. Before 1650, the growth rate was less than .1% per year. The current growth rate is about 1.7% per year. The time a population takes to double decreases as percent growth increases. The doubling time for exponential growth can be calculated using the following equation.

$$\text{doubling time} = \frac{70}{\text{yearly percent rate of growth}}$$

1. If the world's population is increasing at a rate of 1.7% each year and if the rate continues, when will the population be double what it is now?
2. If energy use worldwide is growing at the rate of 3.5% per year and the rate continues, when will energy use be double what it is now?
3. Name two factors that could change the rate of questions 1 and 2.

Because of improved sanitation and better medical techniques, the death rate has decreased in recent times. As a result more people live longer and more have children today than in the past. The sizes of families affect future population.

4. How does the average number of children per family affect the doubling time of population?
5. Why do you think the growth of the human population is sometimes called the population "explosion"?

People need to make informed decisions about how many children to have. The quality of life is affected by the number of people on earth. Many biologists say that the earth is approaching the limit of the number of people it can support with food, energy, and space. They say that the earth cannot support many more people.

26:9   Energy Conservation

Another way to conserve energy is to reduce energy loss from buildings. Heat leaking around and through windows and doors is the biggest source of heat loss from buildings. Weatherstripping and double-pane windows can help reduce the heat loss. Poorly-insulated walls, ceilings, and floors are another major problem. Insulation can be added to existing buildings to reduce heat loss. Insulating materials are assigned R-values according to their resistance to heat flow. (See chapter 11.) The higher its R-value, the better an insulator it is in terms of preventing heat loss.

BACKGROUND   Heat flow through a material depends on type of material, thickness, area, and temperature difference between sides. R-value is defined in English units: $\frac{\text{ft}^2 \times \text{hr} \times °\text{F}}{\text{Btu}}$ Insulation materials have typically higher R-values than other materials of the same thickness.

What does R-value indicate?

FIGURE 26–12. A heat pump is useful for heating and cooling. For heating, as shown, a liquid refrigerant is pumped through an outside coil. The refrigerant picks up heat from outside air, water, or the earth and is vaporized. The temperature of the vapor is increased by a compressor. As the vapor flows through an inside coil, it gives off heat. Then the vapor becomes a liquid as it flows through a condenser and valve. The process is repeated. For cooling, the process is reversed. A refrigerator also works this way.

Who can conserve energy?

Much energy is lost from electrically-heated homes through heating coils. Installation of heat pumps can improve the efficiency of electric heating systems. Figure 26–12 shows how a heat pump works. The addition of flue dampers, devices that close off chimneys to the outside when not in use, can reduce the heat loss from fireplaces by about 25 percent. Other ways to conserve energy in buildings include keeping thermostats at 20°C or lower in cold weather and turning off lights and electrical appliances when they are not needed.

Energy efficiency in industry also can be improved. Friction from industrial processes produces a great deal of heat. Often this waste heat is released into air or water, which is a kind of pollution. The waste heat can be recovered and used, for example to heat water or produce electricity. By attaching an electric generator to a waste steam source, an industrial plant can make some of the electricity it needs to operate. This process is called cogeneration. Replacement of inefficient equipment and better maintenance of equipment can save energy, too.

In the United States, the major use of energy is for transportation. When people travel together on buses, subways, and other forms of mass transportation, energy is conserved. Shipping materials by truck is less energy efficient than shipping by rail, water, or air.

Governments can help save energy. Laws that affect vehicle design, speeds, and shipping procedures can save energy for transportation. Building codes for homes and industries can reduce energy waste. Energy is wasted or saved depending on decisions made by individuals. Individuals help make government policies on energy by electing people with particular points of view.

See Teacher's Guide.

REVIEW AND REFLECT

1. Can all energy be converted into useful work someday? Explain your answer.
2. If one material has a higher R-value than another, what does that mean?
3. Describe three specific ways that you or your family could conserve energy.

Activity: How does insulation affect the flow of heat?

See Teacher's Guide.

MATERIALS

shoe box
tape
gloves
paper towels
room temperature water
5 insulation materials with
  different known R-values

2 thermometers
high-intensity lamp
metric ruler

PROCEDURE

Part A

1. Use a shoe box as a model house. Let the lid be the roof.
2. Place a thermometer in room temperature water. Then dry it off. Put the thermometer inside the house and replace the roof (lid).
3. Place a lamp 30 cm from one edge of the house, shining at an angle of about 45 degrees on the wall of the house.
4. Record the temperature inside the house after 10 minutes.
5. Put on gloves. Line the inside of the house with a 2 centimeter layer of one type of insulation. Line the walls, roof, and floor. **CAUTION:** *Do not allow the insulation to touch your skin.* Repeat steps 1–4.
6. Repeat steps 1–4 with four other insulation materials.

FIGURE 26–13.

Part B

1. Place one thermometer flat against an outside wall within a room at home. Tape it in a place where the wall covering will not be damaged.
2. Place another thermometer in the center of the room in a place where it will not be disturbed.
3. After each thermometer has reached a stable temperature, record the readings.
4. Determine whether the wall is well-insulated. If the difference in temperature between the two thermometers is 2.5°C, the wall is probably not well-insulated.

DATA AND OBSERVATIONS

Insulation Material	R-value	Temperature
None		

QUESTIONS AND CONCLUSIONS

1. Which material used in part A was the best insulator?
2. Does your data support the R-values of the materials?
3. What other considerations, besides R-value, would influence the type of insulation selected for a building?
4. What else, besides wall insulation, is needed to stop heat flow between a building and outdoors?
5. Do you think your home needs more insulation? Explain.

26:10 Information: Energy from Plants

Each time we use fossil fuels, we release the energy of sunlight that shone on the earth millions of years ago. The energy was stored during photosynthesis in the bonds of organic molecules. Today energy from the sun still is being stored in organic molecules of plants during photosynthesis.

We release some of the energy stored in plants each time we burn wood or paper. Wood and paper are mainly composed of cellulose fibers. About a billion tons of cellulose, mostly in the form of wood and paper, are disposed of each year in the United States. A few cities have built trash-burning power plants to use this resource to generate electricity.

While cellulose can be burned to produce heat, it does not produce liquid fuel for cars and trucks. It cannot be distributed easily through pipelines. In addition, petroleum and natural gas are used for purposes other than just fuel. They are raw materials used in the manufacture of plastics, synthetic rubber and textiles, and chemicals such as drugs and pesticides. As a result, many scientists believe that burning is not the most efficient way to use the products of photosynthesis.

In the 1970s, people began to look at plants as possible sources of liquid fuels. Most attention focused on ethanol, C_2H_5OH. In the United States, facilities were built to produce ethanol by fermenting corn. It is not clear whether the energy gained from ethanol fuel is more than the energy put into planting, harvesting, and processing. However, ethanol can replace lead in gasoline, helping to burn fuel more efficiently in engines. This use alone may make ethanol production worthwhile.

Scientists have been working on ways of using plant materials and wastes to produce large amounts of methane, CH_4. Methane is the main component of natural gas. Processes have been developed to turn animal manure, giant kelp, vegetable processing wastes, paper, cornstalks, and other plant material into methane.

Other scientists hope to use breeding techniques and genetic engineering to increase yields of products useful as

How are plants an energy resource?

BACKGROUND   Usable energy from plants and plant products is often referred to as biomass energy.

FIGURE 26–14. At Disney World, water hyacinths are grown in pools of sewage. The hyacinths purify the water. Then they are harvested and decomposed to produce methane fuel.

fuels or chemical raw materials. For example, an alga that produces oil grows slowly. Perhaps the genes for oil production in this alga could be transferred to faster-growing types of algae.

Dr. Melvin Calvin, a professor at the University of California at Berkeley, has concentrated on two plant species. These plants are able to change carbohydrates produced by photosynthesis into hydrocarbons. One species is called *Copaifera multijuga,* a tree that grows in Brazil. Tapping each tree will produce about 20 to 30 liters of oil twice a year. The oil can be refined like petroleum. It also can be used directly in diesel engines. It is not possible, however, to grow *C. multijuga* within the continental United States.

The other plant Dr. Calvin is investigating is *Euphorbia lathyris.* It produces a milky fluid containing both oil and sugar. The plant is called gopher weed. Gophers stay away from gardens where it is used, since the milky liquid burns skin and eyes. The fluid is a latex, which oozes out when a leaf or stalk is broken. The latex cannot be used directly. To make oil, the plants are dried in the sun for a few weeks. Then the stalks are ground up and boiled with heptane. The product is black and sticky, just like oil that comes from the ground. The plant oil can be used for the same purposes as petroleum, even for making plastics.

E. lathyris is particularly attractive as a producer of energy because it can be grown on land where food crops will not grow. Arid regions, such as southwestern parts of the United States, are ideal for *E. lathyris.* Dr. Calvin is confident that plant breeding will double the present yield of *E. lathyris.* Genetic engineering may greatly improve this output.

FIGURE 26–15. Gopher weed produces an oil that is very much like petroleum pumped from oil wells.

How can plants be used to produce oil?

See Teacher's Guide.

REVIEW AND REFLECT

1. Why do you think scientists have concentrated on the production of liquid fuels from solid waste and plant matter? Why are they interested in producing methane gas also?

2. Why do you think there is an emphasis on finding useful plants that will grow on nonagricultural land?

CHAPTER 26 REVIEW

SUMMARY

1. As population grows, energy use increases. 26:1

2. The most-used energy sources today, fossil fuels and nuclear fission, are nonrenewable. 26:2, 26:3

3. Use of fossil fuels to produce energy causes pollution and other problems. 26:2

4. A major problem with nuclear fission power plants is radioactive wastes. 26:3

5. Nuclear fusion does not create large amounts of radioactive wastes, but technology for its large-scale use as an energy source has not been developed. 26:3

6. Passive and active are two methods of solar energy use. 26:4

7. Solar energy is a continuous flow source of energy and is nonpolluting, but the technology for using it currently is more costly than other sources. 26:4

8. Geothermal, wind, tidal, and hydroelectric are continuous flow energy resources that are available at only limited numbers of locations. 26:5, 26:6, 26:7

9. Not all energy from a particular source is converted into useful energy, but the efficiency of energy conversion can be improved. 26:8

10. In each type of energy use, energy is wasted and many opportunities for conservation exist. 26:9

VOCABULARY

active system   6
continuous flow   2
efficiency   7
fission   8

fossil fuels   9
fusion   10
geothermal   1

hydroelectric   4
nonrenewable   5
passive system   3

Choose the correct word from the list to answer each question.

1. What kind of energy comes from hot water and steam within the earth?

2. What term is used to describe energy resources that are always being produced?

3. What kind of solar energy system is based only on building design?

4. What kind of energy can be produced by water flowing over a dam?

5. What energy resources do not increase?

6. What kind of solar energy system requires special mechanical equipment?

7. What is the ratio of useful energy output to energy input called?

8. What is the splitting of atoms called?

9. What nonrenewable sources of energy are most widely used today?

10. What is the combination of light nuclei to form heavier ones called?

QUESTIONS

MAIN IDEAS

Choose the correct answer to complete each sentence.

1. *(Coal, Oil, Uranium)* is not a fossil fuel.

2. Active and passive are two types of *(nuclear, solar, geothermal, water)* energy.

3. *(Most, More than half, A small amount)* of the sun's energy is converted into wind.

4. More electricity currently is produced by *(nuclear fission, nuclear fusion, hydroelectric dams)*.

5. The greatest danger from radioactive wastes is from nuclear *(fission, fusion)* power plants.

6. Most people first became aware of a world energy crisis in the *(1950s, 1960s, 1970s, 1980s)*.

7. The demand for fossil fuels *(increases, decreases, is not affected)* as population growth increases.

8. Hydroelectric energy is not a major energy alternative for the future because *(we do not have the technology to use it, most of the acceptable sites are already in use, it causes too much water pollution)*.

9. Geothermal energy is *(renewable, nonrenewable, continuous-flow)*.

10. Doubling the thickness of insulation *(increases, decreases, does not change)* its R-value.

11. Tidal energy is the result of gravitation mainly between the *(sun and moon, moon and earth, earth and sun)*.

12. A major problem of fossil fuel use is *(tar sands, acid rain, corroded pipes, radioactive wastes)*.

See Teacher's Guide.

APPLICATIONS

Answer each question in one or more paragraphs.

1. How did the energy crisis of 1973 develop?

2. Since so many cities are located along rivers, why do more of them not use their rivers as sources of hydroelectric power?

3. Although mass transit conserves energy, what are some problems of developing and maintaining good mass transit systems?

4. In terms of energy production, why are blades on wind towers, which generate electricity, placed high above the ground?

5. Why is the efficiency of any energy converter, such as an automobile or a power plant, always less than 100 percent?

6. Since the materials from which fossil fuels formed are present today, why are usable fossil fuels not replacing those that are being used up?

7. How can relatively few neutrons result in billions of nuclear reactions per second within a fission reactor?

8. Why is the efficiency of a hydroelectric power plant greater than that of a fossil fuel power plant? How does efficiency relate to cost of the equipment in a power plant?

FURTHER STUDY

INVESTIGATIONS

1. Visit a power plant. Learn what source is used to produce electricity. Find out the conservation measures practiced by the power plant.

2. Learn how much a solar hot water heater would cost that would satisfy your family's needs. Calculate how long it would take to pay off the cost of the solar water heater based on savings of energy cost over your present water heater.

READINGS

0 Cook, Brian. *Gas.* Franklin Watts: New York, 1981.

− Davis, Bertha, and Susan Whitfield. *The Coal Question.* Franklin Watts: New York, 1982.

+ Meade, Dale M. "Energy for the Eons." *Science Year, 1983.* 1982. pp. 142–155.

+ United States. Department of Energy. *Home Wind Power.* Garden Way Publishing: Charlotte, VT, 1981.

SOME people say we live in a "throwaway" society. Many of the items we commonly use are meant to be thrown away. Often large items are junked when they are no longer useful. Many items, like the foods the students in the picture are enjoying, are sold in disposable packaging. When you throw something away, where does it go? What is the waste problem? How can environmental quality be maintained?

ENVIRONMENTAL QUALITY

INTRODUCING THE CHAPTER Invite students to contribute favorite poems and lyrics to initiate a discussion of human rights and decision-making as they relate to natural resources.

27:1 Types of Pollution

Pollution is broadly labeled as air pollution, water pollution, or land pollution. However, classifying pollutants into one of these groups is not always easy. A single pollutant may affect all three, as well as people and other organisms.

A major form of land pollution is solid wastes. Solid wastes include garbage and refuse, sludge, and many byproducts of mining, industry, and agriculture. Garbage is food wastes. Refuse generally includes nonfood wastes, such as paper, glass, metals, and plastics, which come from homes and businesses. Increasing use of disposable products and packaging contributes to the problems of safe disposal of wastes. Nothing is really disposable. Since matter cycles through our environment, everything ends up somewhere else. As world population increases, so does the waste problem.

Garbage can be a health hazard. It is a source of food for rats and a breeding area for flies. Rats and flies are carriers of harmful diseases. Even when it seems to be properly disposed of, garbage may be a health hazard since rats tear into garbage bags and flies breed in garbage cans. Garbage and refuse often are dumped, which is unsightly and unsafe, or buried in landfills. Sites for sanitary landfills are selected to avoid contamination of groundwater. Each day's deposit of garbage and refuse is compacted

GOAL You will learn how the natural environment is being changed by human activities and what can be done to offset the negative effects of changes.

What are three main classifications of pollution?

What are solid wastes?

and covered with soil. Garbage and some refuse that is buried, such as paper, readily decompose. Many solid wastes, such as glass, decompose slowly or not at all.

Sludge is a waste product of sewage treatment. Most sludge is disposed of on land because it is composed largely of organic compounds that decompose. It may be used as fertilizer. However, sludge often contains harmful organisms, such as bacteria that cause diseases. In addition, sludge may contain heavy metals, such as cadmium and nickel, which accumulate in soil as the sludge decomposes. Plants that absorb large amounts of the metals cannot be used safely for food.

The heavy metals in sludge are toxic chemicals. **Toxic** means that in sufficient amounts a chemical is poisonous. Many of the byproducts of agriculture as well as mining and industry are toxic chemicals or hazardous wastes. **Hazardous wastes** are wastes that may be directly poisonous, like toxic chemicals, or may damage the environment and endanger health and safety in longlasting and unpredictable ways. The radioactive wastes of nuclear power plants are hazardous wastes.

Some major air pollutants are shown in Table 27–1. One form of air pollution that causes breathing difficulties is particulates. Particulates are solid or liquid particles suspended in air. Dust is a particulate. Blasting, drilling, and crushing processes in mining and industry produce particulates. Burning coal in electric power plants and gasoline in vehicles pollutes the air with particulates and with sulfur dioxide, too. Sulfur dioxide is absorbed on the surfaces of particulates, causing additional breathing problems.

What is sludge?
BACKGROUND   The most difficult and expensive aspect of waste-water treatment is the processing of sludge. Between 25 and 50 percent of the budget of a plant goes for disposal of sludge.
What are particulates?

FIGURE 27–1.   Noise pollution is believed to affect physical and mental health. Accidents, absenteeism, and compensation for hearing losses resulting from noisy work environments are believed to cost industry billions of dollars each year (a). Microwave pollution from communications antennas and transmitters, microwave ovens, and industrial equipment that shower the environment with radio waves is increasing. The effects are uncertain, but some evidence indicates that exposure to particular intensities may be harmful (b).

a

b

TABLE 27–1. MAJOR AIR POLLUTANTS	
Description	**Estimated Amounts Per Year Worldwide (metric tons)**
Particulates	24 000 000
Carbon dioxide (from pollution sources)	20 000 000 000
Carbon monoxide	50 000 000
Sulfur dioxide	130 000 000
Nitrogen oxides*	24 500 000
Lead compounds	2 000 000
Other metal and toxic compounds (Zn, Hg, Cd, Se, As, Sn, fluorocarbons)	993 000 000

*Data for United States and Canada only

Many industries and power plants pollute water. Thermal (heat) pollution is one kind of water pollution. Water also is polluted by industrial wastes, sewage, mining wastes, and oil and chemical spills. There are about 20 000 different people-made chemicals that pollute water. About 500 more are added each year. Some of them have been found to be toxic in very small amounts. Many are known or suspected to be compounds that cause mutations and cancer.

A major source of water pollution is agricultural runoff. Some toxic chemicals in pesticides and fertilizers dissolve in groundwater or are carried into lakes and waterways along with eroded soil. For example, TCDD, a dioxin, has been found in rivers and groundwater. Certain pesticides and chemical products contain TCDD. Scientists are not sure how it affects human health, but TCDD is one of the most toxic substances made.

See Teacher's Guide.

REVIEW AND REFLECT

1. Describe the relationship between the waste problem and population growth.
2. Name a major source of each type of pollution.
3. Why is thermal pollution of water by power plants and other industries a problem?

SUGGESTION   Learn some ways that ecosystems are being polluted in your area. The city or county engineer, the Environmental Protection Agency (EPA), and local industries and power plants are sources of information. Discuss how each type of pollution enters the environment.

BACKGROUND   Dioxins are a group of about 75 hydrogen-carbon-chlorine compounds. TCDD (2,3,7,8-tetrachlorodibenzo paradioxin) is the dioxin compound that has received media attention recently. The EPA has set up regulations governing acceptable amounts in pesticides and cleanup of contaminated areas.

FIGURE 27–2. Oil spills and leakage from oil tankers and drilling rigs have caused large-scale death of sea life, including birds, otters, and shellfish. The light fractions of oil evaporate from a spill in about three months, but heavier fractions remain. Since oil is an organic substance, it gradually decomposes. However, it contains many chemicals that are toxic to organisms.

Skill Inquiry

Sometimes scientific data is difficult to understand. You know that scientists often graph data to make it easier to interpret. Glyphs, pictures that represent information, are another way to make interpretation easier. Glyphs are useful for representing many kinds of information. For example, you probably are familiar with the international signs used to provide information on highways and in public places, Figure a. Meteorologists use glyphs to represent information such as cloud cover at various locations, Figure b.

Scientists use x-y graphs to represent relationships between two variables. Glyphs can be combined with x-y graphs when more than two variables need to be represented, Figure c. Refer to Figure c to answer questions 1 through 4.

1. What are the effects of particulates at low concentrations of SO_2 (less than 100 micrograms/m^3)?

2. What are the effects of SO_2 at low concentrations of particulates (100 micrograms/m^3 or less)?

3. How does an increased level of particulates change the effect of a given level of SO_2?

4. How does an increased level of SO_2 change the effect of a given level of particulates?

5. Make up a glyph to represent the information given in Table 23–1 on page 491.

Health Effects of SO_2 and Particulates Averaged Over 24-Hour Period (micrograms/m^3)

27:2 Pollutants in Ecosystems

Some pollutants are natural, such as particulates that come from an erupting volcano or sediments that are eroded into streams. However, unnatural pollutants in ecosystems alter natural processes. A young lake has a low nutrient concentration, and therefore relatively few organisms. As a lake ages, nutrients are washed from land into the lake by erosion. The process of adding nutrients to a body of water is called **eutrophication** (yoo troh fuh KAY shun). As eutrophication occurs, the populations of organisms in the water increase.

What happens as a lake ages?

Natural eutrophication occurs over thousands of years. However, pollutants such as sewage, fertilizers, and organic industrial wastes speed up eutrophication so that it may occur in as little as 20 years. Populations of blue-green algae may increase greatly. When the algae die and decompose, they use dissolved oxygen in the water. As a result of the lower oxygen content, many populations of fish die. This type of eutrophication may be reversed. Lake Erie was considered in advanced stages of eutrophication in the late 1960s. Regulations controlling organic pollutants, such as phosphates, have helped to reverse this trend.

Natural processes cleanse the atmosphere of many pollutants. Air pollutants may be blown away by winds and diluted, combine chemically with other substances and form harmless compounds, or be washed out by precipitation. However, air pollution that is concentrated in certain areas may be complicated by geologic and atmospheric conditions. As shown in Figure 27–3, Los Angeles is located in a geologic area where air circulation is restricted. Temperature inversions prevent smog from rising and becoming diluted.

Although carbon dioxide is listed as an air pollutant in Table 27–1, it is naturally produced as a waste product of respiration and used by plants in photosynthesis. Together these processes form the carbon dioxide–oxygen cycle. The burning of fossil fuels is increasing the concentration of carbon dioxide in the atmosphere. Carbon dioxide and particulate pollution may cause slow temperature changes on the earth. Scientists are not sure if the earth's climate will become warmer or cooler.

Natural processes also break down some land pollutants. Solid wastes such as paper, garbage, cotton, and wool decay as a result of the action of decomposers in soil. Objects that decompose naturally in relatively short periods of time are **biodegradable.** Nitrogen, phosphorus, and other important elements are recycled in the environment as part of this decomposition. However many solid wastes, such as plastics and glass, are not biodegradable. When they are disposed of, they do not decompose naturally at a quick rate. Even though they may be buried in sanitary landfills, they are permanent pollution.

Descending warm air

Temperature inversion layer

Sea breeze

FIGURE 27–3. In summer, smog is common in metropolitan Los Angeles. In sunlight, nitrogen oxides and hydrocarbons, abundant pollutants due to traffic in the city, combine to form photochemical smog. Descending warm air from the mountain region forms an inversion layer. The sea breeze moves the smog toward the mountains, where it is trapped. Auto emission regulations have helped reduce the problems.

What natural processes help reduce pollution?

DEMONSTRATION
Demonstrate dilution in the air of your classroom: open a bottle of perfume or ammonia in one location. Have students indicate when the odor reaches them. Review diffusion.

ACTIVITY A number of products, such as laundry materials, are now specifically labeled as biodegradable. Have students check their home and store shelves for products with this label. Prepare lists.

Describe some biodegradable and nonbiodegradable materials.

Activity: How do water samples vary?

MATERIALS

methylene blue solution
3 250-mL glass-stoppered bottles
labels
3 water samples
graduated pipette with bulb
goggles
apron

PROCEDURE

1. Label three bottles A, B, C.
2. Completely fill each of the bottles with water from one of the samples. Record the source of the water sample in each bottle.
3. Draw 1 mL of methylene blue solution into the pipette. Place the end of the pipette in the water sample in bottle A, Figure 27–4. Release the solution into the water. Rinse the pipette in clean water.
4. Repeat step 3 with bottles B and C.
5. Place the stopper on each bottle. (Some water should overflow when you put the stopper in place.) Take care not to allow any air bubbles to be trapped inside.
6. Gently swirl the bottles to distribute the methylene blue solution.
7. Place the bottles in a dark place at room temperature.
8. Record daily observations of the bottles.

FIGURE 27–4.

DATA AND OBSERVATIONS

Bottle	Water Sample Source	Days for Methylene Blue to Disappear
A		
B		
C		

QUESTIONS AND CONCLUSIONS

1. Methylene blue is an indicator of the dissolved oxygen in water. The blue color in a water sample disappears when all of the dissolved oxygen has been used. Dead organic matter in water decays due to the action of bacteria. These bacteria use oxygen in the decay process. The greater the amount of dead organic matter, the more decay takes place. Therefore, more oxygen is used. How can you account for the differences in the oxygen content of your samples?
2. Why did you need to release the methylene blue solution from the pipette in the water, not above the water?
3. Why did you need to store your bottles in a dark rather than in a light place?
4. How do you think the addition of sewage would affect the oxygen content of water?
5. How could your data be used as a measurement of eutrophication?
6. How could your data be useful in determining whether or not a waterway should be used for recreation and other purposes?

<u>27:3</u> Pollution Chains

The effects of pollution in an ecosystem are widespread. Pollution of the air, water, or land in an ecosystem may lead to a chain of pollution that affects many other parts of the ecosystem. For example, harmful pollutants that are washed out of air by rain may become concentrated in soil. Later the soil may be eroded into streams.

A major pollution chain begins with the tall smokestacks of power plants and industries. Burning fossil fuels pollutes the air with sulfur oxides and nitrogen oxides. The combination of these pollutants with water in the air produces acid precipitation. All forms of acid precipitation are commonly called **acid rain.** Normal rainwater is slightly acidic, with a pH of 5.6. (See section 6:10.) Acid rain has an average pH of 4 to 4.5. Acid rain decreases the pH of lakes, which often destroys populations of organisms. Forests, crops, buildings, and monuments also are damaged by acid rain. Industrial planners thought that building taller smokestacks would allow winds to disperse pollutants over larger areas, reducing the pollution problem. However, taller smokestacks caused acid rain to be distributed over a larger area. Crops, forests, ponds, and structures thousands of kilometers from pollutant sources have been damaged by acid rain.

Another pollution chain begins with pesticides. Pesticides include insecticides used to kill insects, and herbicides used to kill weeds. Pesticides applied to fields and forests move into air, water, soil, and organisms. Pesticides contain chemicals that are toxic to pests. However, many pesticides are toxic to other organisms as well.

During World War II, DDT, a chlorinated hydrocarbon, was used to kill lice and mosquitoes that transmitted diseases. After World War II, DDT was used widely as a pesticide in agriculture and forestry. However, DDT was carried into lakes, waterways, swamps, and coastal waters by runoff. It became concentrated in the fatty tissues of aquatic organisms because it is more soluble in fats and oils than in water. Many of the organisms died. As other organisms ate the aquatic organisms, DDT moved up the food chain. Concentrations of the chemical increased in organisms to the point that birds at the top of the food chain suffered toxic effects.

FIGURE 27–5. Many industries that burn fossil fuels for energy pollute the air with sulfur oxides and nitrogen oxides because combustion of the fuels is incomplete.

What causes acid rain?
DEMONSTRATE Show the effects of acid rain on monuments and structures by putting a few drops of dilute HCl on old mortar, a seashell, or chalk.

Why are pesticides considered to be pollutants?

BACKGROUND Agent Orange, containing TCDD, was used in Vietnam. War veterans exposed to Agent Orange have suffered health damage. TCDD causes chloracne, a skin condition, and nervous system problems. It may also be a carcinogen and cause other ailments. Its long-term effects are not known.

FIGURE 27–6. Most people at the Love Canal site had to abandon their homes since they could not be sold due to the environmental hazards of the area. Attempts are now underway to clean up the Love Canal site.

Why is Love Canal important historically?

BACKGROUND   The wastes in Love Canal had been disposed of in as safe a way as the technology of the time could provide. Developers were not warned about what was beneath the area.

The effects of DDT have been so widespread that it has been found in the fatty tissues of penguins in Antarctica, although it has never been used as a pesticide there. DDT and other chlorinated hydrocarbons have been found in the fatty tissues of almost all living species, including people. The pesticides are believed to cause low fertility in males, damage the genetic code, and cause liver and nervous system damage. Use of some pesticides, including DDT, has been banned in the United States, but many of these still are used in other countries. Since DDT was banned in the United States, some bird populations affected by it are recovering.

The story of Love Canal is the story of another pollution chain. Love Canal was dug in heavy clay soil in New York in the 1890s. It became a dumping ground for drums of industrial wastes until 1953. The clay pit prevented the wastes from escaping into groundwater. Later the dump was "capped" with another layer of clay. It was covered with soil, and a school and homes were built on the site. In 1978, chemicals began oozing out of the ground. Many people living in the neighborhood developed health problems. Eighty toxic chemicals were found in the substances leaking into the ground, water, and air from the landfill site. Since then, most residents have relocated and efforts have begun to clean up the site.

Love Canal marked the beginning of public awareness of the dangers of hazardous waste storage. Similar problems have occurred in other places. Thousands of toxic chemicals and hazardous wastes are dumped into landfills in containers that easily puncture or corrode. There are about 50 000 of these waste sites in the United States. Nearly one third are classified as dangerous.

See Teacher's Guide.

REVIEW AND REFLECT

1. What is eutrophication? What is the difference between natural eutrophication and eutrophication caused by pollutants?
2. Describe two pollution chains.
3. Since DDT use has been banned in the United States, why does it still pose a problem for this country?

<u>27:4</u> Solutions to Pollution

Although there is no simple solution to pollution, many activities can help curb pollution. One way to reduce pollution is to control it at its source rather than cleaning it up elsewhere. Industries can install equipment that cuts down on air pollution. Sulfur oxide emissions from the burning of fossil fuels can be reduced by using coal that is low in sulfur content. Particulates can be reduced by electrostatic precipitators that collect charged particles by attraction to surfaces that are oppositely charged. Sulfur dioxide and other gases can be removed by scrubbers that dissolve gases in liquids.

How can pollution be controlled at its source?

Since the 1960s, automobiles have been modified to reduce pollutants. Most new cars have catalytic converters or similar devices that reduce emission of pollutants. In a catalytic converter, carbon monoxide and hydrocarbons are converted to carbon dioxide and water. A catalytic converter becomes ineffective if gasoline containing lead is used. Lead, added to some gasolines to improve engine performance in older cars, is emitted in exhaust. It becomes concentrated in soil and plants, and thus enters the food chain. Lead is a toxic chemical that damages the nerves, brain, and kidneys. It can cause death. Today new cars use "unleaded" gasoline but lead from other sources is still a pollution problem.

Many methods are useful to reduce the pollution problems of solid wastes. As already discussed, people need to make informed choices about the use of disposable products. Recycling is another important way to reduce solid wastes. Garbage and refuse can be disposed of in sanitary landfills rather than open dumps. Sanitary landfills are safer in terms of environmental health. In addition, the land used for sanitary landfills can be developed later for recreational or other uses. However, many landfills do not qualify as "sanitary." In a sanitary landfill, several centimeters of compacted soil is placed over each day's accumulation of solid wastes. Some cities have incineration and resource recovery programs for disposal of solid wastes. Materials such as aluminum and glass can be recovered when solid wastes are burned. Unfortunately, incineration contributes to air pollution.

Pellets

Exhaust to muffler
(CO_2, H_2O)

Exhaust from engine
(HC, CO, O_2)

FIGURE 27–7. A catalytic converter is part of a car's exhaust system. Exhaust gases are passed through pellets coated with a catalyst. It stimulates a chemical reaction that converts the oxygen, carbon monoxide, and hydrocarbons in exhaust to carbon dioxide and water.

Describe two ways to reduce solid wastes.

FIGURE 27–8. Major sources of pollution are industry, agriculture, and sewage from homes and businesses.

Why are laws regulating pollution not always effective?

Sewage treatment facilities, like landfills, do not always use the best waste disposal methods available. Many facilities provide only basic treatment. More extensive treatment is more costly but renders sewage much less harmful. Thermal pollution of waterways can be prevented with cooling towers. (See section 12:7.) Safe disposal of toxic chemicals and hazardous wastes is a problem that has not been solved satisfactorily. Since Love Canal, more laws have been passed to regulate disposal, but often laws are difficult to enforce or open to many interpretations.

A major obstacle to solving pollution problems is identifying the source of a problem. Some sources of pollution, such as smokestacks and drainpipes, are easy to pinpoint. Single sources of pollution are called point sources. Most pollution is widely scattered and a single source is difficult to identify. For example, pesticides that pollute a waterway may come from a large agricultural area including many farms. Sources of widely scattered pollution are called nonpoint sources.

To reduce pollution from pesticides, alternative methods of pest control can be used. Biocontrol is the use of other organisms to control pests. Methods of biocontrol include introduction of parasites, predators, or pathogens of pests.

TABLE 27–2. GARDEN BIOCONTROL METHODS

Pests	Biocontrol
Snails	Place a wide board at the edge of the garden. Snails will gather underneath the board. Collect the snails each day and drop them in soapy water. Plant a few onions around the edge of the garden to repel snails.
Potato beetles	Plant eggplants nearby to lure potato beetles from destroying potato plants. Pick the bugs off the eggplants and drop them in soapy water.
Harlequin bugs	Plant turnips or radishes throughout the cabbage patch to attract these bugs and prevent them from destroying cabbage leaves.

ACTIVITY If this chapter is studied during spring, encourage students to try biocontrol methods in a school or home garden. Other biocontrol methods are listed in "Fighting Pests With Pests," which appeared in *Ranger Rick Nature Magazine,* January, 1978. For reprints of the article contact the National Wildlife Federation, 1412 16th St. N.W., Washington, D.C. 20036.

Companion planting is a useful method of biocontrol, too. For example, aphids are insects that damage tomato plants. Marigolds repel aphids. Planting marigolds among tomatoes helps prevent aphid damage. Some other biocontrol methods popular with home gardeners are shown in Table 27–2. Cultivation techniques, crop rotation, and other mechanical means are cultural methods of pest control. The best method of pest control may be to combine biocontrols and cultural methods with pesticide use. This combined approach is called integrated pest management, or **IPM.** With IPM, use of pesticides can be reduced. As a result, their effect on the environment is less severe, and the control of pests is longer lasting.

Describe IPM.

See Teacher's Guide.

REVIEW AND REFLECT

1. What is a catalytic converter? How does it work?
2. How do solid wastes pollute water?
3. Name two point sources and two nonpoint sources of pollution.
4. If you planned to plant a garden, what problems might you expect from insect pests? Describe the steps you would take to avoid them.

Activity: How should clothes be washed?

See Teacher's Guide.

MATERIALS

large spoon	soil
phosphate detergent	water
labels	soap flakes
4 large jars with lids	washing soda
clothespins	watch or clock
vegetable or motor oil	apron
light-colored cloth cut in 10 pieces	
low-phosphate or no-phosphate detergent	

PROCEDURE

1. Use soil, oil, and other materials available to make the 10 pieces of cloth equally dirty.
2. Label the first jar "phosphate ," the second jar "low-phosphate," the third jar "soap," and the fourth jar "water."
3. Fill each jar two thirds with water.
4. Place two spoonfuls of phosphate detergent in the phosphate jar, two spoonfuls of low-phosphate in the low-phosphate jar, and two spoonfuls of soap flakes in the soap jar. Add nothing to the water jar.
5. Put a piece of cloth in each jar.
6. Tightly put a lid on each jar.
7. Shake each jar for one minute.
8. One at a time, remove the cloths from the jars, rinse them, and hang them up to dry. Use a clothespin to clip a label to each piece of cloth identifying the product and amount used to wash it.
9. Repeat steps 4 to 7 using the amounts of detergents, soap, and soda listed below.
   1 spoonful phosphate detergent
   1 spoonful low-phosphate detergent
   1 spoonful soap flakes
   ½ spoonful phosphate detergent
   ½ spoonful low-phosphate detergent
   1 spoonful soap flakes +
   ½ spoonful washing soda
10. After the cloths are dry, rate the cleanliness of each cloth from 1 to 10 in the data table. Let 1 be the cleanest and 10 be the dirtiest cloth after washing.

DATA AND OBSERVATIONS

Washing Product	Cleanliness Rating

QUESTIONS AND CONCLUSIONS

1. Based on their cleaning abilities, which product is best for washing clothes?
2. How did the amount used affect the cleaning abilities of the products?
3. How does the use of washing soda affect the cleaning ability of soap?
4. Soap is a nutrient for some harmful kinds of bacteria. How might use of soap harm the environment?
5. Since phosphates are nutrients for plants and some other organisms, how might use of phosphate detergents harm the environment?
6. Why do you think phosphate detergents are more popular than low-phosphate detergents?
7. Considering the pollution, costs, and cleaning abilities of the products used, which is the best choice for washing clothes?

Career Profile

In and around Raleigh, North Carolina, people take aluminum recycling seriously. Every day lines of customers wait in the parking lots at 27 shopping centers to be paid for their empty aluminum cans. When the trailer holding these cans is filled to its 2300-kilogram capacity, a driver delivers it to a recycling center in Raleigh. There the aluminum cans are flattened with heavy machinery. At another location, the flattened cans are shredded to prepare them to be melted. The melted aluminum is formed into ingots that are used to make new aluminum products.

Jerry Johnson is the manager of Raleigh's aluminum recycling center. Jerry began working for the recycling center as a truck driver. He picked up aluminum cans at the collection locations and hauled them to the recycling center. After three and a half years, Jerry was named manager of

the recycling center. Every day paperwork floods his desk with volume and pricing, safety improvement, and cost reduction reports. He is a personnel manager and a sales manager, too. Jerry also must check for safety hazards and arrange for repair of machinery that does not work properly.

Jerry feels his work at the recycling center has given him and all his employees a concern for saving and reusing. Instead of discarding a broken piece of machinery at the plant, Jerry thinks of ways to recycle it.

27:5 Environmental Economics

When, where, and how much money to spend to maintain and improve the environment are questions of environmental economics. Environmentalists have criticized some economists for placing too much emphasis on making a quick money profit. These environmentalists point out long-term effects. The future as well as the present condition of the land, water, air and the health of organisms are issues.

Economic decisions, as well as many life decisions, are based on how much risk exists for how much possible benefit. An evaluation of risks and benefits can be done consciously or unconsciously. For instance, if you sit in a cold drizzle at a football game, you may risk getting sick. However, your enjoyment of the event is a benefit that may be worth taking the risk.

Describe environmental economics.

FIGURE 27–9. The risks and benefits of any action that may affect the environment need to be evaluated.

Why are risks and benefits of environmental issues not easy to determine?

ACTIVITY Have each student do a risk-benefit analysis for one or more situations that are an important part of students' lives. Examples could be effort and good grades, practice and playing a musical instrument or sport well, and possible rejection when asking someone to go on a date. Note that a risk-benefit analysis for such things is a very individual matter.

Why are pollutants not always removed if technology to remove them is available?

How are acceptable risks determined?

A conscious evaluation of risks in relation to possible benefits is called a **risk-benefit analysis.** In environmental economics, risks and benefits usually are not easy to determine. Little reliable data about health effects of specific pollutants is available. The effects of pollution often are delayed. Also, it is difficult to translate the risks of pollution into a money amount or reach agreement on the benefits of preserving the environment.

Some situations have begun to show how pollution does translate into money. Studies of workers in different areas over 10 years show that about $36 billion might be saved each year if air pollution could be reduced 60 percent. Lost days due to illness, early death, medical care and health benefits can be assigned price tags. The cost of removing or preventing pollution also can be figured. However, translating the risk of breathing polluted air or the benefit of preserving a natural waterway into money terms is much more difficult.

Usually, removing only about 50 percent of the pollutants from wastes discharged into the environment is easier and less costly than removing even a portion of the remaining 50 percent. This is the concept of **marginal cost**—that as the percentage of pollutant reduction increases, its cost increases and at some point the cost becomes unreasonable. Removing the last few percent of a pollutant is usually very difficult. Sometimes it is thousands of times more expensive than the cost of removing the first 50 percent. The risk of removing more than 50 percent of pollutants in terms of cost may outweigh the environmental benefits. The concept of marginal cost must be considered in any risk-benefit analysis. At some point the cost of removing a pollutant may no longer be worth the benefit to be gained either now or in the future.

In order to decide how much of a pollutant should be removed, we must decide how much is acceptable. An **acceptable risk** is one that an individual or society is willing to take. Most people find the risk of being in a car accident a small enough possibility that they are willing to ride in cars. The acceptable risk for different activities changes with time. Risks that are voluntary are usually more acceptable to people than risks that are not voluntary. Risks that affect a small segment of society normally are more acceptable than risks that affect everyone. Risks that have existed for many years are usually more acceptable than new risks. Thus, acceptable risk is more than a scientific issue. Acceptable risk involves people's attitudes and values.

27:6 Environmental Ethics

Balancing use of resources with care of the environment is an environmental ethic. Often, questions of environmental ethics involve issues of public versus private benefit. Perhaps you and your friends like the bowling alley across town better than the one close to your home. Going to the one you like best would provide a benefit to you. Going to the one close to home would provide the benefit of reducing air pollution, since you do not have to drive as far.

What are the issues of environmental ethics?

Adopting an environmental ethic may require a change in your attitudes and values. You may decide to repair an old appliance rather than buy a new one. You may recycle newspapers, glass bottles, and aluminum cans instead of throwing them away. You may decide to walk or car pool sometimes.

Describe the importance of personal responsibility in environmental ethics.

In a democratic society voluntary application of environmental ethics is important. Each person needs to be well-informed about risks and benefits involving resource use and pollution. An understanding of natural sciences provides information about the environment and a scientific method for making conclusions. The social sciences provide information about the behavior of people, the way political systems operate, and how costs and profits are determined. Personal responsibility involves applying this knowledge to personal, business, and civic decisions.

See Teacher's Guide.

FIGURE 27–10. An environmental ethic for an individual involves electing political candidates and voting on issues that affect the environment.

REVIEW AND REFLECT

1. What is an environmental ethic?
2. How can risks and benefits of actions that have environmental impacts be determined?
3. Why is natural science information alone not enough for making decisions about the environment?

Describe deposit legislation.

27:7 Choices: Deposit Legislation

If you had to decide to buy soft drinks in disposable or returnable containers, what factors would affect your decision? Cost may be a factor. Beverages in returnable containers cost about one-third less than beverages in disposable containers on the average. However, you must pay a deposit for the returnable containers and return them to get your money back. Convenience may be another factor. It may be easier to throw away empty containers than return them. However, it is important to take responsibility for proper disposal of the containers. Landscapes and highways are littered with containers improperly disposed of by people who did not accept this responsibility. Another consideration is the when-you-throw-something-away-where-does-it-go question. Use of disposable beverage containers adds to the problem of solid waste disposal.

In the United States, some states have deposit legislation. In those states, laws require that certain kinds of beverages be sold only in returnable containers. A deposit is charged for each container at the time of sale. The deposit is refunded when the container is returned. The deposit is designed to encourage people to return the container for recycling rather than disposing of it. Deposit legislation is an example of government regulation to reduce pollution.

ACTIVITY   Ask a student to research periodical literature to find out which states have or may be considering deposit legislation.

In states with deposit legislation, the law was voted for in an election by a majority of people. Some people have proposed that deposit legislation would be a good idea everywhere. Opponents feel differently.

Lobbyists are people who present the ideas of people or groups to legislators. Lobbyists for groups that favor disposable containers, such as the manufacturers of the containers, do not think deposit legislation is a good idea. They have pointed out that since only about 25 percent of all litter is beverage containers, anti-litter laws, such as fines, would be more effective than deposit legislation in reducing litter. They also note that fewer containers would be needed with deposit legislation. Since production of fewer containers would require fewer people to make them, many people might lose their jobs. Equipment in some factories would need to be modified to produce returnable containers. In addition, energy would be needed

FIGURE 27–11.   Some states have laws that require beverages to be sold only in returnable containers.

to transport and clean returnable containers. Costs would be passed on to consumers.

Many supporters of deposit legislation cite what has happened in Oregon, the first state to have deposit legislation. Since the legislation in 1972, the Oregon landscape has been noticeably cleaner. Over 400 jobs have been added in the beer and soft drink industries. Sales of these beverages have increased, with consumers saving about five million dollars and business profits going up about 50 million dollars. Garbage disposal costs have been decreased more than six million dollars. Lobbyists for the bottling and canning industries believe that recycling is economical. Energy is saved overall, since fewer new containers are made. Waste management experts say that glass cannot easily be separated from refuse before it is burned. Glass coats furnace parts, reducing their efficiency. Deposit legislation would eliminate many glass containers from refuse. Recycling would greatly reduce the need for aluminum. Currently, the United States imports more than half its aluminum. A director of the solid-waste division of the United States EPA has said, "Deposit legislation seems to make much more sense economically."

Many opponents of deposit legislation are against increased government regulation of industry. They feel that the consumer should be allowed to decide whether to buy disposable or returnable containers based on cost and convenience factors. People who favor deposit legislation feel that whether or not government regulation is desirable, sometimes it is necessary. The consumer still has a choice based on cost and convenience factors of disposing of or returning a container for deposit.

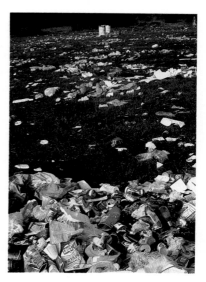

FIGURE 27–12.   Deposit legislation may help to reduce litter.

What are differing views of deposit legislation in terms of government regulation?

See Teacher's Guide.

REVIEW AND REFLECT

1. a. What are some arguments for not having deposit legislation?
   b. Which of these arguments seem justified to you?
2. How are each of the arguments against deposit legislation countered by people who would like deposit legislation?
3. Would you vote for deposit legislation in your community? Why or why not?

SUMMARY

1. The waste problem increases as population increases and technology advances. 27:1

2. Although pollution may be classified as air, water, or land pollution, pollutants are not easily classified because they affect many parts of the environment. 27:1

3. Major land pollutants are garbage and refuse, sludge, and mining, industrial, and agricultural wastes. 27:1

4. Major air pollutants are particulates, carbon dioxide and carbon monoxide, sulfur dioxide, nitrogen oxides, and compounds of lead and other toxic metals. 27:1

5. Major water pollutants are sewage, industrial and mining wastes, oil and other chemical spills, and agricultural runoff. 27:1

6. Many pollutants contain toxic chemicals or are hazardous wastes. 27:1

7. Natural processes may cleanse the environment and recycle nutrients, but pollutants alter natural processes. 27:2

8. A chain of far-reaching pollution may begin with a pollutant originating from a single source. 27:3, 27:4

9. Technology can be used to help curb pollution. 27:4

10. A risk-benefit analysis of an environmental issue depends on determining acceptable risks, which often depend on people's attitudes and values. 27:5

11. Environmental ethics often require decisions on questions of private versus public benefit. 27:6

VOCABULARY

acceptable risk   9
acid rain   6
biodegradable   1

eutrophication   4
hazardous waste   8
IPM   2

marginal cost   3
risk-benefit analysis   5
toxic   7

Match each definition with the correct word from the list.

1. Material that decomposes naturally in a relatively short time

2. Combined approach of using pesticides, biocontrols, and culture techniques to control pests

3. Cost of removing a percentage of pollutants as a function of the total percentage

4. Adding nutrients to a body of water

5. Conscious evaluation of possible outcomes

6. Combination of sulfur oxides or nitrogen oxides with water in the air

7. Poisonous in relatively large amounts

8. Materials that may be directly or indirectly harmful

9. A chance that an individual or society is willing to take

QUESTIONS

MAIN IDEAS

Choose the correct answer to complete each sentence.

1. An example of a point pollution source is a *(pesticide, detergent, smokestack, fertilizer).*

2. In a risk-benefit analysis *(the question must be related to the environment, private benefit and public benefit may be different, marginal cost is unimportant, only risks that involve everyone are acceptable).*

3. Acid rain has a pH of about *(7.0, 5.6, 4.3, 12.0)*.

4. A way to reduce gaseous air pollutants is with *(electrostatic precipitators, catalytic converters, extensive sewage treatment, incineration)*.

5. When you throw a disposable item away it may end up in a(n)*(open dump, sanitary landfill, incinerator, any of these)*.

6. An example of a pollution chain is *(use of pesticides, biocontrol, use of smokestack scrubbers)*.

7. Love Canal was an environmental problem involving *(acid rain, radioactive wastes, chemical wastes, pesticides)*.

8. According to the Law of Conservation of Matter, when you throw something away, it *(is destroyed, ends up somewhere else, is converted to energy)*.

9. Nonfood wastes, such as glass, paper, metals, and plastics, that come from homes and businesses are *(garbage, sludge, sewage, refuse)*.

10. DDT is a chlorinated hydrocarbon that is used in some countries as a(n) *(pesticide, IPM, biocontrol, culture technique)*.

11. One method of reducing solid wastes is *(sanitary landfills, open dumping, resource recovery, incineration)*.

12. An environmental ethic is balancing *(use of resources and care of environment, use of resources and provision of products, private risk and public benefit)*.

See Teacher's Guide.
APPLICATIONS

Answer each question in one or more paragraphs.

1. What could be done to encourage more people to take used items to recycling centers?

2. Describe three point sources and three non-point sources of pollution in your community. Suggest ways to reduce the pollution.

3. List the steps needed to reverse the results of pollution-caused eutrophication.

4. Describe five things that you could do that you are not doing now to apply an environmental ethic in your lifestyle.

5. Suppose you were offered a high-paying job to properly dispose of hazardous wastes. However, you might risk health problems if accidents occur. How would you evaluate the risks and benefits to decide whether to accept the job?

6. Suppose you lived 100 years from now. What would be your evaluation of how people today are managing the environment?

FURTHER STUDY

INVESTIGATIONS

1. Prepare a report on different types of car engines. Include diagrams with a discussion of the environmental impact and economics of the engines.

2. Visit a recycling center. Present an oral report for your class and encourage students to contribute to the center.

3. Indoor air pollution is a topic that is currently receiving attention. Find out what it is and why it is important. Prepare a bulletin board display of your findings.

READINGS

+ Boyle, Robert H., and R. Alexander Boyle. *Acid Rain,* Schocken Books: New York, 1983.

+ Brown, Michael H. *Laying Waste: The Poisoning of America by Toxic Chemicals.* Pantheon Books: New York, 1980.

+ Carey, John. "Is It Safe to Drink?" *National Wildlife.* February/March, 1984. pp. 14–17.

0 Gibbs, L. M. and M. Levine. *Love Canal.* State University of New York Press: Albany, 1982.

+ Piasecki, Bruce. "Unfouling the Nest." *Science 83.* September, 1983. pp. 76–81.

GETTING "back to nature" is a popular phrase. Some people enjoy getting back to nature in a park. Yet, even in a park many changes have been made in the natural environment. Why do people make changes? How do people use the natural environment?

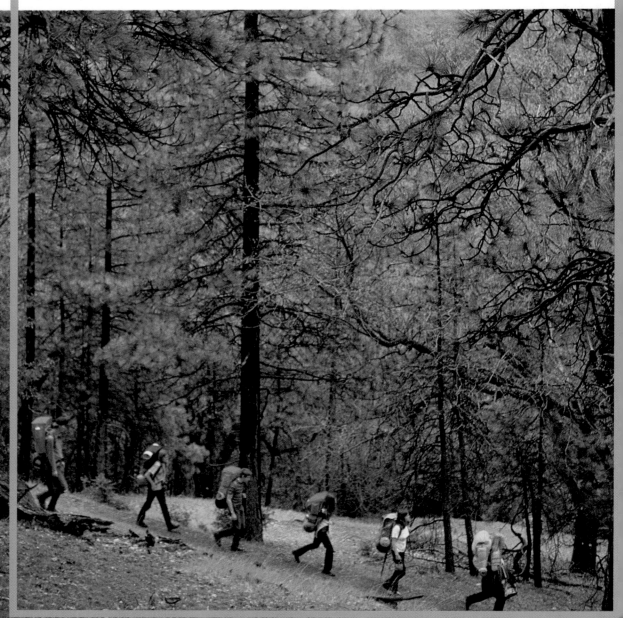

RESOURCE MANAGEMENT

INTRODUCING THE CHAPTER Begin with a discussion of parks students have visited. You may want to invite students to bring snapshots to class to post on a bulletin board. Or, collect pictures of parks from magazines. Continue the discussion, pointing out changes people make in the natural environment. Let students suggest reasons for the changes, whether the changes are necessary or unnecessary, and effects of the changes. Frequently environmental problems are presented in a completely negative way. Help students realize that many environmental problems can be overcome with creative long-range planning.

28:1 Adaptation

Living organisms interact with the environment. Each interaction is balanced by other actions that are part of cycles of changes. A kind of homeostasis on earth is maintained by natural processes. Throughout history, species have adapted to the environment for survival. People have changed the environment in an attempt to adapt.

When agriculture was developed about 10 000 years ago, settlements became more permanent than they had been before. Cities began to become industrialized in the 1600s with the development of modern technology. The growth of large industrial societies is **urbanization.**

Using much of the technology that has made urbanization possible has upset the balance in earth's ecosystems. Many natural cycles of feedback loops that maintain homeostasis may have reached the limits of their adaptability. Our ability to adapt to the changes we have made in the environment is limited, too. We must adapt to the stress that results from the changes in lifestyle that accompany urbanization. Stress is the tension felt in response to a situation. Stress may cause body changes such as increased blood pressure, digestive disorders, and mental illness. In addition, our basic needs for clean air and water, nutritious food, and natural resources for shelter do not change.

GOAL You will learn the nature and importance of some natural resources and problems of their use.

When did cities begin to become industrialized?

How can stress affect the body?

Activity: How can stress be reduced?

See Teacher's Guide.

MATERIALS

paper
pencil

PROCEDURE

1. Some stresssful situations in today's society are listed below. Add any others you can think of to the list.

   > Waiting in a long line when you are in a hurry
   > Traveling out of the country
   > Getting your driver's license
   > Your brother or sister going away to college
   > Moving to a new school district
   > Starting a job
   > Your mother or father beginning to work
   > Being in an auto accident
   > Seeing violence on TV
   > Having divorced parents

2. Survey 10 students in your school. Have them rate the stressful situations in your list from most (1) to least stressful.

3. Ask the students what they do or could do in stressful situations to reduce stress. Encourage them to be specific. For example, if students say they talk to a friend, find out if they talk on the telephone. If they say they exercise, find out if they jog in a park.

4. Tally the ratings to determine a consensus of the three most stressful situations on the list.

5. Rank the stress-reducing ideas in order from the most to least often suggested.

6. Determine the number of stress-reducing ideas that involve

   a. modern technology (such as telephones for talking to friends)

   b. the natural environment (such as jogging in a park)

DATA AND OBSERVATIONS

Situation	Stress Rating

QUESTIONS AND CONCLUSIONS

1. Which three situations in your list are generally most stressful? Which three would you personally rate most stressful?

2. Is all stress the result of something bad? Explain.

3. How are stresses today different from stresses of the past?

4. What are some stressful situations that are unrelated to urbanization?

5. How do people use technology to deal with stress?

6. Why do you think popular vacation spots often are places of natural beauty with recreation facilities?

7. Why is it important in dealing with stress for people to recognize whether they have control over the situation?

8. Suppose that you or a friend is experiencing great stress. What would you suggest to reduce the stress?

28:2   Mineral Resources

Mineral resources are concentrations of useful elements and compounds that can be extracted from minerals and rocks. We use mineral resources in a variety of ways. Metallic minerals are used to make structural alloys, such as steel. Billions of tons of nonmetallic minerals are used in fertilizers and manufacturing. Figure 28–1 shows some consumer products derived from mineral resources.

How are minerals used?

The distribution of mineral resources in the earth's crust is controlled by geologic and biological processes. For example, some ore deposits, such as chromite, form when igneous rocks form. Weathering and erosion also concentrate minerals in soils and sediment deposits. Bauxite, an aluminum ore found in soils, forms from the weathering of aluminum-rich igneous rocks. Abundant deposits of magnesium and manganese are found in the oceans in solution or on the bottom. Some minerals found in sedimentary rocks are produced by organisms. For example, calcium deposits may form from the bones and shells of animals.

Where are metallic ores formed?

The environmental impact of using mineral resources is complex. **Environmental impact** is the effect an activity has on an ecosystem. Air and water pollution from smelting operations and industrial processes are major problems of mineral resource use. Mining can change landscapes and cause pollution. Drainage patterns may be altered. Harmful compounds often become concentrated in

How does use of mineral resources affect the environment?

SUGGESTION   Have students examine Figure 28–1 and then prepare individual lists of products which they have used today that contain minerals.

Steel
Asphalt
Mineral pigments
Plastic
Natural fibers grown with mineral fertilizers
Stone
Cement
Copper
Clay
Synthetic fibers made from minerals
Fiberglass
Grown with mineral fertilizers
Gypsum

FIGURE   28–1.   Many of the items in a typical home are mineral products.

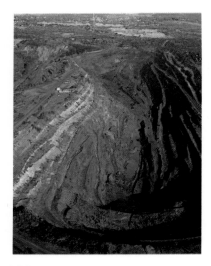

FIGURE 28–2. Surface mines usually cause more environmental damage than underground mines. However, safety and economic considerations often lead mining companies to build surface mines.

What is reclamation?

How can demand for some mineral resources be reduced?

DEMONSTRATION While wearing gloves and an apron, examine the contents of the classroom trash container at the end of a day. Let students suggest materials that could be recycled or ways refuse could be reduced.

soils and water supplies. Dust from mining operations pollute the air. In addition, mining operations cause social changes that affect land use. For example, new towns may be built around large mining operations.

Surface mines, Figure 28–2, are common because they are usually less costly and safer in some ways than underground mines. However, the environmental impact of surface mines is greater. Erosion becomes a major problem if the mines are abandoned when the resources in surface mines are exhausted. Most plants and animals cannot live in the environment. Many of the pollution problems remain. Reclamation is one solution to some of these problems.

Reclamation involves grading and reforesting land. Some mines in the United States have been reclaimed and converted to parks, farmland, residential and industrial areas. Government regulations in some states require various degrees of reclamation. Many mines are never reclaimed, although the cost of reclamation would be less than the amount saved by using surface rather than underground mines.

Technological development demands an increasing supply of mineral resources. But, like fossil fuels, mineral resources are nonrenewable. Once fossil fuels have been used to produce energy, they are no longer useful as energy resources. However, when mineral resources are extracted and used, their value may not be lost. Remember, matter is neither created nor destroyed in a chemical reaction. A mineral resource may be unavailable for use for a long time, for example if it is converted into the structural steel of a building. However, many mineral resources can be recycled once they have been used and discarded.

The solid wastes and sewage of many cities contain a variety of mineral resources. These resources are called urban ores because they are economical sources of minerals. In addition to increasing supplies of mineral resources, recycling can reduce pollution. Technological research can reduce demand for some mineral resources by development of materials that can be used in place of mineral resources. For example, plastic pipes often are used for plumbing in new homes instead of copper pipes, which were used in the past.

28:3 Forest Resources

Forests are ecological communities of large trees and many other organisms. The trees may be used for industrial materials. Forests also are used for recreation. They are important parts of watersheds because they intercept rainfall before it causes erosion and flooding.

About one fifth of the land on earth is forests, but their abundance is declining. An increasing human population has an increasing demand for forest resources. Technological developments also have increased demand for forest resources and land. Since the colonists arrived, about half of the forests in the United States have been cut down. Great destruction of tropical rain forests is occurring. Logging, poor agricultural methods, and clearing of forests for cattle grazing reduces the size of the tropical rain forests each year. The tropical rain forests contain a large percentage of the earth's approximately ten million species of life. Many species are destroyed each year.

Forests are considered renewable resources. A **renewable** resource is one that can be replaced within a person's average lifetime. Natural processes of succession eventually may replace the trees removed from a forest or people may replant trees. Reforestation is the replanting of trees after a forest area has been cleared. Reforestation helps prevent soil erosion and water loss. It is an important part of forest management. Conservation of forest resources involves forest management as well as reducing waste in processing and recycling wood products.

The goal of good forest management is a sustained yield of trees without permanent damage to the forest or the land. A **sustained yield** means that even though some trees are cut, the environment is maintained so that a supply of trees always will be available for future use. Forest management techniques include thinning to remove undesirable trees, fertilizing to promote growth of desirable trees, controlling fire, and protecting trees from insect damage and disease. Considering the forest as an ecosystem is important in forest management. Many variables, such as climate, soils, populations, and community relationships, affect how a forest should be managed.

Different methods of harvesting trees should be used depending on the ecosystem. Clearcutting is harvesting all

What is happening to forest land?

BACKGROUND A standard procedure is the quantitative evaluation of a forest, as well as other resources, before a land is either developed or when forest resource management begins. Forests are often evaluated by the numbers and sizes of different types of trees.

What is the value of reforestation?

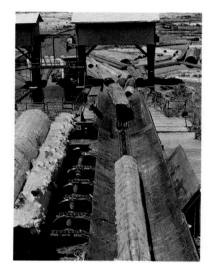

FIGURE 28–3. Some logging operations clearcut forest areas for economic reasons. Although this method may provide timber quickly and cheaply for immediate use, it may result in environmental damage that will prevent future harvests.

FIGURE 28–4. In selective cutting, only large mature trees are marked for harvest. Selective cutting is a more effective method of management for sustained yields than clearcutting.

Why is maintaining a variety of tree species important in a forest?

ACTIVITY   Have students use books about birds and trees to learn which trees depend on fire-cleared soil, and which birds depend on these trees for nesting sites.

What is the purpose of controlled fires?

SUGGESTION   Compare selective cutting to thinning of radishes, carrots, or other plants in a garden if most students are familiar with gardens. Note the difference: in clearcutting the largest trees are taken, while in garden thinning the most mature and strongest are left to grow.

of the trees in a large area of a forest. Although clearcutting is economical for logging operations, a major drawback is erosion of topsoil. Another problem is that some species of trees will not grow back in open areas. Clearcutting is useful where rainfall and slope are low enough to minimize erosion and desirable species require open areas for growth. Harvesting timber by selective cutting involves removing only large, mature trees. Small, young trees continue to store water, hold soil on slopes, provide wildlife habitat, and ensure natural reforestation. Selective cutting is more costly for loggers in the short run than clearcutting, but it is more effective for sustained yields over long periods of time.

A major problem in forest management is pest control. Maintaining a variety of species in a forest ecosystem helps control pests by limiting pest populations. For example, a forest with a variety of tree species will not be destroyed by infestation of a pest that affects only one of the species. Development of resistant species and use of pesticides are also methods of controlling pests. Integrated pest management (IPM) is important in forest management.

Prevention of forest fires that are dangerously destructive and threaten human life and property is necessary. However, controlled fires are becoming a useful tool in forest management. In recent years, foresters have found that natural fires are a necessary part of some forest ecosystems. Certain species of trees take root only in areas cleared by fire. Others release their seeds only in the intense heat of a fire. Controlled fires caused by lightning or prescribed by foresters improve wildlife habitat and prevent severe fires by periodically destroying accumulations of dry materials that fuel fires.

See Teacher's Guide.

REVIEW AND REFLECT

1. How has urbanization affected the earth's ecosystems?
2. Why is the demand for mineral and forest resources increasing?
3. How can recycling of urban ores found in sewage and solid wastes reduce pollution?
4. Why do you think tree farms are more likely to be severely damaged by pests than most forests?

28:4 Land Resources

The value of land as a resource has many dimensions. **Open spaces,** which are undeveloped land, are the sites of forest, wildlife, mineral, and energy resources and have recreational and agricultural uses. Sites, such as the Grand Canyon, are valuable open spaces because they are spectacular and unique. Highways are built in open spaces and cities expand into open spaces.

The increased demand for open space continues as the population grows. A related factor that has increased the need for recreational open space is urbanization. In less urban societies, people's daily activities require them to spend more time in the open. The value of open space seems to increase with urban living because open space in cities is limited.

Farmland is an important resource in the United States. Products from U.S. farmland provide food for the nation and supply about 60 percent of all the food and livestock feed grains that are imported by other countries. Yet, each year about one million acres of U.S. farmland are paved with roads and parking lots, or developed for housing and shopping centers. Imagine a strip of land as wide as four football fields stretching from New York to California. That is the amount of U.S. farmland converted to other uses annually. Developers often can afford to pay higher prices for the land than farmers can profit by planting it. So, the farmers may feel they should sell to developers.

Why are open spaces valuable?

BACKGROUND   The uniqueness of natural landscape, such as terrain set aside for national parks, is a factor in quantitatively determining the value of the landscape to society.

SUGGESTION   Discuss how, when, and the total amount of time that students spend outdoors. Also discuss the factors that influence these answers.

What is happening to U.S. farmland?

FIGURE 28–5. Open space is a source of many natural resources.

FIGURE 28–6. Many national parks, such as the Grand Canyon, have had problems with traffic. Some parks have developed mass transportation systems requiring visitors to park their cars and ride park buses into the main park areas.

Describe some methods of managing open space.

BACKGROUND   Two types of political process, privatization and the so-called Sagebrush Rebellion, are reducing the amount of government-owned land in the U.S. Privatization is selling land to private companies, and the Sagebrush Rebellion is movement of state groups to transfer federal property to states.

Preserving a resource, such as farmland, as open space is easier than acquiring new land for open space. Prime farmland is not easily regained. New land that is less productive is obtained for farming by draining swamps, irrigating deserts, and clearing woodlands. These changes often are harmful to other living resources, such as forests and wildlife.

As a resource similar to forest or wildlife resources, open space needs to be managed. Preserving some open spaces is an important part of management. Planning to make the best use of land is needed when open spaces are developed. Many regions have land use planning commissions that make decisions about the use of land for highways, industries, and so on. Some cities have zoning regulations that control which land areas will be used for residential, commercial, and industrial development.

Much open space is protected or owned by governments. About one third of the land in the United States is owned by the federal government. Rights to extract minerals, harvest timber, graze livestock, and hunt wildlife on these public lands may be sold or given to private companies and individuals. However, many of these uses are controversial. Use of some public lands may need to be limited in order to preserve the nature of the open space.

Many people visit national parks in the U.S. that have unique natural attractions. As a result, the parks often are overcrowded. Overcrowded conditions damage park ecosystems. Auto traffic in Grand Canyon National Park has become so congested in summer that the main park road is closed in the busiest season. Visitors must take a bus from a parking area to the Canyon. Campsites, which were once available on a first-come first-served basis, must now be reserved months in advance. Without such restrictions, damage to the park from overcrowding would severely reduce its scenic and recreational value.

28:5 Soil

Soil, on farmlands and elsewhere, is a natural resource. It is a source of nutrients for land plants, the main producers in land ecosystems. Soil provides the basis for food crops, livestock feed, forest resources, textiles, and industrial materials.

Soil is considered a nonrenewable resource because it forms very slowly, over hundreds or thousands of years. Recall from chapter 18 that soils form from the weathering of rock. Humus, organic matter, is added to topsoil by biological processes. The downward movement of water removes soluble minerals from topsoil, a process called leaching, and deposits them in subsoil.

Although you may think that all soils are alike, there are many different kinds of soils. The properties of soils are determined by climate, topography, the rocks from which they formed, biological processes, and their ages. Soils are classified according to their properties.

The properties of soils affect their suitability for various uses. For example, structure, fertility, and organic content are important properties for agricultural use. Different crops have different soil requirements.

The size and arrangement of the particles in soil determine its structure. Particle sizes range from very fine to coarse. The structure of soil affects its release of nutrients to plants. A soil's content of elements needed for plant growth determines its fertility. The organic content of soil includes dead organic matter and living organisms. Living organisms such as bacteria break down and release nutrients from organic matter.

Other properties of soils affect their suitability for engineering uses, such as housing developments, highway construction, landfill sites, and recreation. Two important properties to be considered are permeability—how easily water moves through soil, and porosity—the amount of air space in the soil. Slope, natural drainage, seasonal wetness, erodibility, pH, depth to bedrock, depth to water table, and ability to support weight are other important soil properties.

Information about the properties of soils in a certain location can be found in a soil survey. **Soil surveys** contain detailed descriptions, maps, and test results of the properties of soils. Soil surveys are useful to farmers, engineers, land use planning commissions, developers, and even home-buyers. Soil surveys are used to identify specific soil conservation problems, such as decreasing fertility and erosion, and to plan solutions for them.

Topsoil is the main source of the nutrients that plants need to grow. The roots of plants help prevent topsoil from

Why is soil considered a nonrenewable resource?

How are soils classified?

ACTIVITY Obtain samples of soil from different locations. Study them with a hand lens to classify them as gravel, sand, silt, or clay, well-graded or poorly-graded.

Describe the importance of understanding soil properties.

DEMONSTRATION Have water poured through two pipes or other columns each containing the same volume of beads of a different diameter. Time how long 200 mL of water takes to pass through each column to find the permeability rate for each. The procedure can be tried with different soils as well, but the time will be much greater and the rate much slower.

Who uses soil surveys?

being eroded. The U.S. Soil Conservation Service estimates that about four billion metric tons of topsoil in the United States are lost each year. The topsoil is eroded and carried by streams to the oceans. Soil erosion is found mainly on new farmland. Where land is drained, deserts are irrigated, or forests are cleared, conditions that hold soil are destroyed. Without topsoil, few plants can grow and ecosystems become unbalanced. Also, eroded soil often contains fertilizer and pesticides that pollute water. Some methods used to conserve soil are shown in Table 28–1.

What are some ways to conserve soil?

TABLE 28–1. SOIL CONSERVATION METHODS		
Method	**Purpose**	**Explanation**
Shelter belts (windbreaks)	Reduce erosion of topsoil by the wind	Planting rows of evergreen trees to block wind
Contour plowing/planting	Reduce erosion of topsoil by rain	Plowing and planting crops by following natural contours
No-till farming	Reduce erosion of topsoil by wind and rain	Using herbicides to control weeds, planting seed without plowing
Crop rotation	Maintain soil fertility	Planting different crops each year in a cycle of three or more years
Strip cropping	Reduce erosion of topsoil by rain	Alternating rows of crops that hold water with crops that absorb runoff
Terracing, retaining walls	Reduce erosion of topsoil by rain	Changing the contour of land to form a series of steps, erecting walls of soil, rocks, or wood to block runoff
Check dams	Reduce erosion of topsoil by rain	Erecting dams of boards, logs, or brush to form steps that slow the flow of water in gullies

See Teacher's Guide.

REVIEW AND REFLECT

1. Why are open space and soil considered valuable resources?
2. a. How is soil eroded?
   b. What can be done to prevent soil erosion?
3. Make three recommendations for preserving the quality of a national park.
4. How might earthworms affect the properties of soils?
5. What process that occurs in soils forms mineral resources such as bauxite?

See Teacher's Guide.

Career Profile

Tim Carter always liked maps, even in elementary school. He read every issue of *National Geographic* and hoped that someday he might work for the National Geographic Society. After teaching geography at a junior high school for six years, Tim applied to the Society for a job. He became a research compiler in the cartographic division where maps are made.

Tim researches many different topics for map development, and a common one is

natural resources. National Geographic does not do its own field work, so Tim must rely on external sources to acquire knowledge about natural resource distribution. First, other cartographers draw the format of a map with its shorelines, boundaries, and drainage. Then Tim identifies specific natural resource areas. Any information or names must be printed to the scale of the map in their proper locations. If the locations of coal seams are to be mapped, for example, Tim might need to color code the different types of coal. He might need to identify areas where the coal is transported for use by industries or power plants.

Tim brings many different skills to his work at National Geographic. His geography background helps him compile research on a topic. Also important is his technical ability to focus attention on details. When Tim prepares a map at publication size, he sometimes needs to print words no larger than .13 centimeters. Tim needs to be concerned about the appearance of a map as well as its geographic accuracy. Communication with people both inside and outside the office are important to Tim's work, too. When many individuals contribute to the creation of a single product, cooperation is essential.

a

b

FIGURE 28–7. Species most in danger of becoming extinct due to human activities are large animals that have low reproductive rates or animals with very specialized habitat requirements. Timber wolves (a) are endangered. They need a large habitat, produce only 4 to 6 offspring per year, and require a large food base. Blue pike (b), once common in the Great Lakes, have become extinct due to overfishing and pollution.

What are some strategies of wildlife management?

How can wildlife habitats be maintained?

28:6 Wildlife Resources

Wildlife resources, like mineral, forest, or land resources, are economically valuable. Hunting and fishing are popular recreational activities along with nature photography, birdwatching, and so on. Millions of dollars are spent each year for licenses, permits, and equipment for these activities. Good wildlife management is as profitable as most agricultural and other uses of land. In addition, many people feel that wildlife is valuable regardless of its economic benefits to people.

A passive strategy of wildlife management is to let natural succession take control. However, few if any environments today are completely free of human influences. So, the natural succession strategy may not be practical.

Active strategies include management for species diversity or a single species. For species diversity, the greatest variety of habitats is maintained and thus a large variety of species. Single species management is used to maintain populations of game species or endangered species.

When the population of a species has dwindled to relatively few members and its survival is seriously threatened, it is said to be endangered. If all the members of a species die, the species is **extinct.** Extinction may occur naturally. For example, dinosaurs probably became extinct largely due to changes in climates. Today human activities have joined natural processes in causing extinctions. As people have altered and polluted ecosystems, wildlife has declined.

Techniques of wildlife management to maintain habitats include using controlled fires to create habitats for animals that live at the edges of forests. Also, water can be impounded to provide food and habitat for waterfowl and shore plants and animals. The plant life of an area may be managed to make the area a more suitable habitat for one or more animal species. For example, the natural succession of an area to a forest may be prevented so that deer populations, which thrive in earlier stages of succession, may increase.

Parks in cities can be managed to attract a variety of wildlife. You can develop a plan to attract wildlife to the area around your home. The basic considerations are the food, water, shelter, and reproductive needs of the species you want to attract. Table 28–2 lists some ideas that could be included in a home wildlife management plan.

A major wildlife management technique is hunting. People have eliminated the natural factors that limit the populations of species in many ecosystems. Hunting that is regulated by licensing, seasonal restrictions, and limits of the number and kinds of animals that can be taken, is a substitute for these factors. The regulations help prevent overhunting that might endanger species. Also, the sale of hunting and fishing licenses is an important source of wildlife conservation funds.

What can you do to provide wildlife habitats?

ACTIVITY   At school or home have students attract wildlife with one or more of the procedures suggested in Table 28–2.
What is the role of hunting in wildlife management?

TABLE 28–2. ATTRACTING WILDLIFE

What to Do	What Is Provided	What Is Attracted*
Plant sunflowers	Food	Seed-eating birds
Plant oak or nut trees	Food/nesting habitat	Squirrels/birds
Plant berry bushes	Food	Songbirds
Let mature trees stand	Insect habitat	Insect-eating birds, such as woodpeckers
Hang bird feeders	Food	Seed-eating birds
Plant a lawn or garden	Earthworm habitat/food	Worm-eating birds/rabbits
Plant flowers in a border or window box	Food	Bees, butterflies
Hang birdhouses	Nesting habitat	Birds
Set out a birdbath or let a garden hose drip	Water	Birds, rabbits, rodents
Plant hedges, shrubs, tall grasses	Habitat	Rabbits, rodents

*Species attracted vary depending on species planted and geographic location.

Activity: How can resources be managed?

MATERIALS

graph paper
pencil

PROCEDURE

1. About one million acres of land north of the Grand Canyon are called the Kaibab (KI bab) Plateau. In 1906, this region was set aside as a National Game Preserve for a large population of mule deer. Use reference books to learn about mule deer. Write a description of mule deer, including what they eat and what animals are their predators.

2. After the Kaibab Plateau became a preserve, deer hunting was banned. From 1906 to 1931, 4889 coyotes, 781 mountain lions, 554 bobcats, and 20 wolves were killed by U.S. government hunters to help protect the deer. Many more predators were killed by private hunters. Prepare a histogram of this data.

3. Censuses were taken of the Kaibab deer population between 1906 and 1931. (See the data table.) Graph the data.

4. Based on what you have learned about mule deer and the Kaibab Plateau, note any cause-effect relationships that may explain the shape of your graph in step 3. (In 1923, little vegetation was found on the Kaibab Plateau; deer were starving to death. In 1924, deer hunting was permitted again. Conditions were improved to encourage deer hunting and prevent livestock grazing.)

5. Describe how the conditions of many starving deer and stripped vegetation found in 1923 might have been avoided. List when and what resource management actions you would have taken. Consider the effects of hunting, cattle control, and predator control. Tell why you would have taken each action.

6. Discuss your decisions within a small group. Identify the merits and problems with each set of recommendations. Make a new set of group recommendations based on the discussion. Report your recommendations.

DATA AND OBSERVATIONS

Year	Deer Population
1906	3000
1908	5000
1910	10 000
1918	15 000
1922	20 000
1923	100 000*
1931	20 000

*unofficial estimate

QUESTIONS AND CONCLUSIONS

1. What served as natural controls for the deer population before 1906?

2. List the ways that people interfered with the natural balance of wildlife.

3. How is the importance of considering each step in a food chain shown by this resource management project?

4. What conditions helped reduce the deer population between 1923 and 1931?

5. How is what is good for the individual different from what is good for a population in this management project?

6. When people interfere with an ecosystem, what responsibility do you think they have for the survival of the populations in that ecosystem?

28:7 **Managing Resources**

Resource management would be easy if one way of managing a resource clearly was best. But, not everyone agrees which action is least costly, least damaging to the environment, or provides the most benefits. As with other environmental topics, public benefit may be different from individual benefit.

An example of disputed resource management is what to do about brush growing along the right-of-way areas of roads. For a long time, herbicides have been sprayed to kill the brush. Although, the brush is not a safety hazard, some people prefer lawnlike vegetation along roads. The spraying is an expensive procedure. It pollutes land, water, and air. Some people think selective cutting of tall vegetation would be better resource management. This procedure would cost less than spraying and would pollute the environment less.

How do ideas about resource management differ?

ACTIVITY   Identify an example of disputed resource management in your community, perhaps even at your school, such as how a particular room (classroom, gym) or piece of land is to be used. List possible uses. Have students individually or in teams prepare a case (recommended use and reasons for a particular use over other possible uses). As a class, examine the cases and reach a consensus on the best use of the resource. Note any other decisions and recommendations. Try to reach compromises to satsify the majority. This activity is an example of policy-making by democratic procedures, often applied when use of a resource affecting many people is disputed.

FIGURE   28–8. Permafrost is permanently frozen ground that becomes unstable if it melts. The Trans-Alaska pipeline crosses permafrost. Since the pipeline transports hot oil, it was engineered to avoid damage to the permafrost.

FIGURE 28–9. Several alternative routes for the Trans-Alaska pipeline were considered before the final route was chosen. However, none of the routes considered was clearly better in every way than all others.

In 1975, construction began on the Trans-Alaska pipeline that transports oil from Prudhoe Bay to Valdez, Figure 28–9. Before construction of the pipeline, many people argued about the best plan of resource management. Some people thought the pipeline should not be built. They said the tundra is a fragile ecosystem that would be severely damaged by an oil spill or machines working on the line. Other people pointed out that the oil was a needed energy resource. Studies were made of the physical, biological, social, and economic effects of the pipeline. When the pipeline was built, extra expense and care were taken to protect the environment. Part of the pipeline was elevated so that heat from the oil would not melt the permafrost. Permafrost is permanently frozen ground that becomes very unstable when melted. Careful studies were made to determine how the pipeline would affect migrating caribou (reindeer).

The positive and negative results of proposed environmental actions should be considered in terms of ecosystems, not just in terms of what people want. An integrated approach to resource management combines many different values. Each value must be weighed against the others. Compromises must be made based on information and reasoning. Planning is an important part of good resource management. A risk-benefit analysis, with public benefit for now and the future as high priority, is essential to any large-scale project affecting the environment. Soil surveys, and environmental impact statements are useful tools for resource managers. They are sources of information for decision makers like you.

Resource management depends on the judgment of many individuals and groups of people. For instance, recycling of metals will only be effective if many people are willing to take metal items to recycling centers. Governments are important in resource management. Governments can help educate the public about natural resources. They also can make and enforce laws so that a few careless people do not spoil the efforts of many. For example, people caught littering along some roads in the United States are fined. As a citizen, you are responsible for effective resource management. Ultimately, everyone benefits from sound resource management decisions.

Describe an integrated approach to resource management.

On whom does resource management depend?

See Teacher's Guide.

REVIEW AND REFLECT

1. How have human activities affected wildlife?
2. What are some physical, biological, and socioeconomic effects of strip mining that should be considered before a mine site is chosen?
3. Describe a resource management plan that
   a. uses a variety of procedures to minimize environmental damage.
   b. not everyone agrees upon.
4. Describe an integrated approach to resource management on your school grounds. Consider what natural resources are there, how they can be conserved, and what information you would need to gather to develop a plan.

See Teacher's Guide.

Skill Inquiry

Data may be qualitative or quantitative. Remember, quantitative data are measured observations. Qualitative data are evaluations of characteristics observed.

As you know, diagrams are useful tools for analyzing data. Diagrams can be made with quantitative or qualitative data. It is important to recognize the difference. Diagrams based on qualitative data show the relationships between variables in relative terms. However, they do not show numerical relationships, such as percentages or amounts, as do quantitative diagrams. Graphs are quantitative diagrams. Qualitative diagrams may be used to show trends when quantitative data is not available.

1. Which diagram in the figure is qualitative? Which is quantitative?
2. Summarize what you can and cannot interpret for each of the natural resources shown in each diagram.
3. When is a qualitative diagram useful? When is a quantitative diagram preferred? Why?

a

b

28:8 Information: Tropical Resources

The human population in tropical regions is expected to double over the next 30 years. The rapidly-growing population is expanding into tropical rain forests. When a tropical rain forest is completely leveled, new growth may take approximately 1000 years. For this reason, scientists and engineers are looking for and finding ways to maintain these forests.

How is wood from tropical rain forests used?

The forests are an important resource for the region. Wood from harvested trees provides fuel for cooking and heating. Wood also is used to build homes and make paper. The roots of trees in the forests help prevent soil erosion and floods. In addition, the rain forests provide important wildlife habitats. Researchers are finding that tropical rain forests do not need to be set aside as isolated parks in order to maintain them as resources.

How can wood be used more efficiently?

First, better use can be made of cut wood because most of the cut wood has been used for cooking and heating. Better ways to cook and heat are being tried. A stove made of mud and sand that contains a metal pipe and a damper is twice as efficient as the type of stove normally used by the native people. Also, better use can be made of wood cut for building homes. In hot, damp climates, the wood rots easily and is eaten by termites. However, if the wood is soaked in certain safe chemicals, it will not need to be replaced as soon. Ways are examined to use some of the previously unused tree species. In normal papermaking, chips of only one type of tree are used at a time. A new "press-dry process" allows the use of wood chips of different species.

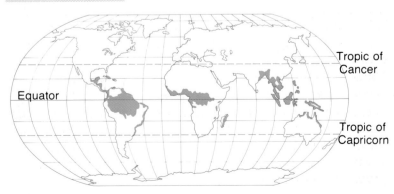

FIGURE 28–10. Tropical rain forests are found in the region between the tropic of Cancer ($23\frac{1}{2}°$ N latitude) and the tropic of Capricorn ($23\frac{1}{2}°$ S latitude).

Within forests, better wildlife management is important. Many native tropical animals are endangered. By purposely promoting the environment that aids a species or by raising animals, natives can increase species number. In some cases, they can produce an economic product, too. Crocodile ranching has been made an industry in Papua, New Guinea. Crocodiles breed in the wild. People gather and raise the tiny crocodiles after they hatch from eggs. The number of crocodiles has increased dramatically. The process also has produced enough crocodiles for export to zoos or to use for hides. Butterfly farming is another important industry in Papua, New Guinea. Native people plant hibiscus and bougainvillea to attract butterflies. Then, after training by wildlife officers, they gather and pack the fragile butterflies for shipment to museums, schools, and collectors throughout the world.

Scientists are promoting certain under-used animal species as important sources of protein. The babirusa of Southeast Asia, a tusked piglike animal, is an example. The babirusa is easily tamed and eats tough leaves and stems that other animals do not digest well. The meat of the babirusa is nutritious and flavorful.

Studies of tropical rain forest soil have shown that some crops can be raised next to and among strands of tropical trees and shrubs. This method of agriculture conserves the protective cover that the forests provide. The optimum amounts of natural growth and crops vary with the terrain. Ongoing research is helping to establish the limit and patterns of agriculture in tropical regions, so that the forests can be saved.

See Teacher's Guide.

FIGURE 28–11. The clearing of tropical rain forests has eliminated many wildlife habitats, endangering many species.

How can agriculture be used in forest management?

REVIEW AND REFLECT

1. Why is leveling a tropical forest usually not good resource management?
2. Name three ways that science and technology have shown that the tropical rain forests can be conserved.
3. Some people living in tropical regions are not familiar with conservation practices and the importance of conserving the rain forests. What problems might this lack of knowledge cause resource managers? How might the problems be solved?

CHAPTER 28 REVIEW

SUMMARY

1. Urbanization has had positive and negative results for people. 28:1
2. Natural resources include minerals, forests, land, soil, and wildlife. 28:2–5
3. Mineral resources are used in many ways, and the impact of their use on the environment is complex. 28:2
4. The goal of good forest management is a sustained yield of trees without permanent damage to the forest or land. 28:3
5. Land is a resource for recreational development, agricultural use, and the sites of forest and mineral resources. 28:4
6. Soil is a nonrenewable resource. Different soils have different properties, which make them suitable for different purposes. 28:5
7. Active strategies of wildlife management include using fire to create habitats, impounding water to provide habitats and food, and growing plants to attract certain animals. 28:6
8. Resource management can help preserve and conserve natural resources. 28:7
9. Resource management depends on the judgments and actions of individuals and groups of people. 28:7

VOCABULARY

endangered 8
environmental impact 6
extinct 1

open space 4
reclamation 5
renewable 2

soil survey 9
sustained yield 3
urbanization 7

Choose a word from the list to complete each sentence correctly.

1. When all the members of a species die, the species is _____.
2. A(n) _____ resource can be replaced in a relatively short time.
3. Maintaining a supply of a resource so that some will always be available for future use is the _____ method of resource management.
4. _____ is undeveloped land.
5. _____ involves grading and reforesting land that has been surface mined.
6. The effect of an activity that changes an ecosystem is a(n) _____.
7. The growth of a large industrial society is called _____.
8. A(n) _____ species is a very small population, and its survival is threatened.
9. A detailed description of the properties of soils, including maps and test results, is a(n) _____.

QUESTIONS

MAIN IDEAS

Choose the correct answer to complete each sentence.

1. Technology that has made urbanization possible has had many (*environmental impacts*, *adaptations*, *sustained yields*).
2. The Trans-Alaska pipeline was built (*without*, *before*, *after*) careful studies of its predicted impact on the environment.
3. The value of open space seems to (*increase with*, *decrease with*, *be unaffected by*) increased urbanization.

4. About *(one half, one third, one fourth, <u>one fifth</u>)* of the land on earth is forests.

5. An active wildlife management technique is *(to let natural succession take control, <u>regulating hunting</u>, being careful never to allow fire in forests)*.

6. Abundant deposits of magnesium and manganese mineral resources are found in *(igneous rocks, sedimentary rocks, groundwater, <u>oceans</u>)*.

7. An effective method of reducing wind erosion of topsoil is *(crop rotation, check dams, terracing, <u>shelter belts</u>)*.

8. Good forest management for sustained yields may involve *(clearcutting, use of pesticides, controlled fires, <u>all of these</u>)*.

9. Soil is a(n) *(renewable, <u>nonrenewable</u>, endangered, extinct)* resource.

10. Minerals extracted from the solid wastes and sewage of cities are called *(city-sources, <u>urban ores</u>, refuse resources)*.

11. Replanting of trees after a forest area has been cleared is called *(<u>reforestation</u>, reclamation, sustained yield, IPM)*.

12. One way to attract seed-eating birds to an area is to plant *(<u>sunflowers</u>, berry bushes, gardens, hedges)*.

See Teacher's Guide.

APPLICATIONS

Answer each question in one or more paragraphs.

1. Why is an integrated approach to resource management important?

2. How might it be possible to tell if water pollution was due to an unreclaimed strip mine, rather than other sources?

3. Why is soil erosion more of a problem on farmland in the United States and Canada than in Europe?

4. Why is cattle-raising on land that could support crops a less-efficient food production choice?

5. How can a potential home buyer use a soil survey in making a decision about buying land on which to build a home?

6. How does everyone ultimately benefit from good resource management decisions?

7. Suppose you own sloping land that is forested. A lumber company wants to harvest the trees. They offer you twice as much to clearcut as to selective cut the first time. They assure you the same price for clearcutting as selective cutting every fifteen years thereafter. Which first-time logging procedure would you accept and why?

FURTHER STUDY

INVESTIGATIONS

1. Find out what large predators are endangered in your area. Make posters including recommendations for ways to preserve the animals.

2. Visit a farm. If possible, take pictures of soil conservation methods. Interview the farmer about the methods used. Prepare a report including a map of the farm and the pictures.

3. Join a local conservation club. Participate in a group project sponsored by the club.

READINGS

+ Cousteau, Jacques-Yves, and the Staff of the Cousteau Society. *The Cousteau Almanac.* Doubleday: New York, 1981.

0 Graham, Ada and Frank. *Careers in Conservation.* Sierra Club Books: San Francisco, 1980.

+ Parfit, Michael. "Groundwater Proves a Hidden Element Whose Time Has Come." *Smithsonian.* March, 1983. pp. 50–61.

– Ridgeway, James. *Who Owns the Earth?* Macmillan: New York, 1980.

Appendix A: Units of Measurement

TABLE A–1. SOME SI BASE UNITS		
Measurement	**Unit**	**Symbol**
Length	Meter	m
Mass	Kilogram	kg
Temperature	Kelvin	K
Time	Second	s
Electric current	Ampere	A

TABLE A–2. OTHER COMMON UNITS			
Measurement	**Unit**	**Symbol**	**Relationship**
Length	Kilometer	km	1000 m
	Decimeter	dm	0.1m
	Centimeter	cm	0.01 m
	Millimeter	mm	0.001 m
	Nanometer	nm	0.000 000 001 m
Mass	Gram	g	0.001 kg
Volume	Liter	L	1 dm^3
	Milliliter	mL	$0.001 \text{ L } (1 \text{ cm}^3)$
Temperature	Degrees Celsius	°C	K + 273
Force	Newton	N	kg·m/s^2
Energy, work	Joule	J	N·m
Pressure	Pascal	Pa	N/m^2
	Kilopascal	kPa	1000 Pa
	Millibar	mb	0.1 kPa
Thermal energy	calorie	c	4.18 J
	Calorie	C	1000 calories
Quantity of electric charge	Coulomb	C	A · s
Electric potential difference	Volt	V	J/C
Electric resistance	Ohm	O	V/A
Power	Watt	W	J/s
	Kilowatt	kW	1000 W
Energy usage	Kilowatt-hour	kWh	KW · hours
Frequency	Hertz	Hz	1/s

Appendix B: Science Classroom Safety

Science activities are safe to perform if you are careful. You must take responsibility for both your own safety and the safety of your classmates. The following guide will help you carry out science activities safely.

B:1 Personal Safety

1. Always obtain your teacher's permission before performing any activity.
2. Always read and understand an activity thoroughly before beginning any part. If you do not understand some part, ask your teacher to explain it.
3. Never eat or drink anything in the laboratory.
4. Always know the location of the fire extinguisher, fire blanket, safety shower, eyewash bath, first aid kit, fire alarm, and the nearest telephone, and how to use them.
5. Always wear goggles and aprons when you see these symbols at the beginning of an activity.
6. Never block aisles with equipment, books, or electrical cords. Never run or play in the laboratory.
7. Always report a fire, accident, or incorrect procedure to your teacher *immediately*.
8. Always tie back long hair and never wear clothing with loose sleeves.
9. Always know how to smother a fire and how to use the fire extinguisher. If hair or clothing should catch fire, use a fire blanket or safety shower. DO NOT RUN.

B:2 Using Equipment Safely

1. Never use chipped, cracked, or broken glassware. Dispose of all broken glass properly as instructed by your teacher.
2. Never dispose of any solid material in the sink.
3. Never place hot objects or any chemicals directly on the balance pan.

4. Never use open flames unless instructed by your teacher.
5. Never insert any object other than standard electrical plugs into electrical outlets.
6. Always be cautious when using cutting instruments.
7. Always clean up your workspace when finished. Return all materials to their proper places. Make sure electric devices are disconnected and gas and water are turned off.

B:3 Using Chemicals Safely

1. Always use proper containers and utensils for chemicals. Never handle chemicals with your hands.
2. Never taste or put any chemical into your mouth.
3. Never return unused chemicals to the original bottle. Dispose of them as instructed by your teacher.
4. Always clean up spills immediately. Use plenty of water. Acid spills may be treated with baking soda; base spills may be treated with boric acid.
5. Always keep combustible materials away from flames, sparks, and hotplates.
6. Always wear goggles and aprons when working with chemicals.

Appendix C: Solving General Science Problems

In science, people often need to use scientific laws to make calculations. You will find these calculations are not hard if you always follow the same steps.
1. Write the equation you are going to use.
2. Manipulate the equation so that the term you need to calculate is alone on one side of the equals sign.
3. Do not forget that whatever you do on one side of the equals sign must be done exactly the same way on the other side.
4. Substitute values for the terms of the equation.
5. Complete your calculations.

Here are examples to show how this procedure works in the kinds of equations you will find in this book. In each example, the value of x is being calculated.

EXAMPLE:

$a = x + b$

Subtract b from both sides.

$a - b = x + b - b$

Simplify the equation.

$a - b = x$

Put in values of a and b; calculate x.

EXAMPLE:

$a = x - b$

Add b to both sides.

$a + b = x - b + b$

Simplify

$a + b = x$

Put in values of a and b; calculate x.

EXAMPLE:

$a = b \times x$

Divide both sides by b.

$$\frac{a}{b} = \frac{b \times x}{b}$$

Simplify.

$$\frac{a}{b} = x$$

Put in values of a and b; calculate x.

EXAMPLE:

$$a = \frac{b}{x}$$

Multiply both sides by x.

$$a \times x = \frac{b}{x} \times x$$

Divide both sides by a.

$$\frac{a \times x}{a} = \frac{b}{a}$$

Simplify.

$$x = \frac{b}{a}$$

Put in values of a and b; calculate x.

EXAMPLE:

$$a = \frac{x}{b}$$

Multiply both sides by b.

$$a \times b = \frac{x}{b} \times b$$

Simplify.

$a \times b = x$

Put in values of a and b; calculate x.

GLOSSARY

Pronunciation Key

a . . . **back** (BAK)	i(i + con + e) . . . **idea, life** (I DEE uh, LIFE)	sh . . . **shelf** (SHELF)
er . . . **care, fair** (KER, FER)	oh . . . **go** (GOH)	ch . . . **nature** (NAY chur)
ay . . . **day** (DAY)	aw . . . **soft** (SAWFT)	g . . . **gift** (GIHFT)
ah . . . **father** (FAHTH ur)	or . . . **orbit** (OR but)	j . . . **gem, edge** (JEM, EJ)
ar . . . **car** (KAR)	oy . . . **coin** (KOYN)	ing . . . **sing** (SING)
ow . . . **flower, loud** (FLOW ur, LOWD)	oo . . . **foot** (FOOT)	zh . . . **vision** (VIHZH un)
e . . . **less** (LES)	yoo . . . **pure** (PYOOR)	k . . . **cake** (KAYK)
ee . . . **leaf** (LEEF)	ew . . . **food** (FEWD)	s . . . **seed, cent** (SEED, SENT)
ih . . . **trip** (TRIHP)	yew . . . **few** (FYEW)	z . . . **zone, raise** (ZOHN, RAYZ)
	uh (u + con) . . . **comma, mother** (KAHM uh, MUTH ur)	

absolute age: the actual age of rock

abyssal plain: a flat, almost level area in the deepest part of the ocean basin

acceleration (ak sel uh RAY shun): a measure of the rate at which the velocity of an object changes

acceptable risk: a risk that an individual or society is willing to take in deciding how much of a pollutant should be removed

acid rain: a combination of sulfur oxides or nitrogen oxides with water in the air; rain with a pH average of 4.5

acoustics: the science of production, control, transmission, reception, and effects of sound

active system: a kind of solar energy system that uses special collectors, storage units, and circulation systems

active transport: a system of moving materials through the cell membrane using certain molecules to act as carriers, and requiring energy from the cell

air mass: a body of air that acquires the same properties (temperature and moisture) as the surface under it

alkali metals: the family of elements in Group IA of the periodic table; have one electron in the outer energy level and are the most reactive of all the metals

alkaline earth elements: the family of elements in Group IIA of the periodic table; have two electrons in the outer energy level

alloy: a combination of a metal with one or more other elements

alpha particle: a particle consisting of two protons and two neutrons; a helium nucleus

alternating current: a type of electric current that continually reverses direction

alveoli (al VEE uh li): tiny sacs in the lungs where carbon dioxide is released and oxygen is absorbed by the blood

ampere (AM pihr): the unit used to measure electric current; the rate of electron flow through a circuit

amplitude: the distance a wave rises or falls as it travels; the amount of energy being transferred by a wave; for transverse waves, the depth of a trough or the height of a crest

antibody (ANT ih bohd ee): a protein that destroys pathogens and toxins

antiparticles: subatomic particles that are identical in mass to electrons, protons, and neutrons but opposite in electric charge

asphalt: a heavy fraction product of petroleum used mainly for road construction and roofing

atomic mass: the sum of an atom's protons and neutrons

atomic mass unit: the approximate mass of a proton or neutron; one-twelfth the mass of an atom of carbon-12

atomic number: the number of protons in the nucleus of an atom

ATP: adenosine triphosphate; a substance found in living things that can store energy in its bonds

audible range: the range of sound frequencies that a normal human can hear; frequencies between 20 Hz and 20 000 Hz

beta particle: an electron given off during radioactive decay

Big Bang: a theoretical model of the origin of the universe based on scientific observation; the universe began as an explosion flinging matter and energy in all directions

biodegradable: a material that can be decomposed by organisms in a relatively short time

biomes (BI ohms): large regions of earth with similar plants, animals, and climate

black hole: the collapsed remains of a star whose gravity is so great that radiation cannot leave

calorie: the amount of thermal energy needed to raise the temperature of one gram of water one degree Celsius

carcinogen: a cancer-causing substance

cardiovascular: the body system consisting of the heart, blood, and blood vessels

cell membrane: the outermost living part of a cell

cell respiration: the process by which glucose molecules combine with oxygen, forming carbon dioxide and water, and releasing energy

cell wall: nonliving material surrounding the cell membrane of some cells; provide support and protection for the cell

cement: a ceramic material used to make concrete

centripetal (sen TRIHP ut ul) **force:** the inward force that keeps an object moving in a circular path

ceramic: a material made primarily from nonmetallic elements fired at high temperatures

chemical equation: a shorthand description of what takes place in a chemical reaction

chemical formula: a shorthand way of indicating the elements in a compound and the relative proportions of those elements

chloroplast (KLOR uh plast): cell structure in which photosynthesis takes place; contains chlorophyll needed for photosynthesis

chromatography: a process used to separate some mixtures into parts with similar polarities

chromosomes (KROH muh sohmz): parts inside the nucleus that contain the genes that determine the traits living things have

climate: the average range of weather conditions during the year at a particular location

colloid: a mixture made up of particles larger than those of a solution but smaller than those of a suspension

color addition: the process of combining different colors of light

combustible: word describing a substance that will burn, such as wood

comet: a body in the solar system consisting of a mass of frozen materials, along with bits of rock and dust

community: the living part of an ecosystem in which producers, consumers, and decomposers interact with each other

compressional wave: a wave which transfers energy by means of a series of compressions and rarefactions traveling through matter

concave lens: a type of lens that is thickest at the edges

conduction: the transfer of thermal energy or electricity through direct contact; can occur in solids, liquids, and gases

conductor: a material that readily transmits thermal energy or electricity

consumers: organisms that eat other living organisms

continental shelf: the zone of the ocean floor nearest to land; an extension of the continental crust covered by seawater

continental slope: the steeply sloping surface between the outer edge of the continental shelf and the ocean basin

continuous flow: describes an energy source, such as the sun, that is always producing energy

convection: the transfer of thermal energy by currents in liquids or gases

convex lens: a type of lens that is thickest in the center

coral reef: an ocean feature found in warm, shallow water; formed by calcium carbonate deposits secreted by coral, a marine animal

coriolis (cor ee OH lus) **force:** a force caused by the earth's rotation; deflects wind from its original path

correlation: a comparison of the ages of rocks from different locations

coulombs (KOO lahms): the unit of measurement for the amount of electric charge

covalent bond: a bond formed by the sharing of one or more electrons between atoms

creep: a type of slow mass movement on most slopes as a result of changes in moisture and temperature

critical angle: the angle at which light is refracted along a boundary between two substances

current electricity: the flow of electrons through a conductor

cyclone: a large area of low pressure that develops between air masses sometimes producing severe weather conditions

cytoplasm (SITE uh plaz um): a fluid within the cell membrane; where many cell reactions take place

deceleration (dee sel uh RAY shun): the rate of decrease in velocity; negative acceleration

decibel: a unit used to measure the intensity of sound

decomposer: an organism, such as bacterium or fungus that breaks down organic matter

deep sea vent: an opening in the ocean floor from which a hot solution containing hydrogen sulfide is released

density: the measure of matter contained in a given volume; expressed in grams per cubic centimeter, g/cm^3

dependent variable: the variable that is being measured in an experiment; it responds to the change of an independent variable

dew point: the temperature at which water vapor begins to condense from the air; depends on humidity

diffraction: the bending of waves as they pass the edges of objects and through openings in their path

direct current: the flow of electrons in only one direction through a conductor

distillation (dihs tuh LAY shun): a process of evaporation and condensation used to separate the parts of some mixtures

DNA: deoxyribonucleic acid; complex molecules that hold the code for an organism's traits

dominant (DAHM uh nunt): a genetic trait that is always expressed

Doppler effect: change in pitch occurring when either the sound source or the observer is moving

ductility: a physical property that describes the ease with which a material can be drawn into wire

ecosystem (EE koh sihs tum): an interaction of a community of living organisms with its environment

efficiency: for any machine or process, the ratio of work (energy) output to the work (energy) input

electric power: a measure of the rate at which the energy of flowing electrons is used

electrons: negatively-charged particles in an atom

elliptical galaxy: a galaxy with a smooth, round or oval outline with old stars and little gas

emulsifying agent: a substance that causes two liquids to form a colloid

endangered: a species whose survival is threatened because its population has become very small

endocrine (EN duh krun): a system of ductless glands that release hormones into the blood

endoplasmic reticulum (en duh plaz mink · rih TIHK yuh lum): system of tubes that transport proteins and other materials within a cell

endothermic (en duh THUR mihk): a type of process that absorbs energy

energy: the ability to do work

environmental impact: the effect an activity has on an ecosystem

enzymes (EN zimz): protein molecules that carry out cell reactions

eukaryote (yew KER ee oht): an organism with cells that have nuclei and distinct structures, such as mitochondria and chloroplasts, within the cell membrane

eutrophication (yoo troh fuh KAY shun): addition of nutrients to a body of water causing an increase in the populations of organisms; can be harmful when too rapid

exothermic (ek soh THUR mihk): a type of process that releases energy

exponent: a superscript that appears with a number and indicates the power to which the number is raised

extinct: a species with no living members

extrusive: igneous rocks that form as magma flows out on the earth's surface

fault: a fracture in a mass of rock along which movement can occur

fertilization: the combining of a sperm and an egg

fiber-reinforced plastic: plastic strengthened with fibers such as fiberglass

fission: the process of splitting atoms' nuclei

flammable: word that describes a material that will ignite easily and burn vigorously, such as gasoline

flare: a burst of energy from the sun, associated with sunspots

fluorescence: the emission of light by a material as a result of the absorption of radiation

food web: all the possible feeding relationships of populations in a community; the interactions of producers and consumers in a community

formation: a grouping of rocks that can be used in correlation

fossil: any evidence of ancient life

fossil fuels: nonrenewable fuels formed from the organic matter of ancient plants and animals by heat and pressure; examples are oil, coal, and natural gas

fractional distillation: a process that separates a mixture into fractions that have different boiling points

frame of reference: in the study of motion, the surroundings an observer uses to determine the position of an object

front: a boundary separating differing air masses

fundamental forces: the three kinds of forces—electromagnetic, gravitational, and nuclear

fundamental frequency: the lowest frequency at which an object will vibrate naturally

fungus: the kingdom of plantlike eukaryotes that do not contain chlorophyll, therefore cannot make their own food

fusion: the combining of lighter atomic nuclei to form heavier ones

gamma rays: electromagnetic radiation similar to X rays but having shorter wavelength

genes (JEENZ): long molecules that contain DNA which forms the code for hereditary traits

genetics (juh NET ihks): the study of inherited traits

genus (JEE nus): the classification division between family and species; the first name in the scientific name of an organism

Geologic Time Scale: a sequence of geologic events based on rock record and related to absolute ages

geothermal: word that describes heat energy from within the earth

gravitational force: a force of attraction between any two objects because of their masses

greenhouse effect: a process by which the atmosphere is heated when water vapor and carbon dioxide absorb infrared waves re-radiated by the earth

group: a vertical column in the periodic table; elements within a group have similar chemical properties

gyre (JIRE): a type of surface current with a loop-like circulation

habitat: a place that provides an organism with what it needs to survive, such as food and shelter

hadron: a class of subatomic particles that respond to strong nuclear forces; includes protons and neutrons

halogens: the family of elements in Group VIIA of the periodic table; the most chemically active nonmetals whose atoms have 7 electrons in the outer energy level

hazardous waste: wastes that may either be immediately harmful or may cause damage in long-lasting and unpredictable ways

heat: the amount of thermal energy that an object is able to transfer to another object; measured in joules

heat of fusion: the amount of thermal energy required to change a substance at its melting temperature from the solid to the liquid state

heat of vaporization: the amount of thermal energy required to change a substance from a liquid to the gaseous state without changing its temperature

homeostasis (hoh mee oh STAY sus): a state of balance within a cell or an organism; maintained by a system of controls and feedback

hormone (HOR mohn): a substance produced by endocrine glands; circulates in the blood and affects reactions in cells in other locations in the organism

H-R Diagram: a graph that shows the relationship between the spectral class of a star and its luminosity

hybrid (HI brud): a trait for which the gene pair consists of one recessive gene and one dominant gene

hydrocarbon: an organic compound that contains only the elements hydrogen and carbon

hydroelectric: electricity generated by water falling over a dam

hypothesis (hi PATH uh sis): a possible answer to a question or solution to a problem

illuminance: the amount of light that strikes a unit of surface area

immunization: making the body resistant to a disease by stimulating its production of antibodies with a vaccine

incandescence: the production of light from atoms excited by heat

independent variable: a variable that is changed by the experimenter

index fossil: a fossil of an organism that lived in only a specific geological period; useful in dating geological layers

indicator: a substance whose color change is used to determine if a solution is an acid or a base

inertia (ihn UR shuh): the tendency of matter to remain at rest or in uniform motion unless acted upon by a force; resistance to a change of motion

inference: a logical conclusion based on observations and data

insoluble: incapable of being dissolved in a solvent

insulator (IHN suh layt ur): a material that resists the flow of heat or electricity

interference: the interaction of two or more waves producing momentary reinforcements and cancellations of energy

intrusive: igneous rocks that form as magma forces its way into spaces between other rocks

invertebrate: an animal without a backbone, such as an arthropod, mollusk, or echinoderm

ion: an atom with a charge as a result of losing or gaining one or more electrons

ionic bonding: bonding between two atoms that results from the transfer of one or more electrons from one to another; produces oppositely charged ions that attract each other

IPM: integrated pest management, the combined approach of using pesticides, biocontrols, and culture techniques to control pests

irregular galaxy: a galaxy with a patchy, noncircular appearance

isotopes: atoms of the same element that differ in the numbers of neutrons

jet stream: a narrow belt of wind flowing west to east at high speed in the tropopause

joule: a unit for measuring work or energy; the work done in moving a force of one newton through a distance of one meter

kelvin: SI unit for measuring temperature, abbreviated K

kinetic (kuh NET ihk) **energy:** the energy of motion

kingdom: the first and broadest classification of living organisms; the five kingdoms are animals, plants, protists, fungi, and monerans

landslide: a type of mass movement that results when weathered rock and soil are suddenly loosened from a hillside and slip rapidly down the slope

law: a description of a natural occurrence that has been observed many times

Law of Conservation of Matter: matter cannot be destroyed in an ordinary chemical reaction

lepton: a class of subatomic particles that have relatively small masses and do not have strong nuclear interactions; an electron is an example

limiting factors: things such as water, temperature, and food supply that control the size of a population in a particular community

longshore current: a current flowing parallel to the shore; caused by waves breaking at an angle to the shore

luminosity: the rate at which a star radiates energy

lunar eclipse: an eclipse of the moon which occurs when the full moon lies in the plane of the ecliptic (in the earth's shadow)

lymph (limf): a fluid that diffuses from the blood into the lymph capillaries and exchanges materials with the cells

main sequence: a star whose radiation pressure is balanced by the force of gravity; characterized by its position on the main sequence of the H-R diagram

malleability (mal ee uh BIHL uh tee): a physical property that refers to the ease with which a material can be pressed, rolled, or hammered into thin sheets

marginal cost: the cost of removing the remaining small percentage of a pollutant; may not be worth the benefit gained

mass: the amount of matter in an object

matter: anything that has mass, takes up space, and resists a change in motion

mechanical advantage: the measure of how much a machine changes the magnitude of an applied force

meiosis (mi OH sus): a type of cell division that produces sex cells, in which the number of chromosomes has been reduced by half

menstruation (men STRAY shun): the release of blood and tissues lining the uterus wall; occurs when the egg is not fertilized

metabolism (muh TAB uh lihz um): the chemical reactions in the cells of a living organism

metalloid (MET ul oyd): any element having properties of both metals and nonmetals

metamorphism (met uh MOR fizm): the process by which rocks undergo changes in composition and texture as a result of heat and pressure

meteor: rock fragment from space that becomes hot and glows upon entering the earth's atmosphere

meteorite: rock fragment from space that reaches the surface of an object, such as the earth or moon, creating craters upon impact

meteoroid: an object, smaller than a minor planet, in orbit around the sun

metric: a commonly used system of measurement in which many, but not all, units are the same as SI units

mid-ocean ridge: an underwater mountain range, rising from the ocean basins, from which submarine lava flows

mimicry (MIHM ih kree): characteristics or behaviors of an organism that make it appear to be a different organism or to look like its surroundings

minerals: solid, earth materials that have a definite chemical composition and molecular structure

minor planet: an object that orbits the sun like a planet, but is smaller

mitosis (mi TOH sus): cell division in which one cell divides into two identical cells, each having the same number and type of chromosomes as the original cells

mixture: a physical combination of two or more substances that are not chemically combined

model: anything, either physical or mental, used to help visualize occurrences and objects that cannot be directly observed

moneran: a kingdom of prokaryotes; includes blue-green algae and bacteria

monsoon: a seasonal wind that blows between a continent and an ocean; brings rains during hot months and dry weather during cold months

moraines: layers or ridges of boulders and rock fragments deposited by a glacier

mudflow: a type of mass movement that occurs in dry mountain regions when heavy rains saturate loose sediments and cause them to move down slope

mutation (myew TAY shun): a change in the DNA code of a gene

mutualism (MYEW chuh lihz um): a relationship in which organisms live in a mutually beneficial association

nebulae: concentrations of interstellar matter

nebular theory: describes the origin of the solar system from a rotating cloud of gas

nephron (NEF rahn): a tiny tube in the kidneys in which materials are filtered from and reabsorbed into the blood leaving wastes behind

neuron (NOO rahn): a nerve cell, which consists of a cell body and nerve fibers

neutralization: a type of chemical reaction in which acids and bases combine to produce water and a salt

neutron: a particle with no electric charge found in the nucleus of an atom

neutron star: a very dense object, consisting entirely of neutrons, formed by the remains of a supernova

newton: the SI unit of force; the force required to accelerate a mass of one kilogram one meter per second per second

niche: the role of an organism in an ecosystem

noble gases: the family of elements in Group VIIIA of the periodic table; stable gases that do not readily combine chemically

nonpolar: the type of covalent bond formed between two atoms having equal attractions for electrons; a molecule that has no charged ends

nonrenewable: word that describes a resource that cannot be replaced once it is used up

nonvascular (nahn VAS kyuh lur): plants, such as algae and mosses, that do not have conducting tissues for transporting food and water

nova: an explosion of a star, sending clouds of matter from the star

nucleus: a cell's control center; contains DNA molecules that form the code for cell functions

ohm: the unit used to measure electrical resistance

open space: undeveloped land

operational definition: a description of a variable in terms of how it will be measured

overtones: natural vibrations of an object, such as a guitar string, that are whole number multiples of the fundamental frequency; vibrations that give a sound a characteristic quality

ovulation (ahv yuh LAY shun): the release of an egg from an ovary

oxidation number: a number that describes the combining capacity of an element by telling how many electrons an atom of that element gains, loses, or shares when combining with another element

paleomagnetic dating: a method for finding the absolute age of a rock by examining orientation of magnetic minerals in the rock

Pangaea: a large supercontinent formed that contained all of the earth's present continents

parallel circuit: an electric circuit in which electric current that passes through each electric device does not have to pass through any others

pascal: the SI unit of measurement for pressure; one newton per square meter

passive system: a kind of solar energy system that uses only the design of the building to collect the sun's energy for heating

pathogen (PATH uh jun): an organism that can cause an infection

period: a horizontal row in the periodic table, characterized by increasing numbers of electrons in the outer energy levels as the elements are read from left to right

periodic law: the properties of elements repeat at regular intervals if the elements are arranged by increasing atomic number

petroleum: a mixture of hydrocarbons formed from decayed organisms which have been buried deep in the earth by geological activity

phase cycle: a complete set of changes in appearance that the moon makes from new moon to new moon

photon: visualized as being a tiny bundle of electromagnetic radiation

photosynthesis (foht oh SIHN thuh sus): the process in which light energy from the sun is changed to chemical energy and stored in the chemical bonds as food molecules

phylum (FI lum): the largest classification division of a kingdom

pitch: the highness or lowness of a sound; the way we perceive the frequency of a sound

plane of the ecliptic: an imaginary plane in which the planets revolve around the sun

plasma: a state of matter, existing only at extremely high temperatures, in which electrons are separated from atoms

plasma: the colorless fluid that makes up about 55 percent of a person's blood; mostly water with dissolved minerals, proteins, and nutrients

plastic: a synthetic material that can be molded easily; used to replace many natural materials

platelet (PLAYT lut): a cell-like part in the blood that aids in clotting

plate tectonics: the theory of continental movement; the drift of rigid crustal plates over the earth's hot, molten interior

polar: a covalent bond in which one atom has a greater attraction for electrons than the other; a molecule that has slightly charged ends

polarized: a type of electromagnetic radiation that has waves vibrating in only one direction

polymerization (pahl uh muh ruh ZAY shun): a synthesis reaction in which large molecules are formed by combining many smaller molecules

population: the total number of a single species found in an ecosystem

potential difference: the difference in potential energy between an electron at the negative terminal and one at the positive terminal; often referred to as voltage

potential energy: the energy of position

power: the rate at which work is done; the amount of work done per unit of time

pressure: the amount of force on a surface per unit area

predators: second-or-third-order consumers that kill animals for food

producer: an organism that makes its own food using sunlight as a source of energy

products: the new substances that are formed in a chemical reaction

prokaryote (proh KER ee oht): an organism whose cells have no distinct structures within the cell membrane

protist: a kingdom of mostly one-celled, microscopic eukaryotes; includes amoeba and paramecium

proton: a positively-charged particle in the nucleus of an atom

Punnett (PUN ut) **square:** a diagram used to show the probability of offspring inheriting certain traits

pure: a trait for which both genes are the same; may be pure dominant or pure recessive

qualitative: observations that do not involve measurements

quantitative: observations based on careful numerical measurements

quark: a subatomic particle thought to make up other subatomic particles

quasar: an early stage through which most galaxies may have passed; very distant objects that emit large amounts of radiation

radiation: the transfer of energy by electromagnetic waves

radiometric dating: a method for finding the absolute age of rock by measuring the quantities of radioactive minerals the rock contains

reactants: the original substances that undergo a chemical change

reactivity: the chemical property of a substance that indicates its tendency to interact chemically with other substances

recessive (rih SES ihv): a trait that is expressed only if two genes for that trait are present

reclamation: the process of restoring land to nearly its original state; involves reforesting, grading, and developing land that has been strip-mined

red giant: an unstable stage in a star's life when fusion converts helium to carbon, and the heat causes the star to expand

refining: the removal of impurities from a material

refraction: the bending of waves when they change velocity while passing from one material to another at an angle

relative age: the age of a rock determined by its position in a sequence of a rock column

relative humidity: the ratio of the actual amount of water vapor in the air to the maximum amount the air can hold at the current temperature

renewable: word used to describe a resource that can be replaced in a relatively short time

resistance: a measure of the degree to which a conductor holds back the movement of electrons; opposition to the flow of electricity

revolution: the motion of an object in its orbit around another object

ribosome: a small sphere on the surface of the endoplasmic reticulum in which proteins are manufactured

rip current: a strong, narrow surface current that moves swiftly out from the shore for a short time

risk-benefit analysis: the conscious evaluation of the risks involved in an undertaking in relation to possible benefits

rotation: the spinning motion of an object on its axis

R-value: a measure of a material's resistance to transfer of thermal energy

salinity: the amount of solid material dissolved in one kilogram of water

saturated: a solution that contains as much solute as can be dissolved in the solvent at that temperature

scavenger: an animal that feeds on dead organisms

scientific methods: organized processes of gaining information by asking questions, making observations, and trying things out in a systematic way

scientific name: the genus and species names of a living organism

scientific notation: a method of expressing very large and very small numbers by using powers of ten

seafloor spreading: the process that moves crustal plates; occurs when magma is forced upward and adds new rock to the seafloor

semiconductor: substance that can conduct electricity under certain conditions

series circuit: an electric circuit in which electric current must pass through all the electric devices while completing the circuit

SI: Systeme Internationale; an internationally agreed upon measurement system based on the metric system

soil survey: a detailed description of the properties of soils in a certain area, including maps and testing results

solar eclipse: an eclipse of the sun which occurs whenever the moon lies in the plane of the ecliptic and casts a shadow on the earth

solubility (sahl yuh BIHL ut ee): a physical property that describes how readily a substance dissolves in another substance

soluble: capable of being dissolved in a solvent

solute: the substance in lesser quantity in a solution; the substance being dissolved in a solvent

solution: a homogeneous mixture in which a substance (solute) is dissolved into another substance (solvent)

solvent: the substance in greatest proportion in a solution; the substance in which a solute is dissolved

species: a group of organisms that can breed and produce fertile offspring; the second name in the scientific name of an organism

specific heat capacity: the amount of thermal energy required to raise one gram of a material one Celsius degree; depends on the nature of the material

spectrum: the full range of wavelengths of electromagnetic radiation

speed: a measure of the distance an object moves per unit of time

spiral galaxy: a disk-shaped galaxy with a center bulge of old stars and spiral arms of gas and young stars

standard: a defined, fixed quantity used as a basis for comparison

standard atmospheric pressure: the average pressure of the air at sea level

standing wave: a wave pattern that stores the energy of a vibrating object most efficiently; in a string, a wave pattern that vibrates without seeming to travel from one end to another

static electricity: the charge on an object resulting from a deficiency or an excess of electrons

steel: an alloy of iron and carbon, usually containing small amounts of other elements

sublimation (sub luh MAY shun): the direct change of a solid to a gas or a gas to a solid

substance: homogeneous matter that always has the same composition; consists of elements or compounds

succession: a series of changes in the community of an ecosystem during its development

supernova: a tremendous explosion following the violent collapse of a very massive star

superposition: the geologic principle that younger layers of rock are deposited over older layers

supersaturated: a solution containing more solute than the amount it would normally take to saturate it at a given temperature

suspension: a type of mixture in which relatively large particles are scattered throughout and can be filtered out and will settle out if left standing

sustained yield: a method of resource management designed to maintain a continuing supply of a resource

synapse (SIHN aps): the gap between neurons across which chemicals carry nerve impulses

technology: the practical application of science to everyday matters

temperature: the measure of the average kinetic energy of the particles in an object

terminal velocity: the highest velocity that can be reached by a falling object

textile: a type of material made from natural fibers (cotton, flax, wool), or manufactured fibers (nylon, rayon, polyester) or a combination of both

theory (THEE uh ree): a reasonable explanation of a natural occurrence

theory of evolution by natural selection: an explanation of how species have changed with time; based on the survival of organisms having traits that best help them compete for food, places to live, and mates

thermal conductance: the amount of thermal energy that passes through a material in one hour

thermal energy: the total amount of internal kinetic energy in an object

tide: the periodic rise and fall of ocean water caused by the gravitational pull of the sun and moon on the earth

total internal reflection: the reflection that occurs when light strikes a boundary between two substances at an angle greater than the critical angle

toxic: poisonous

transformer: a device used to increase or decrease the voltage of alternating current

transition metals: the metallic elements located in the B columns of the periodic table; have one or two electrons in the outer energy level

transmutation: a process in which one element changes into another by radioactive decay

transverse wave: a wave which transfers energy by means of crests and troughs perpendicular to the direction of the wave travel

trench: a deep, long, and narrow trough in the abyssal plain of the oceans

tropopause: the upper boundary of the troposphere; contains the jet streams and is the ceiling of the weather zone

troposphere (TROP uh sfihr): the layer of atmosphere nearest the earth's surface; the layer in which most weather changes occur

unconformity: a buried erosion surface; a break in the rock record

uniformitarianism: the geologic principle that continuous slow changes create the earth's geologic changes

upwelling: a vertical upward ocean current that brings deep; cold water containing nutrients to the surface

urbanization: the growth of a large, industrial society

vacuole (VAK yuh wohl): fluid-filled space in a cell where food and water are stored

variable: a changeable factor in an experiment that may affect an outcome

vascular (VAS kyuh lur): word describing plants that have specialized tissues for transporting food and water

velocity (vuh LAHS u tee): Tthe speed and direction of an object's movement

vertebrate (VURT uh brayt): an animal with a backbone; also has an internal skeleton, and organ systems

virus (VI rus): composed of a molecule of nucleic acid (gene) surrounded by a coating of protein; not usually considered to be a living organism

volts: the unit of measurement for potential difference; the potential difference that enables one coulomb of electrons to do one joule of work while passing through a circuit

volume: the loudness of sound; the way we perceive the intensity of a sound

watershed: the land that supplies water for a main stream and its system of tributaries

water table: the top of the saturation zone in permeable rock

watt: the SI unit for power; one joule of work per second

weathering: the changes that rocks undergo at or near the surface of the earth; includes both mechanical and chemical weathering

weight: measure of the force of gravity between an object and another object; on earth, one object is the earth

white dwarf: an unstable stage in a larger star's life when it collapses from the inward force of its own gravity

work: the result of a force moving an object through a distance; expressed in joules and equal to the force applied multiplied by the distance through which it moves

Index

Photo Credits